Aega Dinh
18 Dumbar to
Guelph, Ont   824-09

A PERIODIC CLASSIFICATION OF THE ELEMENTS

The atomic number is given above the symbol of the element. The Groups are arranged vertically, and the Periods horizontally.

Periods → **Groups**

1	2											3	4	5	6	7	0
1 H																	2 He
3 Li	4 Be											5 B	6 C	7 N	8 O	9 F	10 Ne
11 Na	12 Mg											13 Al	14 Si	15 P	16 S	17 Cl	18 Ar
19 K	20 Ca	21 Sc	22 Ti	23 V	24 Cr	25 Mn	26 Fe	27 Co	28 Ni	29 Cu	30 Zn	31 Ga	32 Ge	33 As	34 Se	35 Br	36 Kr
37 Rb	38 Sr	39 Y	40 Zr	41 Nb	42 Mo	43 Tc	44 Ru	45 Rh	46 Pd	47 Ag	48 Cd	49 In	50 Sn	51 Sb	52 Te	53 I	54 Xe
55 Cs	56 Ba	57-71 see below*	72 Hf	73 Ta	74 W	75 Re	76 Os	77 Ir	78 Pt	79 Au	80 Hg	81 Tl	82 Pb	83 Bi	84 Po	85 At	86 Rn
87 Fr	88 Ra	89-103 see below†	104 Unq	105 Unp	106 Unh												

*LANTHANIDE SERIES

57 La	58 Ce	59 Pr	60 Nd	61 Pm	62 Sm	63 Eu	64 Gd	65 Tb	66 Dy	67 Ho	68 Er	69 Tm	70 Yb	71 Lu

†ACTINIDE SERIES

89 Ac	90 Th	91 Pa	92 U	93 Np	94 Pu	95 Am	96 Cm	97 Bk	98 Cf	99 Es	100 Fm	101 Md	102 No	103 Lr

71 - Lutetium - is not a rare earth but a transition element.

THE
OUTLINES
OF
CHEMISTRY

THE OUTLINES OF CHEMISTRY

NEW EDITION

W. A. E. McBRYDE,
M.A. (Toronto), Ph.D. (Virginia), F.C.I.C.,
Professor of Chemistry, University of Waterloo

R. P. GRAHAM,
M.A. (Queen's), A.M., Ph.D. (Columbia), F.C.I.C.,
Professor of Chemistry, McMaster University

CLARKE, IRWIN & COMPANY LIMITED
TORONTO/VANCOUVER

Metric Commission Canada has granted use of the National Symbol for Metric Conversion.

© 1978 by Clarke, Irwin & Company Limited

ISBN 0-7720-1215-6

Canadian Cataloguing in Publication Data
McBryde, W.A.E., 1917-
    The outlines of chemistry
For first year chemistry course
Includes index.
ISBN 0-7720-1215-6
1. Chemistry. I. Graham, Ronald Powell, 1915-
II. Title.
QD33.M32 1978   540   C78-001469-3

ILLUSTRATIONS BY Helen Fox

3 4 5 6 7 BP 84 83 82 81 80

Printed in Canada

CONTENTS

PHOTO CREDITS

The authors and publisher would like to thank the following individuals and organizations who have made available the photographs on the pages listed.

D.W. Hitchens, University of Waterloo, 14; Environment Canada, 15; Inco Metals Company, 24; Ohaus Scale Corporation, 30 (right and top left); D.W. Hitchens, University of Waterloo, 30 (bottom); National Portrait Gallery, 35; The John Rylands University Library of Manchester, 39; Muspratt's "Chemistry", 1860, 43; The Toronto-Dominion Bank, 46; Shell Canada Ltd., 69; Agriculture Canada, 72; The National Museum of Natural Sciences, The National Museums of Canada, 76; International Minerals & Chemical Corporation (Canada) Limited, 81; Aluminum Company of America, 84; United States Steel Corporation, 103; Photographic Services, Geological Survey of Canada, 107; F.W. Smith, Institute for Materials Research, McMaster University, 115; Aluminum Company of America, 130; Dr. I.D. Brown, McMaster University, 146; John L. Brown, Engineering Experiment Station, Georgia Institute of Technology, 149; The National Museum of Natural Sciences, The National Museums of Canada, 151; General Electric Research and Development Center, 167; Photographic Services, Geological Survey of Canada, 169; Asbestos Corporation Limited, 171; Bell Laboratories, 172; Gulf Oil Corporation, 179; Imperial Oil Limited, 184; Royal Canadian Mounted Police, 199; Audio Visual Center, Simon Fraser University, 200 (left); Petrosar Limited, 200 (right); Imperial Oil Limited, 203; The Marconi Company Limited, 210; Canadian Industries Limited, 214; VG-Organic Limited, 238; Fisher Collection, Fisher Scientific Co., 262; Eastern Forest Products Laboratory, Environment Canada, 267; Ward's Natural Science Establishment, Inc., 271; The National Museum of Natural Sciences, The National Museums of Canada, 272; Gulf Oil Canada Ltd., 274; Popperfoto, 288; D.W. Hitchens, University of Waterloo, 296; C. Jernigan, The Mearl Corporation, 299; Cornell University, 304; The Vancouver Sun, 309; The Royal Institution of Great Britain, 318; Allied Chemical Corporation, 329; Corning Glass Works, 333; National Aeronautics and Space Administration, 337; Bermuda News Bureau, 357; A.J. Whorwood, Department of Geology, McMaster University, 367; McMaster University, 386.

Most of the photographs of postage stamps were taken by Mr. A.J. Whorwood, Department of Geology, McMaster University.

ACKNOWLEDGEMENTS

To write a book is one thing; to produce a book is another. We wish to say our thanks to the typists and typesetters, the graphic artists and engravers, the designers, the printers and photographers, and the editorial and production staffs of our publisher—all of whom contributed to making this book what it is.

We are particularly indebted to Ms. Brenda Molloy of Bay Ridge Secondary School and to Dr. Douglas Melville of Etobicoke Collegiate Institute for their advice and criticisms. They will see the fruit of several of their suggestions, but may not know in how many instances they have influenced what we say or how we say it.

To our wives we owe much, proofreading and patience being not the least of their contributions.

W.A.E. McBryde
R.P. Graham

PREFACE

The Preface to a new edition of a textbook commonly includes a recitation of the ways in which the new edition differs from the first one. We are not observing that tradition: those who know our earlier book will recognize the many changes in content and mode of presentation, and those unfamiliar with the earlier book will not be interested in such historical comparisons.

The Outlines of Chemistry is intended as a textbook for a first course in chemistry at the secondary school level. We are well aware that we have included more material than may reasonably or properly be "covered" in one school year. We have done this in the knowledge that, in the absence of a set curriculum, teachers have considerable freedom to choose the topics they teach and to decide the depth to which they teach them. We hope that what we have provided will meet these varying preferences and needs.

We have tried to write the book, too, to allow flexibility in the order in which topics are taught. For example, with encouragement from teachers who like their students to do laboratory work almost at the beginning of their study of chemistry, we have presented several chapters of so-called descriptive chemistry early (Chapters 5-9), but teachers who prefer first to treat modern atomic theory may move directly from Chapter 4 to Chapters 10, 11 and 12. There are other chapters, particularly in the second half of the book that may be "re-ordered." To facilitate re-arrangements, there is an abundance of cross-references by chapter and section number.

Portions of the book are set in smaller type, in the style of what you are now reading. This type has been used for illustrative material, for describing experiments, for carrying topics further than the average student requires at this stage, and for other kinds of "enrichment".

We have included a large number of questions with each chapter— more than any one reader is likely to try—enough to provide variety and to suit different needs. Because we recognize that the ability of students will vary considerably, we have included questions covering a wide range of difficulty. Some of them have been marked with an asterisk; these are intended to challenge the very able students and to show them some of the power of scientific deduction and correlation.

Books on chemistry differ somewhat in the values they cite for densities, melting points, heats of fusion, etc. This is not the place to discuss reasons for this; we merely record that our data are mostly taken from *Physical Data for Inorganic Chemists,* by M.C. Ball and A.H. Norbury (Longman, 1974). In matters of nomenclature, abbreviations, and the like, our guide has been the practices adopted by the International Union of Pure and Applied Chemistry (IUPAC).

Finally, let us stress that we shall welcome comments—favourable or otherwise (and the "otherwise" are often the more helpful toward improving a later edition)—from the teachers and, no less so, from the students who use this book.

W.A.E. McBryde
R.P. Graham

FOREWORD ON UNITS

This book has been written with due regard to SI practice, although aficionados of SI will recognize that we have introduced a number of non-conforming and non-coherent units. We have not found it easy to make a complete and consistent conversion of chemistry to recommended SI units. We console ourselves in this respect by noting that throughout the worldwide chemical literature only partial accommodations to SI practice have been achieved at best.

There are two fundamental problems, as well as one practical one, at the root of this difficulty. The first is that the *mole*, that uniquely chemical base unit, was developed within the cgs system of units, whereas the base units of mass and length in SI came from the mks system. In order to retain familiar magnitudes of quantities such as molar mass, concentration, equilibrium constants, etc., and to express them in units derived from base units, the magnitude of the mole should be revised upward by 10^3. There has been some urging to do this by the introduction of the kilomole in all these derived units. Apart from the semantic complications of then having effectively two base units with *kilo-* prefixes (kilograms per kilomole, for instance), there is the practical consideration that all these units are too large for the use of chemists. At the scale on which many laboratory operations are carried out, the *milligram, millimole,* and *millilitre* are the practical working units of the chemist. It is not surprising, therefore, that the international chemical community has displayed reluctance to traffic in units that are a million times larger.

The second fundamental problem is the rejection within SI of the atmosphere as a unit of pressure. Although at the level of this book there is no necessity to express the pressure of gases in atmospheres, at only a slightly more advanced level of study of chemistry, the atmosphere becomes an indispensable unit. This is so because the "standard state" of all gaseous substances is *defined* as one atmosphere, and that unit is chosen because of the mathematical convenience that the logarithm of unity is zero (a property not shared by 101 325!)

In spite of the commendable wish of many people to see a uniform and universal system of units in use in physical science, we feel bound to urge against the teaching and learning of chemistry *at this time* exclusively in SI units. There is a vast literature of chemistry already in service and not apt to be replaced quickly in which quantities are expressed in units "whose use is to be progressively discouraged". As long as people must rely on this reference literature they must be able to work within the schemes of units employed therein, and must be able to relate these units to SI. Any student desiring to proceed further in chemistry, or other fields in which chemistry is utilized, who cannot recognize or handle units outside SI is going to be severely disadvantaged. It is for this reason that we have included a number of Questions and Problems intended to give users of this book some exposure to, and experience with, units which are still very much in common use.

Chemistry – the Science of Substances

1. One of the outstanding chemists of the twentieth century is Linus Pauling. He has been honoured in many ways for his contributions to science and to the well-being of society, and has the unusual distinction of being the recipient of *two* Nobel Prizes: one for chemistry and the other for his efforts on behalf of world peace. In one of his textbooks he gives a description of chemistry which, with slight change, we use to introduce the subject.

> *Chemistry is the science of substances, their properties, their structure, and their transformations.*

Let us enlarge on the ideas in this statement.

2. THE SCIENCE OF CHEMISTRY. Chemistry is one branch of *natural science,* which is an organized effort to understand and explain the phenomena of nature. We expect that you are already aware of the general way in which scientists observe and measure natural occurrences, then set about looking for regularities among these, and finally try to account for the regularities by means of theories. As you read on in this book, we hope that the methods of science will become clearer as we show you examples of their application in chemistry.

3. SUBSTANCES AND PROPERTIES. Chemistry is that part of natural science concerned with *substances.* Most people know what a substance is. Or do they? Although there are nine definitions of "substance" in our dictionary, none of them quite fits the usage of the chemist. The closest definition is "any particular kind of material," but this doesn't really convey the special meaning that this word has in chemistry. To a chemist the almost infinite variety of materials is more easily classified and understood if they are considered to be made up of a smaller, more

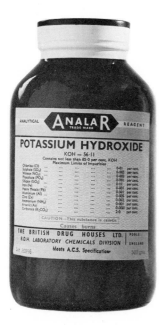

The purest chemicals that can be purchased still contain some impurities, if only in "trace" amounts. Manufacturers of laboratory chemicals commonly show on the label the limits of impurities in their product.

The word "pure" has several meanings. When we speak of pure water we may have in mind its fitness for drinking, and water from a well may be entirely safe and palatable to drink. Nevertheless, if you evaporate a cupful of water and a residue remains in the cup, you are justified in assuming that something else was in the water and, therefore, it was not pure in the chemical sense.

manageable number of individual substances. *Each substance can be recognized or identified by its characteristic properties.* This may be made clearer by some examples.

Granulated sugar is considered a substance, so is water. A syrup made by mixing the two is not regarded by a chemist as a substance, but some of the properties of the syrup are predictable from those of the sugar and water. Baking soda and cream of tartar are regarded as substances in chemistry; when these are mixed together with a little starch (also a substance), the resulting material is called "baking powder." The action of baking powder in the making of a cake can be understood by a chemist because of the known properties of the substances in baking powder. But baking powder is not regarded as a substance in its own right.

Part of the method of chemistry is to break down materials—either in reality or in the mind—into their constituent substances. Each substance then becomes a distinct chemical "individual" whose properties or behaviour can be observed, recorded, and hopefully explained.

4. THE PURE SUBSTANCE. There is in this idea of "substance" in chemistry the requirement of *purity*. Granulated sugar is regarded as a substance but brown sugar is not; brown sugar has not been as highly refined as white sugar and contains other substances that modify its taste, colour, and other properties. Household salt comes close to being the substance a chemist calls sodium chloride, but it usually contains about 1% of other substances. We said a moment ago that water was a substance, but most water is not really pure; well water contains small amounts of dissolved solids which accumulate as kettle scale when the water is boiled. Although water can be made purer by distillation (Sec. 17-12) even distilled water contains foreign substances, such as gases dissolved from the air. The purest forms of sugar or sodium chloride we can buy still contain traces of impurities, and the labels on the bottles of these may list impurities known to be present. However, even if a chemist cannot isolate substances in absolutely pure condition, the *idea* of the *pure substance* is essential to an understanding of events in chemistry. To some extent the idea of a pure substance, free of every possible contaminant, is an idealization. Nevertheless, a chemist devotes much time and effort to isolating and studying substances in the purest state obtainable.

5. A CHECK ON PURITY. You may well ask: how does a chemist decide whether or not a particular material is a pure substance? In most cases the decision is not too difficult; and this is where the careful study of properties comes in. Properties of matter can convey two kinds of information. They can, for instance, enable us to *distinguish* chalk from cheese, or in general one substance from another. Of course this is a little more difficult if the substances are more alike, for example, when distinguishing chalk from gypsum, or cheddar from Colby. The other purpose that properties can serve is as a *check on purity*. Many proper-

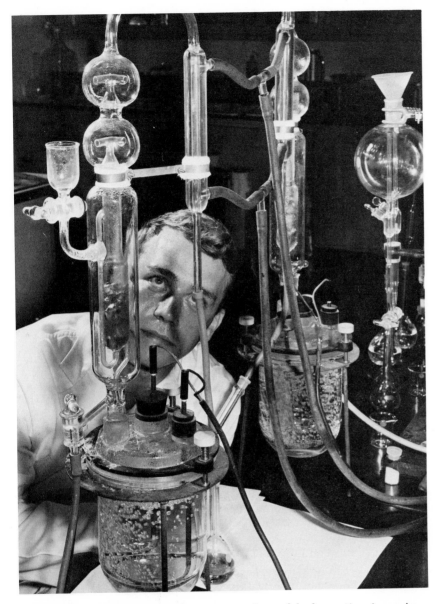

Chemistry is an experimental science, and careful observation is an important part of experimentation.

ties of substances are greatly affected by impurities. You would have no difficulty in distinguishing sea water from fresh water. A chemist could quickly distinguish tap water from distilled water and, morever, could tell you exactly what and how much foreign material was in the tap water. It is this foreign matter that makes tap water more interesting to drink than distilled water, but disqualifies it as a pure substance.

In the next few sections we shall consider some of the properties that are particularly useful for recognizing substances and for checking their purity.

6. CHANGES OF STATE. Some properties are obvious. For example, water is a liquid at room temperature, not a gas or a solid. Matter can exist in any of the three *states*: solid, liquid, or gaseous, but it generally occurs in just one of these, depending on the conditions. We customarily think of water as a liquid, but on a colder planet such as Jupiter the normal state is the solid ice.

Changes from one state to another are usually easily recognized, and experience has shown that a pure substance almost always changes its state at a particular and characteristic temperature. Thus water freezes to ice or ice melts to water at 0°C, and we call this characteristic temperature the *freezing point* of water or the *melting point* of ice. Another liquid that freezes at, for instance, 18°C is clearly, on the basis of this property alone, not water. Similarly, water boils, that is, changes rapidly to vapour, at about 100°C. The exact boiling temperature depends on the atmospheric pressure, and as this changes somewhat from day to day, the temperature of boiling changes somewhat accordingly. What we call the *boiling point* is the boiling temperature when the atmospheric pressure is 1.013×10^5 Pa; by this definition, the boiling point of water is 100°C. A liquid found to have a boiling point other than 100°C is by this property judged not to be water.

7. QUALITATIVE AND QUANTITATIVE PROPERTIES. Before we leave freezing and boiling points, we should note a couple of their important features. For one thing, these are properties capable of measurement with a suitable thermometer; with a little care they can be found very accurately. Properties such as these, which depend on the measurement of some quantity, we call *quantitative* properties. Other properties which depend only on the observation of some quality, like smell or appearance, we describe as *qualitative* properties. Quantitative properties are much better for identifying a substance than qualitative properties. Furthermore, and this is very important, it has been found that pure substances almost always have sharp melting or boiling points. By "sharp" we mean that the melting or boiling takes place all at one temperature. Contrast the behaviour of water boiling sharply at 100°C with that of sugar syrup. Anyone who has made toffee or fudge with a candy thermometer knows that when the ingredients are set to boil for a few minutes the initial temperature may be about 104°C (which on many candy thermometers may still be read, in the old Fahrenheit units, as 220°F) and that with continued boiling the temperature slowly rises; at about 114°C ("soft-ball stage") most recipes call for the heating to be stopped. Obviously, the candy mixture is not a pure substance and equally obviously it does not have a unique boiling point. The same kind of difference is observed between the freezing of pure water at 0°C and the freezing of a brine (containing salt and water). The brine may start to freeze two or three degrees below zero, but the temperature may have to be lowered to below −20°C before the whole solidifies. Evidently, in such a solution, freezing takes place over a range of temperatures. What has been described for sugar syrup and brine is typical of the behaviour of all solutions and enables them to be distinguished from pure substances.

You probably know that Pa stands for "pascal," a unit of pressure.

When recording physical quantities that are very large or very small it is customary and convenient to express them as a number multiplied by a power of ten. For each positive power of ten added, the number shown increases tenfold: thus $10^3 = 10 \times 10 \times 10 = 1000$, while $10^4 = 10 \times 10 \times 10 \times 10 = 10\ 000$ and so on. Usually the number written before the ten raised to a power is shown with one digit before a decimal place and any other digits after. Thus, the distance to the sun, 150 million kilometres, is written 1.50×10^8 km rather than 150×10^6 km.

8. SOLUTIONS AND SOLUBILITY. In the last paragraph we spoke of *solutions* of sugar in water and of salt in water. Many other substances, too, will dissolve in water, but there are substances, like chalk or starch, that do not dissolve much in water. Evidently, dissolving in water is a property possessed by some substances and not by others and it is, therefore, a property that may be used to distinguish one substance from another.

Substances that form solutions are said to be *soluble*; those that do not are called *insoluble*. In considering solutions, we need not restrict ourselves to solutions in water. Sulphur doesn't dissolve in water, but will readily dissolve in another liquid called carbon disulphide, and common salt, which dissolves in water readily enough, is scarcely dissolved by carbon disulphide. We can thus recognize or distinguish substances by their *solubility* in another substance. In Chapter 25 we shall describe how the amount of dissolving is expressed and how solubility thus becomes a measurable or quantitative property like melting point or boiling point.

9. HOMOGENEITY AND HETEROGENEITY. Pure water and a solution of salt in water have several properties in common. Each is a colourless, transparent liquid; and a sample of either taken from one region in its container has identical properties with a sample taken from any other region. All parts of a sample of water are the same, and all parts of a sample of salt solution are the same. There is a word to describe this uniformity: each liquid is called *homogeneous*. Homogeneity—the condition of being homogeneous—is a property of all pure substances and all solutions. A material that is homogeneous could then be a pure substance, but it could also be a solution; you would have to make a decision between these alternatives on the basis of some other property, for example, a sharp or not-sharp melting point or freezing point. A solid substance can also be homogeneous. One sugar crystal in a bowl is just as sweet and, in all other respects, the same as any other. Although fragments turned from a piece of brass on a lathe will obviously differ greatly in size and shape, they will still have identical properties.

The opposite of homogeneous is *heterogeneous*. Heterogeneous materials often may be seen with the unaided eye to consist of different parts. For instance, a piece of granite is commonly seen to contain white, pink, and black particles and is obviously composed of more than one substance. In other cases, we may have to perform certain operations on a material to show that it is heterogeneous. Whole milk, for example, will in time settle into two layers, cream and skim milk; the process can be accelerated and made more complete by a centrifuge. In chemistry the expression *mixture* or *mechanical mixture* is used to describe heterogeneous materials. Sometimes the operations required to separate a mixture into its parts are very complicated. Since many naturally occurring materials are mixtures, the art of separating these into useful and valuable substances becomes important, both in the laboratory and in industry.

Interestingly enough, the Dutch word for chemistry, *scheikunde,* means "the art of separating."

10. A CLASSIFICATION OF MATERIALS. Although we began discussing properties, we have found that examination of properties leads to a useful classification of materials. A pure substance is regarded as a unique chemical individual. Each substance has its own characteristic properties by which it can be recognized. But many materials, especially as we find them in nature, are made up of two or more substances. These *composite* materials fall into two categories, homogeneous and heterogeneous; the former are called solutions, the latter mixtures. We can now construct a simple classification of matter that embodies these ideas:

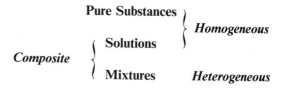

When we organize information into a compact scheme such as the above, we often realize that the finished product has some exceptions. A glass of ice-water contains pieces of ice floating in liquid water. The contents are obviously heterogeneous; they are also obviously one pure substance. Similarly, a flask of boiling water clearly is seen to have bubbles of water vapour forming within the liquid and is heterogeneous. The existence of one substance in two states, such as the examples just cited, constitutes an exception to the classification above. Otherwise, it gives a reasonably good picture of the relationship of pure substances to all other forms of matter.

11. SOME OTHER CHARACTERISTIC PROPERTIES. There are a few other properties that we often look for or measure and which are important for the recognition of substances. One of these is *density*. To understand what is meant by density, consider Fig. 1-1. On the scale are two identical bottles; one is filled with water, the other with carbon tetrachloride. From the position of the pointer, the bottle containing the carbon tetrachloride is heavier than that containing the water. The volume of liquid is the same in each bottle, but the mass is not. Often people will say that carbon tetrachloride is heavier than water; what they mean to say is that carbon tetrachloride is heavier than an equal volume of water; what they should say is that carbon tetrachloride is *denser* than water. Density compares equal volumes of materials: it is defined as the mass per unit volume. In SI the preferred unit of density is kilograms per cubic metre. The density of water is 1.0×10^3 kg/m³ and that of carbon tetrachloride is 1.6×10^3 kg/m³. However, for many operations in the laboratory the subsidiary units grams per cubic centimetre or grams per millilitre are more convenient, the latter being preferred for liquids. Thus, the density of water may be written as 1.0 g/mL and that of carbon tetrachloride as 1.6 g/mL.

The *conduction* of an electric current is a property shared among metals and a very few other substances. It can be measured exactly and is one of the best tests of the purity of highly refined metals, such

The values of density, like many other properties, depend on the conditions of measurement, such as temperature and pressure. Usually these conditions should be specified with the numerical value of density. The values given here refer to substances at room temperature; the density of solids or liquids does not change greatly with changes in temperature or pressure.

In 1960, a world conference on weights and measures adopted the International System of Units. This system is abbreviated SI, from the French title of *Le système international d'unités.*

Carbon tetrachloride   Water

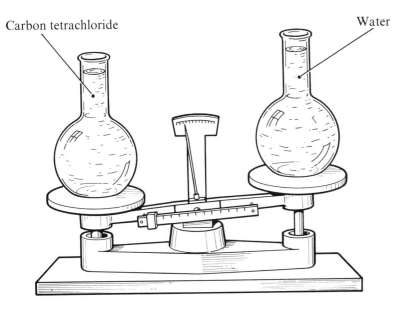

Fig. 1-1: *This depicts in a very simple way the notion that two substances may differ in density. The flask of carbon tetrachloride is heavier than the flask of water although both flasks contain the same volume of liquid. But a small flask of carbon tetrachloride might have had a mass less than a large flask of water. The significant thing is that here we are comparing the masses of equal volumes of these liquids. Density is made up of two factors—mass and volume.*

as platinum. Substances that are good conductors of electricity are usually also good conductors of heat.

Some other properties that we shall mention are given only in descriptive or qualitative terms. For example, we shall refer to *colour*, but anyone who knows anything about paint or fabrics will be aware how difficult it is to express the quality of colour in words. There are other words that apply to the passage of light and one of these, applied mainly to metals, is *lustre*. This relates to the amount of light reflected from the surface of an object. The opposite of shining or lustrous is dull or matte. It is often worth noting whether a material is transparent or opaque. *Transparency* is usually found only in homogeneous bodies. *Odour* is sometimes used to recognize substances and so is *taste*. Both of these properties must be examined with great caution, for many substances are very poisonous to inhale or to ingest. Fortunately, the odour of some chemicals is pronounced enough that very minute amounts can be recognized—hydrogen sulphide, which smells of rotten eggs, being a case in point.

Textbooks usually speak of hydrogen sulphide smelling like rotten eggs. It would be more correct to say that rotten eggs smell of hydrogen sulphide, which is formed during the decomposition of certain substances in aging eggs.

12. The above list of properties is far from complete, but you will see that the observation or measurement of properties occupies a prominent place in chemistry. We shall now introduce another word from the definition of chemistry given at the beginning of this chapter. Chemistry, we said, was concerned with the *transformation* of substances and in the next chapter we shall explain what is meant by this term.

QUESTIONS

1. State the essential difference between (a) a mechanical mixture and a solution; (b) a mechanical mixture and a pure substance; (c) a solution and a pure substance.

2. Why are chemists so particularly interested in pure substances?

3. (a) Explain what is meant by a *property* of a substance. (b) Explain the difference between a qualitative property and a quantitative property. Give one example of each, other than the examples mentioned in the text.

4. The mass of a particular sample of a pure substance furnishes no clue to the identity of the substance, but the density of the sample may. Explain why this is so.

5. A sheet of glass and a sheet of plastic may appear very similar. What properties might be used to distinguish them?

6. Express in your own words the meaning of:

(a) the states of matter   (e) heterogeneous

(b) sharp melting point   (f) impurity

(c) solution   (g) metallic lustre

(d) homogeneous   (h) density

7. List five household substances or materials that are reasonably soluble in water, and five that are not.

8. Define the expression: *boiling point of a liquid*. If the temperature at which a liquid boiled continued to rise on evaporation, what would that indicate?

9. On the basis of your observations, or with the aid of a dictionary, decide whether each of the following materials should be classified as a pure substance, a solution, or a mixture: clear honey, crystallized honey, aspirin, vinegar, brass, diamond, glass, sapphire, paint, tincture of iodine, arsenic, turpentine, air, methylated spirit, chalk, granite, soda water.

10. How is whole milk "separated" by a cream separator? What are the products of this separation? What properties of the products make this separation possible? How was the separation made before the invention of the cream separator? How is separation avoided in most milk today?

11. A chemist in the laboratory has isolated a substance that might be *brucine*. The melting point observed for this preparation is 175°C. Handbooks give the melting point of brucine to be 178°C. Suggest two reasonable explanations for this difference in temperature.

12. Suggest how you might decide whether solder, said to be composed of tin and lead, is a pure substance, a solution, or a mixture.

*13. Suppose that the two flasks shown in Fig. 1-1 each contain 1.00 L of fluid. What volume of carbon tetrachloride must be removed from the flask on the left in order to cause the pointer on the scale to move to a perfectly upright position? (Hint: The data you will need are in Sec. 1-11.)

14. Charcoal is made from hardwood by cooking it, out of contact with air, in a special oven. Vapour is given off by the heated wood; then by chilling the vapour a brown liquid is obtained, known as "pyroligneous acid." Devise and describe some tests by which you could decide whether pyroligneous acid is a pure substance, a solution, or a mechanical mixture.

15. On the basis of the evidence supplied, decide whether each of the materials described below is a pure substance, a solution, or a mechanical mixture. There may be examples where a single choice cannot be made, and you should answer accordingly, making whatever deduction the evidence permits.

(a) A colourless liquid is allowed to evaporate in an open dish; when all the liquid is gone, a white crystalline residue remains.

(b) A colourless liquid is set in a cold bath to cool. At 18°C white crystals begin to form in the liquid. More and more crystals form, with the temperature remaining at 18°C, until the whole mass is solidified.

(c) A liquid having a density of 0.90 g/cm³ is set in an open dish to evaporate. After half of it is gone, the density of the remainder is found to be 0.95 g/cm³.

(d) A liquid is set to evaporate in an open dish; eventually it all evaporates, leaving no residue.

(e) A brown-coloured liquid is set in a centrifuge tube and subjected to high-speed spinning in a centrifuge. After this there is seen to be a light brown material at the bottom of the tube, and a dark brown, clear liquid at the top.

(f) A piece of metal was placed in a porcelain cup which was in turn placed in a furnace. The temperature of the furnace was slowly raised. At 300°C the metal began to melt, but it was not all liquefied until the temperature had reached 440°C.

Transformations
of Substances

2

1. When water freezes or boils it undergoes a transformation that is called a *change of state* but, as you know, the ice can easily be melted by heating it and the vapour can be condensed on a cold object. By either means, the original water can be restored. In ice or in water vapour we still have the substance water; it merely has adopted a rigid form in ice or become greatly dispersed in vapour. When you dissolve a few grams of salt in water, the salt undergoes a transformation; the crystals disappear and the saltiness becomes uniformly distributed throughout the solution. If this solution is left in an open vessel so that the water evaporates, in time all the salt is left behind as a crystalline residue. Just as liquid water becomes dispersed into a much larger space as vapour and can be recondensed into droplets by cooling it, so the dissolved salt becomes distributed throughout the much larger volume of water and can subsequently be recovered as small crystals when the water is removed from the solution. The process of dissolving has not destroyed the salt.

2. CHEMICAL TRANSFORMATIONS. Changes of state and dissolving are not the only transformations of interest in chemistry. Consider the following experiment. If a piece of platinum wire (sealed at one end into some glass tubing which serves as a handle) is heated in a burner flame, it becomes bright red. After the wire is removed from the flame and allowed to cool, examination will reveal that it has suffered no permanent change. (This property of platinum makes it valuable for use at high temperatures.) If a piece of iron wire (held by tongs) is similarly heated in the burner flame, it becomes incandescent, too, but when the wire is taken out of the flame, the heated portion is seen to be coated with a dark, brittle material very unlike the original iron. This coating has properties different from the original metal and must, therefore, be a different substance. A much more dramatic illustration of a transforma-

That the essence of chemistry is change is reflected in the Chinese expression for chemistry, *hua hsüeh*, which is, literally, "the study of change."

tion displayed by a metal when heated in air is seen when a "ribbon" of the metal magnesium is heated in the burner flame. The metal takes fire and burns with a brilliant, white flame and continues to burn even when the ribbon is removed from the burner. A white ash falls from the flaming region and the strip of metal is rapidly consumed. In its place, a new, very different substance is produced.

A great many of the transformations that are of interest in chemistry result in the production of new substances. It is convenient to designate such changes as **chemical changes.** Those processes, such as melting, which do not convert one substance into another are, by contrast, called **physical changes.** As a rule, there is no difficulty in perceiving that a new substance has been formed, so there is no difficulty in recognizing a chemical change or in distinguishing between a physical change and a chemical change. Another term that is frequently used to convey the same meaning as chemical change is *chemical reaction,* or often just *reaction.*

3. PHYSICAL AND CHEMICAL PROPERTIES. We said before chemistry is concerned with the properties of substances and with their transformations. We use properties for the identification and classification of chemical substances. After seeing the different consequences of heating platinum, iron, and magnesium in air, we can see how the chemical changes that substances undergo are, themselves, important properties of those substances. We call any chemical change that a substance undergoes a *chemical property* of that substance. Thus, it is a chemical property of magnesium that it burns in air to a white ash; and it is a chemical property of platinum that it does not burn or is not tarnished when heated in air. Properties such as density or melting point or electrical conductance, which do not involve chemical changes, are called *physical properties.* You will see that we shall come back again and again to describe physical and chemical properties of substances. You will find, too, that part of the systematic organizing of chemical facts consists of listing, predicting, and explaining properties.

THE ZINC-SULPHUR REACTION

We can easily illustrate some physical and chemical changes, and the use of properties for the recognition of individual substances, by a detailed consideration of a simple but typical chemical reaction which occurs when zinc and sulphur are intimately mixed and heated.

4. THE MIXING OF ZINC AND SULPHUR. *Zinc* is an important metal with many uses. You will be familiar with it as the outer case of dry cells and as the protective coating on "galvanized" pails and fencing wire. In the form in which it is to be used here—zinc dust—it is a dark blue-grey powder. *Sulphur* is an important substance that is an indispensable constituent of all living things. Sulphur can exist in several forms but the one most suitable for our purpose is the powdered variety, often called "flowers of sulphur." In this form it is a light, yellow powder.

If the two powders are stirred together (in roughly equal proportions by mass), nothing much happens, no matter how thoroughly they are stirred, nor how long the mixture is allowed to stand. The resulting mixture is still a powder—a powder with a colour intermediate between that of zinc and sulphur.

5. THE REACTING OF ZINC AND SULPHUR. If now a little of the mixture —*just enough to fill the curved end of the test tube*—is heated in a test tube made of borosilicate glass (such as Pyrex) over a hot flame, interesting things happen. Signs of melting appear around the edges of the mixture. Then a yellow liquid shows up on top, getting browner as the heating continues. Then an orange-yellow vapour appears above the mixture. Suddenly there is a bright red flash and a loud hissing, and white and yellowish vapours swirl in the test tube. When the test tube is removed from the flame and things settle down, three different zones are observed: a silvery metallic mirror coating the bottom, a white powder on it and coating the walls above it, and a yellow powder still further up (Fig. 2-1).

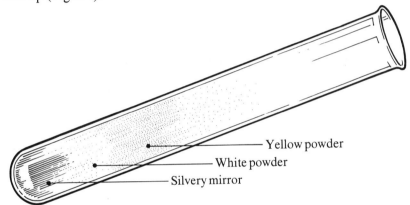

——— Yellow powder
—— White powder
—— Silvery mirror

Fig. 2-1: *Products of the zinc-sulphur reaction*

6. SOME CHARACTERISTIC PROPERTIES OF ZINC AND SULPHUR. The zinc and sulphur with which we started were both in powder form. But in other respects the two are very different. These differences in properties can be used to distinguish zinc from sulphur, or to assist in the recognition of each.

(a) Zinc is dark blue-grey; sulphur is yellow.

(b) Zinc is denser than sulphur. When the portions of equal mass were measured out, the portion of zinc was smaller. Had equal volumes been taken, the portion of zinc would have been heavier.

(c) Sulphur will dissolve in the liquid known as carbon disulphide. Zinc will not. If a small sample of powdered zinc is added to a little carbon disulphide and the mixture stirred, the solid zinc and the liquid remain as separate phases. The zinc can be sepa-

"Phase" is the word used to denote a portion of a substance which is uniform throughout in properties and composition. A jug of water and ice cubes contains a two-phase system. Water is one phase; the ice cubes together make up the second phase.

rated from the liquid by pouring the mixture through a filter paper in a funnel. The zinc stays on the filter paper; the liquid passes through. If several drops of the liquid are gently heated, the carbon disulphide evaporates, and no residue is left. This proves that no zinc had dissolved in the carbon disulphide.

(Take care in heating carbon disulphide; it is very flammable.)

When, on the other hand, sulphur is stirred with carbon disulphide and the mixture is filtered and a few drops of the clear liquid is evaporated, a solid residue, of yellow crystals of sulphur, remains. (The clear liquid formed by mixing two different phases, carbon disulphide and sulphur, is a *solution*, with only one phase.)

(d) Zinc is much more resistant to heating than sulphur is. If little mounds of zinc and sulphur are placed side by side on a metal spatula and the spatula is heated gently and evenly, the sulphur first melts, and then burns, before anything appears to happen to the zinc. (The sulphur burns with a blue flame and gives off a very choking odour.)

If the zinc and sulphur are gently heated, separately, in test tubes they again behave quite differently. The sulphur melts, without burning, to a yellow liquid which gradually turns dark brown, and then boils, forming an orange-yellow vapour which condenses to a yellow powder on the cooler upper wall of the test tube. The zinc, on the other hand, neither melts nor burns, unless heated much more strongly.

(e) Zinc warmed with dilute hydrochloric acid in a test tube reacts with it to form bubbles of a gas which has no colour and little odour and ignites with a "pop" when a burning splint is held at the mouth of the test tube. (The gas is hydrogen, by the way. If it were pure it would be odourless.) Sulphur, on the contrary, does not react with warm hydrochloric acid.

7. **MORE ABOUT THE MIXTURE OF ZINC AND SULPHUR.** When the zinc and sulphur were mixed together, nothing much seemed to happen. Knowing what we now know about zinc and sulphur, we are able to prove that indeed nothing much did happen. Here are some tests:

(a) If a sample of the mixture is examined with the aid of a low-power microscope, two different kinds of material can be clearly distinguished. These can be compared with separate samples of the zinc and sulphur.

(b) If a sample of the mixture is stirred into carbon disulphide and the mixture is filtered, a dark powder remains on the filter paper and a liquid passes through. If a few drops of this liquid are evaporated, the liquid disappears leaving crystals of a yellow solid. This solid can be identified as sulphur. (It melts easily to a yellow liquid which turns dark brown on heating; it

A sheet of zinc reacts vigorously with dilute hydrochloric acid to form bubbles of hydrogen, a very flammable gas.

burns with the characteristic choking odour of burning sulphur, etc.)

(c) If a sample of the mixture is warmed with dilute hydrochloric acid, there is a reaction which consumes part of the powder and generates a gas which has no colour and little odour and which ignites with a "pop" when a burning splint is held at the mouth of the test tube. When the reaction is over, a yellow powder remains in the liquid. This is sulphur.

Clearly, then, the zinc and sulphur had both retained their characteristic properties in the mixture. They were still there as zinc and sulphur, though all mixed up.

8. MORE ABOUT THE REACTION AND ITS PRODUCTS. When the zinc-sulphur mixture was heated, a yellow liquid was formed which gradually turned dark brown and then formed an orange-yellow vapour. This, clearly, is sulphur behaving as sulphur ought to behave.

But then there was a vigorous reaction with the evolution of heat and light and sound. Afterwards there were three phases visible. From top to bottom, these were: a yellow powder, a white powder, and a metallic mirror. These can be tested separately. (To make the separation, the test tube may have to be broken.)

See how useful that word "phase" is!

The yellow powder can be shown to be sulphur. How?

The mirror can be shown to be zinc. How?

The white powder, however, does not behave like either sulphur or zinc. For example, it will not dissolve in carbon disulphide, and when warmed with dilute hydrochloric acid, it reacts to give a gas which is certainly not one with "little" odour.

The white powder is in fact a new substance having properties very different from those of the original zinc or sulphur or the mixture of them. Here then is the product of a chemical change; and, as we have suggested already, we can recognize the occurrence of this chemical transformation by the appearance of the new substance.

A new substance requires a new name, and chemists give to most substances names that are indicative of their parentage. This one is called *zinc sulphide*.

9. We now return to the description of chemistry given in Chapter 1. *Chemistry is the science of substances, their properties, their structure, and their transformations.*

We have by now introduced you to the idea of a substance as a distinctive kind of material; to the idea of properties, both physical and chemical, by which substances are characterized and recognized; and to the principal sorts of transformations, physical and chemical, that substances may undergo. It remains for us to make a few introductory remarks about the term *structure* as applied to substances.

10. THE STRUCTURAL APPROACH TO CHEMISTRY. As you read on in this book you will see that this idea of structure is a recurrent theme. Later we shall describe the structural units of which matter is believed to consist, and then you will see an intimate connection between structure and properties. In fact, the chemist's understanding of how different substances are put together from the basic structural units has reached the point where reasonably reliable correlations between structure and properties can be made. New substances having desirable combinations of properties can now be predicted and put together to order. Some of the remarkable applications of chemistry today depend on the ability of the chemist to apply a knowledge of the structure of matter to produce materials with desired properties. Examples of this include plastics, synthetic fibres, corrosion-resistant alloys, and chemicals to control disease.

11. THE BUILDING BLOCKS OF CHEMISTRY. The known facts of chemistry are made easier to understand if we picture matter as made up of extremely small, simple building units. These are called *atoms*. In order to explain *all* the facts we must picture the atoms themselves as having a structure composed of even simpler particles. An important thing for you to grasp about atoms is that they and their constituent particles *cannot be seen*. What we believe about them has all been deduced from observations in thousands of carefully designed investigations.

According to this idea of the construction of matter one substance differs from another because there are different sorts of atoms in each. When we look at a drop of water or a grain of salt we picture each consisting of incredibly large numbers of atoms; and we think there are different kinds of atoms in water than there are in salt. It is one of the chemist's jobs to find out what kinds of atoms are in each pure substance.

But there is more to the structure of substances than just a list of the kinds of atoms in them, in much the same way that there is much more to the structure of a house than wood, bricks, cement, and so forth. For instance, natural gas, gasoline, and paraffin wax are all made up of substances composed of two kinds of atoms: carbon atoms and hydrogen atoms. But why is one of these materials a gas, another a liquid, and the third a solid at ordinary temperatures? We think that in substances the atoms are organized into structures or *aggregates* characteristic of that substance. Thus, natural gas and gasoline contain the same kinds of atoms, but the atoms are differently arranged, and the different arrangement results in different properties. The aggregates in a substance are often called *molecules* when they consist of only a moderately small number of atoms. Other aggregates, of vast numbers of atoms, are called *crystals* or *polymers* according to their properties.

There is a lot more to be said about atoms and about the ways in which they aggregate; we shall return to this later.

SCIENTIFIC EXPLANATION

12. Before we leave this introduction to atoms and molecules, however, we should inject a few thoughts about *kinds of scientific explanation*. We said that we could explain chemical phenomena more easily by a mental picture of building units called atoms. But why a *mental* picture? Wouldn't it be more satisfactory to say matter *is* made up of atoms? The fact is, though, that since we cannot see atoms, the way we visualize them is based entirely on what lawyers might call "circumstantial" evidence. If we cannot directly observe an atom, the concept we have of it obviously has developed only in our mind. And the evidence on which this is based may be incomplete. Perfect or imperfect, the picture of an atom that we have proves useful in our understanding of chemistry. We should make clear, however, that many explanations in science are given in simplified and perhaps only tentative ways.

13. SCIENTIFIC LAWS. Science is a human endeavour to understand and explain the phenomena of nature. To do this, the scientist probes nature—that is, asks questions by performing experiments. Often, to get results that are meaningful, the scientist has to pick simple, isolated occurrences to study. The next step is to try to organize the observations into simple generalizations. Given enough experimental information, particularly quantitative measurements, there may next emerge a law, which is a statement that sums up things that have been observed and enables the prediction of observations in experiments yet to be made.

We use the word *law* in science in an altogether different way from that used in connection with the laws of society. A scientific law is a statement of regular behaviour which has been observed in naturally occurring events. Scientists may agree that a certain law, such as the Law of Gravitation, applies to objects on the earth and even to objects such as satellites and planets. But apples falling from trees or satellites orbiting the earth follow their predictable courses not out of any respect for a law laid down by scientists. On the other hand, little girls and boys are discouraged from stealing apples from a farmer's tree by laws which govern the privacy of personal property; and the astronaut who may have had the remarkable experience of traversing space around the earth in a spacecraft at speeds of many thousands of kilometres per hour is subject to laws governing the speed with which he may drive his automobile. The latter are man-made laws laid down by some recognized authority for the protection of individuals and society. As individuals, we may conform to these laws or we might decide to break them on occasion. In the latter event, however, society may impose strictures on our action as a punishment for the violation.

14. Now we should ask ourselves: do scientific laws actually *explain* anything, or are they merely summaries of regular behaviour in nature? The laws themselves contain no explanation; but regular occurrences tend to be associated with a cause, and so the recognition of a scientific law prompts us to try to find an explanation. Human curiosity being what it is, we wonder why this or that thing happens. Why are some substances denser than others? Why do some conduct electricity but others do not? Why do most substances expand when heated? Why does a compass needle point north and south? The list of questions is endless. The scientist approaches this list of questions with the conviction that there is a rational answer or explanation for each. And what makes the subject more interesting is that several, seemingly unrelated phenomena may turn out to have a common explanation. Here and there in this book we shall point out cases where the explanation of one property may also explain several others.

To try to explain regularities in nature, we often make use of "models" and theories. One such model is the atom. We have said that many facts of chemistry can be explained by an intellectual model in which atoms are the building blocks, and we contrive that our description of the atom will fit all or as many as possible of the facts we are seeking to explain. There is a very important difference, however, between saying matter *is* made up of atoms which look like such and such and saying we can best *explain* what we observe by *assuming* that matter is made up of atoms. Chemists have been explaining many of the facts of chemistry by means of atoms for over one hundred and fifty years, but the model or description of an atom that was thought satisfactory a hundred years ago is quite unsatisfactory today. Actually, our description of an atom has been undergoing continual revision for the best part of a century. The atoms themselves haven't been changing, but our ability to describe a model of an atom has increased again and again as we have probed the mysteries of nature with increasingly elaborate and sensitive tools.

In the New Testament, Christ is portrayed as a teacher who sought repeatedly to explain the mysteries of God and man by means of parables ("The Kingdom of Heaven is like . . . "). It is probably a fair comparison to say that many scientific "explanations" are based on models ("A gas is like . . . "). As we develop these scientific models later in this book, we shall try to show how they seem to "explain" scientific laws and the properties of substances.

QUESTIONS

1. Distinguish between a physical change and a chemical change. Give five examples of common physical and chemical changes.

2. List three reasons for believing that the process described in Sec. 2-5 is a chemical reaction.

3. List four properties that may be used to distinguish zinc from sulphur. How does zinc sulphide differ from these two substances?

4. Express in your own words the meaning of:

(a) physical property
(b) chemical property
(c) change of state
(d) condensation
(e) filtration
(f) separation

5. List five properties each for ice and for water. Why is the change from ice to water considered a physical change?

6. Which of the following do you think are physical changes, and which are chemical changes? Crystallization of honey, tarnishing of silver, evaporation of moth balls, burning of a candle, melting of solder, fermentation of grape juice, drying of paint, a cake "rising," brewing of tea.

7. List four properties each for iron and for rust. Why is the change from iron to rust considered a chemical change?

8. List as many properties as you can think of by which it would be possible to distinguish between the members of each of the following pairs of substances:

(a) gold and fool's gold
(b) silver and lead
(c) powdered sugar and starch
(d) water and gasoline
(e) diamond and quartz
(f) air and oxygen
(g) gasoline and kerosene

9. Explain the chemist's use of the word "phase." In which of the following materials is there only one phase?

Corn syrup, granite, milk, clear tea, gold, tincture of iodine, fog, glass, zinc sulphide, sulphur, slush, clean air, smog.

10. Suggest methods for separating the phases in the following mixtures:

(a) powdered zinc and powdered iron
(b) powdered zinc and sulphur
(c) milk of magnesia
(d) olive oil and vinegar
(e) cigarette smoke
(f) salt and pepper

11. A mixture is prepared by stirring together 50 g of common salt and 50 g of water at room temperature. These are called the *components* of the mixture. (The maximum quantity of salt that can dissolve in 50 g of water at room temperature is 17.5 g.) After the mixture has been stirred sufficiently for no further changes to take place, what will be the amounts and compositions of the *phases* in the mixture? Suggest a mixture in which the phases and the components will be the same.

12. Find out all you can, by making use of the school library, about the substance iodine. Then devise and describe an experiment by which you could determine whether powdered zinc and iodine undergo a chemical reaction comparable to that between zinc and sulphur. If the reaction *did* occur the product would be a new substance with the name zinc iodide. Find out about its properties, so that you can describe how you might decide whether or not it had formed. (This investigation could be carried out in the laboratory.)

*13. Scientists account for experimental observations by referring to *laws* and to *theories*. The use of these terms will be made clearer as more examples are introduced throughout this book. By means of the Law of Gravitation and the Atomic Theory (about which you probably have already heard) try to explain how a scientific law differs from a scientific theory.

The Composition
of Substances

3

1. Chemical reactions were described in Chapter 2 as transformations in which one or more new substances were produced. To gain much understanding of chemical change requires that the *masses* of the substances taken and produced be considered carefully.

Until late in the eighteenth century chemistry was not so much a science as a special kind of cooking. Sketches and descriptions of early chemical laboratories show them to be similar to kitchens of that era. The chemists used a variety of vessels and utensils to wash, measure out, mix, extract, heat, or cool the substances they worked with. It is little wonder that they often used their wives' kitchens as laboratories. A modern laboratory and a modern kitchen still have much in common: work benches, hot and cold running water, glassware of various shapes and sizes, ovens and refrigerators, blenders and stirrers. The essential difference between them is that a weighing device—the balance—is indispensable in a chemical laboratory but not in a kitchen. It was, in fact, the introduction of the balance and the practice of weighing the materials produced or consumed in chemical reactions that changed chemistry from an art to a science.

2. MASS AND WEIGHT. Mass and weight are defined differently, although in popular usage the difference is often overlooked. The *mass* of a body is a measure of the quantity of matter in it. The *weight* of a body is proportional to the downward force exerted on it by gravity, and hence varies somewhat because the value of the acceleration due to gravity varies slightly from place to place on the earth's surface. Nowhere has the distinction between mass and weight been made more dramatic than in the activities of astronauts: a man out in space beyond any significant pull of the earth's gravitational field is essentially weightless—and can "float" in his cabin—but he still has all his matter and so retains his mass.

At a given place on the earth, however, two bodies of equal mass will have equal weight, and vice versa; and at the same place the ratio of

Each of these balances has a capacity of 200 g, but they differ in sensitivity. The one on the top right (a Harvard trip balance) can detect a difference of 0.1 g and the one on the top left (a multiple-beam balance) a difference of 0.01 g. The one above, called an analytical balance, can detect a difference of 0.1 mg and so permits the mass of an object to be determined to the nearest 0.000 1 g.

All these sensitivities depend on the balances being kept clean and in good repair.

the masses of bodies of different mass will be the same as the ratio of their weights. In this discussion and elsewhere, when we use the verb *to weigh,* we mean *to find the mass of.*

A two-pan balance of equal arms compares forces: the force acting downwards on the left-side pan with the force acting downwards on the right-side pan. When the instrument is "in-balance" these forces are equal:

(mass on left pan)   ×   (acceleration of gravity at that point)

= (mass on right pan)   ×   (acceleration of gravity at that point)

or $$m_l g_l = m_r g_r$$

If the masses (m) are expressed in kilograms and the accelerations of gravity (g) are expressed in metres per second squared, then the forces are in newtons (N); $1N = 1$ kg·m/s^2. These forces are properly called *weights,* and so such a balance is a *weighing device.*

Although the value of g varies from place to place on the earth's surface, it is not significantly different on the two sides of a balance. Hence the equation above can be simplified to:

$$m_l = m_r$$

Accordingly, such a balance is also a device for comparing *masses.* If one of the masses is known, then the other is determined.

3. MASS RELATIONSHIPS IN A CHEMICAL REACTION. Now, suppose we put an analytical balance to work, and look into some mass relationships. Remember the burning of magnesium ribbon? Suppose we weighed a piece of this metallic ribbon, and then ignited it in air, catching and weighing all the ash produced. To do this conveniently, and in such a way as to recover all the ash, we proceed in the following fashion:

1. We weigh a clean porcelain crucible and lid.

2. We put into it a length of magnesium ribbon (7 to 8 cm), curled up to fit.

3. We weigh crucible, lid, and magnesium.

4. We set the crucible and contents on a wire triangle as shown in Fig. 3-1. The lid is placed off centre so that some fresh air can

enter the crucible but ash will not be blown out by the burner gases. By means of a Bunsen burner we play a small flame on the crucible, gradually increasing the flame until the metal catches fire. If this is done properly the ash will all be caught inside the crucible and lid. The crucible is then allowed to cool.

5. We weigh again the cooled crucible, lid, and contents.

The significant thing that this investigation discloses is that the mass of the ash is more than that of the metal. For instance, in one experiment the following observations were made:

Mass of crucible + lid   = 25.2910 g

Mass of crucible + lid + magnesium = 25.3538 g

Mass of crucible + lid + ash   = 25.3953 g

Thus, mass of magnesium = (25.3538 – 25.2910) g = 0.0628 g

and mass of ash   = (25.3953 – 25.2910) g = 0.1043 g

4. Given a proper amount of scientific curiosity we should wonder why the ash weighs more than the metal. By our previous statements, we regard the ash as a new substance. What became of the metal? Is it *in* the new substance? Is it *all* in the new substance? What *else* is in the new substance? Did something add itself to the metal to form the ash? Where did this something come from? The heat? The burner gas? The crucible? The air? You can see that starting with no preconceived ideas a great many questions are suggested by this experiment. The early chemists, up to about the end of the eighteenth century, found simple burning experiments like this very difficult to explain. Most of the difficulty lay in their unawareness of the role played by air, and specifically of one gaseous substance in the air called oxygen. Looking back, it seems strange that this now familiar fact was not known, nor its significance understood for so long.

In the experiment with magnesium, we observed a chemical transformation in which the substance magnesium *combined* with the substance oxygen to form a new chemical substance, magnesium oxide. As far as we can detect, all the magnesium is in the new substance, and so is a measurable mass of oxygen. In fact, if 0.1043 g of ash (magnesium oxide) is obtained from 0.0628 g of magnesium, we may infer that the mass of oxygen combined with the magnesium is (0.1043 – 0.0628) g, or 0.0415 g.

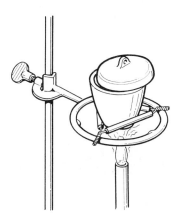

Fig. 3-1: *Changes in mass in a chemical reaction at high temperatures may be studied by doing the reaction in a porcelain crucible which is itself unchanged by the heating. The crucible is kept covered to prevent fine particles formed in the reaction escaping or particles of dust entering the crucible.*

We shall gloss over the fact that a small fraction of the magnesium does something different, that is, combines with the nitrogen from the air forming a different substance, magnesium nitride.

TABLE 3-1

COMPARISON OF PROPERTIES OF MAGNESIUM AND MAGNESIUM OXIDE		
PROPERTY	MAGNESIUM	MAGNESIUM OXIDE
State	Compact solid	Powdery solid
Colour	Grey, metallic	White
Density (g/cm³)	1.74	3.58
Electrical conductance	Conductor	Non-conductor

5. CONSERVATION OF MASS. There is a subtle principle buried in this last statement. Are we *really* justified in the inference just made, namely, that the mass of oxygen in 0.1043 g of magnesium oxide is found by subtracting the mass of magnesium initially taken from the mass of ash found in the crucible? What we are saying, in fact, is that the sum of the masses of magnesium and oxygen equals the mass of magnesium oxide. Experience has shown that in transformations, whether physical or chemical, the mass of the starting materials *is* equal to the mass of the materials formed. This generalization is the first chemical law to be introduced in this book; it is called the **Law of Conservation of Mass.**

In any change, chemical or physical, the total amount of matter (that is, the total mass) is the same after the change as before it.

6. Incidentally, in chemical reactions we customarily call the starting substances (in this case magnesium and oxygen) *reactants,* and the new substances produced (in this case the single substance magnesium oxide) *products*.

In our magnesium oxide reaction we have applied the Law of Conservation of Mass when we deduced the amount of oxygen that had combined with the magnesium.

REACTANTS	PRODUCT
0.0628 g of magnesium + x g of oxygen	0.1043 g of magnesium oxide

Therefore, $(x + 0.0628)$ g $= 0.1043$ g
and so $\qquad\qquad\quad x = 0.0415$ g

7. ANOTHER CONSERVATION EXPERIMENT. Here is another, chemically related, transformation that takes place in a self-contained, sealed vessel. A photoflash bulb contains a web of fine aluminium wire (usually) and is filled with oxygen gas. When the bulb is "flashed" by an electric current a chemical reaction takes place suddenly, with the emission of much light. The aluminium and oxygen combine to form a new substance called aluminium oxide, which afterwards can be seen as a powdery substance inside the bulb. We can use this device to demonstrate the Law of Conservation of Mass. We weigh a new photoflash bulb carefully on an analytical balance, and record the mass. Then we "flash" the bulb and set it aside to cool. When cool, we carefully weigh it again. Except for any minor discrepancy, which might be due to fingerprints or some such cause, we find the mass of the bulb unchanged. Mass is conserved during the rather violent chemical change that occurs when the bulb "flashes."

8. DEFINITE PROPORTIONS. In the magnesium-oxygen reaction, we saw that 0.0628 g of magnesium and 0.0415 g of oxygen reacted to form 0.1043 g of magnesium oxide. These are numbers from one experiment. Another remarkable principle shows up if we do the experiment several times. Suppose that each member of your class followed the same set of directions, and turned in his or her results. Some variation is bound to occur in the amounts of magnesium taken, and this will cause different amounts of ash to be produced. Suppose Smith misread his instructions and took only a 5-cm length of magnesium ribbon, while Jones, hoping to see a bigger flash when the magnesium burned, took a 10-cm length. Let us compare their results with ours.

	OURSELVES	SMITH	JONES
Mass of magnesium (g)	0.0628	0.0411	0.0830
Mass of ash (g)	0.1043	0.0681	0.1380
Mass of oxygen (g)	0.0415	0.0270	0.0550
Mass of oxygen per gram of magnesium (g)	0.661	0.657	0.663

From these figures it is quickly seen that the masses of ash obtained, and therefore also those of oxygen, are directly proportional to the masses of magnesium taken. This can be shown by dividing in each case the mass of oxygen by that of magnesium, to give the *mass of oxygen per gram of magnesium*. Notice that this is practically a constant. Each time we burn magnesium in air, the proportions of magnesium and oxygen that combine are the same! In other chemical reactions the same sort of observation is found to apply; the proportions (by mass) in which substances react is always constant. This can, therefore, be stated as a second generalization or law, usually called the **Law of Definite Proportions**.

That these numbers are not identical illustrates what is often called *experimental error*. The class could with profit discuss how errors might arise in this experiment.

> *In any chemical change the participating substances always react with one another in a definite proportion by mass.*

9. Much of science, as we said before, consists in wondering why. Here is something indeed to wonder at. How does it happen that, whenever magnesium reacts with oxygen, the proportions are always 0.66 parts of oxygen for each part of magnesium? Why is there never more than 0.66 g of oxygen per gram of magnesium, nor ever less? Here you see the scientific method at work. We have discovered a remarkable regularity in the masses of substances taking part in a chemical reaction, and the sequel is an attempt or series of attempts to explain the regularity. *Part of science involves "detecting" regularities*—and it usually requires some probing with experiments to reveal these—*and the other part consists of devising a reasonable explanation for them.*

10. COMPOSITION OF SUBSTANCES. If we go back just once again to the magnesium oxide, our experiments showed that 1.00 g of magnesium consistently reacted with 0.66 g of oxygen to form magnesium oxide. We could say that the *composition* of magnesium oxide is magnesium and oxygen in a certain proportion, and we could easily calculate that this proportion is 60% magnesium and 40% oxygen. Notice that we are

More accurately, the composition is 60.3% magnesium and 39.7% oxygen.

expressing the composition of one substance in terms of two others. It is clear that this composition is fixed in accordance with the Law of Definite Proportions. In fact, we might propose the following corollary of this law:

Each pure chemical substance that is composed of other substances will contain these substances in some fixed proportion by mass.

This statement is sometimes called the **Law of Constant Composition.**

11. COMPOUNDS. There isn't any doubt about magnesium oxide being a chemical substance; it meets the criteria mentioned in Chapter 1. Yet in the preceding paragraph we described its composition in terms of two other substances from which it can be made. We convey the idea that magnesium oxide is more complex than the magnesium and oxygen from which it can be made by saying that magnesium oxide is a *compound* of magnesium and oxygen. It follows that we should be able to express the composition of every compound in terms of simpler substances. The composition of magnesium oxide can be given qualitatively, as magnesium and oxygen, or quantitatively, as 60% magnesium and 40% oxygen. And the Law of Constant Composition can be restated to say: *Every compound has a fixed composition by mass.*

Experience has shown that magnesium oxide is not easily turned back into the simpler substances from which it may be produced. Indeed, one practical use of this compound, when pressed into bricks, is to line furnaces for use at high temperatures. At 2000°C magnesium oxide neither melts nor breaks down into simpler substances. We say such a compound is very stable.

12. COMPOSITION AND DECOMPOSITION. Not every compound is so stable. Near magnesium oxide on the shelves of a chemical storeroom you will probably find a bottle of mercury(II) oxide, or mercuric oxide. This substance is a dense, red powder. A rather simple experiment shows that it breaks down or *decomposes* on heating at about 500°C. Let us put a gram or so of mercuric oxide at the bottom of a Pyrex test tube, and then clamp it nearly horizontally, as illustrated in Fig. 3-2. Then we heat this compound with the flame of a burner, being careful to avoid heating the tube except at the closed end. The compound soon darkens, turning almost black. Along the cooler walls of the tube, a silvery deposit gradually accumulates; this proves to be the *familiar liquid metal mercury.* The other product of this reaction is not visible; it is the gas oxygen which gradually passes out of the mouth of the tube. We can demonstrate the presence of this oxygen quite dramatically because it supports the burning of many objects better than air itself. If we put a glowing wooden splint into the mouth of the tube, the wood bursts into flame because of the pure oxygen in the tube. As we continue heating the mercuric oxide, it gradually disappears, leaving only the silvery deposit higher up the test tube.

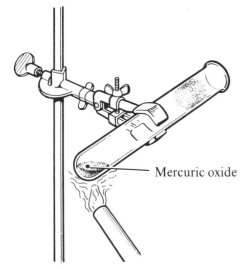

Mercuric oxide

Fig. 3-2: *Because glass is a poor conductor of heat the end of this tube not in the flame is comparatively cool. On this cooler surface the mercury vapour, formed when mercuric oxide is decomposed at the hot end, is able to condense into small drops. The oxygen gas also formed is not visible, but its presence can be demonstrated as described in the text.*

13. In the laboratory you may do this experiment quantitatively by weighing the mercuric oxide taken and the mercury remaining in the tube. If the decrease in mass of the former is taken to be the mass of oxygen in the compound, then it is a simple matter to calculate the percentage composition of mercuric oxide in terms of mercury and oxygen. Each time this experiment is carefully repeated the composition will be found to be the same, so we may infer that mercuric oxide is a pure substance. Here is a representative set of results:

Mass of test tube   = 22.519 g
Mass of test tube + mercuric oxide = 23.501 g
Mass of test tube + mercury residue = 23.428 g

Accordingly, mass of mercuric oxide = (23.501 – 22.519) g = 0.982 g
and the mass of mercury (assuming that none escaped)
$$= (23.428 - 22.519) \text{ g} = 0.909 \text{ g}$$

Therefore, the mass of mercury per gram of mercuric oxide
$$= 0.909/0.982 = 0.926 \text{ g}$$

The percentage composition of mercuric oxide is:

mercury $0.926 \times 100 = 92.6\%$
oxygen $(1.000 - 0.926) \times 100 = 7.4\%$

14. The heating of mercuric oxide is a famous experiment historically. By doing this, Joseph Priestley in 1774 isolated pure oxygen and studied some of its properties. Mercury does not combine vigorously with oxygen as magnesium does, but the red oxide (which floats on the surface of the mercury) is slowly formed when the mercury is heated in the air at about 350°C. Priestley heated this red substance by means of a "burning glass" (a large lens to focus the sun's rays) to produce what is credited as the first pure oxygen.

Carl Wilhelm Scheele, a Swedish apothecary, isolated oxygen (1773) before Priestley did, but the honour of discovery does not go to him because his studies were not published until some years later. A scientific discovery, to be "counted" as such, must be made widely known to other scientists, so that they may verify it.

15. ELEMENTS. We have described magnesium oxide and mercuric oxide as compounds. The name properly suggests that they have been "compounded" from, or are composed of, something simpler. Indeed, we have seen for ourselves how magnesium oxide may be produced or *synthesized* from magnesium and oxygen, and how mercuric oxide may be decomposed into mercury and oxygen. From the mass relationships

(i) 0.60 g magnesium + 0.40 g oxygen forms 1.00 g magnesium oxide
(ii) 1.00 g mercuric oxide forms 0.93 g mercury + 0.07 g oxygen

we saw that the composition of these two compounds may be quantitatively expressed in terms of the substances oxygen and magnesium or mercury. The latter three are, therefore, simpler substances than the former.

Joseph Priestley (1733-1804) was a clergyman, teacher of languages, and librarian, but his fame was made as a scientist, especially by the discovery of oxygen. He also discovered the pleasant taste of water in which carbon dioxide had been dissolved; although he recommended this beverage to his friends, it is doubtful that he foresaw the modern soft-drink industry. Incidentally, his carbon dioxide came from a brewery adjacent to his parsonage.

Priestley was persecuted because of his liberal religious views and his sympathy with the American and French Revolutions, and he emigrated from England to America in 1794.

Can we carry this process any further? That is, can we show by synthesis or decomposition that oxygen or magnesium or mercury consists of still simpler substances? Can we, for instance, convert magnesium completely into two or more other substances? The answer is apparently not. Magnesium (and oxygen and mercury) are special substances which cannot be broken down by chemical reactions into simpler substances. Magnesium, mercury, and oxygen are known as elements, or, more formally, as *chemical elements.*

16. We can now add to what we have said about the classification of matter in Chapter 1. Every pure substance known is either an element or a compound; every compound is composed of elements; the elements represent the limit of decomposition of compounds. What a simplification this represents! Of the practically limitless variety of naturally occurring materials, we can make some sort of order by listing the substances of which they consist. The situation is made even simpler when we realize that all the chemical substances known are made up of just over a hundred elements. This opens up the possibility of reducing the great complexity of the world around us. It is rather like the simplification in our language achieved by reducing all words to representation by an alphabet of twenty-six letters. Think how much more complicated the situation is for the Chinese in whose language every word is represented by a different symbol.

17. In addition to the three elements already named, there are others whose names will be familiar to you: iron, copper, silver, gold, platinum, sulphur, carbon, nitrogen, chlorine, phosphorus, calcium, lead, tin, aluminium, chromium, nickel; and you probably have heard of others such as fluorine, iodine, arsenic, uranium, and radium. Of the hundred-odd elements, some are very common and widely distributed, some are very rare, and a few that do not occur on the earth have been made artificially. (Ninety have been found on earth.) The eight elements that are most prevalent in the earth's crust are listed in Table 3-2, in the order of decreasing abundance. These eight elements account for almost 98% of the mass of the earth's crust. The order in Table 3-2 does not indicate the relative importance of the elements. Notice, for example, that such indispensable elements as carbon, nitrogen, phosphorus, sulphur, chlorine, and hydrogen do not appear in the list.

TABLE 3-2

ABUNDANCES OF ELEMENTS IN THE EARTH'S CRUST

ELEMENT	ABUNDANCE (% by mass)
Oxygen	46.9
Silicon	26.9
Aluminium	8.1
Iron	5.1
Calcium	5.0
Magnesium	2.3
Sodium	2.1
Potassium	1.3

QUESTIONS

1. Make clear the meaning of each of the following terms, and also the difference between each member of the given pairs:

(a) mass, weight
(b) element, compound
(c) reactant, product
(d) mass, density
(e) combination, decomposition
(f) composition, decomposition

2. State in your own words the Law of Conservation of Mass. Give an illustration of the law, but not one taken from Chapter 3.

3. One thousand kilograms (one tonne) of coal, when burned, forms about thirty kilograms of ash. Is this an exception to the Law of Conservation of Mass? Explain.

4. Briefly explain how a relatively small number of elements can form a very large number of compounds.

5. Which is the simpler substance: magnesium or magnesium oxide? Give reasons for your answer.

6. A pure brown-coloured substance on heating produces a shiny metallic residue and gives off a colourless gas. Was the original substance an element or a compound?

7. In Question 6 would you expect the mass of the metallic residue to differ from that of the brown substance? How, and why?

8. At one time air was considered to be an element. Why is this view not held today?

9. By calculation show that the following statements are equivalent, and state what chemical law they embody:

(a) Iron combines with oxygen in the mass-ratio 3.49:1.00.

(b) A compound of iron and oxygen contains 77.8% iron by mass.

(c) A mass of 0.186 g of iron and 0.0533 g of oxygen combine to form a compound.

10. Given that 3.04 g of pure zinc sulphide contains 1.00 g of sulphur and the remainder zinc, calculate the mass of sulphur that would combine with (a) 1.00 g of zinc; (b) 40.0 g of zinc. Also calculate the maximum mass of zinc that you could expect to obtain by chemical treatment of 1000 kg of a mineral that is pure zinc sulphide. Why is the question phrased "*maximum* mass"?

11. Why do chemists say that magnesium oxide is a more *stable* substance than mercuric oxide?

12. Check with the aid of a dictionary the meanings of the words *synthesis* and *analysis*. Which of the experiments described in this chapter constitutes a synthesis, and which an analysis? Justify your answers.

13. The densities of magnesium and magnesium oxide are given in Table 3-1. Calculate the mass and the volume of magnesium oxide that would be produced by the complete burning of 1.0 cm³ of magnesium metal.

14. Would it be suitable to use the triple-beam balance illustrated in the text for determining the masses required in the experiment described in Sec. 3-3? Explain why or why not.

15. Copper and sulphur react together much as zinc and sulphur do in the experiment described in Sec. 2-5. A known mass of copper powder is mixed with excess sulphur, and the mixture is heated to induce a reaction. Afterward the unreacted sulphur is allowed to burn away to gaseous sulphur dioxide, which escapes. From the following data, calculate the ratio by mass in which copper and sulphur react:

mass of test tube	21.511 g
mass of test tube + copper	22.524 g
mass of test tube + copper sulphide	22.776 g

16. Show that the following data are in accord with the Law of Definite Proportions:

(a) 6.54 g of zinc + 3.21 g of sulphur →
9.75 g of zinc sulphide

(b) 7.00 g of zinc + 3.21 g of sulphur →
9.75 g of zinc sulphide
+ 0.46 g of zinc

(c) 6.54 g of zinc + 4.00 g of sulphur →
9.75 g of zinc sulphide
+ 0.79 g of sulphur

17. Individual members of a class of students carried out the experiment on the heating of magnesium in air, and when all the results were compared it was found that the gain in mass per gram of magnesium ranged from a low of 0.63 g to a high of 0.67 g. The class average was 0.66 g. Are we justified, in the face of this evidence, in our belief in the Law of Definite Proportions? Discuss.

18. Name the five most abundant elements in the earth's crust, and rank them in the order of decreasing abundance. In what common forms do these occur on earth? (You may need to consult some reference books to answer this.)

19. Although the atmosphere contains about four parts of nitrogen (by volume) for each part of oxygen, nitrogen is not listed in Table 3-2. Can you account for this?

20. At 25°C the following substances have the densities stated: copper, 8.9 g/cm³; sulphur, 2.1 g/cm³; copper sulphide, 5.7 g/cm³. One gram of sulphur will react with four grams of copper to form copper sulphide. Compare the volumes of reactants and product. Does the reaction result in a shrinkage or an expansion?

*21. Early in the seventeenth century J. B. van Helmont, in a famous experiment, grew a willow tree in a pot of earth. The shrub had an initial mass of 5 lb and the tree at the end had a mass of 169 lb. Helmont had added nothing to the "system" except rainwater or distilled water, and so concluded that water was the primary stuff of which everything else consisted. Comment on his interpretation, and indicate whether the Law of Conservation of Mass (not at that time recognized) was violated.

*22. When we use the phrase "conservation of mass," what precisely does the word *conservation* mean? Is this the same meaning as the word conveys in the phrase "conservation of fuel"?

4 The Structure of Substances: An Atomic Theory

1. People have speculated for centuries about how matter is made up. An Athenian philosopher, Democritus, taught about 400 B.C. that the world was made up of tiny particles. He described these as imperceptible (unable to be perceived by the senses), indivisible, and indestructible. One could doubtless arrive at such a description of matter by lying out in the sun in some Olympian vineyard and gazing at the sky. Somebody else could devise an altogether different model of matter; and various people, including the much more influential Aristotle, did just that. These Greek philosophers did not put their ideas to the test by making measurements or doing experiments, and so there was no basis for choosing one theory of the structure of matter in preference to another. Democritus' idea of tiny particles being the building blocks of all matter reappeared from time to time, but did not gain general acceptance until the nineteenth century.

2. DALTON'S ATOMIC THEORY. The man who deserves the credit for putting this theory on a scientific basis is the school teacher, John Dalton (1766-1844). The great intellectual leap that he made was the suggestion that the Law of Conservation of Mass and the Law of Constant Composition could be explained by the following five assumptions:

1. All substances are made up of tiny, invisible particles.

2. Each chemical element is composed of characteristic particles which cannot be further subdivided. (These particles he called atoms.)

3. In each element the atoms are all alike and have the same mass; the atoms of different elements differ in mass.

4. Atoms cannot be created or destroyed during physical or chemical changes.

5. Compounds result from the union of atoms in some simple numerical ratio to form "compound atoms."

The word "atom" is derived from Greek roots meaning something that cannot be cut or divided.

The term "compound atom" was used by Dalton, who believed that compounds too had their own characteristic particles. Although the term is a bit archaic, we shall retain it in the next few pages until we explain what we now think the union of atoms produces.

How very simple that makes it all seem. One element differs from another because each has its own special kind of atom. An element cannot be broken down into simpler substances because its atoms are indivisible. When two elements combine, atoms are neither created nor destroyed; so the mass of the product is the same as that of the reactants. And, if an atom of element A and an atom of element B unite to form a "compound atom," or for that matter, if a billion atoms each of A and B form a billion "compound atoms," the proportions by mass of the elements in the compound will be constant. The constancy of composition of the compound is the result of the event on the atomic scale happening the same way each and every time.

3. RELATIVE MASSES OF ATOMS. Moreover, Dalton believed that, in spite of the fact that he couldn't see or handle the atoms of his theory, he could deduce something about their *relative masses*. To explain this, we shall go back to the reaction between magnesium and oxygen which we examined in the last chapter. There we saw that each time magnesium oxide was formed from the elements, 1.00 g of magnesium combined with 0.66 g of oxygen—neither more nor less.

John Dalton was an English school teacher who knew how to study by himself, for his own schooling ceased when he was only eleven years old.

He made several contributions to science, but it was the publication of his atomic theory in 1808 that brought him fame.

$$\frac{\text{mass of magnesium}}{\text{mass of oxygen}} = \frac{1.00}{0.66} = \text{approx.} \ \frac{3}{2}$$

If we assume that Dalton's proposals are correct, and if we *assume* (and Dalton encountered some snags here) that the "compound atom" of magnesium oxide is made up of one atom each of magnesium and oxygen, *then* we may infer that a magnesium atom is $3/_2$ times as heavy as an oxygen atom. This doesn't tell us the mass of either atom *absolutely*, but does tell us the mass of one *relative* to the other.

Some people find the idea of the relative masses of atoms somewhat difficult to grasp. Perhaps we could illustrate the idea of relative masses by an example that has nothing to do with chemistry. Imagine going to a clerk in a hardware store to buy 5 kg of a certain size of bolt. When these have been weighed into a paper bag you suddenly realize that you must have an equal number of nuts to thread onto the bolts. The clerk obligingly goes away and counts out the nuts and adds them to the bag, and the scale now registers 6 kg. You may have no idea how many nuts and bolts are actually in the bag, but you should be able to figure out that each bolt weighs five times as much as a nut. By similar reasoning nineteenth-century chemists were able, by making certain assumptions, to deduce the relative masses of atoms that they couldn't see.

By this sort of reasoning Dalton produced the first table of relative masses of the atoms of the different elements. Our understanding has greatly increased since 1808 when the foregoing was introduced, but we have had only to modify, not greatly change, the principles enunciated by John Dalton.

4. Dalton didn't prove the existence of atoms; it would be better to say he *inferred* it, in the same sense that Columbus inferred the western route to the Indies from the supposition that the earth was spherical. In the nineteenth century many chemists were not altogether convinced that atoms were real or necessary to explain chemical phenomena. The evidence on which Dalton based his inferences certainly did not permit a very precise description of this model for the structure of matter. There was no way of telling how big atoms were or anything about their shape; there was no way of obtaining the mass of a single atom. Towards the end of the nineteenth century there began a flood of experiments and observations which in about two decades gave convincing evidence of the existence of atoms and made possible a much more detailed description of them.

5. From these investigations we now recognize that the name atom, meaning something indivisible, is a misnomer. Experiments have shown that atoms have constituent parts and an internal structure that can be revealed in certain ways. Perhaps the most dramatic demonstration that atoms are *not* indivisible came in the closing weeks of World War II when the United States Air Force dropped a new kind of weapon on the Japanese city of Hiroshima. The power of the new weapon, called an atomic bomb, was provided by the sudden splitting of atoms of uranium. Today every enlightened citizen of the world has heard of nuclear fission and nuclear energy, even if he or she doesn't understand them. One very good reason for studying science is so you may be enlightened concerning the power and the danger of this development in man's control over nature.

6. AVERAGE ATOMIC MASSES. Dalton was mistaken in assuming that all the atoms of a given element have the same mass. They are certainly very alike; but, for many of the elements, experiments performed long after Dalton's time have shown that the masses of the atoms of a given element can differ slightly. For a century after Dalton proposed his ideas, chemists were not aware of this difference because, in handling substances in bulk, they were dealing with enormous numbers of atoms. The atomic masses they used were *average* relative values of the masses of the atoms. We shall be going into this in some detail in Sec. 10-14 but for the present we shall treat the atoms of any one element as if they were all alike.

It is often quite safe to treat average values of some quantity as "representative" or "typical" values. Here is an example. The average age of school pupils entering Grade 9 in Ontario is 14. We all know of pupils who for one reason or another enter Grade 9 when they are 13 or 15, or even 16. Nevertheless, the "representative" or "typical" Grade 9 student is 14 on entry. And this average age applies not only to the Province of Ontario as a whole, but to any large sample of pupils taken in one location or another—say Ottawa or Windsor. Since we are dealing with large numbers of pupils, the average age is the same each time we check it, and so serves as a representative value. For atomic masses the same principle applies. Even though all iron atoms do not have the same mass, the average—when a large number of atoms is taken—appears to be constant. Ordinary amounts of iron contain vast numbers of atoms.

7. "COMPOUND ATOMS." Dalton stressed that the union of atoms produces "compound atoms." This tended for a long time to create the impression that in elements and compounds we are dealing with tiny particles in all cases. But, as we shall see in later chapters, enormous numbers of atoms can combine to form single structures.

8. RELATIVE ATOMIC MASSES. In tracing the gradual acceptance of Dalton's atomic theory during the nineteenth century, we find confusion arose for some time because of the following problem. In Sec. 4-3 we said of the magnesium-oxygen reaction:

$$\text{magnesium} + \text{oxygen} \rightarrow \text{magnesium oxide}$$
$$3g \qquad\qquad 2g \qquad\qquad\qquad 5g$$

We then said *if* the combination proceeded according to the following:

1 atom of magnesium + 1 atom of oxygen → 1 "compound atom"

we could deduce that a magnesium atom was $3/2$ times as heavy as an oxygen atom. But there is a big "if" in this reasoning. We might as readily have assumed:

2 atoms of magnesium + 1 atom of oxygen → 1 "compound atom"

or

1 atom of magnesium + 2 atoms of oxygen → 1 "compound atom"

From *these* assumptions we should have drawn different conclusions. A little thought and a little arithmetic should convince you that, if the former of these alternatives were true, the magnesium atom would only be three-quarters as heavy as the oxygen atom, whereas if the second alternative applied, a magnesium atom would be three times as heavy as an oxygen atom.

The composition by mass, which comes directly from an experiment, cannot alone reveal the numbers of atoms undergoing a chemical reaction. As we showed in Sec. 4-3, if the ratio in which atoms combine and the composition by mass are known, we can calculate the relative masses of the atoms. Or, if we know the composition by mass of a compound and the relative masses of the atoms in it, we can deduce the ratio in which the atoms are combined.

Example. Sulphur dioxide is a compound containing 50% sulphur and 50% oxygen by mass. A sulphur atom is known to be twice as heavy as an oxygen atom. It is evident, then, that it will take twice as many oxygen atoms as sulphur atoms in the compound if the two elements each make up 50% of its mass.

The position for fifty years after Dalton's theory was introduced was that neither the ratio of atoms in many compounds nor the relative masses of atoms were known with certainty. This difficulty was sorted out about 1860, and from that time onward chemists agreed to a scale of relative masses for atoms.

See Chapter 20.

Here we are disregarding the extremely minute amounts of naturally occurring plutonium (Pu).

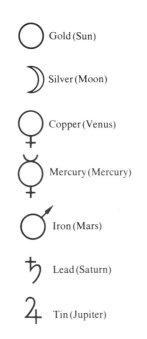

Fig. 4-1: These are a few of the symbols used by the alchemists. Do you recognize, in the symbols for copper and iron, Venus' mirror and Mars' shield and spear?

Fig. 4-2: Some of Dalton's symbols for elements

9. Any scale of relative values has to have a standard for reference: a familiar example is the practice of giving elevations of land in relation to sea level. It has proven convenient to compare the mass of atoms of any given element to the mass of carbon atoms. The carbon atoms selected to make this comparison are represented by a mass of 12.00. In relation to this standard the masses of other atoms are spread out on a scale ranging from 1 for hydrogen, the lightest atom, to 238 for uranium, the naturally occurring element with the heaviest atoms. For each element a number, called its **relative atomic mass** (but for many years called its "atomic weight") can be found by careful measurement (Sec. 20-8). This is the relative average mass of the atoms of that element on a scale based on carbon = 12.00. On this scale the value for magnesium turns out to be 24.31 and that of oxygen to be 16.00. This signifies that magnesium atoms are roughly twice as heavy (accurately, 2.026 times) as carbon atoms; oxygen atoms are 16.00/12.00 or $^4/_3$ as heavy as carbon atoms; and magnesium atoms are 24.31/16.00 or 1.52 times as heavy as oxygen atoms.

There is a slight complication in the above description. Not all carbon atoms have exactly the same mass; we shall be explaining this more fully in Chapter 10. It turns out that approximately 1% of *naturally occurring* carbon atoms are a bit heavier than the rest. Now, does that reference mass of 12.00 apply to the average of all carbon atoms, or to the more abundant species? In fact, the practice adopted by scientists has been to use the mass of the more abundant carbon atoms as the reference standard. The heavier carbon atoms have masses of 13 compared with the more common value of 12. The relative atomic mass of naturally occurring carbon is 12.01. (See Question 10.)

SYMBOLS

10. Dalton made another contribution. He introduced the use of a symbol for each atom, and hence for each element. The very early chemists, called alchemists, had previously used symbols for the seven metallic elements in which they were most interested; these were the symbols of the planets to which the metals were supposed to be astrologically related (Fig. 4-1). Dalton, recognizing the advantage of having a different symbol for each kind of atom, used a circle with a distinguishing mark for each atom, leaving the open circle for oxygen (Fig. 4-2). He represented a compound atom by placing two or more of these symbols together with the circles touching.

11. THE NAMES AND SYMBOLS OF ELEMENTS. Dalton's symbols were an improvement on the alchemists', but they were still very cumbersome. In 1811, the Swedish chemist Berzelius introduced the system of symbols now used, a system based on abbreviation of the names of the elements. Since there are many more elements than letters in the alphabet, it was not sufficient to use the first letter only of the name. Most of the symbols, therefore, have two letters—the first two in the name, or the first and third, or the first letters of two syllables.

For most elements, chemists of all countries and languages have agreed on an international name, often one ending in *-ium*. Elements discovered in ancient times had, however, acquired different names in different languages. For these Berzelius used the Latin name as a safe compromise. For example, *plumbum* is the Latin word for lead, so the symbol chosen for lead is Pb. Many of the best known elements, therefore, have symbols that seem to bear no relation to their names. This makes them harder to learn, to be sure, but equally hard for students in all countries. The result of Berzelius' decision is that chemical symbols—and the combination of these into so-called formulas—are the same in every language. In a Russian or Japanese or Czechoslovakian scientific paper they may be the only parts you can read.

The names, symbols, and relative atomic masses of twenty-four common elements are listed in Table 4-1. Where the symbol is based on a Latin name, that name is given in brackets.

Iron is variously called iron, *haearn* (Welsh), *iarunn* (Gaelic), *eisen* (German), *yzer* (Flemish), *ijzer* (Dutch), *yster* (Afrikaans), *jern* (Danish and Norwegian), *järn* (Swedish), *yergat* (Armenian), *dzelzs* (Latvian), *gelezis* (Lithuanian), *zeljezo* (Croat and Serbian), *zelezo* (Czech and Slovakian), *zelazo* (Polish), *vas* (Hungarian), *demir* (Turkish), *raud* (Estonian), *rauta* (Finnish), *fer* (French), *ferro* (Italian and Portuguese), *ferul* (Rumanian), *hierro* (Spanish), *hadid* (Maltese), *sideros* (Greek).

TABLE 4-1

SOME IMPORTANT ELEMENTS

NAME	SYMBOL	RELATIVE ATOMIC MASS
Silver (Argentum)	Ag	107.87
Aluminium	Al	26.98
Bromine	Br	79.91
Carbon	C	12.01
Calcium	Ca	40.08
Chlorine	Cl	35.45
Copper (Cuprum)	Cu	63.54
Fluorine	F	19.00
Iron (Ferrum)	Fe	55.85
Hydrogen	H	1.008
Helium	He	4.00
Mercury (Hydrargyrum)	Hg	200.59
Iodine	I	126.90
Potassium (Kalium)	K	39.10
Magnesium	Mg	24.31
Nitrogen	N	14.01
Sodium (Natrium)	Na	22.99
Oxygen	O	16.00
Phosphorus	P	30.97
Lead (Plumbum)	Pb	207.19
Sulphur	S	32.06
Silicon	Si	28.09
Tin (Stannum)	Sn	118.69
Zinc	Zn	65.37

Jöns Jakob Berzelius (1779-1848) was a Swede who for many years was the world's greatest authority on chemistry. He originated our symbols of the elements and their use in the formulas of compounds, discovered several elements, made what were in his day the best determinations of relative atomic masses, advanced chemical theory through his textbooks and other writings, and was the teacher of many whose names and work are a part of the history of chemistry.

12. FORMULAS AND EQUATIONS. Just as Dalton placed together the symbols of two or more elements to show how a compound is formed, so in the Berzelius system compounds are represented by a grouping of symbols of the constituent elements. Magnesium oxide is represented by MgO; this grouping of symbols is called a *formula*. And you probably already know that the formula for water is H_2O. Notice that the formula for magnesium oxide conveys the information that one atom of magnesium is united with one atom of oxygen, whereas the formula for water tells us that two atoms of hydrogen are united with one atom of oxygen.

> The **symbol** *stands for the element, but it can also stand for an atom of that element.*

> The **formula** *shows which elements are in a compound, and also the ratio(s) in which the atoms of these elements are united.*

The chemist uses symbols and formulas as a sort of shorthand. The formula of a compound, in addition to being briefer than the name, tells something of its composition.

By means of the relative atomic masses we can calculate the fraction or percentage of each element in a compound. From Table 4-1 we note that the relative masses of the hydrogen and oxygen atoms are

$$\text{hydrogen} = 1.008 \qquad \text{oxygen} = 16.00$$

In water, then, 2×1.008 or 2.016 parts (by mass) of hydrogen are united with 16.00 parts of oxygen. The Law of Conservation of Mass tells us that in this union nothing is added or taken away, so there must be 18.016 parts (by mass) of water. The fraction of each element in water thus is

$$\text{hydrogen} = 2.016/18.016 = 0.1119$$
$$\text{oxygen} \quad = 16.00/18.016 = 0.8881$$

and the percentages are

$$\text{hydrogen} = 0.1119 \times 100 = 11.19\%$$
$$\text{oxygen} \quad = 0.8881 \times 100 = 88.81\%$$

> *The formula indirectly expresses the composition of a substance by implying the relative amounts of the elements in it.*

Also, the essential information about a chemical reaction may be given in abbreviated form by means of these symbols. Notice, for example, the following:

$$\text{Mg} + \text{O} \rightarrow \text{MgO}$$

This brief statement is called a *chemical equation*. It states that magnesium atoms and oxygen atoms unite in equal numbers to form the compound magnesium oxide. However, there is still another complication: under most conditions the atoms of oxygen occur paired in molecules for which the formula O_2 is written. So a better shorthand description of the magnesium–oxygen reaction would show oxygen by formula rather than by symbol, thus:

$$Mg + O_2 \rightarrow MgO$$

This equation correctly shows that oxygen occurs as molecules of O_2 and that in magnesium oxide the atoms of magnesium and oxygen are combined 1:1, but the equation is unsatisfactory in that the Law of Conservation of Mass is not being "obeyed": there is more oxygen on the left-hand side than on the right-hand side. It is in fact not a true equation.

We correct this by putting appropriate coefficients in front of Mg and MgO:

$$2Mg + O_2 \rightarrow 2MgO$$

Such an equation is said to be *balanced*.

As we proceed in this book we shall see how a great deal of information about substances and reactions can be represented by formulas and equations.

QUESTIONS

1. State the five main postulates or assumptions of Dalton's atomic theory.

2. Explain how Dalton's theory accounts for (a) the Law of Conservation of Mass; (b) the Law of Definite Proportions.

3. List all the information conveyed by the statement that the formula of a certain gaseous substance is NO_2.

4. List all the information conveyed by the equation

$$2Ag + S \rightarrow Ag_2S$$

5. Why is it customary to balance a chemical equation?

6. From the formula ZnS for zinc sulphide, calculate the percentage of zinc in this compound, using the relative atomic masses of Table 4-1 (or the set given to one decimal place inside the back cover).

7. From the information given in Sec. 3-13 calculate the value of x in the following ratio, which applies to mercuric oxide:

$$\frac{\text{mass of mercury}}{\text{mass of oxygen}} = x$$

Does this prove that a mercury atom has a mass x times that of an oxygen atom? Explain.

8. Two compounds are known to contain only carbon and oxygen. One of these contains 57.1% oxygen, and the other 72.7% oxygen. Calculate for each compound the mass of oxygen combined with 1.00 g of carbon. Show how the results are consistent with an atomic theory of matter.

9. With the table of relative atomic masses, calculate formulas for the compounds described in Question 8. Are these the only possible formulas for these compounds? Explain.

10. The relative masses of all atoms are compared with the mass of certain carbon atoms, which are assigned the value 12.00. Yet the relative atomic mass of carbon is given in Table 4-1 as 12.01. Explain why there appear to be two values for carbon.

11. Suppose that the basis for comparing masses of atoms were changed from carbon = 12.00 to carbon = 100.0. What effect would this have on (a) the relative mass of an atom of magnesium; (b) the actual mass of an atom of magnesium?

12. A compound called cupric oxide (a black solid) is found to contain 4.0 g of copper for each 1.0 g of oxygen. Another compound, called cuprous oxide (a red solid) is found to contain 8.0 g of copper for each 1.0 g of oxygen. With no other information than this can you make a guess concerning the formulas of these compounds? Can you make a different guess for these formulas? If your first guess is correct, what are the relative masses of copper and oxygen atoms. What if your second guess is correct?

13. Methane, the most abundant constituent of natural gas, is composed of 75% carbon and 25% hydrogen by mass. Assuming that you know nothing of the numbers of atoms of each element in the molecule of methane, what deductions (if any) may be made about the relative masses of carbon atoms and hydrogen atoms?

14. From the information in Question 13, and the relative atomic masses in Table 4-1, deduce what you can about the numbers of atoms of each element in the molecule of methane.

15. Make clear the meaning of the terms *symbol* and *formula*. When oxygen is represented by O_2, is this a symbol or a formula?

5

Oxygen – the Vital Element

1. Oxygen is the breath of life, and has been for as long as *Homo sapiens* has been breathing. The species from which we evolved depended on it, too. Every fire that has been made has required oxygen. Yet tens of thousands of years passed by with no one being aware of this element. Gold and iron, copper and silver, lead, mercury, and sulphur have been known for thousands of years; but oxygen has been known for only two hundred years.

2. Why did this substance escape notice for so long? Partly because oxygen is by its nature elusive. It is ordinarily a gas, which makes it intangible, and it is colourless, tasteless, and odourless. However, the chief reason that it went undiscovered for so long is that no one was really looking for it! Until the eighteenth century, scientists didn't think much about what we now call gases. They knew there was air, and dry air and wet air, but the very idea of *different kinds* of "air"—that is, gases composed of different substances—is largely a product of eighteenth-century thinking and experimenting. When the idea was grasped, however, discoveries came rapidly: within a few years three of the most important gases, oxygen, hydrogen, and nitrogen, were recognized as distinct and elemental substances.

SOURCES OF OXYGEN

3. OCCURRENCE. Oxygen occurs both as the element itself and in the form of compounds. The most common compound is water. There are hundreds of millions of *cubic kilometres* of water on the earth, and oxygen constitutes 89% (by mass) of water. Moreover, oxygen in combined form is plentiful in rocks and minerals: almost half the mass of the earth's crust is oxygen (Table 3-2).

The building on the left is the Toronto Dominion Bank Tower, in downtown Toronto. How much air do you think is contained in that building? Well, it's more than seven hundred tonnes (7 × 10⁵ kg) —and a change of only 1°C in the temperature changes this by nearly 2500 kg!

The air is a vast reservoir of oxygen—not combined oxygen, but elemental oxygen. The composition of dry air is given in Table 5-1; slightly more than one-fifth of air is oxygen.

TABLE 5-1

COMPOSITION OF DRY AIR		
	PER CENT BY VOLUME	PER CENT BY MASS
Nitrogen	78.0	75.5
Oxygen	21.0	23.1
Other gases	1.0	1.4

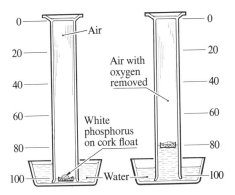

Fig. 5-1: *Determining the proportion by volume of oxygen in air*

4. That about one-fifth of air is oxygen can be demonstrated by a very simple experiment. Place a piece of white (sometimes called yellow) phosphorus, about half the size of a pea, on a thin piece of cork that is floating on water in a tray. Invert over the cork a 100-mL graduated cylinder, thereby trapping a definite volume of air (Fig. 5-1).

The phosphorus will react with the oxygen of the air in the cylinder, producing a white smoke that soon dissolves in the water. The water will move up into the cylinder to take the place of the oxygen consumed by reaction with the phosphorus. After all reaction has ceased, the water will occupy a fifth of the volume of the cylinder. Oxygen, then, constitutes one-fifth (by volume) of air. The water does not fill the cylinder because the other components of air, mainly nitrogen, do not react with phosphorus.

5. **LABORATORY PREPARATION.** Oxygen can conveniently be prepared in the laboratory by heating mercury(II) oxide (mercuric oxide, HgO), which readily decomposes to mercury and oxygen (Sec. 3-12). The equation is

$$2HgO \rightarrow 2Hg + O_2\uparrow$$

Here and elsewhere, we use an arrow pointing upwards ($\uparrow$) to *emphasize* the formation and expulsion of a *gas*.

A method for preparing oxygen that is better, because it is cheaper, is the heating of potassium chlorate ($KClO_3$) to form potassium chloride (KCl), and oxygen:

$$2KClO_3 \rightarrow 2KCl + 3O_2\uparrow$$
potassium   potassium
chlorate   chloride

A suitable apparatus is shown in Fig. 5-2.

If a little manganese dioxide (MnO_2), a black powdery substance, is added to the white potassium chlorate, the evolution of oxygen will be more rapid and more vigorous. Manganese dioxide acts in this reaction as a *catalyst*. A catalyst is a substance that speeds a chemical reaction without itself being used up.

"Handle" white or yellow phosphorus with forceps, never with your fingers. If you ignore this advice, you'll wish you hadn't. White phosphorus causes very nasty burns; its fumes are poisonous; and, unless it's wet, it may spontaneously catch fire in the air.

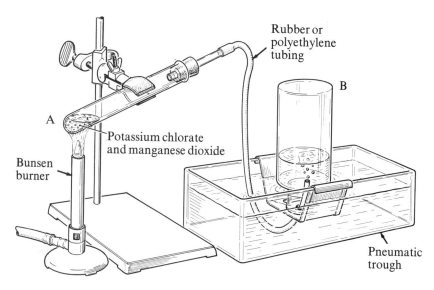

Fig. 5-2: *Potassium chlorate, in the test tube A, is heated gently; oxygen is evolved and led into the inverted bottle B, initially filled with water. The oxygen rises and pushes the water down and out. This method of collection is called displacement of water.*

6. COMMERCIAL PRODUCTION. Oxygen for industrial uses is sometimes made from water by the action of electricity (Sec. 26-15), but more often it is extracted from air. Air is liquefied (to "liquid air") by cooling and compressing it, and then the liquid is distilled (Sec. 17-12) in a manner that separates the oxygen, nitrogen, and the other (minor) components of air. This separation·takes advantage of the difference in the boiling points of liquid nitrogen (bp –196°C) and liquid oxygen (bp –183°C).

SOME REACTIONS OF OXYGEN

7. Oxygen is one of the most reactive of chemical elements: it reacts with a great many elements and compounds. In general, the product of the reaction of oxygen with other elements is a simple compound known as an **oxide**. Familiar examples of oxides are lime, or calcium oxide (CaO); iron rust, which is mainly iron oxide (Fe_2O_3); carbon dioxide (CO_2); and white sea sand, which is mainly silicon dioxide (SiO_2).

We shall first consider reactions of oxygen with elements and then, in Sec. 5-10, reactions of oxygen with compounds, particularly with compounds that contain carbon.

8. REACTION OF OXYGEN WITH METALS. The elements include the substances we know as metals (iron, copper, aluminium, etc.); in fact, most of the elements are metals. With very few exceptions, among them gold and platinum, all the metals react with oxygen.

For example, the rusting of iron is due mainly to a slow combination of iron with the oxygen of the air. The reaction can be represented by the equation:

$$4Fe + 3O_2 \rightarrow 2Fe_2O_3$$
iron oxide
(a brown-red solid)

Finely divided pure iron, when sprinkled into pure oxygen, catches fire immediately and burns up rapidly in a shower of sparks. The product of this reaction is also an iron oxide; however, under these conditions, a black oxide, of composition Fe_3O_4, is the product formed.

A more active metal, calcium, is converted to an oxide more rapidly than iron when exposed to the air. Similarly, calcium will burn more vigorously than iron; in fact it can be set on fire in the air. The product is calcium oxide:

$$2Ca + O_2 \rightarrow 2CaO$$
calcium oxide
or lime
(a white solid)

A reaction, such as either of these, in which there is a chemical union of a substance with oxygen, is called an **oxidation.** If the reaction is rapid, with fire and obvious evolution of heat and light, the oxidation is called a *combustion* or *burning.* If the reaction is slow, and a metal is involved, it is called a *rusting.* Whether they occur slowly or rapidly, heat is evolved in all these oxidation reactions. A chemical reaction in which heat is evolved or generated is said to be *exothermic.*

9. REACTION OF OXYGEN WITH NON-METALS. Oxidations occur with the elements known as non-metals, too. A discussion of this will lead us presently to one of the properties of an element that is used to classify it as "metal" or "non-metal."

Let us state, without explanation for the moment, that three typical non-metals are carbon (C), sulphur (S_8), and phosphorus (P_4). Each of these elements will burn in air, and even more vigorously in pure oxygen, to an oxide. The reactions are

$$C + O_2 \rightarrow CO_2$$
carbon dioxide
(a colourless,
odourless gas)

$$S_8 + 8O_2 \rightarrow 8SO_2$$
sulphur dioxide
(a colourless,
pungent gas)

$$P_4 + 5O_2 \rightarrow P_4O_{10}$$
phosphorus pentoxide
(a white solid)

Each of these reactions is an oxidation: each involves a chemical union or combination with oxygen, and each yields an oxide as the product. And each is an exothermic reaction.

"Burning" is a term of wider application than "combustion." "Burning" refers to any rapid reaction in which heat and light are evolved, whether or not oxygen is concerned in the reaction; "combustion" refers to reaction with oxygen. The reaction of zinc and sulphur (Chapter 2) is a "burning," but not a "combustion."

We write the formula for sulphur as S_8 rather than S because sulphur exists in the form of molecules, each of which contains eight atoms (Fig. 15-2). White phosphorus consists of molecules of P_4 (Fig. 22-2).

"Phosphorus pentoxide" seems an odd name for a compound of formula P_4O_{10}. In an earlier day the formula was thought to be P_2O_5, and so the compound was quite reasonably given this name, which has become very well established. It is now known that the molecule of this compound consists of four phosphorus atoms and ten oxygen atoms.

Antoine-Laurent Lavoisier (1743-1794) first put forward the view that combustion consists of reaction with oxygen. He was led to this idea, which was contrary to the chemical theories of his day, by careful measurements of the gain in mass of substances undergoing combustion and the loss in mass of the air involved.

Among much else, Lavoisier helped to devise our chemical nomenclature—words such as "oxide" and "sulphide"—whereby a compound has a name derived from the names of the elements of which it is composed.

Perhaps his greatest contribution was showing chemists the importance of weighing and measuring quantities carefully—something we take for granted today.

Litmus paper is paper impregnated with litmus, a plant pigment.

10. COMBUSTION OF FUELS. The combustion or oxidation of carbon to carbon dioxide, the equation for which is given just above, is the main reaction that occurs when *coal* is burned—for the simple reason that coal is mainly carbon. (The same equation serves to represent the burning of *coke*, which is more nearly all carbon than is coal.)

Coal is burned in tremendous amounts every day for the heat that is produced in its combustion. We call coal a *fuel*, by which we mean a substance from which energy (usually in the form of heat) can be obtained (usually by burning it) at reasonable cost.

Other important fuels are *natural gas* and *fuel oil*. These are not pure substances; they each consist of several compounds, mainly compounds of carbon and hydrogen known as **hydrocarbons.** A typical hydrocarbon is methane (CH_4), the main constituent of natural gas. The combustion of methane yields carbon dioxide and water (vapour):

$$CH_4 + 2O_2 \rightarrow CO_2 + 2H_2O + heat$$

The ease with which natural gas can be pumped through pipelines, and the supply of natural gas in (or, rather, under!) Western Canada, contribute to its importance as a fuel in Canada today.

A hydrocarbon that is chemically related to methane is propane (C_3H_8). It can readily be liquefied, and in this form stored or transported in steel cylinders. Many cottagers and campers use propane for cooking. Its combustion products are the same as those of methane:

$$C_3H_8 + 5O_2 \rightarrow 3CO_2 + 4H_2O + heat$$

Paraffin, as in a "wax" candle, is composed of several hydrocarbons. It likewise burns to carbon dioxide and water (vapour).

11. GASOLINE consists mainly of hydrocarbons, but more volatile ones than those of fuel oil or paraffin. When gasoline is burned in an automobile engine, hot gases are produced, and it is the expansion of these that furnishes the power to drive the automobile. It is also the expansion of hot gases from the combustion of fuel, but in different types of engine, that drives jet planes, rockets, and spacecraft.

The combustion of fuels furnishes much of the *heat* that keeps us warm in our homes, and the combustion of foodstuffs in our bodies (with the necessary oxygen being taken into our blood stream through our lungs) furnishes our body heat. Much *electricity* is generated from the energy of expanding steam, produced by the heat of burning coal or natural gas. Planes, trains, tractors, trucks, and ships depend for their *motive power* on the energy released in the combustion of fuels. In all these instances, energy is released as a consequence of, or as a product of, chemical reactions.

SOME PROPERTIES OF OXIDES

12. When the oxide of carbon (or of sulphur or of phosphorus) is dissolved in water the resulting solution turns litmus paper red and tastes sour. A solution that has these properties is said to be *acidic*, or to contain an **acid.** Such oxides are known as *acidic oxides*, and elements whose oxides are acidic are known as *non-metals*.

Although later we shall be discussing acids more fully, it is worth pointing out here that their formation in these cases results from a chemical reaction between the oxide and water, and that the product of this reaction is the acid substance. For the oxides mentioned we may write:

$$CO_2 + H_2O \rightarrow H_2CO_3$$
carbonic
acid

$$SO_2 + H_2O \rightarrow H_2SO_3$$
sulphurous
acid

$$P_4O_{10} + 6H_2O \rightarrow 4H_3PO_4$$
phosphoric
acid

By contrast, when the oxide of calcium (or magnesium or sodium) is dissolved in water the resulting solution turns litmus paper blue and feels "slippery." A solution that has these properties is said to be *alkaline* or *basic*, or to contain a **base.** Such oxides are known as *basic oxides*, and elements whose oxides are basic are known as *metals*. The acidic or basic character of the oxide of an element is one of the properties—there are others (Sec. 9-3 and 13-5)—used in classifying that element as a metal or a non-metal.

In the solutions that have alkaline properties a new substance has been formed as a result of a reaction between the metal oxide and water. For instance:

$$Na_2O + H_2O \rightarrow 2NaOH$$
sodium   sodium
oxide   hydroxide

$$CaO + H_2O \rightarrow Ca(OH)_2$$
calcium   calcium
oxide   hydroxide

The formula for calcium hydroxide introduces another point to be noted. We write $Ca(OH)_2$ rather than CaO_2H_2 because experience has shown that the pair of atoms OH recurs in substances with alkaline properties and elsewhere. Such groups of atoms that appear to pass intact through chemical reactions and to have associated with them certain characteristic properties (in this case alkalinity) came to be known as groups or radicals. The OH group or radical is named *hydroxide*. Other groups indicated in this section include SO_4 (sulphate), CO_3 (carbonate), PO_4 (phosphate).

The bases that react with water as shown above are also known as *alkalis* or are said to show alkaline properties. An important property of alkalis is their reaction with acids to give a new class of substances known as **salts,** for example:

$$2NaOH + H_2CO_3 \rightarrow Na_2CO_3 + 2H_2O$$
carbonic   sodium
acid   carbonate
(a salt)

Salts are also formed by the reaction of acids with many oxides that do not appreciably dissolve in water. For example:

$$CuO + H_2SO_4 \rightarrow CuSO_4 + H_2O$$

sulphuric
acid

copper
sulphate
(a salt)

Such an oxide—always the oxide of a metal—is also called a base although not called an alkali.

All alkalis are bases. Not all bases are alkalis.

IMPORTANCE OF OXYGEN

13. A long time ago, oxygen was called "vital air"—and a rather good name it was, too, because this element is essential to life as we know it.

When we inhale, oxygen from the air passes through the lungs into the blood, where it loosely combines with a complex compound known as hemoglobin. By this means oxygen is carried in the blood stream to the tissues and made available there for reaction with foodstuffs and body constituents. These reactions are exothermic, and it is the energy that is released that maintains our body heat, keeps our hearts pumping, activates our muscles for walking and talking and breathing, and in fact makes possible all our body functions.

Our bodies are—among other things—furnaces that "burn" fuels, such as the carbohydrates and fats in our diet, to obtain the energy needed for heat and for work. One such carbohydrate is the sugar known as glucose; its combustion can be represented by the equation:

$$C_6H_{12}O_6 + 6O_2 \rightarrow 6CO_2 + 6H_2O + heat$$

The carbon dioxide from this and related reactions in our bodies is carried by our blood to our lungs and escapes in exhaled breath.

The name "oxygen" is not at all good. It is from the Greek, meaning "acid-former." Lavoisier (1743-1794) coined this name, being of the opinion that this element was a constituent of all acids. He was very wrong about this, although he was very right about much else in chemistry—so much so that he is regarded as one of the founders of modern chemistry. He lost his head by the guillotine in the French Revolution, though not for chemical reasons.

Hemoglobin is an iron-containing red pigment in the red corpuscles of the blood. Every year far too many people die, accidentally or deliberately, by being in a closed garage with an automobile whose engine is running. One of the products of the combustion of gasoline is carbon monoxide (CO), an odourless and colourless gas. Carbon monoxide can combine with hemoglobin in much the same way oxygen can, and in fact hemoglobin prefers carbon monoxide. So, if you breathe carbon monoxide, your hemoglobin preferentially picks up carbon monoxide, and your tissue cells starve for lack of oxygen. The successive symptons of carbon monoxide poisoning are headache, irritability, confusion, unconsciousness, and death. All this may occur within a few minutes.

Joseph Priestley was prophetic when he wrote, just over 200 years ago, that pure "dephlogisticated air," which was his name for oxygen, "might be peculiarly salutary to the lungs in certain morbid cases."

14. When lungs are impaired, or breathing is difficult, or normal air is not available (as in high flying and deep diving), an artificial atmosphere is needed. So, an "oxygen tent," which furnishes an atmosphere enriched in oxygen, is helpful to a patient with pneumonia, and an "oxygen inhalator" may revive a victim of near-drowning or carbon monoxide poisoning. Astronauts, of course, have to carry oxygen or substances from which oxygen can be obtained.

We have seen that the combustion of fuels (Sec. 5-10) depends on oxygen to furnish much of the heat that warms our homes, offices, and factories. Normally, combustions take place in ordinary air, of which 21% (by volume) is oxygen. If the air is "enriched" by the addition of oxygen, combustion will be more vigorous and more rapid. The effect is further enhanced by using pure oxygen, as in some rockets, which carry oxygen for the burning of their fuel. More and more, combustions in industry are being facilitated by using a higher concentration of oxygen than ordinary air can supply. For example, oxygen is used in this way at Hamilton, Ontario, and elsewhere, to burn out impurities in iron in a

"Oxygen is for burning or breathing, depending on whether you are rockets or people." (Nine-year-old student)

steelmaking process, and at Sudbury, Ontario, during the smelting of sulphide ores to extract nickel and copper, to speed and make more efficient the conversion of sulphides to gaseous sulphur dioxide.

An important use for oxygen is in "oxy-acetylene" torches, for cutting and welding metals and alloys. Acetylene (C_2H_2) is a gas that burns with a hot flame in air, but with an even hotter one in pure oxygen. This you might expect from the increased rate of combustion of the acetylene and from the fact that a lot of the energy produced isn't "wasted" in heating up the nitrogen of the air which flows through an ordinary burner. The temperature of the oxy-acetylene flame is about 3300°C.

A growing use for oxygen is in the purification of sewage water; oxygen sustains micro-organisms that, in turn, convert waste materials into carbon dioxide and water.

15. SLOW BURNS. The oxygen in the air around us causes many oxidations to occur which are slower and less spectacular than those just described. For instance, we have mentioned the rusting of iron. Iron and steel (which is mostly iron) are used to construct automobile bodies, railroad cars, ship's hulls, bridges, and so on. When exposed to air containing moisture and carbon dioxide, iron is slowly converted to an oxide, the actual process being more complicated than that suggested by the equation given in Sec. 5-8. One estimate of the cost to society of this rusting, a cost made up of the deterioration of the metal itself and the efforts to prevent this, is a minimum of $6 billion annually. To limit this corrosion or rusting, exposed iron and steel is covered with paints and enamels which protect the surface from attack by the atmosphere. These paints and enamels often contain oils, many of them produced by chemists, which dry and harden as a result of chemical oxidation in the air.

Natural rubber is obtained from a milky latex tapped from special trees grown in tropical countries; synthetic rubber is produced chemically from suitable hydrocarbons. Rubber from either source is a polymer—that is, it is made up of enormous numbers of carbon and hydrogen atoms linked together in a certain way. A typical "formula" for rubber can be written $(C_5H_8)_n$, where n is a large number. Rubber, as we use it in tires, hoses, footwear, and the like, contains a variety of added substances to give it desirable properties. Virtually all rubber compositions include *antioxidants*, which are substances (as the name implies) that inhibit oxidation of the hydrocarbon by air. Oxidized rubber becomes hard and brittle, and therefore useless for its intended purpose.

16. OXYGEN AND CARBON DIOXIDE IN BALANCE. The process of breathing (Sec. 5-13) or respiration, involves taking oxygen from the air and giving carbon dioxide to the air. If it were not for a process that does the reverse—consuming carbon dioxide and producing oxygen—our atmosphere would become unfit for life. That process is *photosynthesis*, which occurs in all green plants under the influence of sunlight. Photosynthesis involves a very complicated series of reactions, but the net result of these can be represented by the equation:

$$6CO_2 + 6H_2O + \text{light energy} \longrightarrow \underset{\text{glucose}}{C_6H_{12}O_6} + 6O_2$$

This is essentially the reverse of the reaction shown in Sec. 5-13, which describes the combustion of glucose taken into the body as a "fuel." In the case of the photosynthesis reaction, the glucose and oxygen together have more chemical energy than the carbon dioxide and water from which they were formed—by an amount equal to the amount of energy absorbed from the sunlight. In a very real sense, some of the sun's energy is "stored" in every molecule of glucose that is formed by this reaction in a green plant.

The reactions of photosynthesis serve to produce glucose and other sugars, and also various polymers of glucose, such as starch. These are important to animals and humans as food. But the same reactions also form oxygen which is returned to the atmosphere. The chemical processes associated with respiration and photosynthesis are part of the *carbon cycle,* an intricate pattern of inter-relationships between living and non-living matter, which has kept the concentration of carbon dioxide and of oxygen in air almost constant for centuries. There is some concern, however, that human activities may be upsetting this balance. The demands of an ever expanding world population for fuel to keep warm, and especially to produce greatly increased amounts of electrical energy for industrial and other purposes, have resulted in the burning of ever increasing quantities of so-called fossil fuels—coal and petroleum and natural gas—created in the long-distant geological past. This combustion of fuels containing carbon is causing a slow but steady increase in the carbon dioxide content of the atmosphere. There are reasons for believing that carbon dioxide in the atmosphere limits the amount of heat energy that radiates from the earth into outer space. The consequence of a greater accumulation of this gas is that the whole planet may start to warm up. One serious result of such a warming trend is the possibility of vast quantities of ice in the polar regions melting and raising the level of the oceans.

Along with the increased generation of carbon dioxide into the atmosphere, there is a second perturbation in the carbon cycle. This is the gradual reduction in the amount of green vegetation, especially forests, as the human race spreads itself more and more across the land areas of the world. In particular concern has been expressed at the inroads upon the tropical rain forests in the Amazon River regions of Brazil.

QUESTIONS

1. Summarize the information given about oxygen in this chapter, under the following headings:

(a) occurrence

(b) laboratory preparation

(c) commercial production

(d) physical properties (see also Table 6-1)

(e) chemical properties

(f) importance

2. What is the proportion of oxygen in air, by volume? Describe an experiment to measure this proportion.

3. How could you show that oxygen comes only from potassium chlorate when a mixture of potassium chlorate and manganese dioxide is heated?

4. Although oxygen may be prepared rapidly and easily from potassium chlorate in the laboratory, it is not prepared commercially in this way. Account for this.

5. What mass of oxygen can be obtained from the complete decomposition of 1.00 g of potassium chlorate? Making use of the density of oxygen given in Table 6-1, calculate the volume of oxygen (measured under standard conditions) that can be obtained from 1.00 g of potassium chlorate.

6. When a sample of liquid air is left standing in a thermos flask (which prevents its *rapid* evaporation), it becomes richer in oxygen than ordinary air. Why?

7. The air in an average school laboratory contains over 50 m^3 of oxygen. Why does a wooden splint, which just glows in the laboratory, burst into flame when thrust into a 25-mL test tube filled with oxygen?

8. Where combustion is concerned, what air will do, oxygen will do better. Discuss with three or four examples. Why does an oxy-acetylene torch produce a hotter flame than can be attained with acetylene burning in air?

9. Write five equations representing oxidation reactions. Indicate what reactant has been oxidized in each reaction (by underlining its formula in the equation).

10. Name three oxides that are gases, three that are solids, and one that is a liquid, at ordinary temperatures.

11. When a metal rusts, is there a change in mass? Explain your answer.

12. Explain what is meant by: an oxide, a basic oxide, an acidic oxide. Give examples of the reactions of several oxides with water to form acids or bases.

13. Arsenious acid, As_2O_3, does not dissolve in water to any significant extent. It will dissolve in a dilute solution of sodium hydroxide. Can you draw any conclusion from this as to whether this oxide shows acidic or basic properties, and hence whether arsenic shows metallic or non-metallic properties?

14. The metal calcium can be burned in air to form calcium oxide. Calcium oxide will dissolve in water to form calcium hydroxide. When carbon dioxide is bubbled into a solution of calcium hydroxide a white precipitate forms consisting of calcium carbonate, which does not dissolve in water. Write a series of equations to describe this set of reactions. (You will need to consider what happens to carbon dioxide in water.)

15. Salt is the term popularly applied to the substance sodium chloride. Yet in chemistry the same word is used for a whole class of substances. Explain this chemical meaning of salt, and give two examples other than sodium chloride.

16. Make clear in your own words the meaning of:

(a) oxidation

(b) combustion

(c) burning

(d) rusting

(e) fuel

(f) hydrocarbon

(g) antioxidant

(h) exothermic reaction

17. Matter cannot be destroyed. Nevertheless, the gasoline in the tank of a car disappears as the car is driven. Why doesn't one of these statements contradict the other?

18. State how the conditions for burning are removed by: (a) stepping on a burning match; (b) blowing out a candle; (c) using a carbon dioxide fire extinguisher; (d) wrapping a blanket around a person whose clothes are burning; (e) blasting buildings in a fire area.

19. Indicate the meaning and importance of the following terms as they relate to the production of oxygen in the laboratory, in industry, or in nature: catalyst, distillation, photosynthesis.

*20. Explain what is meant by the carbon cycle in nature. How is carbon dioxide put into the atmosphere? How is it removed?

6 Hydrogen – the Universal Element

English is a peculiar language: "flammable" and "inflammable" mean the same thing. When a substance won't burn, it is "non-flammable" or "non-inflammable."

1. Hydrogen was first prepared and studied at a time when gases were called "airs." Because hydrogen burns readily it was named *inflammable air*, thereby distinguishing it from other "airs" such as "dephlogisticated air" (oxygen) and "fixed air" (carbon dioxide). The modern name of *hydrogen* is equally good in reflecting a property of this element, for it comes from the Greek meaning "water-former," and water is what is formed when hydrogen burns in air or oxygen.

2. OCCURRENCE. The most important occurrence of hydrogen on the earth is in water, a compound that is about 11% hydrogen (by mass). Hydrogen is also a constituent of hundreds of other compounds that are essential to living organisms, and it is a constituent of the many compounds that make up natural gas and petroleum. Moreover, it is in almost all acids and bases.

Only a trifling amount (0.01%) of elemental hydrogen occurs in our atmosphere, but it is very plentiful in the sun and other stars. In fact, when account is taken of the stars in our own and other galaxies, hydrogen atoms comprise 93% of all the atoms in the universe. Hence the title we use for this chapter.

3. LABORATORY PREPARATION. Hydrogen is usually made in the laboratory by the reaction of zinc and an acid, either hydrochloric acid or dilute sulphuric acid:

$$Zn + 2HCl \rightarrow H_2\uparrow + ZnCl_2$$
hydrochloric   zinc
acid   chloride

$$Zn + H_2SO_4 \rightarrow H_2\uparrow + ZnSO_4$$
sulphuric   zinc
acid   sulphate

A suitable apparatus is shown in Fig. 6-1.

Information about elements in the sun and stars comes from study of the light they emit. The element helium (Greek, helios, sun) was discovered in this way in the sun long before it was known on earth.

This photograph, taken during an eclipse, shows masses of glowing gas above the surface of the sun. Such "prominences," as they are called, are often projected upward like fiery geysers.

The sun's light shows the presence of almost 70 elements, of which hydrogen and helium are the most abundant.

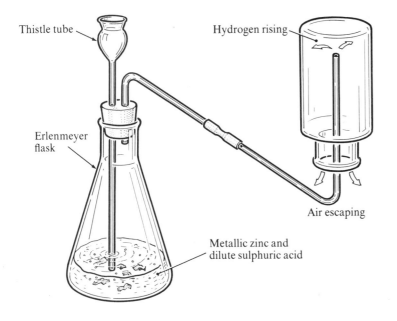

Fig. 6-1: Hydrogen can be collected by the downward displacement of air, as shown, because its density is so much less than that of air.

In these reactions, zinc is said to *displace* hydrogen from the acids. Iron and tin also displace hydrogen from hydrochloric acid and from dilute sulphuric acid. More active metals, such as magnesium and calcium (Chapter 29), and particularly sodium and potassium, displace hydrogen from acids with great vigour, often violence.

Do not do any experiments with potassium or sodium until you have become familiar with the properties of these metals.

Very active metals displace hydrogen even from water:

$$2K + 2H_2O \rightarrow H_2\uparrow + 2KOH \text{ (violent reaction)}$$
potassium   potassium
                             hydroxide

$$2Na + 2H_2O \rightarrow H_2\uparrow + 2NaOH \text{ (vigorous reaction)}$$
sodium   sodium
                             hydroxide

$$Ca + 2H_2O \rightarrow H_2\uparrow + Ca(OH)_2 \text{ (brisk reaction)}$$
calcium   calcium
                             hydroxide

Magnesium, less active than calcium, does not react detectably with cold water, but reacts with boiling water or steam, to yield hydrogen

$$Mg + H_2O \rightarrow H_2\uparrow + MgO$$
                            magnesium
                            oxide

Steam and water vapour are not the same thing. Water vapour is water in the gaseous state and it is invisible, whether hot or cold. If you look just beyond the spout of a kettle when the water in it is boiling briskly, what do you see? Nothing — and that is where hot water vapour is. A little further out you see a fog, which is steam, consisting of minute droplets of liquid water that have condensed from the vapour state as the vapour cooled somewhat.

and iron, a still less active metal, reacts with steam or hot water vapour if the metal is first heated to redness

$$3Fe + 4H_2O \rightarrow 4H_2\uparrow + Fe_3O_4$$
                              iron
                              oxide

4. COMMERCIAL PRODUCTION. Some of the hydrogen needed for industry is made by the electrical decomposition, or electrolysis, of water (Sec. 26-15) or of an aqueous solution of common salt (Sec. 26-14). The electrolysis of water is represented by the equation:

$$2H_2O + \text{electrical energy} \rightarrow 2H_2\uparrow + O_2\uparrow$$

Another method is the reaction of steam with white-hot coke (which is largely carbon):

$$H_2O + C \rightarrow H_2 + CO$$

The gaseous "mixture" of hydrogen and carbon monoxide (CO) obtained by this method is called *water gas*, and is used either as a source of hydrogen or as a fuel.

Other methods for obtaining hydrogen include the decomposition of ammonia, NH_3 (Sec. 7-8):

$$2NH_3 + \text{heat} \rightarrow 3H_2 + N_2$$

and the reaction (under appropriate conditions) of steam with natural gas, the main constituent of which is methane (CH_4):

$$2H_2O + CH_4 \rightarrow 4H_2 + CO_2$$

This latter reaction is in fact the chief source of hydrogen for industry.

5. USES. Several important chemicals are made from hydrogen. Among these are hydrogen chloride, ammonia, and methanol:

$$H_2 + Cl_2 \rightarrow 2HCl$$
hydrogen chloride

$$3H_2 + N_2 \rightarrow 2NH_3$$
ammonia

$$2H_2 + CO \rightarrow CH_3OH$$
methanol

Vegetable oils, such as cottonseed oil and peanut oil, are converted to solid or semi-solid substances, used as cooking fats and in margarine, by treating the oils with hydrogen under pressure, at about 200°C, in the presence of a suitable catalyst (usually nickel).

Hydrogen is used to inflate small weather balloons, because of its "lightness"; to cool some electrical equipment, because of its good conductivity for heat; and to convert some metal oxides to the metals themselves, because of its affinity for oxygen.

Liquid hydrogen is an important fuel for rocket propulsion, because in its reaction with oxygen a large amount of energy is released per gram of reactants.

6. SOME PROPERTIES OF HYDROGEN. At ordinary temperatures, hydrogen is a colourless, tasteless, and odourless gas. Some of its properties are given in Table 6-1. The density of hydrogen is only about one-fifteenth the density of air; in fact, hydrogen is the least dense (expressed loosely, the "lightest") of all gases.

TABLE 6-1

SOME PROPERTIES OF HYDROGEN AND OXYGEN

	HYDROGEN	OXYGEN
Relative Atomic Mass	1.008	16.000
Molecular Formula	H_2	O_2
Boiling Point (°C)	–253	–183
Freezing (or Melting) Point (°C)	–259	–219
Solubility in Water (mL gas/L water at 25°C)	19.1	30.9
Density (g/L at standard conditions)	0.090	1.429

As we shall see later, the density of gases varies appreciably according to the prevailing temperature and pressure. For this reason standard conditions, Standard Temperature and Pressure (STP), are often specified with such properties. These are 0°C and a pressure of 101.3 kPa.

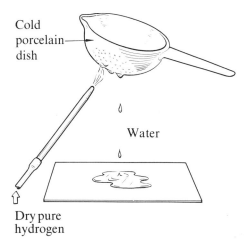

Cold
porcelain
dish

Water

Dry pure
hydrogen

Fig. 6-2: *Water is produced from the burning of hydrogen.*

7. Dry hydrogen burns in air or in oxygen, with a pale blue flame. The product is water, but, since the temperature of the combustion is well above 100°C, the water is in the form of water vapour. This will condense to liquid water on a cool surface, as indicated in Fig. 6-2. The equation for the reaction is

$$2H_2 + O_2 \rightarrow 2H_2O$$

This reaction is exothermic and, accordingly, a more complete description of the reaction is

$$2H_2 + O_2 \rightarrow 2H_2O + \text{heat}$$

Pure hydrogen burns quietly; but if hydrogen containing some air or oxygen is ignited, by a spark or flame, the combustion is *explosive*. Thus when an inverted bottle full of *pure* hydrogen is ignited, the hydrogen burns quietly and slowly at the mouth of the bottle, where the hydrogen

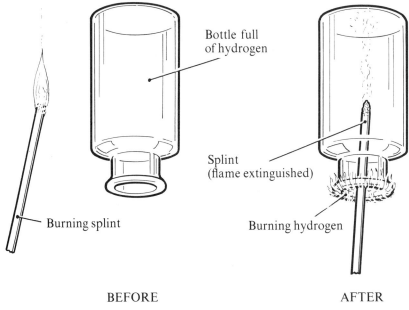

Bottle full
of hydrogen

Splint
(flame extinguished)

Burning splint

Burning hydrogen

BEFORE

AFTER

Fig. 6-3: *A splint will not burn in hydrogen but it starts the hydrogen burning where it is in contact with air.*

The purity of hydrogen can be judged by such an experiment. Hydrogen from a generator should **never** be ignited at the outlet from the generator until an inverted test tube of gas obtained from the generator will burn quietly. But don't try to ignite the gas until it has been moved several feet away from the generator!

meets the oxygen of the air (Fig. 6-3). If, however, the hydrogen has been mixed with an appropriate quantity of air, it all burns in a flash, with an explosive "pop." If anyone is foolish or careless enough to do this experiment with a large volume of hydrogen, the "pop" may be heard for half a kilometre or so. Such an explosion can be devastating.

Hydrogen's affinity for oxygen can be demonstrated in other ways. For example, hydrogen reacts with the oxides of the less active metals, abstracting the oxygen from the oxide to form water, and leaving the metal itself as the other product of the reaction. An interesting illustration of this is the reaction of hydrogen with hot copper oxide; the dull black oxide is changed to the shiny reddish metal, and water is formed (Fig. 6-4):

$$CuO + H_2 \rightarrow Cu + H_2O$$

copper
oxide   copper
                                (metal)

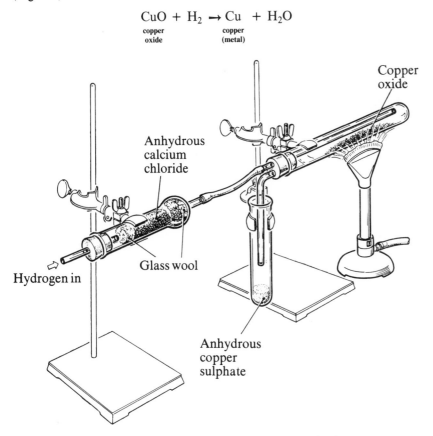

Copper
oxide

Anhydrous
calcium
chloride

Glass wool

Hydrogen in

Anhydrous
copper
sulphate

Fig. 6-4: *Hydrogen takes oxygen from hot copper oxide, becoming water (vapour). The copper oxide is reduced to copper metal. The water manifests itself by changing white anhydrous copper sulphate to blue hydrated copper sulphate (bluestone). To make sure that the water was not in the stream of hydrogen, but was actually formed in the reaction, the hydrogen is first passed through anhydrous calcium chloride, a drying agent.*

The reaction of hydrogen with metal oxides is used in industry to prepare certain metals. A good example is tungsten, the metal from which the filaments of incandescent electric light bulbs are made.

  8. THE REDUCING ACTION OF HYDROGEN. The reaction of hydrogen with copper oxide is an example of a type of chemical reaction known as *reduction. When a metal is formed from a compound of the metal the compound is said to be* **reduced.** *The substance that brings about the reduction is a* **reducing agent.** In our example, hydrogen is the reducing agent:

$$CuO + H_2 \rightarrow Cu + H_2O \qquad (1)$$

_{substance reduced}   _{reducing agent}   _{product of the reduction}

Conversely, *when a metal is converted to a compound, the metal is said to be* **oxidized;** *and the substance that brings about the conversion is an* **oxidizing agent.** For example, when copper (metal) is heated in air or oxygen it is converted to copper oxide. In this reaction, copper is oxidized and oxygen is the oxidizing agent:

$$2Cu + O_2 \rightarrow 2CuO$$

_{substance oxidized}   _{oxidizing agent}   _{product of the oxidation}

Hydrogen is by no means the only reducing agent in chemistry. Hot coke or carbon, for example, is an important reducing agent in industry, and is so used in the making of iron from iron oxide in a blast furnace. Nor is oxygen the only oxidizing agent. For example, in Equation (1) above, we have indicated that copper oxide is being reduced to copper by means of hydrogen, but we might just as properly have written the equation as:

$$CuO + H_2 \rightarrow Cu + H_2O \qquad (2)$$

_{oxidizing agent}   _{substance oxidized}   _{product of the oxidation}

This indicates that hydrogen is being oxidized to water, by means of copper oxide. Equations (1) and (2) are both correct because oxidation and reduction go hand in hand.

By comparing the labels in Equations (1) and (2) you will notice that the reducing agent (H_2) is oxidized and that the oxidizing agent (CuO) is reduced. Perhaps an analogy will make this less confusing than it appears on first reading. Suppose that you expose a wet towel to the air of a room, either to dry the towel or to make the air more humid. Whatever your purpose, the towel becomes drier and the air becomes wetter. The towel is a wetting agent and the air is a drying agent. So the wetting agent is dried and the drying agent is wetted—just as a reducing agent is oxidized and an oxidizing agent is reduced.

9. REVERSIBLE REACTIONS. We mentioned earlier (Sec. 6-3) that hot water vapour will react with hot iron:

$$4H_2O + 3Fe \rightarrow Fe_3O_4 + 4H_2 \qquad (3)$$

Any amount of iron can be oxidized to iron oxide if sufficient hot water vapour is brought into contact with it and the hydrogen that is produced is swept away.

It is also true that hydrogen will react with hot iron oxide:

$$4H_2 + Fe_3O_4 \rightarrow 3Fe + 4H_2O \qquad (4)$$

Here, hydrogen is reducing iron oxide to metallic iron. And any amount of iron oxide can be reduced if sufficient hydrogen is brought into contact with it and the water vapour that is produced is swept away.

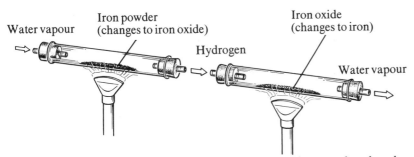

Fig. 6-5: *Water vapour passed over heated iron powder is reduced to hydrogen, the iron changing to iron oxide. If the process is reversed and hydrogen is passed over heated iron oxide, the iron oxide is reduced to iron and hydrogen is oxidized to water vapour.*

The two reactions can be demonstrated very simply as illustrated in Fig. 6-5. Notice that the reaction of Equation (4) is the exact reverse of that of Equation (3). These reactions are said to be *reversible,* and this may be indicated by the use of double arrows, thus:

$$4H_2O + 3Fe \rightleftharpoons Fe_3O_4 + 4H_2$$

The direction in which a reversible reaction predominantly "goes" depends on the substances taking part in the reaction, their concentrations, and the temperature. There is much to be learned from reversible reactions, but this will have to be left for more advanced study.

QUESTIONS

1. Summarize the information given in this chapter about hydrogen, under the following headings:

(a) occurrence (d) physical properties

(b) laboratory preparation (e) chemical properties

(c) commercial production (f) importance

2. In the laboratory preparation of hydrogen could the gas have been collected, as oxygen was, by the displacement of water?

3. Describe two different methods for producing hydrogen from water in the laboratory.

4. Write equations representing the reactions of (a) sodium, potassium, calcium, and magnesium with water; and of (b) zinc with hydrochloric acid, and with sulphuric acid.

5. Would you use water to extinguish the flame of burning sodium? Why?

6. Write equations for: (a) the formation of water by the burning of hydrogen; (b) the decomposition of water by electricity.

7. Explain the distinction between water gas and water vapour.

8. What is a safe way for lighting hydrogen from a jet? Explain why.

9. Why is it important to know the test for pure hydrogen? Outline a procedure by which you could find out whether or not the gas from a generator was pure hydrogen.

10. The explosive nature of a mixture of hydrogen and oxygen has been described in this chapter. What is the nature and the cause of the explosion?

11. Outline a demonstration to show that hydrogen has a density less than that of air.

12. Hydrogen, because of its low density, can be used to inflate balloons. Why is it rarely used for this purpose? Do you know what is used instead, and why?

13. Explain the meaning of:

(a) displacement reaction (c) reduction

(b) reversible reaction (d) reducing agent

14. (a) Outline the method and observations of an experiment to show that hydrogen is a reducing agent.

(b) Write the equation for the reaction in this experiment, and label the substance reduced and the product of its reduction.

15. Suggest a chemical test for distinguishing between powdered charcoal and powdered cupric oxide (both of which are black).

16. Contrast the properties of oxygen and hydrogen with respect to:

(a) occurrence; (b) density; (c) ability to support combustion; (d) flammability; (e) oxidation and reduction.

17. You are given three stoppered but unlabelled bottles, one containing hydrogen, one oxygen, and the other air. How could you decide which was which?

18. Write an equation for the decomposition of water to its constituent elements. Suppose this is done by an electric current (electrolysis) so that the hydrogen and oxygen are produced and collected separately. Suppose, in addition, that the current runs long enough to cause the decomposition of 0.100 g of water. By means of the densities given in Table 6-1 calculate the volume of each gas produced. How do the volumes compare?

*19. The exact composition of water has been determined by an investigation similar to that described in Sec. 6-7. Hydrogen is passed over a known mass of heated copper oxide long enough to reduce part of the oxide. The water vapour thereby formed is passed through a tube containing a known mass of solid phosphorus pentoxide, with which it reacts completely (Sec. 5-12). The loss in mass of the copper oxide indicates the quantity of oxygen converted to water; the gain in mass of the phosphorus pentoxide indicates the quantity of water formed. From the following experimental information calculate the percentage composition of water. (Compare your result with the data in Sec. 4-12.)

Loss in mass of copper oxide on reduction = 0.6565 g

Gain in mass of phosphorus pentoxide = 0.7392 g

Nitrogen – a Lazy Element

7

1. The French word for nitrogen is *azote*. This is a very apt name for this relatively lazy or unreactive element because it comes from the Greek meaning "without life." In molecules of nitrogen, N_2, the two atoms are strongly linked to each other, much more so than are the atoms in the O_2 or H_2 molecules. This strong "bond" hinders the reaction of nitrogen with other substances.

This chemical laziness does not extend to nitrogen compounds in which nitrogen atoms are not linked to each other. Included among these are important foods and fertilizers, all the proteins, and most explosives.

2. OCCURRENCE. You will have already seen, from Table 5-1, that in ordinary air there is about three times as much nitrogen as oxygen. And there is a lot of air: above every square metre of the earth's surface there are 7800 kg of elemental nitrogen.

Nitrogen occurs in many compounds, too. One that is important, as a fertilizer, is sodium nitrate, $NaNO_3$, known as *Chile saltpeter* from its extensive occurrence in that country. The most important nitrogen compounds, however, are the proteins: these primary and essential constituents of our bodies have very large molecules in which nitrogen atoms have a key role.

3. LABORATORY PREPARATION. A method that would be excellent for making pure nitrogen, if it were not dangerous, is the *very gentle* heating of a solution of ammonium nitrite (NH_4NO_2). This is prepared by mixing solutions of ammonium chloride and sodium nitrite, which react as follows:

$$NH_4Cl \ + \ NaNO_2 \rightarrow NH_4NO_2 \ + \ NaCl$$

ammonium chloride   sodium nitrite   ammonium nitrite   sodium chloride

Then the ammonium nitrite decomposes into nitrogen and water:

$$NH_4NO_2 \rightarrow N_2\uparrow + 2H_2O$$

CAUTION: *Ammonium nitrite is a dangerously unstable substance. Once the decomposition has been started by gentle heating, it proceeds rapidly with the evolution of heat, and may become explosive unless the vessel is cooled.*

A safer way to obtain nitrogen for laboratory experiments is to use up the oxygen of ordinary air by putting into the air something that reacts with the oxygen to give a solid product. Steel "wool" (from which the grease has been removed by washing) serves very well—although you will have to wait a day or two for all the oxygen to be consumed. The steel rusts by taking oxygen from the air, leaving the nitrogen. A related but faster method is to allow phosphorus to react with the oxygen. For either method, the apparatus pictured in Fig. 5-1 is appropriate.

Neither of these latter methods yields pure nitrogen because air does not consist solely of oxygen and nitrogen. But the nitrogen is reasonably pure, because the proportions of carbon dioxide and the other gases in air total only about 1%.

4. PHYSICAL PROPERTIES. Like oxygen and hydrogen, gaseous nitrogen is colourless, odourless, and tasteless. And, like them again, it does not dissolve much in water. Nitrogen has a density somewhat less than that of oxygen, but decidedly greater than that of hydrogen (Table 7-1).

TABLE 7-1

SOME DENSITIES	
GAS	DENSITY AT STP (g/L)
Air	1.29
Nitrogen	1.25
Oxygen	1.43
Hydrogen	0.09
Carbon dioxide	1.98
Ammonia	0.77

When it is sufficiently cooled and compressed, nitrogen first becomes a liquid (boiling at $-196°C$) and then a solid (melting at $-210°C$).

5. CHEMICAL PROPERTIES. Although nitrogen is not reactive the way that oxygen or hydrogen is, under suitable conditions it will combine with oxygen, with hydrogen, and with some metals.

With hot calcium or magnesium metals, nitrogen reacts to form what is called a *nitride*, for example:

$$N_2 + 3Ca \rightarrow Ca_3N_2$$
$$\text{calcium nitride}$$

The formation of a little magnesium nitride when magnesium is heated in air was mentioned in a marginal note with Sec. 3-4.

At high temperatures, nitrogen reacts with oxygen:

$$N_2 + O_2 \rightarrow 2NO$$
nitric
oxide

This reaction occurs during the ignition stroke in an ordinary automobile engine. The nitric oxide so formed is among the exhaust gases. After escaping from the tailpipe, this oxide combines with the oxygen of the air to form nitrogen dioxide, NO_2. This, by the action of the ultraviolet light of the sun, is decomposed to very reactive substances which combine with unburnt gasoline molecules in the air; such reactions yield chemicals that irritate our eyes and respiratory passages. These substances are in the smog that afflicts Los Angeles and, in varying degrees, most large cities.

Nitrogen's reaction with hydrogen at about 500°C, under high pressure, in the presence of a suitable catalyst, is particularly important:

$$N_2 + 3H_2 \rightarrow 2NH_3$$
ammonia

By this means, in what is known as the **Haber process**, ammonia for industry (Sec. 7-10) is produced in very large amounts.

6. PRODUCTION AND USES OF NITROGEN. Nitrogen for industrial uses is obtained the way that oxygen is, from liquid air (Sec. 5-6). Ordinary air is liquefied by cooling and compressing it and then, to separate the components, the liquid is distilled (Sec. 17-12).

Because nitrogen is unreactive toward most substances, it is used as an inert atmosphere, that is, as a protective gas to surround or "blanket" a substance and so shield it from the oxygen of the air as, for example, during the heat treating of metals. The most important use for gaseous nitrogen is for making other chemicals, especially ammonia (NH_3) and nitric acid (HNO_3). A growing use for liquid nitrogen is in the fast freezing of foods.

Fritz Haber (1868-1934) was a brilliant German chemist who devised a practical method for making ammonia directly from nitrogen and hydrogen.

With the help of Carl Bosch, a chemical engineer, he developed this into a large-scale industrial process that, with minor modifications, has been used for more than 60 years and continues to be the way in which most of the world's ammonia is made.

OXIDES OF NITROGEN

7. There are seven oxides of nitrogen. Yet nitrogen and oxygen exist together in the air without uniting to form any of them. (This shows how unreactive nitrogen is.) The oxides are usually made from other nitrogen compounds.

Of the seven oxides (N_2O, NO, NO_2, N_2O_3, N_2O_4, N_2O_5, and N_2O_6), only three—those listed in Table 7-2—are of much importance. These three oxides are all gases under ordinary conditions.

Dinitrogen oxide (nitrous oxide, N_2O) may be prepared from ammonium nitrate. *The heating of ammonium nitrate should be done* **very cautiously,** and should be discontinued before more than two-thirds of the nitrate has decomposed. Nitrous oxide prepared from ammonium ni-

However, oxygen and nitrogen do unite during thunderstorms (when the lightning brings about some reaction of the nitrogen and oxygen of the air, with the formation of oxides of nitrogen) and in the upper reaches of the atmosphere (where ultraviolet rays induce some reactions between nitrogen and oxygen).

The explosion of ammonium nitrate in a freighter in the harbour of Texas City in 1947 killed more than 500 people.

TABLE 7-2

SOME OXIDES OF NITROGEN

FORM-ULA	NAME*	SOME PROPERTIES	LABORATORY PREPARATION	USES
N_2O	dinitrogen oxide nitrous oxide "laughing gas"	colourless; odourless; induces mild hysteria, then anaesthesia	*gentle* heating of NH_4NO_3; $NH_4NO_3 \rightarrow 2H_2O + N_2O\uparrow$	anaesthetic; propellant and "whipping" agent in whipping cream substitutes
NO	nitrogen oxide nitric oxide	colourless; low solubility in water; reacts with oxygen to form NO_2	$3Cu + 8HNO_3$ *(dilute)* $\rightarrow 3Cu(NO_3)_2 + 4H_2O + 2NO\uparrow$	both NO and NO_2 are intermediates in the production of nitric acid (HNO_3) from ammonia (NH_3) by the Ostwald process:
NO_2	nitrogen dioxide	reddish-brown; irritating odour; poisonous; dissolves in and reacts with water	$Cu + 4HNO_3$ *(concentrated)* $\rightarrow Cu(NO_3)_2 + 2H_2O + 2NO_2\uparrow$	$4NH_3 + 5O_2 \rightarrow 6H_2O + 4NO$ $2NO + O_2 \rightarrow 2NO_2$ $3NO_2 + H_2O \rightarrow 2HNO_3 + NO$

*Where more than one name is given, the first name is the "proper" one and the others the more common (just as Robert and William are more proper but less popular than Bob and Bill).

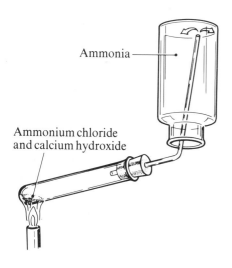

Ammonia

Ammonium chloride and calcium hydroxide

Fig. 7-1: *A laboratory preparation of ammonia.*

The name "ammonia" comes from *sal ammoniac* or *salt of Ammon*. Ammon was an Egyptian god of three thousand or so years ago, to whom there was a temple at the Oasis of Ammon in the Libyan desert. It is thought that the priests at that temple first discovered "salt of Ammon" (which we now know as ammonium chloride, NH_4Cl) as a product of the burning of dung from the camels of the caravans that stopped at the oasis.

trate has a somewhat sweet odour due to impurities; the pure oxide is odourless. Nitrous oxide is fairly soluble in water, but can be collected over hot water (which dissolves much less of it than cold water). Many substances will burn in nitrous oxide because it decomposes readily, releasing oxygen.

AMMONIA

8. LABORATORY PREPARATION. The gas ammonia, NH_3, is conveniently prepared by the gentle heating of a mixture of solid ammonium chloride (NH_4Cl) and either calcium oxide (CaO, often called *lime*) or calcium hydroxide ($Ca(OH)_2$, often called *slaked lime*):

$$2NH_4Cl + CaO \rightarrow CaCl_2 + H_2O + 2NH_3\uparrow$$
$$2NH_4Cl + Ca(OH)_2 \rightarrow CaCl_2 + 2H_2O + 2NH_3\uparrow$$

Since ammonia is much less dense than air (Table 7-1), it may be collected by the downward displacement of air, as depicted in Fig. 7-1.

Some nitrides react with water to yield ammonia, for example:

$$Mg_3N_2 + 6H_2O \rightarrow 3Mg(OH)_2 + 2NH_3\uparrow$$

9. PROPERTIES. At ordinary temperatures ammonia is a colourless gas that has a sharp and penetrating, but not unpleasant, odour. It is easily condensed to a liquid and to a solid.

In oxygen, ammonia will burn to yield nitrogen:

$$4NH_3 + 3O_2 \rightarrow 6H_2O + 2N_2$$

or, under carefully controlled conditions, nitric oxide, NO (Table 7-2).

Ammonia and the gas hydrogen chloride, HCl, readily react to form a white cloud of ammonium chloride, NH_4Cl:

$$NH_{3(gas)} + HCl_{(gas)} \rightarrow NH_4Cl_{(solid)}$$

If the ammonia and hydrogen chloride are separately dissolved in water, and the two solutions are mixed, solid crystals of ammonium chloride are obtained by evaporating the solution.

Ammonia dissolves readily and extensively in water or, put another way, water is a very good *solvent* for ammonia.

An aqueous solution of ammonia is sometimes called *ammonium hydroxide*, though a better name is *aqueous ammonia* or *aqua ammonia*. The solution smells of ammonia; all the ammonia can in fact be removed by boiling the solution. (This is a convenient way of preparing small amounts of the gas.)

In Sec. 5-12 we spoke of certain substances such as sulphur dioxide, SO_2, whose aqueous solutions we labelled *acidic*, and of others, such as calcium oxide, CaO, whose solutions we called *basic* or *alkaline*. An aqueous solution of ammonia also turns litmus paper blue. Later on (Sec. 27-3) we shall have more to say about acidic and basic solutions and at that time we shall be better able to account for the alkaline reaction of aqueous ammonia.

Compressed ammonia from steel cylinders is here being added in controlled amounts to an irrigation system that will carry it to the roots of plants all over the field.

A process, developed largely by Professor F. A. Forward of the University of British Columbia, takes advantage of the ability of ammonia to form soluble compounds with nickel, cobalt, and copper but not with the other elements in the ore.

10. USES. Liquefied ammonia is an excellent fertilizer (because it provides nitrogen to plants in a form they can readily use), and is the refrigerant in many industrial refrigerators (for example, for meat-packing plants) and ice-making equipment (for example, for hockey and curling rinks). Aqueous ammonia is used at Fort Saskatchewan, Alberta, and elsewhere to recover metals from suitable ores. The largest use for ammonia, however, is for making other chemicals. In addition to the important ones shown in Fig. 7-2, these include urea, $CO(NH_2)_2$ (an animal feed and fertilizer, and a reactant in the manufacture of some plastics), hydrazine, N_2H_4 (a rocket propellant), and hexamethylene diamine, $(CH_2)_6(NH_2)_2$ (for making nylon).

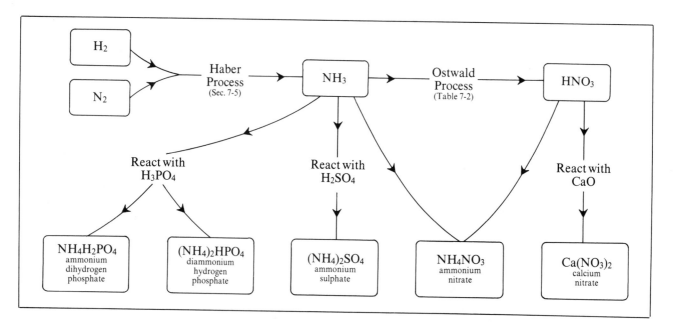

Fig. 7-2: *This diagram illustrates how important ammonia is and how "one thing leads to another." All the chemicals shown in the lower boxes are made in Canada by the reactions indicated, and all are sold as fertilizers.*

NITRIC ACID

11. PREPARATION. In the laboratory, nitric acid is usually made by heating sodium nitrate with concentrated sulphuric acid:

$$NaNO_3 + H_2SO_4 \rightarrow NaHSO_4 + HNO_3\uparrow$$

This preparation depends on the fact that, of the four substances in the reaction, only nitric acid is appreciably volatile. On heating, then, nitric acid distils off, as a vapour, leaving the other substances behind. When the vapour is cooled, liquid nitric acid is obtained.

Most of the nitric acid for industry is made by the **Ostwald process,** which involves a sequence of reactions (given in Table 7-2) starting with ammonia. The reactions can be briefly indicated as follows:

$$NH_3 \xrightarrow{\;O_2\;} NO \xrightarrow{\;O_2\;} NO_2 \xrightarrow{\;H_2O\;} HNO_3$$

ammonia   nitric   nitrogen   nitric
oxide   dioxide   acid

12. PROPERTIES. Pure nitric acid is a colourless liquid that boils at 83°C. It mixes with water in all proportions. Concentrated nitric acid decomposes slowly in light and on heating, liberating the gases oxygen and nitrogen dioxide (NO_2). The yellow or brown colour of concentrated nitric acid is due to dissolved nitrogen dioxide. Since this substance is poisonous, the fumes of nitric acid **should not be inhaled.**

Nitric acid is a strong acid and, particularly when hot and concentrated, will attack almost everything. It has, for example, a very rapid and never-to-be-forgotten corrosive action on human flesh. Nitric acid is also an effective oxidizing agent; it can oxidize almost every element. (Gold is one of the few exceptions.)

13. USES. Nitric acid is used in extracting uranium from ores, and in making dyes and many other products, but by far the largest amounts are consumed in the production of fertilizers and explosives (Fig. 7-3). All nitrogen-based explosives contain either the NO_2 or NO_3 group.

14. NITRATES. The salts of nitric acid are called *nitrates*; they all contain the group NO_3. They can be made by treating nitric acid with an appropriate basic substance; for example:

$$2HNO_3 + CaO \rightarrow Ca(NO_3)_2 + H_2O$$

All the nitrates are soluble in water, and they are rather readily decomposed by heat, for example:

$$2KNO_3 \rightarrow 2KNO_2 + O_2\uparrow$$

potassium   potassium
nitrate   nitrite

$$2Pb(NO_3)_2 \rightarrow 2PbO + 4NO_2\uparrow + O_2\uparrow$$

lead   lead   nitrogen
nitrate   oxide   dioxide

The first of these reactions hints at why potassium nitrate ("saltpeter") is effective as a constituent of gunpowder (Sec. 22-1).

NITROGEN AND SOIL FERTILITY

15. All living matter consists in part of *proteins*—very complex substances containing carbon, hydrogen, oxygen, nitrogen, and sulphur.

The pure substance corresponding to the formula HNO_3 is properly called "hydrogen nitrate" rather than "nitric acid." The expression "nitric acid" ought to be restricted to solutions of hydrogen nitrate in water — but it isn't!

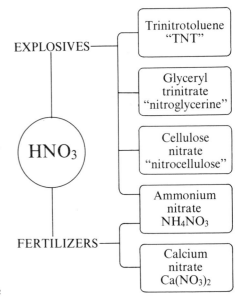

Fig. 7-3: *This shows some important compounds made from nitric acid. Notice that ammonium nitrate is a fertilizer and also—when used under very different conditions—an explosive.*

These rounded "nodules" on the root of this alfalfa plant are the homes of bacteria. These bacteria convert nitrogen, from the air in the soil, to nitrogen compounds that the plant can absorb. The plant changes these relatively simple compounds into complex nitrogenous compounds called proteins.

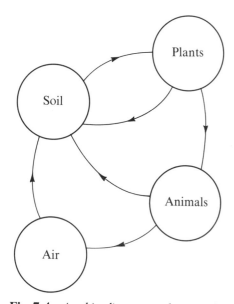

Fig. 7-4: *As this diagram indicates, the nitrogen in the air, in the soil, in plants and in animals is always on the move. Moreover, as the diagram doesn't indicate, it is constantly changing its form.*

For the building up of proteins, our bodies require nitrogen compounds. These are furnished by the plants and the animals that we eat. The animals depend for their proteins on plants or on other animals that depend on plants. Plants, then, are our basic foodstuffs. They obtain the necessary nitrogen compounds from the soil, and therefore the reaping of crops depletes the soil of an essential element. Farms would soon become unproductive if the soil were not in one way or another provided with fresh supplies of suitable nitrogen compounds.

16. Two "natural" processes provide the soil with nitrogen compounds. One depends on bacteria that live in little rounded lumps ("nodules") on the roots of legumes, among them peas, clover, and alfalfa. These useful bacteria convert nitrogen from the air into nitrogen compounds that plants can use. (This is called "fixation" of atmospheric nitrogen.) This explains why the growing and ploughing under of a crop of clover or alfalfa is a common and effective method of replenishing the soil with nitrogen compounds. But it is a slow method.

Another "natural" process depends on lightning. Under its urging some of the nitrogen and oxygen of the air combine to form oxides of nitrogen and these dissolve in rain and are brought down to the soil. This is a welcome contribution but a minor one. The lightning of thunderstorms "fixes" about 1100 kg of nitrogen per square kilometre per year. The bacteria on the roots of a crop of alfalfa or clover, working more quietly and less spectacularly, do much better—fixing ten to twenty times that amount.

If good crops are to be garnered year after year, the farmer himself must add nitrogen compounds to the soil. A common fertilizer is manure, a substance that reeks with nitrogen compounds. Nitrogenous fertilizers of the so-called "chemical" kind include ammonia and the ammonium compounds and nitrates shown in Fig. 7-2.

Nitrogen is by no means the only essential plant nutrient, though it is certainly of great importance. Calcium and phosphorus, for example, are essential, too.

17. THE NITROGEN CYCLE. The nitrogen of this planet certainly leads a busy life. Nitrogen, in the form of simple compounds such as nitrates, is constantly being taken up from the soil by living plants and transformed into proteins. In forests and on uncultivated land the plants die and the nitrogen of their proteins is returned to the soil, in the form of simple compounds, by the process of decay. In this, bacteria play an important part. The plants grown on cultivated land are eaten by animals (ourselves included) and the plant proteins are converted into animal proteins. But the animals, too, die eventually and, again by the process of decay, the complex proteins are broken down by bacteria to simple compounds that are returned to the soil. Moreover, during the life of every animal, nitrogenous compounds are excreted; the nitrogen of these compounds ultimately goes back to the soil or to the air. And, as we mentioned earlier, lightning and bacteria convert nitrogen of the air to compounds in the soil.

So nitrogen is constantly changing from simple compounds to complex ones and back again to simple ones; from the air and soil to living organisms and back again to the air and soil. If the nitrogen atoms in the cells of your body could talk they would certainly have some fascinating stories about where they have been! You may have in you more of Cleopatra or Shakespeare (or a dinosaur!) than you know.

QUESTIONS

1. Summarize the information given about nitrogen in this chapter, under the following headings:

(a) occurrence   (d) physical properties

(b) laboratory preparation   (e) chemical properties

(c) commercial production   (f) importance

2. A laboratory preparation of nitrogen is to heat ammonium nitrite (or substances that produce ammonium nitrite) gently. A laboratory preparation of nitrous oxide is to heat ammonium nitrate gently. Write equations to represent the reactions in these two preparations. Why is so much emphasis placed on the *gentle* heating?

3. What evidence is there that nitrogen does not react with iron at ordinary temperatures? With phosphorus at ordinary temperatures?

4. Nitrogen and oxygen remain permanently as elements in the atmosphere at ordinary temperatures. At very high temperatures, or during electrical storms, some combination between these elements occurs. What product or products are formed? Give equations.

5. As a library research project, find out about the role of nitrogen oxides (known as NO_x to the "initiated") in promoting photochemical smog.

6. Write a balanced chemical equation for the formation of ammonia from nitrogen and hydrogen. Calculate what mass of nitrogen and what mass of hydrogen, by reacting completely together, would form 1.54 g of ammonia. With the aid of the densities listed in Table 7-1 calculate the volumes (under standard conditions) of all three gases in the reaction. Comment on the result.

7. In Sec. 3-3 and 3-4 we described an experimental investigation into the composition of magnesium oxide. We implied in a marginal note that when heated in air a certain amount of the magnesium might be converted to magnesium nitride instead of to the oxide. Deduce whether this would cause the apparent mass of magnesium oxide to be greater or less than the mass if magnesium oxide had formed exclusively.

8. Write a balanced equation to represent the formation of magnesium nitride from the elements. When magnesium nitride is treated with water a chemical reaction takes place with the formation of ammonia and magnesium hydroxide. Work out a balanced equation for that reaction.

9. From the equations of Question 8 and a table of relative atomic masses, work out the mass of magnesium nitride that might be formed from 1.00 g of magnesium. Then work out the mass of ammonia that could be produced from that mass of magnesium nitride.

10. Many substances that burn in air to form oxides will also burn in nitrous oxide gas with formation of the same products. Work out a balanced equation for the combustion of sulphur in nitrous oxide.

11. Write down a sequence of balanced equations showing the oxidation of ammonia to nitric oxide, the oxidation of nitric oxide to nitrogen dioxide, and the dissolving of nitrogen dioxide in water to form nitric acid (Sec. 7-11).

12. Write formulas for the following substances:

(a) nitric acid   (d) ammonia

(b) lead nitrate   (e) ammonium sulphate

(c) calcium nitrite   (f) ammonium chloride

13. A solution of ammonia in water will neutralize a solution of nitric acid, forming the salt ammonium nitrate. Write an equation for this reaction. Notice that ammonia here acts as a base.

14. List some important uses of nitrogen, nitrous oxide, ammonia, and nitric acid.

15. It is important to realize that you will rarely encounter pure hydrogen nitrate, that is, 100% nitric acid. The "concentrated" acid of commerce contains about 70% hydrogen nitrate. Calculate the mass of ammonia required to neutralize 1.00 kg of concentrated nitric acid.

16. The same reacting substances may, under different conditions or concentrations, yield different substances as products of a chemical reaction. Illustrate this by (a) reactions of copper with nitric acid, and (b) oxidations of ammonia. Write balanced equations in all cases.

*17. If you visit a plant where nitric acid is made by the oxidation of ammonia you will be shown a tower consisting of stainless steel tanks in which water is admitted at the top and air and oxides of nitrogen are admitted at the bottom. Nitric acid, about 60% hydrogen nitrate, is collected from the bottom of the tower. You will probably see some red-brown gas escaping from a chimney at the top of the tower. Account for what happens in the tower, for the red-brown gas, and suggest a reason why the acid is only 60% in concentration. Can you draw any conclusion from the fact that the units of the tower are made of stainless steel?

18. An explosive used especially in floating mines that were scattered about the seaways during World War II is known as "amatol." It consists of a mixture of ammonium nitrate and TNT. What do you think would be the function of ammonium nitrate in such an explosive? Ammonium nitrate by itself has proven to be a dangerous explosive; what does an explosion of this substance produce?

19. Contrast the decompositions of potassium nitrate and lead nitrate caused by heating these compounds. How would you easily recognize whether, on heating a metal nitrate, it decomposes as potassium nitrate does or as lead nitrate does?

20. Explain what is meant by the term "fixation" of atmospheric nitrogen. Why is it a matter of interest to chemists? By careful review of this chapter list ways in which nitrogen can be fixed: (a) by natural events; (b) by the activity of chemists.

21. Fertilizers are often sold bearing three numbers on the label of the bag or package, for instance "7-7-7." These numbers are respectively the percentage of nitrogen, of phosphorus pentoxide, and of potassium oxide in the product. Work out the nitrogen numbers for the four fertilizer substances identified in Fig. 7-2. Which has the highest, and which the lowest, nitrogen content?

22. The name *nitrogen* comes from Greek roots meaning "nitre-former." (Nitre is another name for saltpeter.) In France the same element is called *azote*, from Greek roots meaning "without life." In Germany it is called *stickstoff*, meaning "suffocating substance." Comment on the appropriateness of each of these names.

23. Nitrogen and oxygen resemble each other in many physical properties but are very different in chemical properties. Illustrate the truth of this statement with examples.

24. The nitrogen and oxygen of the atmosphere are both important to life, but for very different reasons. Discuss.

25. The composition of dry air is given (in Table 5-1) as:

nitrogen = 78.0%; oxygen = 21.0%; other gases = 1.0%

all percentages being on a volume basis. With the aid of densities given in Table 7-1 calculate: (a) the mass of 100 L of dry air; (b) the mass of the oxygen and nitrogen in 100 L of dry air. The difference between (a) and (b) is the mass of the other gases. Calculate the average density of these other gases. Are the other gases more or less dense than the oxygen and nitrogen that make up the bulk of the air?

Chlorine and some Related Substances

1. In this chapter we shall discuss another gaseous element, chlorine, and some of its compounds, and show the importance of these substances. Then we shall compare chlorine with some elements that resemble it.

2. OCCURRENCE. Chlorine is much too reactive to remain "free" or uncombined. (It is belched from some volcanoes, but soon reacts with other substances.) Chlorine is very abundant in the form of compounds known as *chlorides*. In this form there are 2×10^{10} kg of chlorine in every cubic kilometre of sea water—and over the earth there are almost one and a half billion cubic kilometres of sea water! Moreover, enormous quantities of common salt (sodium chloride, NaCl) occur in underground beds, as residues from ancient seas. Very large Canadian deposits are in (or, rather, under) southwestern Ontario (Fig. 8-1) and parts of the Maritimes. And across a great portion of Saskatchewan, beneath the wheat fields, there are vast deposits of *potash*—minerals that contain potassium chloride, KCl—and even greater deposits of common salt.

3. PREPARATION. Chlorine is conveniently made in the laboratory by warming manganese dioxide, MnO_2, either with hydrochloric acid (HCl) or with sodium chloride and sulphuric acid (H_2SO_4), using apparatus illustrated in Fig. 8-2.

$$MnO_2 + 4HCl \rightarrow MnCl_2 + 2H_2O + Cl_2\uparrow$$

$$MnO_2 + 2NaCl + 3H_2SO_4 \rightarrow 2NaHSO_4 + MnSO_4 + 2H_2O + Cl_2\uparrow$$

Chlorine for industry is obtained from the decomposition of an aqueous solution of sodium chloride by means of an electric current (Sec. 26-14). A chemical reaction that is brought about in this way is called an *electrolysis*.

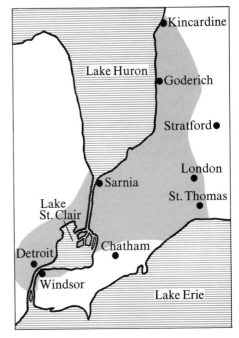

Fig. 8-1: *The shading indicates how extensive are the deposits of sodium chloride under southwestern Ontario. At Windsor, the main bed is 75 m thick. There is enough salt here to satisfy the needs of the entire world for hundreds of years.*

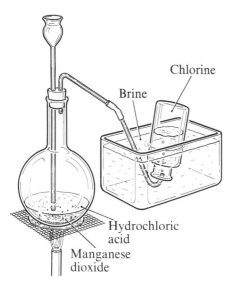

Chlorine

Brine

Hydrochloric
acid

Manganese
dioxide

4. PHYSICAL PROPERTIES. At ordinary temperatures, chlorine is a dense, greenish-yellow gas with a pungent and choking odour. It is irritating; moreover, it is poisonous. At low temperatures chlorine can be condensed to a liquid and to a solid. The gas dissolves in water (0.64 g/100 g of water at 20°C).

5. CHEMICAL PROPERTIES. Chlorine is a very reactive element. It combines spontaneously, and often vigorously, with most metals to form *chlorides*, for example:

$$Cl_2 + 2Na \rightarrow 2NaCl$$

sodium
chloride

$$Cl_2 + Cu \rightarrow CuCl_2$$

copper
chloride

Fig. 8-2: *Chlorine may be collected, as indicated here, by the downward displacement of brine (water saturated with sodium chloride), or by the upward displacement of air (Fig. 8-3). But, if you collect chlorine by displacing air, be sure to use a hood or do the experiment outside. Brine is used instead of water because it dissolves less chlorine than water does—only about one-sixth as much.*

These cubes, which look rather like ice cubes, are naturally occurring crystals of sodium chloride, in the form of the mineral known as halite. (The largest crystal is 2 cm to the side.)

If you sprinkle a tiny "pinch" of table salt onto a piece of black paper and look at it through a magnifying glass, you will see these same cubic crystals which sodium chloride always forms.

The production of familiar and harmless sodium chloride (common salt) from the dangerous substance sodium and the poisonous substance chlorine is peculiarly fascinating.

With sodium, the reaction is very vigorous: brilliant yellow light is emitted and a white fluffy mass of sodium chloride is rapidly produced. With copper, a less reactive metal, the reaction is less vigorous.

The copper, preferably in the form of foil, should be heated before being brought into contact with the chlorine: it will then glow brightly and produce a poisonous green salt, copper chloride (which is better named copper(II) chloride, as we shall explain in Sec. 21-9).

Gaseous hydrogen and chlorine should not be mixed, because they react explosively, particularly in sunlight or other bright light, to form hydrogen chloride:

$$H_2 + Cl_2 \rightarrow 2HCl$$

This reaction can be demonstrated safely by lowering a burning jet of hydrogen into a bottle of chlorine; be careful that the hydrogen is pure before igniting it (Sec. 6-7). That the product of the burning is hydrogen chloride can be demonstrated by bringing near the top of the bottle a stirring rod moistened with aqueous ammonia. The ammonia from this reacts with hydrogen chloride to form a white smoke of ammonium chloride (Sec. 7-9).

Phosphorus is another element that reacts vigorously with chlorine:

$$P_4 + 6Cl_2 \rightarrow 4PCl_3$$
phosphorus trichloride

In Chapter 22 you will learn why we use the symbol P_4 rather than P for phosphorus.

If there is an excess of chlorine, there is a further reaction:

$$PCl_3 + Cl_2 \rightarrow PCl_5$$
phosphorus pentachloride

6. CHLORINE WATER. A solution of chlorine in water is often called *chlorine water*. But chlorine does not merely dissolve in water: it reacts with it. Slowly, chlorine water changes into two acids:

$$Cl_2 + H_2O \rightarrow HCl + HClO$$
**hydro-   hypo-
chloric   chlorous
acid   acid**

Chlorine water and moist chlorine gas are effective bleaching and sterilizing agents largely because of the hypochlorous acid formed in this way.

Chlorine water gradually (more rapidly in sunlight) changes into hydrochloric acid alone, because the hypochlorous acid is not very stable and decomposes in the following way:

$$2HClO \rightarrow 2HCl + O_2\uparrow$$

7. USES OF CHLORINE. Chlorine is one of the most useful of chemicals, which is why billions of kilograms of it are produced annually.

It is used to make hydrochloric acid, the solvent chloroform ($CHCl_3$), the refrigerant and aerosol propellant "Freon" (CCl_2F_2), insecticides, weed killers, plastics, dry-cleaning fluids, and a host of other substances. Much chlorine is used for bleaching wood pulp to be made into paper or rayon.

A familiar application of chlorine (or, rather, an aqueous solution of sodium hypochlorite, NaClO, made from chlorine) is as a house-

A Canadian chemical engineer, Dr. W. H. Rapson of the University of Toronto, has developed an important process for bleaching wood pulp by means of chlorine dioxide, ClO_2.

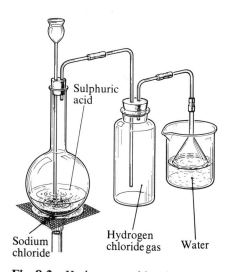

Fig. 8-3: *Hydrogen chloride, formed when sodium chloride is heated with concentrated sulphuric acid in the flask, is collected in the bottle by upward displacement of air. It can also be dissolved in water (as shown) to form hydrochloric acid.*

hold agent, such as "Javel" and "Javex," for bleaching, cleaning, disinfecting, and deodorizing.

Of great importance is the use of chlorine for the treatment of municipal water supplies to reduce bacterial contamination.

In the period 1888-1910, when the citizens of Ottawa, Ontario, drank untreated Ottawa River water, the average annual death rate from typhoid fever was 33 per 100 000 of population. In each of 1911 and 1912, an epidemic of this disease claimed more than 90 per 100 000. The chlorination of Ottawa's water supply began in 1913, and the death rate from typhoid fever fell rapidly. In the last 20 years there have been no cases of typhoid fever (let alone deaths from it) among residents of Ottawa, a city with a population of over 300 000. This is what one part (or even less) of chlorine in a million parts of water can do!

HYDROGEN CHLORIDE

8. PROPERTIES. Hydrogen chloride under ordinary conditions is a colourless gas, with a very sharp and irritating odour. By lowering the temperature sufficiently, it can be condensed to a liquid or a solid. When hydrogen chloride is dissolved in water—and it dissolves readily and copiously—the aqueous solution is called *hydrochloric acid.* Some of the properties of this and other acids will be discussed in Sec. 27-3.

9. PREPARATION. Hydrogen chloride is conveniently made in the laboratory by the action of concentrated sulphuric acid on sodium chloride:

$$H_2SO_4 + NaCl \rightarrow NaHSO_4 + HCl\uparrow$$

A suitable apparatus is depicted in Fig. 8-3.

10. USES. Hydrogen chloride is most useful in the form of its aqueous solution, hydrochloric acid. Large amounts of this are forced underground into oil-bearing and gas-bearing rock formations, to increase the yield of oil and gas by "opening-up" the structures in which they occur. Hydrochloric acid is also used as a catalyst in the conversion of corn starch to the sugar glucose; for cleaning metals; and in the recovery of metals from some ores.

CHLORINE AS ONE OF A FAMILY

There are really four other halogen elements, but astatine, At, is a very rare element that may not occur in nature; very small amounts of it have been made artificially, by methods that are beyond the scope of this book.

11. There are three other elements that have properties that resemble those of chlorine, though varying in degree. Such a group of elements is called a *family* of elements, and is often given a collective name. This one is known as the **halogen family** of elements, and comprises fluorine (F_2), chlorine, bromine (Br_2), and iodine (I_2).

12. SOME PROPERTIES OF THE HALOGENS. At ordinary temperatures and pressures, fluorine and chlorine are gases, bromine is a liquid, and iodine is a solid, of the varying colours described in Table 8-1. All the halogen elements are poisonous, and thoroughly unpleasant in other ways.

TABLE 8-1

SOME PROPERTIES OF THE HALOGENS

PROPERTY	FLUORINE	CHLORINE	BROMINE	IODINE
Relative Atomic Mass	19.00	35.45	79.91	126.90
State at Room Temp.	gas	gas	liquid	solid
Colour of Gas	light yellow	greenish-yellow	reddish-brown	violet
Colour of Solid	light yellow	yellow	dark red	violet-black
Density of Solid (g/cm³)	1.3	1.9	3.4	4.9
Melting Point (°C)	–218	–101	–7	114
Boiling Point (°C)	–188	–34	59	184

Fluorine is highly toxic; more than one chemist died attempting to isolate it. Chlorine has been used in chemical warfare; Canadian troops suffered heavy casualties from it in World War I. Liquid bromine attacks the skin rapidly, and causes painful burns that heal only slowly. Bromine takes its name from the Greek word for "stench", and it is well named. The vapours of all halogen elements are pungent, and irritating to the eyes, nose and throat.

Notice from Table 8-1 how, as the relative atomic masses of these elements increase from fluorine through chlorine and bromine to iodine, there is a *gradation* in physical properties—for example, the densities, melting points, and boiling points all steadily increase. As you learn more about other elements and other families of elements, watch for similar sorts of gradations.

13. MORE PROPERTIES OF THE HALOGENS. These elements undergo many similar chemical reactions, but the intensity or vigour of a particular reaction depends on which halogen is involved. We illustrate this in what follows.

All the halogen elements are reactive, with fluorine the most reactive —in fact, fluorine is more reactive than any other element. Each of the halogens will react with hydrogen and with most metals—but fluorine is so reactive that some elements ignite spontaneously in fluorine gas, and most metals when warmed take fire in it. (Even normally inert substances like asbestos and glass are attacked by fluorine.) Chlorine, bromine, and iodine, in that order, are less vigorous in their reactions than fluorine.

All the halogens dissolve somewhat in water, and react with it in varying degrees. Fluorine reacts rapidly, chlorine slowly (Sec. 8-6), bromine only in bright sunlight, and iodine scarcely at all.

Iodine dissolves only very slightly in water, but it dissolves abundantly in an aqueous solution of potassium iodide (KI). The antiseptic "tincture of iodine" is a solution of iodine and potassium iodide in ethyl alcohol (C_2H_5OH).

Such gradations in properties exist among compounds of the halogens, too. Consider, for example, the compounds of formula HF, HCl, HBr, and HI—the so-called *hydrogen halides*. All these are colourless gases at ordinary temperatures, and all have sharp, irritating odours. All dissolve plentifully in water, yielding acidic solutions. But they vary in the extent to which they dissolve in water and, as shown in Table 8-2,

TABLE 8-2

SOME PROPERTIES OF THE HYDROGEN HALIDES

PROPERTY	HYDROGEN FLUORIDE (HF)	HYDROGEN CHLORIDE (HCl)	HYDROGEN BROMIDE (HBr)	HYDROGEN IODIDE (HI)
Stability	very stable	stable	less stable	relatively unstable
Solubility in Water (g/100 g at 20°C)	35	42	49	57
Melting Point (°C)	−83	−115	−87	−51
Boiling Point (°C)	20	−85	−67	−35

TABLE 8-3

USES OF SOME METAL HALIDES

COMPOUND	FORMULA	USES
Sodium fluoride	NaF	insecticide; additive to water supplies in an effort to reduce tooth decay*
Sodium chloride (common salt)	NaCl	essential foodstuff; melting snow and ice on roads (and rotting cars!); preserving fish; making other chemicals such as Cl_2, HCl, NaOH, $NaHCO_3$
Potassium chloride	KCl	fertilizer (in the form of potash)
Sodium bromide *Potassium bromide*	NaBr } KBr }	sedatives in medicine
Sodium iodide	NaI	additive to table salt**
Silver chloride *Silver bromide*	AgCl } AgBr }	light-sensitive agents in photography
Silver iodide	AgI	"seeding" clouds in rain-making***

Salt has been known and used for thousands of years. Rebellions and wars, superstitions and religious practices, routes of trade and sites of cities, and taxes (always taxes!) — salt has had something to do with all of them.

The word "salt" is rich in associations. For example, "salary" comes from the Latin word *salarium*, for the portion of a Roman soldier's pay that was in the form of salt. We still say that a man is "worth his salt" if he does a good job. In the castles of early England, only those of noble birth sat above the large vessel of salt: they were "above the salt." Perhaps you can think of other allusions to salt in our language.

*Sodium hexafluorosilicate (or "silicofluoride"), Na_2SiF_6, also serves as a source of fluoride in the treatment of municipal water supplies. Another use for this compound is as a moth-proofing agent (for rugs, not people).

**Iodine in the form of complex organic compounds is found in the human body, particularly in the thyroid gland, which is in the neck. This gland cannot function properly unless iodide-bearing substances are included in the diet. The requirement is very small, but if it is not met conditions like goitre develop. To guard against an iodide deficiency, much of our table salt now contains a small proportion of sodium iodide—hence the name *iodized salt*.

***In 1967-72, during the Vietnam War, the United States Air Force tried to "rain-out" opposing troops and hamper the transport of their supplies by "seeding" clouds with tiny crystals of silver iodide. These apparently induce exceedingly small, cold water droplets to freeze; the resulting ice crystals attract water vapour, whereupon they increase rapidly in size and fall out of the cloud, reaching the ground as raindrops. A constructive form of "weather warfare" is inducing rain to fight large forest fires, an application of silver iodide now being investigated in Canada.

there are gradations in other of their properties, too. (You will notice that, in some of its properties, hydrogen fluoride is "out-of-line"; so also in some respects is fluorine itself, for reasons that must be left for more advanced study.)

METAL HALIDES

14. The compounds that metals form with halogen elements are known by the collective name of **metal halides.** This term embraces *fluorides* such as sodium fluoride (NaF), *chlorides* such as copper chloride ($CuCl_2$), *bromides* such as silver bromide (AgBr), and *iodides* such as potassium iodide (KI).

In Table 8-3 we list important metal halides and some of their uses.

In this largest potash mine in the world, a thousand metres below Esterhazy, Saskatchewan, the walls, ceiling, and floor are solid potash. The deposits under southern Saskatchewan are immense enough to supply the potash fertilizer needs of the entire world for the next two thousand years.

QUESTIONS

1. Summarize the information given about chlorine in this chapter, under the following headings:

(a) occurrence (d) physical properties
(b) laboratory preparation (e) chemical properties
(c) commercial production (f) importance

2. Sodium chloride, also known as the mineral halite or rock salt, occurs widely in underground deposits throughout the world. What is the origin of these deposits? Where are the principal Canadian deposits?

3. With the aid of reference books in your school library find out which are the major chemical elements present in dissolved form in sea water, and what is the abundance of these. Which element is the most abundant? Which is the next most abundant?

4. Manganese dioxide is commonly used in a laboratory preparation of chlorine. Is it a catalyst in this case, as it was in the preparation of oxygen? Explain.

5. Why is chlorine collected in the laboratory by displacement of a concentrated salt solution, rather than water?

6. Chlorine was used as a "war gas" in World War I. Why did it, a gas, flow downwind, close to the ground, rather than rise and disperse as ammonia (for example) would have done? (The density of chlorine at STP = 3.17 g/L.)

7. Write balanced chemical equations representing the reaction of chlorine with (a) copper metal; (b) phosphorus; (c) water.

8. Suggest an explanation why dry chlorine has little effect on dry litmus paper, but bleaches moist litmus paper.

9. When water, through which chlorine has been bubbled, is allowed to stand, it gradually becomes more and more acid. Why?

10. If chlorine gas is passed through a glass tube immersed in crushed "Dry Ice" (Sec. 15-15), will the gas liquefy or not? What would you expect the liquid to look like?

11. Prepare a chart showing the importance of chlorine in the chemical industry. This should show the various products of commercial importance in which chlorine is a constituent. (This exercise can be made much more meaningful by consulting reference volumes in your school library before you start.)

12. Describe how chlorine and substances easily obtained from chlorine are used for bleaching and sterilizing. Why does drinking water in many urban areas smell and taste of chlorine? Why are swimming pools "chlorinated"?

13. Suppose you wanted to produce one litre of pure chlorine gas by the action of sulphuric acid on manganese dioxide and sodium chloride. Calculate the mass of chlorine that would occupy one litre at STP (see Question 6). What is the minimum mass of sodium chloride required to produce this mass of chlorine?

14. How is hydrogen chloride prepared in the laboratory? How is a sample collected for further study?

15. "Concentrated" hydrochloric acid is a solution containing about 37% by mass of hydrogen chloride in water. It has a density of 1.20 g/mL. Calculate the mass of hydrogen chloride present in 1.00 L of this acid. The density of hydrogen chloride *gas* at STP = 1.63 g/L. Calculate what volume of this gas, measured at STP, is contained in 1.00 L of concentrated hydrochloric acid.

16. Look up in a dictionary the meaning of the word *halogen*. On the basis of this definition, explain how the word *halide* is used in chemistry.

17. Write a brief report on the commercial importance of metal halides.

18. If hydrogen chloride gas is passed over heated, finely divided iron, the metal is converted to a compound of iron and chlorine containing 44.0% iron by mass. If chlorine is passed over a second portion of heated iron, a compound of iron and chlorine is formed which contains 34.4% iron. With the aid of the table of relative atomic masses, determine the formulas of the two iron chlorides formed, and give balanced equations for their formation from the starting materials named.

19. Write formulas for the following substances:

(a) silver iodide (d) sodium hypochlorite
(b) hydrogen fluoride (e) manganese chloride
(c) chlorine dioxide (f) "Freon"

20. Name the elements that make up the halogen "family." Give some reasons (others will be disclosed later in the book) for grouping these elements together in a family.

21. Note that in addition to many similarities, the halogen elements and compounds show a gradation in properties as, for instance, their molecular mass increases. Give examples of such trends in properties.

*22. With reference to some properties of the halogens given in Table 8-1, suggest possible reasons for the progressive increase in density in the solid state, shown in the fifth row. Can you think of any reason why the melting and boiling points also show a progressive increase in moving across the table?

*23. If your reason for the second part of Question 22 is correct, what can be concluded from the corresponding information for the hydrogen halides (Table 8-2)?

A Look at Metals

9

1. The elements we have just discussed—oxygen, hydrogen, nitrogen, and chlorine—are each a gas, at least at ordinary temperatures. The elements bromine and mercury are ordinarily liquids, and you are familiar with iron, copper, and zinc as solid elements. This is one way of classifying the chemical elements: dividing them into those which under ordinary conditions are gases, those which are liquids, and those which are solids. But there are other ways of classifying or grouping elements. We saw this in the preceding chapter, where fluorine (ordinarily a gas), chlorine (ordinarily a gas), bromine (ordinarily a liquid), and iodine (ordinarily a solid) were grouped together. This grouping, into the so-called halogen family of elements, is based on the similarities in many of the properties of these four elements, though obviously one property that is not similar is their state (gaseous, liquid, or solid) under ordinary conditions.

There is still another way of classifying elements: one group composed of those elements which are *metals*, and another group of those which are not—the latter being called, reasonably enough, *non-metals*. In this chapter, we shall describe some characteristics of metals.

2. WHY CLASSIFICATION? You may be thinking: why all this fuss about classification? And, even if there is a need for classification, why all these different kinds of classification? The answer to both questions is the same, and it is brief and simple: because classification is useful. It is an aid to memory. It helps us to organize, summarize, and correlate our knowledge. It makes it easier to talk about substances that have some characteristics or properties in common.

In much of our ordinary talking, writing and thinking, we use classification almost unconsciously. For example, think of people: for some purposes we classify them by age—we speak of babies, children, adolescents, and adults. At other times we classify people by their economic circumstances: the poor, the low-income group, the middle-income group, the wealthy. In other contexts we think of people as female or male, or we group them according to their religion, or their citizenship, or their occupation, or their skin-colour, and so on and so on.

All of us constantly use classification, and many different kinds of it. Each kind "brings out" or highlights a different kind of information. A given purpose may be well served by one classification but poorly served, or not served at all, by another. So it is in chemistry, too, and the division of the elements into metals and non-metals is one of the several useful forms of chemical classification.

Gallium is a metal that melts in your hand. This very low melting point is one of its unusual properties. Another is that it expands on solidification—so does water, but it is a bit odd, too!

3. WHAT IS A METAL? Do you think of a metal as something that is hard? Well, many metals are indeed hard, but aluminium is not, and the metal potassium is so soft that it can be cut with a knife as easily or more easily than some cheeses. (And diamond, the hardest substance known, is a non-metal.) One can't usefully speak of a liquid being "hard," yet the metal mercury is a liquid at temperatures down to well below 0°C—witness its use in thermometers. In fact it is not easy to define a metal in a simple and precise way, though we shall see later (in Sec. 13-5) that certain chemical properties are a good basis for distinguishing metals from non-metals.

Here, it will be useful to cite some physical properties that most metals have in common. First, though, let us stress that the term "metal" (and "non-metal," too) is applied only to an element. Thus steel, which always consists of several elements, is not a metal; it is properly called an *alloy* (Sec. 9-4).

Of the slightly more than 100 elements, more than 70 are considered to be metals. Each of these has different properties that enable it to be distinguished from all the others, but nonetheless they all (or almost all) have certain features in common. These are

i)   they are good conductors of heat and of electricity;

ii)   they can be drawn out into wires (that is, they are *ductile*);

iii)   they can be pounded into thin sheets (that is, they are *malleable*);

iv)   generally, they do not readily break when stretched (that is, they have high *tensile strength*);

v)   they have a shiny appearance, or *metallic lustre*, as a consequence of their marked ability to reflect light (hence the use of silver in mirrors);

vi)   with two exceptions (copper and gold), their colour is grey;

vii)   most of them have high melting points (mercury and gallium are not among the "most") and high boiling points.

These are all physical properties. A distinctive chemical property of metals is that

viii)   their oxides are bases (Sec. 5-12).

4. WHAT IS AN ALLOY? An alloy is a material that has metallic properties and is composed of two or more elements, at least one of which is metal. Steel, brass, and solder are familiar alloys. Each of these is really a family of alloys: there are dozens of different steels, for example, each of different composition (although always with iron as the major component), and varying in properties such as hardness, tensile strength, corrosion resistance, machinability, etc.

Alloys are designed for particular applications, to have the properties that are most important for the intended use. For example, because of its low density ("lightness"), aluminium is a desirable material for the construction of aircraft, but the pure metal is not sufficiently strong. However, a strong and suitable alloy is made from aluminium by adding to it small but appropriate amounts of copper, magnesium, silicon, and zinc. But an aluminium alloy of different composition is made for certain architectural applications, where an attractive, corrosion-resistant surface finish is desired.

So it is that there are many hundreds of different alloys—based on iron or copper or nickel or magnesium or zinc or almost any metal—each alloy having different properties to suit different purposes.

5. Gold jewellery is always made of an alloy, pure gold being much too soft to withstand wear. Copper is the common alloying element: it increases the hardness without unduly affecting the lovely colour and lustre of gold. The term *carat* is used to express the proportion of gold in the alloy, pure gold being designated 24-carat. Thus "16-carat gold" is 16/24 or 66.7% gold.

Incidentally, when you are talking about diamonds, "carat" means something very different. Here a carat is strictly a unit of mass equal to 200 mg.

And there are 100 "points" in the carat used to measure the mass of a gem-stone. Thus a 30-point diamond in an engagement ring, or in anything else, has a mass of 60 mg or 0.060 g. But the size of a diamond is only part of the story; its worth is also very dependent on the quality of the "cut," its colour (or lack of it), and the nature and extent of any microscopic cracks or inclusions of foreign matter. A diamond of the best quality of cut, colour, etc., can cost as much as a twice as large (or even larger) diamond of poor quality.

Names, too, can be misleading. "Sterling silver" sounds as though it were pure silver, but it is not: it is silver alloyed with several per cent of copper. And "German silver," the base for much silver-plated ware, contains no silver at all; it is an alloy of copper, zinc, and nickel.

6. We turn now to consider some of the chemical properties of some representative metals. We shall be pointing to similarities among these properties, and stressing differences, too.

7. REACTIVITY TOWARD AIR AND OXYGEN. Metals vary greatly in their reactivity toward pure oxygen and also toward oxygen in the more dilute form in which it occurs in air.

If you cut the soft metal **potassium** (K) with a knife, to expose a fresh surface, you will need to be on the alert to see the pure metal because it promptly reacts with the oxygen of the air: you can see the colour changing as an oxide coating is formed.

Sodium (Na), a brother or sister element to potassium, reacts similarly, although not quite so rapidly. These metals (and some others, too) are so reactive that they have to be stored out of contact with air—say, in liquid paraffin ("mineral oil").

As you might expect from this, each of these metals reacts even more vigorously with pure oxygen. In fact, each will burn rapidly in pure oxygen.

In very sharp contrast, **gold** (Au) is unaffected by air or even pure oxygen. Ornaments and artifacts of gold that have been found in Egyptian tombs are as good as the day they were left with their Pharaoh owners thousands of years ago.

These are the extremes: the very high reactivity of potassium and sodium, and the inertness of gold. The reactivities of all the other metals, though they vary among themselves, are intermediate between these extremes. Let us illustrate this by reference to some familiar metals.

Calcium is a metal that you know in the form of compounds—in limestone and chalk, as calcium carbonate; in gypsum, as calcium sulphate; in bones, as calcium phosphate.

Metallic calcium is a grey metal that is harder than potassium or sodium, being about as hard as tin. Like potassium and sodium, it corrodes or tarnishes by reaction with the oxygen of the air, producing calcium oxide, CaO, a white solid that is often called *lime*:

$$2Ca + O_2 \rightarrow 2CaO$$

In pure oxygen, calcium will burn readily, to the same product. But these reactions are not as vigorous as the reactions of potassium and sodium with air and with oxygen.

Magnesium, a member of the same chemical family of elements as calcium (the alkaline earth family), appears to be unreactive toward air, but an appearance can be deceptive and in this instance it is. What happens is that magnesium reacts with oxygen and carbon dioxide from the air to produce a thin layer of compounds that is adherent and which effectively "seals-off" the underlying magnesium metal. This thin "skin" is transparent and so the silvery metallic lustre of magnesium shows through it, and the metal appears not to have been attacked. If a portion of this coating is removed, say by scratching, the freshly exposed metal promptly reacts with more oxygen and carbon dioxide to rebuild the coating. The wound heals itself!

Before you reached this page, you knew from your study of Chapter 3 that magnesium ribbon, if heated sufficiently, burns in air to magnesium oxide, MgO, a white solid sometimes called *magnesia*:

$$2Mg + O_2 \rightarrow 2MgO$$

Magnesium in the form of wire or powder reacts the same way, and the reactions with pure oxygen are distinctly more lively.

Aluminium, too, is more reactive than it appears to be. Here, again, a very thin oxide coating is formed when the metal is exposed to the air:

$$4Al + 3O_2 \rightarrow 2Al_2O_3$$

This white aluminium oxide, or *alumina*, is dense and adherent; it protects the rest of the metal from attack, without detracting significantly from the metallic appearance of the aluminium. Thus it is that aluminium alloys can be used for sheeting on buildings, window frames, and doors that will retain their strength and attractive appearance for years.

Aluminium in powder form or as fine wire burns readily in pure oxygen (to Al_2O_3), giving off a very bright light; hence its use in flash bulbs for photography. Aluminium is certainly a reactive metal, although not quite as reactive as magnesium.

The metal **zinc** is fairly reactive: its vapour will burn in air to zinc oxide, ZnO. But, like magnesium and aluminium, zinc does not corrode appreciably in air at ordinary temperatures. Again, as with magnesium and aluminium, the cause of this apparent inertness is the formation of a tightly adhering compound (by reaction of the zinc with oxygen and moist carbon dioxide) that protects the underlying metal from further attack by oxygen.

This helps to account for a very important use of zinc: the coating or *galvanizing* of steel to prevent it from rusting, as in galvanized fencing.

You are very familiar with the fact that objects or structures of **iron** rust readily, and will eventually crumble away unless the surface of the iron is protected from the air by paint or other suitable impervious coating (Sec. 5-15).

When iron combines with oxygen of the air, as it does fairly readily, the brownish-red oxide (Fe_2O_3) that is formed is not very adherent; rather it expands, buckles and splits, thereby exposing a fresh surface of iron. This reacts with more oxygen, and the process is repeated again

Hans Christian Oersted (1777-1851) was a Danish scientist who is most often remembered as the discoverer of the magnetic action of an electric current. But he was a first-class chemist, too, being the first person to isolate the metal aluminium.

and again until all the iron has reacted or, as we say, rusted away.

As we mentioned earlier (Sec. 5-8), finely divided pure iron, when sprinkled into a bottle of pure oxygen, catches fire immediately and burns up rapidly (to a black oxide, Fe_3O_4) in a shower of sparks.

Copper does not react appreciably with dry air or oxygen at ordinary temperatures, but on heating will yield an oxide:

$$2Cu + O_2 \rightarrow 2CuO$$

This can be demonstrated by heating a piece of bright copper wire (held in a pair of tongs) in a Bunsen burner flame for a minute or so; when the wire is removed, it will be seen to be tarnished with a black coating, which is copper oxide (CuO).

The attractive green patina that copper roofs acquire is due to the reaction of copper with the carbon dioxide, moisture, and oxygen of the air. The substance responsible for the green colour is $Cu_2CO_3(OH)_2$; it is both a carbonate and a hydroxide of copper, known as a basic carbonate. This compound was known to people in ancient times in the form of the naturally occurring mineral malachite.

The tarnishing of household silver is due to the formation of silver sulphide, Ag_2S, from the reaction of the silver with compounds of sulphur that come from industrial fumes, from sulphides in the coal or gas or oil used as fuel, and from the cooking of foods such as eggs, onions, and cabbage.

Silver is practically inert toward air or oxygen, although an oxide will form under conditions of high pressure.

8. REACTIVITY TOWARD WATER. Now let us consider the reactivity of these same ten metals toward water.

The reactions of five of them we have already discussed, in Chapter 6. In Sec. 6-3 we cited the reactions with water of potassium, sodium, calcium, magnesium, and iron, and we pointed out that the vigour of the reactions of these metals decreased steadily in the order in which we have just named the metals.

Aluminium and zinc, if they are very hot and particularly if they are in the form of powder, will react with steam or hot water vapour in a manner similar to magnesium or iron:

$$2Al + 3H_2O \rightarrow 3H_2\uparrow + Al_2O_3$$
$$Zn + H_2O \rightarrow H_2\uparrow + ZnO$$

Neither copper nor silver nor gold react with water.

We shall content ourselves (and perhaps more than content you!) with one more illustration of variation and trends in the reactivity of metals.

Hydrogen is produced so rapidly that the potassium or sodium is often blown out of the container, usually onto the experimenter, who then starts to dissolve as the metal reacts with the water of his or her cells to produce a caustic (KOH or NaOH) that then attacks more cells. It is really very unpleasant.

9. REACTIVITY TOWARD HYDROCHLORIC ACID. Never put potassium or sodium into hydrochloric acid, or into any acid for that matter. This is a route to a nasty and possibly blinding accident: the reactions are of explosive violence.

$$2K(or\ 2Na) + 2HCl \rightarrow H_2\uparrow + 2KCl(or\ 2NaCl)$$

Calcium, too, reacts very vigorously with hydrochloric acid, though not quite so violently as potassium or sodium:

$$Ca + 2HCl \rightarrow H_2\uparrow + CaCl_2$$

Magnesium reacts similarly, and so do aluminium and zinc, but less briskly. You should recall that the reaction of zinc with hydrochloric acid is a convenient way of preparing hydrogen in the laboratory (Sec. 6-3).

Iron, too, reacts in the same way, but not overly vigorously:

$$Fe + 2HCl \rightarrow H_2\uparrow + FeCl_2$$

Neither copper nor silver nor gold react with hydrochloric acid. These metals are completely inert toward this acid.

10. ACTIVITY SERIES. Clearly, the metals vary greatly in their reactivity and there is a rather steady gradation from very active (or reactive) ones to very inactive (or inert) ones. Chemists find it convenient to arrange the metals into a list or series that reflects this variation and gradation.

On the basis of the chemical reactions that we have discussed in this chapter, you should try to arrange into such a series the ten metals that have been considered.

Our arrangement of such an *activity series*, listing the most active metal first, is shown in Table 9-1.

The relative activities of the metals are shown in more ways than we have indicated in Table 9-1. For example, the more readily a metal forms an oxide, the more difficult it is for that oxide to be decomposed or reduced to the metal. Oxides of metals near the top of the series are very stable, and this accounts for some of their uses: for example, magnesium oxide melts only at an extremely high temperature and is therefore very useful for lining furnaces.

TABLE 9-1

AN ACTIVITY SERIES

METAL	ACTIVITY WITH OXYGEN	ACTIVITY WITH WATER	ACTIVITY WITH HYDROCHLORIC ACID
K	Very active	Very active	Very active
Na	Very active	Very active	Very active
Ca	Active	Active	Very active
Mg	Active	Active with steam	Active
Al	Active	Active with steam	Active
Zn	Active	Active with steam	Active
Fe	Active	Active with steam	Active
Cu	Little	None	None
Ag	Almost none	None	None
Au	None	None	None

Iron oxide, Fe_2O_3, is much less stable than MgO and can be decomposed to metallic iron by heating with hot carbon. This is how iron for the making of steel is obtained: haematite ore, which is mainly iron oxide, is strongly heated (in what is called a blast furnace) with coke, which is mainly carbon.

Silver, a metal very low in the activity series, forms an oxide (Ag_2O) only under special conditions, such as high pressure. This oxide is unstable and easily decomposed: modest heating will convert it back to silver and oxygen.

It is as though metals high in the activity series "like" to be in the form of compounds, and those very low in the series "prefer" to remain as metals. Gold always occurs in nature as metallic gold, never as compounds of gold. Silver and copper, too, occur in some deposits as the metals themselves (occur "native" as we say), but the metals above iron in the activity series are found in nature only in the form of compounds.

The activity series is a very important concept that deserves more discussion and, as you continue to read this book, you will see that we return to it.

11. AN APOLOGY. In this chapter, and in earlier ones, too, we have introduced a term or a topic or a concept, and shortly thereafter have said, at least in effect: "Well, that's all we're going to say about that here, but we'll have more to say about it later."

You may very well be thinking that we can't keep our minds on a subject for very long, or that we haven't organized this book very well. We won't argue these points, but think it fair to say that a good part of the difficulty stems from the nature of chemistry. By this we mean that many of the ideas and concepts of chemistry are fairly complex, and cannot be fully explained or understood until you have met and mastered some other aspects of chemistry.

An illustration of the problem is this: early in this chapter we said that metals are good conductors of electricity, but we didn't explain why. To understand the "why," one needs to know something about the structure of metals (Chapter 15) but, to understand that, one needs to know something about the structure of atoms (Chapter 10); to appreciate that, one should know something about ordinary chemical reactions. So, we talk about chemical reactions early in the book, but in so doing find ourselves wanting to use ideas that can be properly developed and discussed only after one is reasonably familiar with chemical reactions! Accordingly, at a particular stage, we can develop a particular topic only so far, and must leave a broader and deeper understanding for later on, after other ideas and concepts have been presented. If at any time you want to know what has been said earlier about a particular topic, or what will be said later, use the Index to guide you to the appropriate pages.

QUESTIONS

1. Describe some of the principal properties of metals in general. Why is it that these properties are shared by almost all metals, rather than being the exclusive property of an individual metal?

2. Explain (with the aid of a dictionary, if necessary) the meaning of the terms: ductility, malleability, tensile strength, lustre.

3. What is the significance of the term *alloy*? As a small research project, find out from a dictionary or encyclopedia what are the principal components in the following alloys: brass, bronze, solder, common steel, stainless steel, monel metal, alnico, nichrome. If you are not familiar with these alloys, make a note of their principal use.

4. Explain the significance of the expression "18-carat gold."

5. Write balanced equations for: (a) the rusting of iron to Fe_2O_3; (b) the burning of iron to Fe_3O_4. Which oxide has the higher oxygen content?

6. Certain metals described in this chapter appear to be less reactive toward oxygen or water than they really are. This is due to the formation of an adherent "skin" of oxide which (like paint) protects the bulk of the metal from attack. List the metals that have this property and are described in this chapter. Why is this property important?

7. Chromium is an important commercial metal (chrome plating, chrome steels, etc.). It is not listed in Table 9-1, but it occurs between zinc and iron. Predict whether chromium would be attacked by hydrochloric acid. Do you think, on the basis of its uses, that chromium metal is or is not protected from rusting by an oxide coat? Explain.

8. Aluminium oxide, as the oxide of a metal, is dissolved by a chemical reaction with hydrochloric acid. Write a balanced equation for this reaction.

9. As indicated in Table 9-1, aluminium is attacked by hydrochloric acid. Predict the products of this reaction, and write a balanced equation for it.

10. The metals known earliest to mankind were gold (pre 5000 BC), electrum, a gold-silver alloy that occurs native (about 4300 BC), native copper (pre 5000 BC), bronze (about 4300 BC), smelted copper (about 3500 BC), and lead (about 3500 BC). Can you suggest why these metals or alloys, but not others, are mentioned in, or found in, archeological evidence?

11. A few metals are produced industrially by reducing their oxides with hydrogen at elevated temperatures. A case in point is tungsten, used for the filaments in incandescent lamps, whose oxide WO_3 can be so reduced. Give an equation for the reaction with hydrogen. What mass of tungsten oxide would be required to produce one kilogram of the metal? (Incidentally, the melting point of tungsten is 3653°C, one of the highest among all metals. Why is this important?)

12. What are the products of the chemical reaction that occurs when water vapour is passed over red hot iron (Sec. 6-3)? Assuming complete conversion, what mass of hydrogen can be obtained from 10.0 g of iron powder by this reaction? From the density of hydrogen at STP (Table 6-1), calculate the volume of the hydrogen, measured under standard conditions, that could be obtained in this way from 10.0 g of iron.

13. What is an activity series of the common metals? What information is conveyed by it?

14. Give some examples of reactions to illustrate the principle that the more reactive a metal is, the more resistant are its compounds (oxides, for instance) to decomposition or reduction back to the metal. Show also that the reverse is true for metals low in the activity series.

10 The Composition of Atoms

1. In Chapter 4 we introduced the idea of matter being constituted of atoms, and of each chemical element having its own kind of atoms. Now that we have examined the properties and reactions of some substances, it is appropriate that we learn more about atoms—their structure and how they make up the different forms of matter. Much of what is to be said in this chapter is deduced from experiments that are more difficult to describe and explain than those discussed up to this point, and we must ask you to take our word for it that the evidence for the facts given is thoroughly convincing. Should you continue with the study of physics or chemistry, and develop the necessary mathematical skills, you will be able to check the proofs and deductions for yourself.

THE DIMENSIONS OF ATOMS

2. A MULTITUDE OF ATOMS. The fact that atoms are very small and extraordinarily numerous can perhaps be made clear with the aid of some numbers. These apply to the gas *neon* of which you have probably heard because of its use in outdoor luminous advertising signs. The reason we select neon for this illustration is that it is one of relatively few elements whose atoms are not paired or clustered; our "model" for neon gas is a host of single atoms distributed throughout the volume occupied by the gas. The density of neon is 0.901 g/L (0.901 kg/m³) at 0°C and 101.3 kPa (STP; see Sec. 6-6). Under these conditions one litre of this gas has a mass of 0.901 g, and evidence has shown that the litre contains 2.69×10^{22} atoms of neon. This is a mind-boggling number!

3. It is not too difficult to comprehend a million, that is 10^6; this is the approximate magnitude of populations of large cities like Toronto and Montreal.

Try then to think of a million million, that is 10^{12}. We cannot really picture such a host of real objects, and yet, as you can see, this still falls short, by many powers of ten, of the number of atoms in a litre of neon gas.

To try to get some feeling for the immensity of this number, you might try calculating the volume of the earth; and then imagine the entire planet being chopped up into 2.69×10^{22} pieces of equal size. The arithmetic shows that each piece would occupy about 40 L; this would be a cube measuring about one-third of a metre across, or about the amount of material you would find in a sandbag. This calculation shows that it would take about as many sandbags of material to produce the entire planet earth as there are atoms in just one litre of neon at STP!

4. MASS OF A SINGLE ATOM. From the foregoing information, we can also calculate the average mass of each atom. Thus, if 2.69×10^{22} atoms have a mass of 0.901 g or 9.01×10^{-4} kg, the average mass of a single atom is (9.01×10^{-4}) kg $\div (2.69 \times 10^{22}) = 3.35 \times 10^{-26}$ kg. Even a billion billion or 10^{18} of these atoms could not be detected by the sensitive analytical balance illustrated in Chapter 3. As we go on, we shall see that, while atoms do differ in mass from element to element, they all have masses about 10^{-27} kg to 10^{-25} kg.

5. SIZE OF A SINGLE ATOM. Can we make any estimates of size in the same way? Atoms or other particles in gases are thought to be spread out with considerable space between them. This is why gases are so compressible, and why they occupy fully any container in which they are placed. Thus, we cannot say that the volume of 2.69×10^{22} neon atoms is one litre because we don't know how much of the litre is really empty space. If, however, we place the container of neon in a very cold bath so as to lower the temperature below the boiling point of neon (which is $-246°C$) the gas condenses to a few drops of liquid neon, the volume of which proves to be 0.75 mL. Presumably the same "indestructible" atoms are still present in the liquid, only much closer together since they occupy so much less volume. Indeed, we may guess that, since the liquid doesn't shrink much under compression, the atoms in the liquid are probably touching one another. If we make this assumption, we can estimate the volume occupied by 2.69×10^{22} atoms to be about 0.75 mL. (We don't know, to be sure, how they are packed together, and whether there are empty spaces between them.)

The average volume per atom then works out to be 2.8×10^{-23} mL, and this corresponds to a particle approximately 3.8×10^{-10} m in diameter. This gives us a rough estimate of the size of neon atoms. A much more elaborate study has resulted in a model of the neon atom which is a sphere of diameter 3.14×10^{-10} m or 314 pm. Most atoms are a few hundred picometres in diameter (Fig. 13-4).

This gives us some idea of the size of atoms—how big and how heavy they are, and of the enormous numbers of them in comparatively small amounts of ordinary matter.

It is possible for objects to *occupy* a space without actually *filling* it. The moving blades in an electric fan can occupy a certain region, from which it is prudent to keep one's fingers, but when the fan is at rest it is clear that the blades did not fill this region.

THE FUNDAMENTAL PARTICLES

6. THE ELECTRON. In the closing years of the nineteenth century, physicists discovered the existence of particles much lighter than any known atom. The lightest atoms are those of the gaseous element hydrogen, but the new particles were roughly 1/2000 as heavy. Moreover, unlike atoms, they were electrically charged. They appeared to be "atoms" of electricity, each bearing a fixed amount of negative charge. They could be produced in a variety of ways, and it gradually dawned on the scientific world that these were constituents of all atoms. The "indivisible" atom thus appeared to have parts. Moreover, the electrified nature of the new particles showed there was a connection between electricity and matter. The new particles were called *electrons*. They are now recognized as fundamental particles present in all atoms.

7. THE CHARGE ON AN ELECTRON. The charge borne by each electron has been measured, and is 1.6×10^{-19} C. This is the smallest quantity of electricity found on any charged object, and it appears to be the fundamental unit of electrical charge. This quantity of charge is represented by the symbol e. We may, therefore, say that the charge on an electron is one unit, and we show that this is negative charge by a minus sign.

C is the symbol for "coulomb," a unit of electrical charge. You are probably more familiar with the unit of current called the "ampere." You can, perhaps, connect these units in your mind by remembering that a current of one ampere consists of one coulomb of charge passing by a point in a conductor in one second.

The charge on an electron is –e

8. THE MASSES OF ATOMS. In Chapter 4 we described how chemists in the nineteenth century developed a scale of the relative masses of atoms based on the ratios by mass in which various elements combined. The masses of all atoms were compared to the mass of the most abundant carbon atom, which was taken as a standard with the value 12.00. The resulting scale of *relative atomic masses* ranges from approximately 1 for hydrogen to just over 238 for uranium. (See the inside back cover for values.) When this scale was established there was no prospect of determining the actual mass of an individual atom, but what could be established was a ratio such as (for oxygen):

$$\frac{\text{Average mass of an oxygen atom}}{\text{Mass of reference carbon atom}} = \frac{\text{Relative atomic mass of oxygen}}{12.00}$$

$$= \frac{16.00}{12.00}$$

In the twentieth century methods for determining the actual masses of atoms were developed, and we shall be describing these in Sec. 20-7. We have already given the mass of a single neon atom in Sec. 10-4; the most striking feature of this quantity is its smallness. Such very small numbers are inconvenient to work with and difficult to remember. A way around having to work unnecessarily with actual atomic masses is achieved by the use of the *atomic mass unit*. This is defined as exactly one-twelfth of the mass of the reference carbon atom. On the scale of relative atomic masses the atomic mass unit has the value one. The actual mass of one atomic mass unit (symbol u) is 1.66×10^{-27} kg.

It follows that the actual mass of a reference carbon atom $= 12.00 \times 1.66 \times 10^{-27}$ kg $= 1.99 \times 10^{-26}$ kg. The average mass of an oxygen atom, in accordance with what is stated above, is

$$\frac{16.00}{12.00} \times 12.00 \times 1.66 \times 10^{-27} \text{ kg} = 16.00 \times 1.66 \times 10^{-27} \text{ kg}$$
$$= 16.00 \text{ u}$$

More generally, the average mass of an atom of any element, in atomic mass units, is the number corresponding to its relative atomic mass.

Problem 10-1: What is the actual mass of a fluorine atom?

Solution: The mass of a fluorine atom is 19.00 u (from inside back cover)

$$1 \text{ u} = 1.66 \times 10^{-27} \text{ kg}$$

∴ the mass of a fluorine atom is

$$19.00 \times 1.66 \times 10^{-27} \text{ kg} = 3.15 \times 10^{-26} \text{ kg}$$

9. MASS OF AN ELECTRON. We have gone into all this at some length because we propose to list the mass of the electron and other atomic particles in atomic mass units. The actual mass of an electron has been found to be 9.1×10^{-31} kg.

To convert this to atomic mass units we divide this mass by 1.66×10^{-27} kg/u.

∴ *the mass of an electron = 0.000 54 u*

As we remarked before, this is much less than the mass of any atom.

10. THE PROTON. Matter is not ordinarily electrically charged, so we must conclude that the atoms of which it is composed are electrically neutral. If electrons, carrying a unit of negative electric charge, are building blocks of all atoms, then there must be some other fundamental unit bearing positive charge. Such a particle *has* been identified, and is called a *proton*. It carries the same amount of charge as an electron, but the charge is positive. It is much heavier than the electron; its mass is 1.0 u (1.0073 u, to be exact).

11. PARTICLES IN A HYDROGEN ATOM. We could now imagine an electron and a proton being brought together in some way to create a neutral particle. Such a particle seems to be a suitable model for the hydrogen atom. Hydrogen is known from chemical reactions to have a relative atomic mass of 1.008. An atom made up from an electron and a proton should have a mass of (0.0005 + 1.0073) u = 1.0078 u, which looks very close to the relative atomic mass of hydrogen. No other combination of protons and electrons would yield a neutral atom with a mass about 1 u.

12. THE NEUTRON. To explain the composition of all atoms heavier than hydrogen, a third particle is required, which will contribute mass but not charge. Such a particle was discovered in 1932, and is called a *neutron*. It is uncharged, and has a mass just about the same as that of a proton, that is, 1.0 u.

The characteristics of the three fundamental atomic building blocks are summarized in Table 10-1.

TABLE 10-1

THE FUNDAMENTAL ATOMIC PARTICLES

PARTICLE	SYMBOL	CHARGE	MASS (u)
Electron	e	$-e$	0.000 54
Proton	p	$+e$	1.0
Neutron	n	0	1.0

13. ATOMIC NUMBER. Atoms of any given chemical element always have a particular constant number of protons and electrons. The number of protons and electrons will always be the same since the atoms must be electrically neutral. We said there were just over a hundred elements, and it has been established that the atoms of each differ in the number of protons and electrons they contain. Hydrogen atoms differ from helium atoms because the former have one proton and one electron, and the latter have two protons and two electrons. What makes one element have different physical and chemical properties from another is their atoms; furthermore, the atoms of one element invariably have a different number of protons and electrons from those of another. In fact, we can assign a kind of serial number to each element according to the number of protons or electrons in its atoms; this is called the *atomic number* of the element, and is represented by the symbol Z.

14. ISOTOPES. We must now examine what is known about the composition of some common atoms in terms of the three fundamental particles listed above. Table 10-2 is an ordered list of the elements with atomic number Z from 1 to 18, and contains for each atom an inventory of the constituent particles. You may be struck by the fact that most of the elements in this list have atoms with more than one characteristic mass. These atoms differ in the number of neutrons they contain, and therefore differ in mass by 1 or 2 or some integral number of u. We said in Chapter 4 that we can no longer accept Dalton's postulate that all atoms of a particular element are identical. You can see from Table 10-2 that, while all atoms of a given element have the same number of protons or electrons (same atomic number), they may have different numbers of neutrons, and therefore different masses. Atoms of a single element which differ in mass are called *isotopes*. For example, all oxygen atoms have 8 protons and 8 electrons but the number of neutrons may be 8, 9, or 10. The isotope with 8 neutrons ($^{16}_{8}O$) is by far the most abundant.

TABLE 10-2

COMPOSITION OF ATOMS OF THE FIRST EIGHTEEN CHEMICAL ELEMENTS

ATOMIC NUMBER z	NAME	SYMBOL	NUMBER OF			MASS (u)	ABUNDANCE (%)
			ELECTRONS	PROTONS	NEUTRONS		
1	Hydrogen (Deuterium)	H (D)	1 1	1 1	0 1	1 2	≈ 100 rare
2	Helium	He	2 2	2 2	1 2	3 4	very rare ≈ 100
3	Lithium	Li	3 3	3 3	3 4	6 7	7.5 92.5
4	Beryllium	Be	4	4	5	9	100
5	Boron	B	5 5	5 5	5 6	10 11	20 80
6	Carbon	C	6 6	6 6	6 7	12 13	98.9 1.1
7	Nitrogen	N	7 7	7 7	7 8	14 15	99.6 0.4
8	Oxygen	O	8 8 8	8 8 8	8 9 10	16 17 18	99.8 rare 0.2
9	Fluorine	F	9	9	10	19	100
10	Neon	Ne	10 10 10	10 10 10	10 11 12	20 21 22	90.5 0.3 9.2
11	Sodium	Na	11	11	12	23	100
12	Magnesium	Mg	12 12 12	12 12 12	12 13 14	24 25 26	79.0 10.0 11.0
13	Aluminium	Al	13	13	14	27	100
14	Silicon	Si	14 14 14	14 14 14	14 15 16	28 29 30	92.2 4.7 3.1
15	Phosphorus	P	15	15	16	31	100
16	Sulphur	S	16 16 16 16	16 16 16 16	16 17 18 20	32 33 34 36	95.0 0.8 4.2 rare
17	Chlorine	Cl	17 17	17 17	18 20	35 37	75.8 24.2
18	Argon	Ar	18 18 18	18 18 18	18 20 22	36 38 40	0.3 0.1 99.6

This statement about deuterium and hydrogen discloses a rather interesting problem. Because deuterium has different properties from common hydrogen, should we regard these as two distinct chemical substances? The criteria for pure substances outlined in Chapter 1 suggest that they should be distinguished, and yet chemically we regard them together as one element. We mention the problem merely to show you how difficult it is to frame a foolproof definition of a pure substance in the chemist's sense of the term.

There is an awkwardness of usage here that it might be well to expose. The term isotope is, strictly speaking, only applicable to one of two or more "strains" of atoms of the same element which differ in mass because of having different numbers of neutrons. Some elements, such as fluorine, occur naturally as a "pure strain" of atoms all of one mass. We prefer not to speak of isotopes in this case; it is rather like talking of a single alternative.

15. Hydrogen, the first element in the list, has a rare isotope of mass 2 u. About one in every 6000 hydrogen atoms has this greater mass. It is possible, with some specialized know-how, to prepare hydrogen gas made up almost entirely of these heavier atoms. This special hydrogen is called *deuterium*, or often just *heavy hydrogen*. Deuterium and common hydrogen differ somewhat in physical properties. Isotopes of other elements, however, are not given special names; and, in cases where they can be separated, differences in properties between them are much less pronounced than between the isotopes of hydrogen.

We can now speak a little more precisely about the reference standard for the scale of relative atomic masses by saying that it is the carbon isotope whose mass is 12 u which is used for this purpose.

16. MASS NUMBER. The mass of each isotope or atom is made up of the masses of the fundamental particles in it. Of these, the protons and neutrons each have a mass of about 1 u, and the electrons by comparison have a mass of only a trifling amount. Roughly, therefore, the mass of each atom or isotope in u is the sum of the numbers of its protons and neutrons. The total number of protons and neutrons is called the *mass number* of the particle; this is always an integer. The exact mass of various atoms in u may be slightly above or below the mass number.

For example, the exact mass of a helium atom is 4.0026 u; its mass number is 4.

17. The mass number is frequently represented by the symbol A. The relationship among the numbers of "heavy" particles in a particular atom or isotope is as follows:

$$A = \text{mass number} = \text{number of protons} + \text{neutrons}$$
$$Z = \text{atomic number} = \text{number of protons} = \text{number of electrons}$$
$$A - Z = \text{number of neutrons}$$

18. SYMBOLS TO REPRESENT ATOMIC SPECIES. In Chapter 4 we introduced the use of symbols for elements, or for atoms of elements. It is sometimes desirable to extend this usage to show the atomic number and mass number for a particular atomic species. The atomic number is written as a subscript to the left of the symbol of the element, thus:

$$_{12}\text{Mg}$$

The mass number is written as a superscript, also to the left of the symbol, thus:

$$^{24}\text{Mg}$$

To represent the three common isotopes of magnesium, we show both numbers in three separate symbols:

$$^{24}_{12}\text{Mg} \quad ^{25}_{12}\text{Mg} \quad ^{26}_{12}\text{Mg}$$

It is probably not really necessary to indicate the atomic number with the symbol. Each element has its own symbol and its own atomic number; if you know one you can always look up the other. We designate a particular isotope in speech by saying, for instance, "magnesium-25" or "carbon-12."

19. If you study Table 10-2 for a few minutes, you will see that the number of neutrons is always about the same as the number of protons. But, before you get the impression that this is a principle applying to all atoms, we should add that among elements of atomic number greater than 20 the number of neutrons increases faster than the number of protons in the atoms. By the time we come to uranium, we find in atoms of the commonest isotope 92 protons and 146 neutrons.

20. RELATIVE ATOMIC MASSES AND ISOTOPES. We must now inquire into the relationship between the masses of atoms or isotopes and the relative atomic masses as listed, for example, on the back cover of this book. Hydrogen and helium consist almost entirely of one isotope, and the relative atomic mass is thus practically the same as the mass in u of the predominant isotope. Lithium (atomic number 3) consists of two isotopes of mass number 6 and 7. There are devices for separating isotopes, and when the lithium isotopes are separated it is found that 7.5% of the atoms are the lighter isotope and 92.5% are the heavier. What is more, these percentages are essentially constant no matter what the source of the lithium. (Remember: the average age of Grade 9 pupils is 14, whether in Ottawa or Windsor.) The relative atomic mass has been determined chemically from the composition of some lithium compounds, and proves to be 6.941. This quantity is thus a "weighted average" of the masses of the isotopes, the weighting being based on their relative abundances.

Perhaps we can make this clearer with an example. Imagine mixing 925 objects (coins, nails, atoms—whatever you like), each having a mass of 7 units, and 75 objects each having a mass of 6 units. There will be 1000 objects in the mixture; the total mass will be (925 × 7 + 75 × 6) units = 6925 units. The average mass per object in the mixture will be 6925/1000 = 6.925 units. This is what we mean by a *weighted average*. An unweighted average for the two different objects would be (6 + 7)/2 = 6.5 units. This should reveal to you how the relative atomic mass of lithium is related to the masses of its isotopes. (There is a slight discrepancy between 6.925 and 6.941, but this is due to the exact masses of the lithium isotopes being slightly greater than 6 and 7.)

Problem 10-2: Calculate the relative atomic mass of magnesium from the distribution and masses of its isotopes given in Table 10-2.

Solution: The easiest way to do this is to assume that we have a representative sample of 1000 magnesium atoms, and to calculate the mass of these.

There will be three groups of these atoms: one group consists of 786 atoms each with a mass of 24 u, another of 101 atoms each with a mass of 25 u, and a third of 113 atoms each with a mass of 26 u.

The mass of 786 atoms, each of 24 u	= 18 864 u
The mass of 101 atoms, each of 25 u	= 2 525 u
The mass of 113 atoms, each of 26 u	= 2 938 u
The total mass of 1000 atoms	= 24 327 u
Therefore, the average mass of each atom	= 24.327 u
and the relative atomic mass of magnesium	= 24.327

We are probably not justified in expressing this answer to the third decimal place, because we used only whole-number values for the isotopic masses. The true masses of isotopes often depart slightly from integral values. If very exact values of the masses of each isotope had been used, this calculation would have yielded a slightly different result. You should compare the answer above with the value on the inside back cover.

In general, the relative atomic mass of an element is derived from the masses of the isotopes of which it is composed in the manner indicated by these examples.

THE MOLE

21. THE AVOGADRO CONSTANT. In Sec. 10-8 we pointed out for the case of oxygen the equality of the two ratios:

$$\frac{\text{Relative atomic mass for an element}}{12.00} = \frac{\text{Average mass of an atom of that element}}{\text{Mass of reference carbon atom } (^{12}C)}$$

Although relative atomic masses are listed as pure numbers without units, it has been a long-established practice in chemistry to attach special importance to a mass of an element equal to its relative atomic mass in grams. We can call this the *gram-atomic mass* of that element; thus 12.01 g is the gram-atomic mass for carbon, 16.00 g is the gram-atomic mass for oxygen, and so forth.

The equation just given could be slightly amended as follows:

$$\frac{\text{Gram-atomic mass of an element (g)}}{12.00 \text{ g}} = \frac{\text{Average mass of an atom of that element}}{\text{Mass of reference carbon atom } (^{12}C)}$$

This can be rearranged to give:

$$\frac{\text{Gram-atomic mass of an element (g)}}{\text{Average mass of an atom of that element}} = \frac{12.00 \text{ g}}{\text{Mass of reference carbon atom } (^{12}C)} \qquad (1)$$

The ratio on the left-hand side of Equation (1) is not specific for any particular element; it can apply to any element. The ratio on the right-hand side applies only to the reference carbon isotope, carbon-12, and has therefore a fixed value. In Sec. 10-8 we saw that the mass of one atom of this carbon isotope was $12.00 \times 1.66 \times 10^{-27}$ kg. Accordingly, the value of the ratio on the right-hand side is:

$$\frac{12.00 \text{ g} \times 10^{-3} \text{ kg/g}}{12.00 \times 1.66 \times 10^{-27} \text{ kg}} = \frac{10^{-3} \text{ kg}}{1.66 \times 10^{-27} \text{ kg}} = 6.02 \times 10^{23}$$

What is the significance of this number? It is the number of atoms of carbon-12 that make up 12.00 g or one gram-atomic mass of this carbon isotope. By the same token, the ratio on the left-hand side of Equation (1) gives the number of atoms of any element that are in one gram-atomic mass of that element. What, then, is the significance of Equation (1)? It states that there is a constant number of atoms in one gram-atomic mass of any element. This number, 6.02×10^{23}, is called the Avogadro constant, and is usually represented by the symbol N_A.

The Avogadro constant = N_A = 6.02×10^{23}/mol

Notice that the constant has units (per mole); the mole is defined in Sec. 10-23.

Amadeo Avogadro (1776-1856) was an Italian scientist whose contributions to physics and chemistry we shall outline in Chapter 19.

22. The idea of relative atomic masses can readily be extended to molecules. When atoms combine to form molecules the mass of the latter will be the masses of the constituent atoms. In the accompanying table are given the relative molecular masses for the indicated substances; you can verify these values with the aid of the table of relative atomic masses (back cover).

SUBSTANCE	FORMULA	RELATIVE MOLECULAR MASS
Hydrogen	H_2	2.016
Oxygen	O_2	32.00
Water	H_2O	18.016
Phosphorus	P_4	123.90
Glucose	$C_6H_{12}O_6$	180.16

These molecular masses are relative to the mass of the standard carbon-12 = 12.00. They are given without units, but it has also proven convenient to deal with an amount of a substance that is its relative molecular mass in grams; this may be called the *gram-molecular mass*.

23. THE MOLE. The amount of a substance represented by the gram-atomic mass or the gram-molecular mass came to be known as the *mole* (symbol mol). However, this usage has been subtly changed in recent years, by international agreement, so that today the mole is a unit (indeed *the* unit) in which to state the *amount of a substance*. The latter, represented by the symbol *n*, is given as some number of moles.

The amount of a substance has been added to a short list of *basic physical quantities*, such as length, mass, time, and electric current, in terms of which other physical quantities can be defined. A physical quantity may be represented by a conventional symbol, and is given by the product of a numerical value (a pure number) and a unit. The unit may also be represented by a symbol. The following examples illustrate this usage:

$$\text{mass } (m) = 50 \text{ kg} \qquad \text{time } (t) = 49.2 \text{ s}$$
$$\text{length } (l) = 7.5 \text{ m} \qquad \text{current } (I) = 0.02 \text{ A}$$
$$\text{amount of a substance } (n) = 0.10 \text{ mol}$$

The **mole** is defined as **the amount of a substance that contains as many particles as there are atoms in 12.00 g (0.012 00 kg) of carbon-12.** The particles may be atoms or molecules or electrons or ions (see Chapter 13) or any other specified entity. Another statement of this definition is that *the mole is the amount of a substance that contains 6.02×10^{23} of the particles represented by its symbol or formula.*

Because the particles may be atoms or molecules, some confusion may arise in this use of the term mole if a substance can occur in more than one form. For instance, in referring to oxygen, are atoms (O) or molecules (O_2) meant? In such cases it is necessary to specify the particles or the state of combination of the substance intended; for instance, a mole of atomic oxygen or a mole of molecular oxygen.

24. MOLAR MASS. Suppose you have in front of you a piece of pure copper, or some pure chloroform in a beaker, or a flask filled with a pure gas. You may speak of the amount of each of these substances by stating the number of moles (n) in your sample, or you may state the amount of matter in each sample by stating its mass (m). The ratio of these two quantities, m/n, is the mass per mole of the substance; this quantity is properly called its *molar mass* (symbol M). The term molar mass applied to elements means the same thing as gram-atomic mass, provided that n refers to atoms as the particles in the definition of the mole. Molar mass, applied to molecular substances, means the same thing as gram-molecular mass. For instance, the molar mass of atomic oxygen is 16.00 g/mol; for molecular oxygen it is 32.00 g/mol.

The term molar mass is more convenient and more general than gram-atomic mass, gram-molecular mass, and several others that have been in use, and should henceforth be used when speaking of the mass of one mole of anything.

25. The practice of expressing quantities of substances in moles is useful in evaluating the masses of reactants or products in chemical reactions. For instance, the equation

$$\text{Zn} + 2\text{HCl} \longrightarrow \text{H}_2 + \text{ZnCl}_2$$

which you encountered in Sec. 6-3 might convey that a zinc atom reacts with two molecules of hydrogen chloride (which in aqueous solution is called hydrochloric acid) to form a molecule of hydrogen and a molecule of zinc chloride. But the equation could equally well be interpreted as showing that a mole of zinc reacts with two moles of hydrogen chloride, producing a mole each of hydrogen (molecular hydrogen, as the

In making steel, quantities of materials must be carefully calculated—and the quantities are in tonnes, not grams.

equation tells us) and zinc chloride. This is because in each case a mole is 6.02×10^{23} times as much as one atom or molecule; if we multiplied each item in the equation, read as atoms or molecules, by the Avogadro constant we end up with the equation read as moles.

We can readily find the molar masses of each substance in this equation. For zinc it is 65.4 g/mol (see relative atomic masses, back cover); for hydrogen chloride it is (1.0 + 35.5) g/mol = 36.5 g/mol; and so forth. Thus we have implicit in the equation the masses of each substance taking part, and we can use this information to calculate the quantity of a reactant required or the yield of a product obtained for a given chemical reaction.

Problem 10-3: How many grams of hydrogen can be produced from the reaction of one gram of zinc with hydrochloric acid?

Solution 1: From the equation cited above, we see that one mole of zinc produces one mole of hydrogen. The molar masses are

for zinc: 65.4 g/mol

for hydrogen: (2 × 1.0) g/mol = 2.0 g/mol

Accordingly, 65.4 g of zinc produces 2.0 g of hydrogen

$$1.00 \text{ g of zinc will produce } \frac{2.0 \text{ g} \times 1.00 \text{ g}}{65.4 \text{ g}} = 0.0306 \text{ g of hydrogen}$$

Solution 2:

$$1.00 \text{ g of zinc} = \frac{1.00 \text{ g}}{65.4 \text{ g/mol}} = 0.0153 \text{ mol of zinc}$$

This will produce 0.0153 mol of hydrogen, and this amount of hydrogen = 0.0153 mol × 2.0 g/mol = 0.0306 g of hydrogen, as before.

In Chapter 16 we shall be expanding on these ideas, which are of great importance in practical chemistry.

QUESTIONS

1. Make clear the meaning of and the distinction between: (a) atomic mass; (b) relative atomic mass; (c) gram-atomic mass; (d) atomic mass unit.

2. Rewrite Table 10-1, but insert the charge in coulombs and the mass in kilograms.

3. Explain the meaning of the terms *atomic number* and *mass number*. What is the significance of the difference between these numbers?

4. Why are the numbers of protons and electrons equal in every atom?

5. In what ways are isotopes of a particular element alike, and in what ways are they different?

6. Fill in the blank spaces in the following table: →

7. Prepare a table similar to Table 10-2, showing the composition of the following isotopic species; cobalt-60, chromium-50, calcium-44, potassium-41, copper-63, zinc-64, bromine-81. (You may need information from the table on the inside back cover to answer this.)

8. What is meant by the phrase "average mass of an oxygen atom"? Why is it necessary to speak of "average" masses in such cases?

9. Explain the distinction between "average" and "weighted average," by reference to a particular example, say, the ages of the students in a class. When is there apt to be the largest difference between these two kinds of averages?

ELEMENT	ATOMIC NUMBER	NUMBERS OF ATOMIC PARTICLES			MASS NUMBERS
		PROTONS	ELECTRONS	NEUTRONS	
Vanadium			23		51
Arsenic	33			42	
Nickel		28			58
Strontium	38				90
Silver			47	60	
Iodine		53			127
Tin		50		70	
Rhodium	45				103

10. Neon (atomic number 10) has three isotopes, but fluorine (atomic number 9) has no isotopes. Explain this distinction.

11. Explain clearly why experiments such as the decomposition of mercuric oxide or the synthesis of magnesium oxide (Chapter 3) fail to disclose the existence of isotopes of the elements involved.

12. From the data in Table 10-2 calculate the relative atomic mass of boron to the second decimal place. Compare your answer with the value given for boron in the table on the inside back cover of the book.

13. Iridium (a metal rather like platinum) occurs with only two isotopes, of mass number 191 and 193. The relative atomic mass of iridium is 192.2. Deduce the relative abundance of the two isotopes of this element.

14. Explain why one might expect relative atomic masses to be very nearly whole numbers, and why, nevertheless, some are not even close to whole numbers.

15. The relative atomic mass of magnesium is 24.32. What proportion of this is contributed by electrons?

16. Why do we believe that the particles in a gas are spread out at some distance from one another? Why do we believe that the particles are bunched close together in a liquid?

17. State the mass, in atomic mass units, of (a) one atom of fluorine; (b) one atom of phosphorus. Calculate the mass, in kilograms, of each of these atoms.

18. Table 10-2 lists two isotopes of hydrogen, and three of oxygen. Water occurs as molecules with the formula H_2O, but in view of the existence of these isotopes not all water molecules will be identical or have the same mass. How many different water molecules can be formed from these isotopes? How many different masses will there be among these? Which molecules will be the lightest? Which the heaviest?

19. The number 6.02×10^{23} is known as Avogadro's number or, with the unit mol^{-1}, is called the Avogadro constant. Explain clearly the significance of this quantity.

20. The atomic mass unit, u, is 1.66×10^{-24} g. Show that 1.66×10^{-24} is the reciprocal of Avogadro's number, and explain why this is so.

21. What is the relationship between the actual masses of atoms and their relative masses? How may relative masses of atoms be found without actually weighing atoms?

22. The sensitive chemical balance illustrated in Chapter 3 can just detect 0.1 mg (10^{-4} g). How many atoms of magnesium is that? How many atoms of mercury?

23. Calculate the actual mass in grams of (a) one rhodium atom, (b) one million sodium atoms, (c) 10^{20} beryllium atoms.

24. Calculate the molar mass for the following substances, all encountered in earlier chapters of this book: hydrogen iodide, nitric oxide, sulphuric acid, propane, phosphorus pentoxide.

25. Suppose we have exactly one gram of each of: magnesium, chlorine, chloride ion, neon, carbon disulphide, sulphur, lead nitrate, sodium iodide, silicon, silane (SiH_4). State the amount of each substance in moles, and for what species (atoms, molecules, etc.) the number of moles refers to.

26. Why is it ambiguous to speak of "a mole of chlorine" or "the molar mass of chlorine." How can you remove the ambiguity?

27. Twenty-eight grams of nitrogen may be represented by 2N or N_2. Explain the difference in these two representations.

28. Seek out the appropriate equations in earlier chapters of this book, and from these, answer the following questions:

(a) What amount of potassium chlorate (in moles) is required to produce one mole of molecular oxygen?

(b) What amount of sulphur dioxide (in moles) is produced by the burning of one mole of molecular sulphur?

(c) What amount of molecular hydrogen (in moles) is produced by the treatment of one mole of methane with excess steam?

(d) What amount of hydrogen nitrate (nitric acid) (in moles) can be produced from one mole of ammonia.

(e) What amount of hydrogen chloride (hydrochloric acid) (in moles) is required for reaction with manganese dioxide to produce one mole of molecular chlorine?

29. The oxidation of aluminium to its oxide is represented by an equation given in Chapter 9. What amount of aluminium oxide (in moles) is formed from one mole of aluminium? What are the molar masses of aluminium and its oxide? What is the amount of aluminium (in moles) in one kilogram of this metal? What is the amount of aluminium oxide (in moles) that can be formed from one kilogram of this metal? What is the mass of this amount of aluminium oxide?

30. Nitrogen dioxide may be produced for study in the laboratory by treating copper metal with an excess of concentrated nitric acid. An equation representing the reaction is given in Chapter 7. What amount of copper (in moles) is required to produce one mole of nitrogen dioxide? Suppose it is desired to produce one gram of nitrogen dioxide; what amount of this substance (in moles) is that? What amount of copper (in moles) would be required to produce one gram of nitrogen dioxide? What is the mass of that amount of copper?

*31. The copper atom is considered to be spherical and 2.55×10^{-8} cm in diameter. How many of these can be laid along a line 1 cm long and just be touching another? In simple square packing, how many atoms could be laid out in a square of area 1 cm^2? In simple cubic packing, how many atoms could be laid out in a cube of volume 1 cm^3? Given that each copper atom has a mass of 63.6 u, calculate the mass of this 1 cm^3 of copper. How does this compare with the density of copper, 8.9 g/cm^3? Can you suggest any explanation for the discrepancy?

11

The Structure of Atoms: A Model of the Hydrogen Atom

1. By now you have made the acquaintance of the fundamental atomic particles—electrons, protons, and neutrons—and have seen how they vary in number from atom to atom among the different elements and their isotopes. Now we turn our attention to the way these particles are arranged within atoms. The evidence on which our ideas about this arrangement are based comes from a variety of observable phenomena to be described in this chapter. We shall begin with a brief account of radioactivity.

2. RADIOACTIVITY. In 1896 Henri Becquerel, a French physicist, showed that uranium and its compounds gave off radiations that would, among other things, darken photographic plates. In subsequent years Marie and Pierre Curie showed that some other elements of high atomic mass shared this peculiar property. Such elements were said to be *radioactive*. The radiation was shown in due course to be of more than one kind. Of the things given off, two proved to be particles hurled out of the atoms of these unusual elements with great force. One of these was called the α particle (alpha particle), and was shown by Ernest Rutherford and Hans Geiger in 1908 to consist of a helium atom stripped of its two electrons. It was therefore positively charged with two electronic units of charge, and had a mass of 4 u. The other particle, called a β particle (beta particle), proved to be an electron.

Some radioactive elements emit α particles; others emit β particles. Both particles are much too small to be seen, but they can be detected by their action on a photographic film or on a fluorescent screen (like a television screen), or by the fact that in passing through a gas they make it capable of conducting an electric current. (This last property is the basis of the familiar Geiger counter for detecting and measuring radioactivity.)

The observation leading to the discovery of radioactivity was that a compound of uranium is capable of affecting a photographic plate that is protected from ordinary light. Radioactive substances can thus take their own photographs: the picture so obtained is called an autoradiograph.

Here, on the left, is an autoradiograph of a sample of uranium ore from Elliot Lake, Ontario. The picture on the right is of the same sample, photographed with ordinary light in the usual way. Clearly, the radioactive substances are largely localized in "veins."

3. THE PASSAGE OF PARTICLES THROUGH MATTER. Since particles from radioactive substances can be detected in these ways, it soon became apparent that they had remarkable powers of penetration through air, paper, metal foils, etc. For instance, the α particle can pass through several centimetres of air or other gases without evidence of a collision. This movement of particles has given some insight into the nature of atoms.

We described in Sec. 10-2 the enormous number of atoms present in a litre of neon under ordinary conditions. In a later chapter we shall show that there are just as many molecules (mainly of oxygen and nitrogen) in a litre of air; these molecules are seven or eight times heavier than α particles. It is surprising, therefore, that an α particle can travel so far through so many heavier particles and not bump into one or more of these.

In another experiment, Rutherford showed that practically all the α particles shot at a thin foil of metal (like aluminium foil) passed through unhindered (Fig. 11-1). From the sizes of the metal atoms used, a typical foil can be shown to be of the order of 10^5 atoms thick. Rutherford's observations indicated that most α particles were whistling

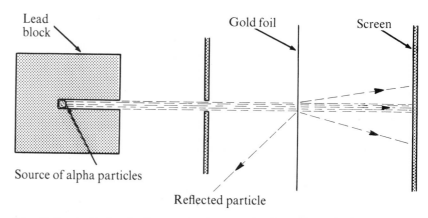

Fig. 11-1: *In Rutherford's experiment on the scattering of alpha particles, most of the latter passed through thin gold (or other metal) foil without deflection. Some were deflected slightly, and a few had their direction altered considerably, even to the extent of occasionally being deflected backwards.*

through something like 100 000 metal atoms without hitting anything!

This evidence compelled Rutherford to conclude that atoms are virtually empty or hollow, offering little resistance to the passage of α particles through them. This is interpreted to mean that the electrons, protons, and neutrons of which atoms are made must be exceedingly small, and must occupy only a tiny fraction of the volume of the atom.

4. THE NUCLEUS OF THE ATOM. During their study of the passage of α particles through metal foils, Rutherford and his students did observe that a few of the α particles *were* deflected from their course. More unexpectedly, a few of these even came out of the foil on the same side they went in. This was a surprising observation, which prompted Rutherford to say that "it was almost as incredible as if you fired a 15-inch shell at a piece of tissue paper and it came back and hit you."

He inferred from these observations that the deflected α particles must have experienced some massive repulsion, and he surmised that this was due to electrical forces. This led him in 1911 to propose a model of the atom in which all the positive charge and practically all the mass (or, as we now can say, all the protons and neutrons) were concentrated in one tiny particle, which Rutherford called the *nucleus*, at the centre of the atom. Surrounding the nucleus, the electrons occupied (but obviously didn't fill) the remainder of the volume of the atom. This model, which is still completely satisfactory as a description of atoms, is known as the *nuclear atom*. This concept of the nuclear atom is based on what is often called Rutherford's scattering experiment (Fig. 11-1).

The emptiness of the atom will be made a little more evident by consideration of the sizes of the nucleus and electrons compared to the size of atoms. We said previously that atoms were a few hundred picometres in diameter. We cannot be as sure of the diameters of nuclei or elec-

Ernest Rutherford grew up on a farm in New Zealand. His ability at school earned him scholarships at Canterbury College in New Zealand and later at the University of Cambridge in England. At one stage of his career (1898-1907) he was a professor at McGill University, but thereafter worked at British universities.

Lord Rutherford, as he became, probably did more than any other person to lay the foundations of modern atomic theory. He introduced the idea of the nucleus, named the proton, predicted the existence of the neutron, and performed, supervised, or inspired most of the brilliant experimental work in nuclear science done in the first third of this century.

trons, but each appears to be about one-thousandth of a picometre. This means that the diameter of an atom is at least 100 000 times as great as the diameter of its nucleus or of any of the electrons it contains. No wonder atoms are so porous to the passage of particles which, being themselves nuclei of helium atoms, are very tiny projectiles.

5. The astonishing thing about this description of what is often called the nuclear atom is that its mass is practically all concentrated in the tiny central nucleus. The heavy particles, the protons and neutrons, are the fundamental nuclear particles, and they are collectively known as *nucleons*. As we have already explained, atoms of one element differ from those of another by the number (Z) of protons in the nucleus, and hence of the number of electrons around the nucleus. Isotopes are species of a single element the atoms of which differ in the number of neutrons in their nuclei, and therefore differ in mass. To distinguish among different atoms and isotopes we can indicate the numbers of protons and numbers of nucleons (mass numbers), and so by difference the numbers of neutrons. Any species that can be distinguished on the basis of the numbers of each kind of nuclear particle it contains is known as a *nuclide*. Two special categories of nuclides are the following:

These dimensions can perhaps be made more dramatic if we try to picture a large-scale model of a hydrogen atom. Suppose we picture the nucleus of this as a golf ball. There is one electron, and it would be represented by another golf ball. The second ball will move around the first within a sphere about 4 km in diameter. How easy it would be to lose a golf ball in all that space!

Isobars: same mass number, different atomic number; for example, $^{24}_{11}Na$ and $^{24}_{12}Mg$

Isotopes: same atomic number, different mass number; for example, $^{32}_{16}S$ and $^{34}_{16}S$

6. **EMISSION OR ABSORPTION OF LIGHT BY ATOMS.** Before we can effectively tackle the next question, namely, whereabouts in atoms are the electrons and what are they doing, we must gather some of the evidence on which to build an answer.

For a long time it has been known that salts of certain metals, lithium, sodium, copper, etc., or even the metals themselves will impart colour to flames. Also, when an electric current passes through tubes filled with certain gases or vapours, the latter glow with a characteristic colour.

With a bit of clean platinum wire sealed into a piece of soft glass which serves as a handle, you can easily demonstrate the colours imparted to a flame by the salts of certain metals. When placed horizontally in a clear gas flame a portion of the wire gets red hot, but if it is clean it adds no colour to the flame. If the wire is then cooled, dipped into a solution of sodium chloride, and again inserted in the flame, a strong amber-coloured flare appears in the flame. This is caused by the very small volume of solution that clings to the wire. The same result is observed if other sodium salts, such as sodium nitrate, are used. You may cool and clean off the wire, and then repeat the test with solutions of lithium chloride or copper chloride, whereupon you will observe different colours. Such *flame tests* have long been used to identify or detect metals in solution. Under suitable conditions the intensity of the flame colouration can be measured by light-sensitive instruments, and a relationship established between flame intensity and the amount of the element responsible for the colour. Such a device is called a flame photometer, and many are used in laboratories for chemical analysis for small amounts of certain metals.

These glows have already been mentioned in connection with neon-filled tubes for advertising signs. Lamps containing mercury vapour are used for street lighting, disinfecting, and other purposes. Lamps containing sodium vapour emit the same amber colour that is observed in the flame test for sodium compounds, and these lamps are used for highway and airport lighting.

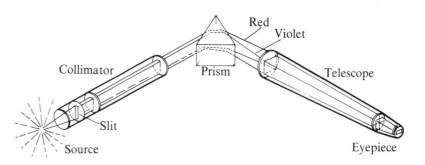

Fig. 11-2: *This sketch illustrates the essential components of a simple prism spectroscope. Rays from the light source pass through a slit, are made parallel by a collimator lens, and are then refracted by the prism. The rays emerging from the latter pass through the first telescope lens which forms an image of the spectrum that is viewed through an eyepiece. The telescope can be moved around horizontally so that the angles of deviation of the rays can be measured.*

The coloured light from these sources can be analyzed by passing it through an instrument called a spectroscope (Fig. 11-2) in which it is resolved into its component wavelengths. When sunlight or white light from a tungsten lamp (the filament of which is incandescent) is examined by the spectroscope it is dispersed into a rainbow-like band of colours. But where the light from a flame test or a discharge tube is similarly examined it is found to consist of only a few narrow coloured "lines," corresponding to only a few isolated wavelengths. The colours or wavelengths that appear in this case depend on the element in the flame or discharge tube; each element that emits light under these conditions has its own characteristic pattern of coloured lines; no two elements emit an identical pattern of wavelengths (Fig. 11-3). The set of

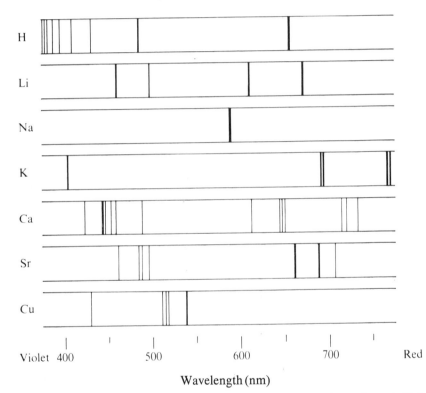

Fig. 11-3: *The spectra of some elements. The diagram shows lines (which are actually images of the spectroscope's slit) emitted at various wavelengths by the atoms of the indicated elements. In a spectroscope such as illustrated in Fig. 11-2 each line would appear as a single colour. The broader lines represent colours that are emitted with greater intensity than the narrower lines. With photographic film and other detectors additional spectral lines can be found in the ultraviolet and infrared regions of the spectrum. It is clear that each element emits its own distinctive spectrum. The spectroscope can reveal differences not visible to the eye; the flame colouration due to lithium and that due to strontium each appears to the eye to be about the same shade of red, but notice here the differences in the actual wavelengths emitted.*

wavelengths given out in this way comprise what is called the *emission spectrum* of the given element (plural *spectra*). The spectrum has been likened to a fingerprint in its ability to identify a given element.

Not only can gases and vapours *emit* light when subjected to flame temperatures or electrical discharges, but at moderate temperatures they can *absorb* certain wavelengths. For instance, if the white light from a tungsten lamp is passed through a tube containing sodium vapour, and is then directed through a spectroscope, the rainbow-like continuous spectrum from the light source appears; but careful examination reveals that there is a black line amidst the orange-yellow colour. This black line is due to a wavelength now missing from the continuous emission from the tungsten filament. That wavelength was absorbed by the sodium atoms through which the white light passed. The light so absorbed has a wavelength of 589 nm, and that is the same wavelength as the amber light emitted by sodium or its compounds in a flame or by the sodium vapour lamp. There is an *absorption spectrum* for sodium, therefore, and it is at least in part observed at the same wavelengths as occur in the emission spectrum.

7. WAVES AND QUANTA. The foregoing facts about emission and absorption of light were known in the nineteenth century, but could not be explained. You probably already know from physics that the transmission of light is described by a "model" based on the motion of waves. This is the only model that will account for certain phenomena, such as the way light is scattered because of diffraction when it passes through narrow slits. A relationship exists between colour and the length of the waves describing the light, and it is possible to measure the wavelength of light of a particular colour. It is also known that light is only a limited region, to which our eyes and brain respond with a sensation that we call colour, within a much greater span of wave motion that we call the electromagnetic spectrum. There are other regions in this that we call ultraviolet, infrared, radio frequency, microwave, etc. (See Fig. 11-4.)

However, there are some properties of light, especially its radiation from glowing bodies, and its ability to eject electrons from some metals (the photoelectric effect), which the wave model does not satisfactorily explain.

"We must imagine radiant energy being thrown out from an atom in pailfuls, as it were, rather than from a hose pipe. A pailful is called a quantum of the radiant energy, and the size of the pail depends upon the wavelength of the radiation." (Andrade, 1927)

8. At the beginning of this century Max Planck, a German physicist, ventured a radical hypothesis that whenever light, or electromagnetic radiation in general, is absorbed or radiated by atoms or molecules, the energy is taken in or given out in tiny pulses. The size of each energy pulse varies inversely as the wavelength of the radiation, or, as is usually stated, is proportional to the frequency of the light. (See Fig. 11-5.) The small pulses of energy came to be known as *quanta* (singular *quantum*).

$$E = h \times \nu$$

| energy of quantum | Planck constant | frequency |

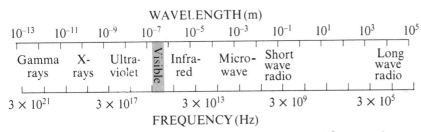

Fig. 11-4: *The range of the electromagnetic spectrum with approximate wavelengths and frequencies of common radiations. The visible spectrum is only a tiny portion of this, between 4×10^{-7} and 7×10^{-7} m.*

The Planck constant is extremely small, 6.62×10^{-34} J·s, so you can imagine that the energy pulses are quite small also.

Five years later (1905) Albert Einstein extended this idea by suggesting that not only was the energy absorbed or emitted in quanta, but that it was actually transmitted through space in the form of small pulses of radiation travelling with the speed of light, and bearing with them their associated quanta of energy. To the pulses of radiation he gave the name *photons*. This extension of Planck's idea was able to account for many features of the photoelectric effect which had previously defied explanation. This amounted to a corpuscular theory of light—an idea virtually abandoned since 1680 when Huygens proposed the wave theory. The situation boils down to this: we need *two* models to account for *all* the phenomena associated with light and similar radiation—wave motion when it suits us, corpuscular when it suits us better. How fickle seem the scientists; how fickle really is nature!

9. NIELS BOHR AND A SIMPLE MODEL OF THE HYDROGEN ATOM. Shortly after Rutherford had proposed his nuclear model for atoms he was joined for a short time by a young assistant called Niels Bohr, freshly graduated from the University of Copenhagen. Bohr soon added some new ideas to Rutherford's theory. He suggested, for instance, that the electrons travelled around the nucleus in orbits, rather like planets around the sun. In the case of the hydrogen atom, where there was only a single electron to keep track of, he developed a model based on simple physical relationships. In this model he permitted a quantity called the angular momentum of the electron to assume only certain values which were 1, 2, 3, etc., times a certain basic amount. This led to only certain orbits being "allowed" for the electron, each with a characteristic radius, and in each of which the electron could have only a certain definite energy. These energies could be labelled E_1, E_2, etc., according to the value of the integer specifying the angular momentum. Bohr was able to calculate these energies; we don't intend to show you how, but you could look it up elsewhere. Thereupon emerged an exciting result (which made Bohr's whole model exciting). The difference in the electron's energy between any two orbits proved to be just equal to the energy, calculated by Planck's relationship, corresponding to some line in the emission spectrum of hydrogen. For example, three prominent

Fig. 11-5: *The essential characteristics of wave motion to which we shall be referring are its wavelength (λ = lambda), its frequency (ν = nu), and the velocity with which a given wave crest appears to move in a forward direction (ν). These are related as follows:*

$$\text{v} = \nu \times \lambda$$
$$\text{velocity} \quad \text{frequency} \quad \text{wave-length}$$

Wavelength has units of length (l), say metres; frequency has units of reciprocal time (t), usually s^{-1}, called hertz (Hz); velocity has units of l/t, usually m/s. In the case of light and all electromagnetic radiation the speed of the wave motion is 3×10^8 m/s, and this quantity is given the symbol c. The distance a is called the amplitude at the point x; as the wave moves forward it causes the amplitude to vary periodically.

"It is well that the reader should appreciate . . . the agony of the physicists of the period. They could but make the best of it, and went around with woebegone faces sadly complaining that on Mondays, Wednesdays, and Fridays they must look on light as a wave; on Tuesdays, Thursdays, and Saturdays, as a particle. On Sundays they simply prayed." (Hoffmann, 1947)

The angular momentum of the electron travelling in a circular orbit is made up of the product of its mass and its velocity divided by the radius of the orbit.

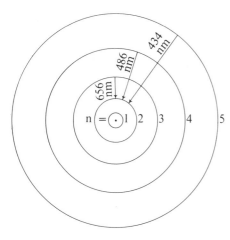

Fig. 11-6: *By making certain assumptions Bohr was able to calculate the radii of a set of circular orbits for the electron, and also the energy of the electron in each orbit. He then showed that the jump of an electron from one orbit to another would be accompanied by absorption or emission of electromagnetic radiation the wavelength of which, in accordance with Planck's relationship, just matched observed spectral wavelengths. The transitions marked on this drawing correspond to three lines in the visible emission spectrum of atomic hydrogen.*

This stamp, commemorating the 50th anniversary of the publication in 1913 of the atomic theory of Niels Bohr (1885-1962), displays the key relationship linking the energies of the electron in two orbits with the frequency (v) of the electromagnetic radiation emitted or absorbed in an electron transition within the hydrogen atom.

lines in the visible spectrum of hydrogen could be matched to differences in the energy of an electron in designated orbits as follows:

OBSERVED WAVELENGTHS IN HYDROGEN SPECTRUM	CALCULATED ENERGIES OF ELECTRON (BOHR)
656 nm	$E_3 - E_2$
486 nm	$E_4 - E_2$
434 nm	$E_5 - E_2$

Bohr concluded that the emission of light in these cases must correspond to the jump of an electron from one orbit to another. The jumps corresponding to the above spectral lines for hydrogen are indicated by arrows in Fig. 11-6.

We can summarize Bohr's ideas by saying that the electron in a hydrogen atom can travel in only one of a set of specified orbits, and that in the latter its energy is quantized. Spectral wavelengths or frequencies correspond to a jump of an electron from one permitted energy state to another.

Bohr's model of the hydrogen atom was a big step forward in our understanding, but it fell short of being a complete and satisfactory explanation of the arrangement of electrons in atoms in general. For one thing, a "solar system" model suggests a flat atom, whereas all other evidence indicates a spherical (or nearly spherical) model. For another, the analogy to the solar system suggests that the electrons travel about the nucleus in fixed orbits, much as individual planets follow fixed orbits around the sun. This picture proves too simple, and fails to give any guidance as to what happens in atoms with more than one electron.

10. MATTER WAVES. Building a scientific theory is somewhat like assembling a jigsaw puzzle. Sometimes unrelated pieces of information (like pieces of the puzzle) suddenly fit together to yield an enlarged glimpse of the whole; sometimes there are long delays while people probe around looking for a relationship between one item and another. So it was that ten years elapsed before the next breakthrough in this problem, and when it came it was a shocker! A French scientist, Louis de Broglie, proposed in 1923 that if light or electromagnetic radiation could have the dual character of waves and particles, why could moving matter not also be described either as particles or as wave motion? His reasoning led him to the following relationship for matter waves:

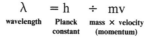

What sort of wavelengths does this lead to? Obviously, because of the presence of the Planck constant in the relationship they will be very small, but for a particle of very small mass there could, nevertheless, be a significant wavelength. A simple calculation reveals that an electron, moving with a speed that can easily be attained in the laboratory, has a wavelength about the same as the diameter of many common atoms!

Scientists have learned how to extract electrons from atoms, how to accelerate those electrons, collect them into a beam, focus them onto very small objects, and put them to use in instruments such as the electron microscope and electron diffractometer.

The picture on the left depicts an amazingly tiny crystal of molybdenum trioxide, MoO_3, much too small to be seen by the naked eye. Here you see it clearly defined in the electron microscope, at a magnification of 60 000.

The pattern on the right was obtained by impinging electrons on the same crystal, whereby the electrons are diffracted by the atoms in the crystal. The symmetry of the pattern is a consequence of the regularity of the spacing of the molybdenum and oxygen atoms that constitute molybdenum trioxide.

Consider an electron (mass = 9.1×10^{-31} kg) moving at 3×10^6 m/s (1% of the speed of light, which is easily achieved in practice). According to the de Broglie relationship its wavelength should be:

$$\lambda = \frac{6.62 \times 10^{-34} \, \text{J·s}}{9.1 \times 10^{-31} \, \text{kg} \times 3 \times 10^6 \, \text{m/s}}$$
$$= 2.4 \times 10^{-10} \, \text{m} = 2.4 \times 10^2 \, \text{pm}$$

We should add briefly that in 1927 two American scientists, C. J. Davisson and L. H. Germer, unexpectedly demonstrated that a beam of moving electrons could be diffracted in passing through a crystal of nickel (in which the regular spaces between the atoms acted as a grating). In that same year G. P. Thomson, in England, also observed electron diffraction by a thin foil of metal. These experimental observations confirmed de Broglie's unproven supposition concerning matter waves since, as we have already stated, the phenomenon of diffraction can be explained only by attributing wave motion to the diffracted beam.

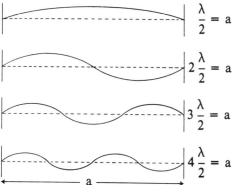

Fig. 11-7: *A violin string may be set into wave motion and, as illustrated, more than one pattern of standing waves can develop on the string between the points of attachment at the ends. In sound, these correspond to a fundamental tone and overtones.*

11. STANDING WAVE PATTERNS. A wave, such as we described in Fig. 11-5, gives the appearance of moving forward; that is, a particular wave crest moves ahead at the speed with which the wave is travelling. However, if a string or wire is tied down at both ends, like a violin string is, and then is plucked to generate waves along its length, the wave crests do not appear to move. (This is a result of reflection from both ends of the string.) The string is now said to describe a pattern of *standing waves*. Fig. 11-7 indicates that more than one such wave pattern can arise on the string, but these are limited because there must be an integral number of half-wavelengths distributed along the string. This limitation can be expressed by a simple relationship:

$$n\left(\frac{\lambda}{2}\right) = \text{length of string}$$

In this statement n is a whole number and λ is the wavelength corresponding to the choice of n. The figure also shows that whenever $n > 1$ there are points along the string at which the latter is not moving; that is, the wave has zero amplitude at these points. They are called *nodes*.

12. ELECTRON WAVES IN ATOMS. After de Broglie had introduced the idea of an electron or other small particle having an associated wavelength, Erwin Schrödinger, an Austrian mathematical physicist, in 1925 linked together this idea and Bohr's model to yield a new description of the hydrogen atom. In simplest terms, what he suggested was that the electron could be in any orbit around which its matter waves could extend in an integral number of wavelengths.

Schrödinger embodied his ideas in some fairly complex mathematics, and his approach to the organization of electrons in atoms and molecules is usually known as *wave mechanics*. He showed that when an electron is "tied down" by the strong electrical attraction of the nucleus it can adopt only certain standing wave patterns in three dimensions. (Compare this with the violin string in one dimension.) There are integers, like n in the example of the violin string, which have to be introduced to distinguish one wave pattern from another. Actually, since the description of the electron wave is shifted to three dimensions, it turns out that three such integers are needed. They are called *quantum numbers*, and are represented by three different symbols, n, l, and m.

n This is called the *principal quantum number*.
  It may assume any positive integral value, commencing at 1, so that permissible values are 1, 2, 3 . . .
  It is somewhat like n in the example of the violin string because it is related to the number of nodes that form in the wave pattern.

l This is sometimes called the *subsidiary quantum number*.
  The value l may have depends on the value of n. The values permitted for l are zero and integers up to $(n - l)$. Thus the higher the value of n the more choices there are for the value of l.

In the next section we shall explain that the value of *l* roughly determines the *shape* of the standing wave pattern for the electron.

m   This (for a reason we don't propose to explain) is usually called the *magnetic quantum number*.

The values permitted for *m* are related to the value of *l*. They may run, in integers, from *l* down through zero and on to –*l*. Thus, if *l* = 2, *m* may be 2, 1, 0, –1, or –2.

The values of *m* are, to some extent, related to the *direction* in space that a particular wave pattern will be orientated.

What all this means is that if you select a set of values for *n*, *l*, and *m* (provided that these conform to the permitted values as described) someone versed in wave mechanics can provide you with a description of the corresponding wave pattern for the electron in the hydrogen atom. This description might very well be in the form of a mathematical equation which you would not find very illuminating, but fortunately some of the simpler wave patterns can be described in ways that can be visualized or represented by models. These simple visual representations enable us to get a feeling for the way in which electrons are arranged in atoms, and as we proceed you will see that this electron arrangement is of prime importance in determining the chemical behaviour of atoms.

The simplest wave pattern for the electron is that for which *n* = 1. We shall describe it first.

13. A FUZZY MODEL OF THE HYDROGEN ATOM. The most curious feature of the wave-mechanical description of the electron in an atom is that it is incapable of fixing the position or the path of the electron at any particular instant. Whereas in Bohr's theory the electron was confined to an orbit of specified radius, according to this newer theory it apparently travels around the nucleus in a capricious way, probably never following the same path twice. In that case what *can* we say about the electron's whereabouts? Wave mechanics enables us only to predict the *probability* or chance of finding the electron at any point we select in the neighbourhood of the nucleus.

To try to give you some feeling for what this statement means, suppose you try to imagine a probability description of yourself "tied down" inside your house. If you were asked to state whereabout in your house you would be at a given moment in the future, your first reaction might be that there was no way of telling in advance where you would be. However, if pressed for some answer, it might occur to you that there are some places where you are more likely to be than others, and that you might try to describe your whereabouts on a probability basis. For instance, there might be a 40% chance of your being in the family room, 30% chance that you would be in the kitchen, 10% in your bedroom, etc. Such a probability description is what we have to resort to in trying to locate an electron in an atom.

If that is all wave mechanics can tell us, how can we represent the distribution of electron probability around the nucleus? One way, for the simplest wave pattern, is to plot probability *vs* distance from the

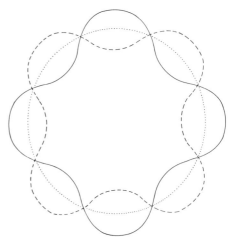

Fig. 11-8: *This drawing may help you see a connection between de Broglie matter waves for electrons and the Bohr model of the hydrogen atom. Bohr calculated for increasing values of an integer n the radius of circular orbits and the energy of the electron in those orbits. For the calculated energies there would be, according to de Broglie, associated wavelengths. It turned out that the permitted orbits were only those that could just accommodate n standing waves for the electron; this is illustrated here for the case where n = 4. Although we no longer uphold the Bohr orbits, we do retain the idea of standing wave patterns (but in three dimensions) for the electron.*

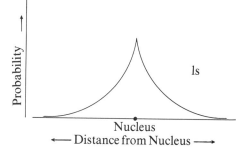

Fig. 11-9: *In the ls orbital the wave pattern is such that there is a high probability of locating the electron near the nucleus, and then this falls off in all directions in the manner shown.*

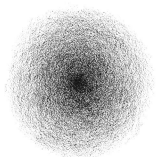

Fig. 11-10: *The dots in this drawing of the ls orbital of a hydrogen atom each represent a fixed small probability of finding the electron in that vicinity at a given instant. It might be helpful to think that a thousand dots could be arranged to surround the nucleus in three dimensions. Each dot would then represent one chance in a thousand that the electron would be near that spot at a particular instant.*

Fig. 11-11: *As Fig. 11-9 and 11-10 suggest, it is difficult to fix the precise outer limit of an orbital. Nevertheless, boundary diagrams such as this for the ls orbital probably best convey the spherical shape of the "electron cloud." The boundary can be set to contain, say, 95% of the electron probability.*

nucleus; this is shown in Fig. 11-9. In this case the plot informs us that there is a high probability that the electron is close to the nucleus, and that this probability diminishes as we get farther away from the latter. The probability in this case does not depend on any particular direction in which we choose to measure distance from the nucleus, so it is said to be **spherically symmetrical**. Wave patterns that are spherically symmetrical about the nucleus are designated by the letter s following the numerical value of the principal quantum number. In this case we label the wave pattern 1s. Such a wave pattern is a description of the whereabouts of the electron in the hydrogen atom. It replaces the notion of an orbit; instead, it is called an *orbital.*

There are some other ways of depicting an orbital. In Fig 11-10 we show one way; in this way the density of the dots around the centre is supposed to correspond to the distribution of electron probability around the nucleus. Someone has said that this speckled sketch representing an orbital might be interpreted thus: suppose that in some magic way we could photograph an atom over and over, and that in each photograph the electron appeared as a little dot; if many hundreds of such photographs were superimposed, the effect would be like Fig. 11-10, with the greatest density of dots in the region where the electron most often appeared. We must add, of course, that this representation has to be imagined in three dimensions; electrons are distributed throughout a volume—not a flat surface.

Because of the visual impression created by drawings such as Fig. 11-10 people often speak of the *electron density*, and how this is distributed in an atom or molecule; they also sometimes use the term *electron cloud* in referring to electrons in orbitals. There is no harm in these descriptions, and we may use them in what follows, but you must understand that it is the electron *probability*—not the electron itself—that is smeared out in this way.

Another way to represent the same orbital is to sketch a sphere, as in Fig. 11-11. Because of the long "tail" in the probability plot (Fig. 11-9) it is almost impossible to fix an outer limit to the electron cloud in such an orbital, and therefore impossible to define the exact size of the atom. However, from Fig. 11-9 it would be possible to decide at what radius a sphere centred on the nucleus would contain some proportion, say 95%, of the electron probability. That is what the spherical drawing of Fig. 11-11 is intended to convey, and the sphere so represented is called the *boundary surface* of the electron cloud or orbital.

14. MORE ORBITALS FOR THE HYDROGEN ATOM. From what has been said in Sec. 11-12 you might expect that more than one wave pattern or orbital can arise in a hydrogen atom. For instance, what happens if $n = 2$? The first thing is that two kinds of orbitals are possible. One of these has spherical symmetry, as the 1s orbital had, but there is a difference; in this case something appears that is akin to a node on the violin string—a place with zero amplitude. However, instead of the node occurring at a point, it is spread out over a whole spherical surface. In Fig. 11-12 the probability is again plotted against distance from the nucleus, but at a certain distance, marked r′ in the drawing, the probability vanishes. It will vanish at this distance in any direction from the nucleus, so there is actually a spherical nodal plane inside this orbital, which, following what was said in the previous section, is designated 2s. In Fig. 11-13 this orbital is represented in cross-section by a dot plot like Fig. 11-10.

Two other features of the 2s orbital should be mentioned. One is that the energy with which an electron with this wave pattern is bound to the nucleus—the so-called *binding energy*—is much less than for an electron in the 1s orbital. The other follows in consequence: since the electron is less tightly bound it can, on average, remain further from the nucleus, and accordingly the 2s orbital is larger than the 1s.

There is a second kind of orbital with $n = 2$. That two different kinds are possible is due to the fact that there is now a choice of value for the subsidiary quantum number l. According to the rules outlined in Sec. 11-12, when $n = 1$, l may only be zero, but when $n = 2$, l may be zero or one. The spherically symmetrical orbitals already described have $l = 0$, and in fact the label s that we used for these is simply another way of saying the same thing. But when $l = 1$, three other orbitals arise whose probability plots look the same except for the direction in which they extend in space. These are represented by boundary surfaces in Fig. 11-14. (Compare with Fig. 11-11.) From the figure it is evident that they are not spherically symmetrical, but instead consist of two lobes on either side of the nucleus; through the nucleus these lobes are divided by a nodal plane. Such orbitals are designated 2p; the letter p following the principal quantum number is another way of showing that $l = 1$, and the letter may also help you remember that the three orbitals lie perpendicular to one another in space.

In the hydrogen atom the 2s and 2p orbitals lead to the same binding energy of the electron to the nucleus.

15. A set of the orbitals with the same principal quantum number is called a *shell*. The smallest shell is the 1s orbital. A second shell, lying on average further out from the nucleus than the 1s orbital, is made up of the 2s and the three 2p orbitals. A third shell, lying further out still, is made up of several orbitals that have $n = 3$. In this case we may have $l = 0$ or 1 or 2. With $l = 1$ there are three perpendicular 3p orbitals as before. There is also a set of five orbitals labelled 3d, for which $l = 2$ (Fig. 11-15). All orbitals in this shell have two nodal surfaces. The binding energy of an electron in any of these orbitals is the same, but less than in the orbitals with $n = 2$.

16. In Table 11-1 we show an inventory of orbitals for the four shells with $n = 1$ to $n = 4$. You will observe that as the value of n increases so does the number and kind of orbitals; in fact, the number of orbitals in a shell is always equal to n^2. The system governing the number of orbitals is based on the rules for permissible quantum numbers given in

The binding energy is the amount of work that must be done to completely remove from the atom the electron in this orbital.

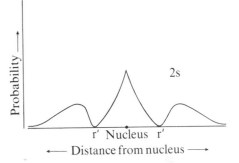

Fig. 11-12: *This plot for the 2s orbital in a hydrogen atom should be compared with that for the 1s orbital, shown in Fig. 11-9. The significant differences are (i) the node at r′, which, taking into account all directions, is really a nodal sphere; and (ii) the fact that more of the electron probability stretches somewhat further out from the nucleus.*

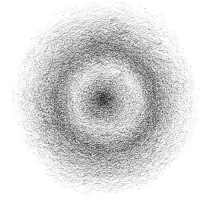

Fig. 11-13: *This "dot plot" suggests a cross-section at the middle of the 2s orbital. You see that the nodal sphere is buried within the entire electron distribution; it cannot be represented in a boundary-surface drawing like Fig. 11-11.*

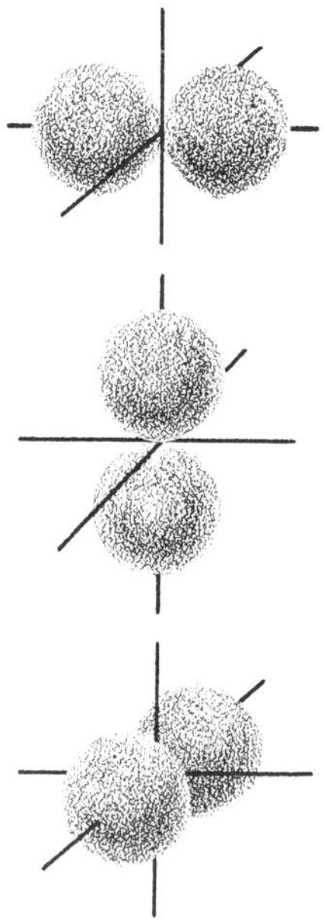

Fig. 11-14: *These drawings represent boundary surfaces for the three 2p orbitals of the hydrogen atom. The straight lines indicate where the Cartesian (x,y,z) axes lie in relation to the orbitals, and how the maximum extension of each of these lies along one of these axes. There is a nodal plane in each orbital, lying at 90° to the direction of maximum extension.*

Fig. 11-15: *This is a boundary-surface drawing for one of the 3d orbitals. Although electrons in d orbitals are not given prominence in this book, they are important in the physics and chemistry of many metals and their compounds.*

TABLE 11-1

RELATIONSHIP AMONG ORBITALS IN SHELLS

SHELL	VALUE OF n	ORBITALS	NUMBER OF ORBITALS	TOTAL NUMBER OF ORBITALS IN THE SHELL
K	1	1s	1	1
L	2	2s	1	4
		2p	3	
M	3	3s	1	9
		3p	3	
		3d	5	
N	4	4s	1	16
		4p	3	
		4d	5	
		4f	7	

Sec. 11-12. By applying these rules you should be able to extend this table to higher quantum numbers if you need to. We have included in the table another method of labelling shells by the letters K, L, M and N; this is an alternative to stating the principal quantum number.

The sets of orbitals that have the same value of l within any particular shell are known as sub-shells; for example, the 3d orbitals comprise a sub-shell within the M shell. Within each sub-shell there are an odd number of orbitals, specifically $(2l + 1)$ orbitals, each corresponding to a different value of the quantum number m (Sec. 11-12).

17. A WRAP-UP ON THE HYDROGEN ATOM. To recapitulate, an orbital is one of a variety of standing wave patterns that an electron can assume around the nucleus of an atom. Where precisely the electron is within the space occupied by the orbital turns out to be something that wave mechanics cannot tell us, but it also turns out to be something that we really don't need to know. When an electron can be described by a particular wave pattern or orbital it is said to *occupy* or *be in* that orbital. In each orbital there is a certain characteristic probability distribution for the electron, and this is often loosely called the "shape" of the orbital.

In the hydrogen atom the electron could occupy any orbital. However, as Fig. 11-16 shows, the various orbitals differ by the amount of energy with which an electron in them is bound to the nucleus.

The scale of energies in Fig. 11-16 has its zero at the top ("A" in the figure), and all values below that have negative signs. Zero energy in this case implies that the electron is just removed from control by the nucleus. (In the usage of Chapter 13, it corresponds to formation of a hydrogen ion by removal of an electron.) When the electron is in any orbital, and therefore more or less bound to the nucleus, its energy is considered negative with respect to this defined zero of energy. An electron, subject to the electrical pull of the nucleus, is comparable to a ball subject to the gravitational pull of the earth. When a ball rolls down hill its potential energy decreases; when an electron moves from an

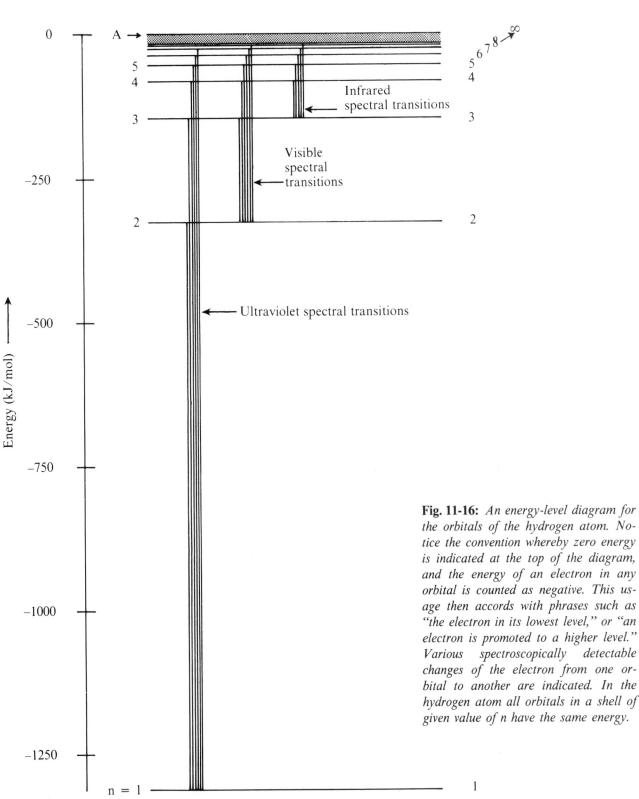

Fig. 11-16: *An energy-level diagram for the orbitals of the hydrogen atom. Notice the convention whereby zero energy is indicated at the top of the diagram, and the energy of an electron in any orbital is counted as negative. This usage then accords with phrases such as "the electron in its lowest level," or "an electron is promoted to a higher level." Various spectroscopically detectable changes of the electron from one orbital to another are indicated. In the hydrogen atom all orbitals in a shell of given value of n have the same energy.*

orbital with $n = 2$ to one with $n = 1$ its energy likewise decreases. In the case of the electron, the energy it loses is given out to the surroundings as light or radiation. If an atom absorbs light, its energy is increased by the energy of the light quantum, and the electron will thereby enter an orbital with higher (that is, more positive or less negative) energy.

The term *binding energy* is used in a slightly different way, since it is usually given as a positive amount. It will help you to avoid confusion if you think of it, in relation to Fig. 11-16, as the work that must be done (or energy that must be added) to remove the electron from the orbital in which it is "bound." Thus the lower the energy of the orbital (or smaller the value of n) the greater will be the binding energy.

In hydrogen the 1s orbital is that of lowest energy; it is the smallest orbital and in it the electron is, on average, closest to the nucleus. A hydrogen atom with its electron in this orbital is said to be in the *ground state*. When, through heat or collision, the electron is driven to an orbital of higher energy, for instance 2s, the atom is said to be *excited*, or in an *excited state*. The spectral wavelengths and their associated energies, which we described in Sec. 11-9, correspond to an electron jumping from one orbital to another of different energy. The frequency of radiation emitted or absorbed can be related exactly to the difference in the orbital's energies in accordance with Planck's relationship (Sec. 11-8). Much of our knowledge of orbitals in all atoms is obtained from the study of spectral frequencies, and it is from such evidence that we can draw energy-level diagrams such as Fig. 11-16 with considerable confidence.

We have mentioned Albert Einstein for his contribution of the photon theory of the propagation of light. A towering intellectual giant (who as a child was so slow in learning to speak that there was some thought that he might be retarded), Einstein is best known for his theory of relativity which includes the famous mass-energy relationship:

$$E = mc^2.$$

18. About a dozen scientists have been mentioned in this chapter. Where were they born and raised? Henri Becquerel—France; Marie Curie—Poland; Pierre Curie—France; Hans Geiger—Germany; Ernest Rutherford—New Zealand; Max Planck—Germany; Albert Einstein—Germany; Niels Bohr—Denmark; Louis de Broglie—France; Clinton Davisson and Lester Germer—United States; George Thomson—England; and Erwin Schrödinger—Austria. Marie Curie's greatest work was done in France, Rutherford's in Canada and England, and Einstein's in Switzerland.

All of these are names that will always have a place in the history of the development of atomic theory. But no country has a monopoly on the production of great scientists. Science is truly an international endeavour.

QUESTIONS

1. State in your own words the meaning of: (a) α particle; (b) β particle; (c) radioactivity.

2. How does an alpha particle differ in structure from a helium atom?

3. What were two important conclusions drawn from Rutherford's scattering experiment?

4. The diameter of an aluminium atom is approximately 300 pm (3×10^{-10} m). Approximately how many atomic diameters thick is a piece of aluminium foil 0.001 in thick? (1 in = 2.5 cm)

5. The nucleus of an aluminium atom is about 2×10^{-13} cm in diameter. Using the atomic diameter given in Question 4, calculate the ratio of the diameters of atom and nucleus.

6. In what respect is the nucleus of the lightest isotope of hydrogen unique among atomic nuclei?

7. Explain the meaning of the terms: (a) nucleus; (b) nucleon (c) nuclide. Give a description of three different nuclides as examples.

8. Argon, potassium, and calcium all have nuclides with mass 40. What name is given to nuclides sharing a common mass number? How many protons and how many neutrons are there in each of the three nuclei?

9. Explain what is meant by an *emission spectrum* and an *absorption spectrum*. How does a spectroscope function to convert the light emitted or absorbed by atoms into a spectrum of separate lines?

*10. The red glow emitted by neon under the influence of an electrical discharge is due to an intense spectral line of wavelength 640 nm. Convert this to a frequency, and use Planck's relationship to determine the corresponding energy. The answer obtained is the energy per single atom. Convert this to energy per mole. (How many atoms are there per mole?)

*11. Convert the prominent wavelengths in the visible spectrum of atomic hydrogen to energies expressed in kilojoules per mole. Check your answers with the transitions shown in Fig. 11-16; are they of the proper magnitude?

*12. In some books you will find the energies of electron transitions and other atomic and molecular events given in units of "electronvolts." Electrical units are so defined that the product of a charge (in coulombs) and a potential difference (in volts) is an amount of work or energy (in joules). When an electron (whose charge you have been given) moves through a potential difference of one volt, the work needed (or given out) is *one electronvolt*. Calculate the equivalent energy in joules per atom and in kilojoules per mole.

13. By means of the de Broglie relationship calculate the wavelength associated with a 1000-kg automobile moving at a speed of 100 km/h (27.8 m/s). Has the result any significance?

14. Make a table summarizing for each permitted value of the quantum number n the permissible values of l and of m.

15. What features of the standing wave pattern can be associated with the different values of the quantum numbers n, l, and m?

16. Explain the following terms: (a) principal quantum number; (b) K shell; (c) s, p, d, and f sub-shells.

17. In Fig. 11-9 to 11-11 three different ways of describing the whereabouts of an electron in the 1s orbital of a hydrogen atom are shown. In your own words, describe what each of these sketches is trying to tell.

18. What is meant by the term *orbital*? What is meant by the statement that s orbitals are *spherically symmetrical*? What does it mean that p and d orbitals are *not* spherically symmetrical?

19. When $n = 2$, there may be two different kinds of orbitals in the hydrogen atom. How do they differ, and what do they have in common?

20. Explain what is meant by the terms *shell* and *sub-shell*. How many sub-shells may be in a shell? How many orbitals may be in a sub-shell or a shell?

21. Explain what is meant by the *ground state* of an atom, and an *excited* state. Show for hydrogen atoms that there is only one ground state but many possible excited states.

*22. It can be shown that the energy of an electron in a hydrogen atom can assume only the values given by $E = -R/n^2$, where E is the energy and n is the principal quantum number of the orbital occupied. R is a constant having the value 1312 kJ/mol (or equivalent). Why is the negative sign in the equation? Calculate values of E for $n = 1,2,3,4 \ldots$ and verify your results by reference to Fig. 11-16. What happens to the energy values when n becomes large?

*23. Indicate which electron transitions would give rise to an emission spectrum in hydrogen, and which would give rise to an absorption spectrum. Can you suggest why many wavelengths observed in emission spectra do not occur in absorption spectra?

*24. Radioactivity is exhibited by certain elements that possess isotopes with unstable nuclei. Radioactive particles are emitted from these with great speed, and thereby these nuclei are transformed into nuclei of a different element. (It is puzzling that a nucleus, supposedly made up of protons and neutrons, can emit electrons! The process is equivalent to a neutron turning into a proton by ejecting an electron.) By referring to the table of elements on the inside back cover, decide which nuclides are formed when the following nuclear changes occur:

(a) $^{238}_{92}U$ gives off an α particle, (b) $^{60}_{27}Co$ gives off a β particle.
Label the resulting nuclides, and name the elements produced.

*25. The isotope strontium-90 emits a β particle. What are the atomic number and mass number of the resulting nuclide. What element is it? This (daughter) nucleus also emits a β particle. Name the element produced by its decay.

The Electron Structure of Atoms: The Periodic Table

1. When we consider atoms with more than one electron, the mathematical description of the motion of any one electron becomes much more complicated. This is because any one electron, in addition to being attracted by the electrical pull of the nucleus, is being repelled by an electrical push from every other electron. And as you have now learned, we cannot be sure where any of these electrons are at any given instant. Accordingly, an exact mathematical analysis of the wave pattern of electrons in such atoms is almost impossible. Nevertheless, we believe that the same general types of wave patterns or orbitals as we have described for the hydrogen atom apply in all atoms, though with certain differences, as we shall shortly see. This belief has proven useful in accounting for a host of chemical and physical observations. Because of its wider applicability, the wave-mechanical description of the atom quickly superseded Bohr's model, and it remains the current theory of the electron structure in atoms and of matter in general.

2. POPULATING ORBITALS WITH ELECTRONS. The first question we must ask is this: can more than one electron adopt the same wave pattern, that is, occupy the same orbital? To be in the same orbital, two or more electrons must occupy roughly the same region in space. Since they repel each other because of electrical forces at close range, it might occur to you that only one electron could be accommodated by each orbital. However, when all the evidence is taken into account, it appears that up to two, but no more than two, electrons can occupy the same orbital. But to do even that the electrons must fulfil a special requirement. On the basis of the behaviour of atoms in strong magnetic fields it has been deduced that electrons appear to spin about an axis, like a top; and like that of a top the spin may be either clockwise or anticlockwise. The only way in which two electrons may share the same orbital is if they have opposite spins.

This is usually represented by assigning to the electron what is called a *spin quantum number,* symbol *s.* This may have the value ½ or –½. A complete description of an electron in an atom is thus given by four quantum numbers, *n, l, m,* and *s;* of these the first three identify a particular orbital in which the electron is found, and the fourth describes its spin. According to this manner of labelling, the rule governing the occupancy of orbitals by electrons is that no two electrons in an atom may have an identical set of quantum numbers. This is known as the *Pauli Exclusion Principle.*

Thus in the case of helium ($Z = 2$) there are two electrons, and they are attracted by a nucleus of charge $+2e$. The extra nuclear pull is partially offset, though, by the mutual repulsion of the two electrons. The two electrons in the helium atom in the ground state occupy the 1s orbital (with opposite spins). This fills that orbital, and thereby also fills the K shell or first shell, since there is only the one orbital in that shell (Table 11-1).

What happens, then, in the atom of lithium ($Z = 3$)? How can three electrons be accommodated around the nucleus? Two of them could obviously go in the 1s orbital in which they would have the lowest possible energy. The third electron must be in a different orbital, and for its energy to be as low as possible it should adopt a wave pattern in the L shell with $n = 2$. But here we encounter a new problem. In the hydrogen atom all four orbitals in the L shell were at the same level of energy. But in *all other* atoms where there are two or more electrons, the orbitals that differ in *l* (the s, p, etc.) also differ in energy. From spectroscopic measurements and other evidence the energies of electrons in these orbitals have been measured for many atoms, and it turns out that within a given shell the s orbitals are lower in energy (the electron is more firmly bound to the nucleus) than the p orbitals, which in turn are lower than the d, etc. On the strength of this information, then, you might expect that the third electron in lithium would be in the s orbital of the second shell—the 2s orbital. And that is just where it is in the normal atom.

3. You may wonder *why* the 2s orbital in lithium is lower in energy than the 2p. There is an easy answer, provided you remember the shapes of the electron probability plots for these orbitals. Let us compare them by referring to Fig. 12-1. Although the total probability (which is the area under the curves) is the same for each plot, the distribution in the case of the 2s orbital puts the electron close to the nucleus for part of the time. This is quite different from the 2p orbital in which the electron is unlikely to be near the nucleus very often. Let us then relate these plots to the situation in the lithium atom where there already are two electrons in the 1s orbital (K shell) close to the nucleus. These will in part shield the electron in the L shell from the full nuclear charge, but how good the shielding will be depends on the kind of orbital the electron in the L shell occupies. Since the 2s orbital puts the electron on occasion close to the nucleus whereas the 2p orbital has a node at the nucleus, it seems logical that an L shell electron will be better shielded from the nucleus in the 2p orbital than in the 2s orbital. On such grounds it is not surprising that in lithium a 2s electron (that is, an electron in the 2s orbital) is more tightly bound to the nucleus, and therefore at a lower energy, than a 2p electron.

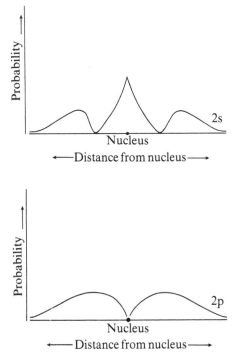

Fig. 12-1: *You have already seen the upper drawing as Fig. 11-12, and will recall that it shows the probability of finding the electron in a 2s orbital as a function of distance (but not direction) from the nucleus. The lower plot shows the same probability applying to a 2p orbital but with the additional limitation that this plot refers to the direction in which the 2p orbital shows its maximum elongation. The probability for electron distribution is "direction-sensitive" for all but s orbitals.*

When we speak here and elsewhere of the energy of an orbital, what we really mean is the energy of an electron occupying that orbital.

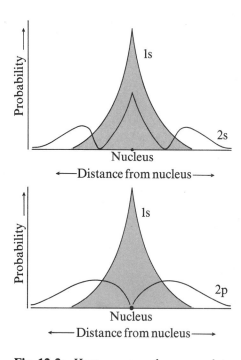

Fig. 12-2: *Here you see the same plots as shown in Fig. 12-1, but with the probability plot for the 1s orbital superimposed (shown shaded). It is clear that the 2s orbital penetrates more into the region of the 1s orbital than the 2p does. (Incidentally, if you think the probability plot for the 1s orbital looks narrower or closer to the nucleus than the one drawn in Fig. 11-9 for the hydrogen atom, that is the case, because here we are concerned with the lithium atom in which the nuclear charge is +3e as compared with +1e for the hydrogen atom.)*

Another way to describe this situation is to consider the penetration of the territory of the 1s orbital in lithium (occupied by two electrons) by the territory of the 2s or the 2p orbitals. The diagrams in Fig. 12-2 suggest that a 2s electron will be more likely to penetrate into the zone of the K shell than would a 2p electron, and the former would accordingly feel more nuclear pull. What we have described for the specific case of lithium applies to all atoms with $Z > 1$, and for all such cases s orbitals are at lower energies than p orbitals with the same principal quantum number. For similar reasons p orbitals are lower in energy than the corresponding d orbitals.

4. THE BUILDING-UP PRINCIPLE. You should now be able to follow the electron arrangements in the succeeding elements. For beryllium ($Z = 4$) two electrons with opposite spins can and do occupy the 2s orbital. With boron ($Z = 5$) the next vacant orbital for occupancy by the fifth electron is one of the three 2p orbitals. In the elements that follow, as the number of electrons increases they can be accommodated in these p orbitals until the latter are all filled. At this point, which occurs with neon ($Z = 10$), a total of eight electrons occupy the orbitals of the L shell. Thereafter, additional electrons must enter the M shell, and the first electron to do so will occupy the vacant orbital of lowest energy, namely 3s. And so it goes.

Chemists and physicists have developed a short notation by which they describe the arrangement or *configuration* of electrons in atoms. This consists of a horizontal list of the orbitals populated by the electrons, and an index number to show how many electrons are in that orbital. We can most easily illustrate this by showing the electron configuration of the 20 elements of lowest atomic number. You should note that the order of occupancy of orbitals, as given in Table 12-1, conforms to the order of increasing energy of the orbitals, particularly with respect to the s orbitals being lower in energy than the p orbitals within a given shell (Sec. 12-3).

TABLE 12-1

ELECTRON CONFIGURATION OF ELEMENTS 1 TO 20					
ELEMENT	Z	CONFIGURATION	ELEMENT	Z	CONFIGURATION
Hydrogen	1	1s	Sodium	11	$1s^2 2s^2 2p^6 3s$
Helium	2	$1s^2$	Magnesium	12	$1s^2 2s^2 2p^6 3s^2$
Lithium	3	$1s^2 2s$	Aluminium	13	$1s^2 2s^2 2p^6 3s^2 3p$
Beryllium	4	$1s^2 2s^2$	Silicon	14	$1s^2 2s^2 2p^6 3s^2 3p^2$
Boron	5	$1s^2 2s^2 2p$	Phosphorus	15	$1s^2 2s^2 2p^6 3s^2 3p^3$
Carbon	6	$1s^2 2s^2 2p^2$	Sulphur	16	$1s^2 2s^2 2p^6 3s^2 3p^4$
Nitrogen	7	$1s^2 2s^2 2p^3$	Chlorine	17	$1s^2 2s^2 2p^6 3s^2 3p^5$
Oxygen	8	$1s^2 2s^2 2p^4$	Argon	18	$1s^2 2s^2 2p^6 3s^2 3p^6$
Fluorine	9	$1s^2 2s^2 2p^5$	Potassium	19	$1s^2 2s^2 2p^6 3s^2 3p^6 4s$
Neon	10	$1s^2 2s^2 2p^6$	Calcium	20	$1s^2 2s^2 2p^6 3s^2 3p^6 4s^2$

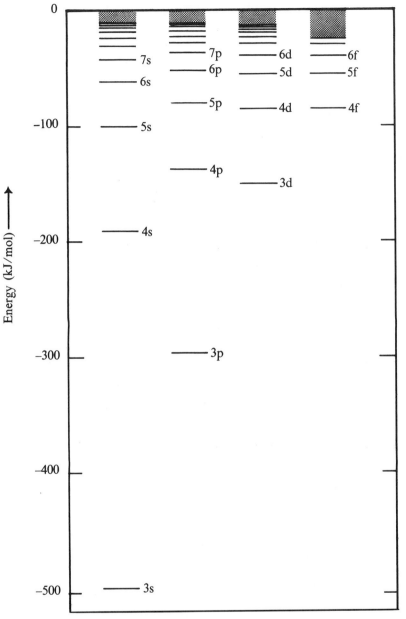

Provided the relative energy levels of the various orbitals are known, it would be possible to predict the electron configuration for any atom of given atomic number. The procedure is to imagine each orbital being filled in succession, starting with that of lowest energy (the 1s) and remembering that the capacity of each orbital is two electrons. As each orbital is filled, we go on to the one of next highest energy, and in this way distribute the Z electrons belonging to the atom of the element of atomic number Z. This exercise is known as the "building-up principle." Broadly speaking, it works pretty well, though a few exceptions do arise among elements of higher atomic number.

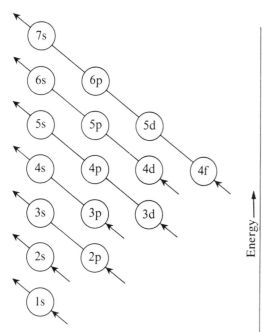

Fig. 12-5: *This is a chart to help you remember the order in which orbitals are filled in the imaginary process of "building up" an atom by adding electrons sufficient in number to balance the charge on the nucleus. The order of orbital filling is indicated by the diagonal lines and the arrowheads. When you have reached the extreme left on one line, you proceed to the next higher line and start at the extreme right, continuing in this way until the appropriate number of orbitals have been populated. This scheme serves the same purpose (though giving less information) as Fig. 12-4.*

The element arsenic, with atomic number 33, has a ground-state configuration of electrons:

$$1s^2 2s^2 2p^6 3s^2 3p^6 3d^{10} 4s^2 4p^3.$$

You should verify that this configuration accords with the filling order shown in this chart. (Notice that the order of writing down the orbitals in an electron configuration is not the same as the filling order.)

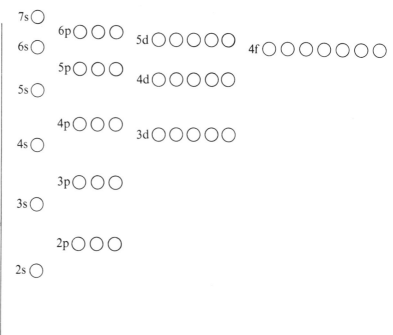

Fig. 12-4: *This is a generalized energy-level diagram for orbitals in atoms. Each circle represents an orbital with capacity for two electrons. The actual energies of the orbitals are different for each atom because of the changing nuclear charge, and, as mentioned in the text, even the relative energies of some of the sub-shells may change as the atomic number gets larger.*

5. Earlier (Table 11-1) we stated that the M shell (*n* = 3) comprised nine orbitals, made up of one s, three p, and five d orbitals. You ought to be wondering why in Table 12-1 we show potassium and calcium with electrons in the 4s orbital (N shell), yet the 3d orbitals of the M shell remain unoccupied. To try to explain this let us examine an energy-level diagram for the sodium atom, the one in which the M shell just starts to fill. This is shown in Fig. 12-3. These energy levels have all been determined very accurately from spectral wavelengths. The important thing to notice is that the energy level of the 4s orbital is lower than that of the 3d orbital. (In an ordinary sodium atom these are unpopulated, but they could be occupied by the 3s electron if a sodium atom were excited (Sec. 11-17).) Evidently the lowering in energy of the s orbitals which results from penetration of the underlying shells, as described in Sec. 12-3, is great enough to bring the 4s orbital below the 3d orbital in energy. This interpenetration of the M and N shells has consequences for the building-up principle.

6. AN ENERGY-LEVEL SCHEME. The orbital theory of electron configurations appears to fit the facts of chemistry well enough to justify learning a sort of *generalized* energy level scheme for orbitals in all atoms. This is shown in Fig. 12-4. The circles are intended to represent orbitals, and they are distributed vertically according to relative energy and horizontally according to type of orbital. The building up of atoms can then be imagined as occurring by the gradual filling of each orbital by one, then by two electrons, starting with the orbitals of lowest energy and working up. To work out or display the electron configuration for a given atom the presence of one or two electrons in an orbital is shown in some way, the commonest being to insert small arrows within each circle. The arrows are pointed in one or the opposite direction to convey the idea of their spin. Two electrons of opposite spin in the same orbital have their arrows shown opposed. This practice is illustrated for nitrogen in Fig. 12-6.

There are grounds, which we mention in the next chapter, for believing that the orbital population shown in Fig. 12-6 is correct, and that when electrons occupy a set of orbitals having the same energy they do so first singly and then, when each orbital in the set is so occupied, additional electrons of the opposite spin are accepted to fill the orbitals. Two electrons in the same orbital, which implies occupying the same region of space, repel each other electrically and on this account are each less firmly bound to the nucleus than they would be if they could occupy separate orbitals of the same energy. The possible electron configuration for a nitrogen atom shown in Fig 12-7 is less stable than the actual state shown in Fig. 12-6.

7. SOME EXCEPTIONS. Concerning the generalized energy level scheme shown in Fig. 12-4 there are two cautionary remarks that should be made. The first is that, as we have hinted already, there are some exceptions to the expected filling order among elements of higher atomic number. These are not gross exceptions, and it may even be possible to suggest explanations for them, but they are certainly not predictable from Fig. 12-4 alone. The second comment is that, although the figure indicates a certain relative order of energy for the orbitals which seems in accord with the building-up principle, there is other evidence based on spectroscopy, magnetic measurements, and the ease of removing electrons from atoms, that this order is not always strictly preserved. For instance, the energy levels of the 4s and 3d orbitals are reversed in many atoms.

One last comment before leaving this topic: the electron configurations shown in Table 12-1 apply to the ground state, or state of lowest over-all energy, of the atoms in question. Any of these atoms may become excited through collisions at high temperatures or through bombardment by moving electrons in an electrical discharge. We described such excitation of the hydrogen atom in Sec. 11-17. In an excited state of an atom an electron will occupy some orbital of higher energy than it did in the ground state, but when the conditions become less exciting this electron will revert in one or more jumps to its energy state prior to excitation. It is in these transitions downward in energy that radiant energy of some characteristic wavelength is emitted, and this is the source of the wavelengths observed in the emission spectrum or the colours observed in the flame tests given by many elements (Sec. 11-6). With the information provided in this chapter you can better appreciate that the flame colours characteristically emitted by the following elements are due mainly to the electron transitions indicated:

Lithium	2p → 2s	670.8 nm	(crimson)
Sodium	3p → 3s	589.3 nm	(amber)
Potassium	4p → 4s	767.2 nm ⎫	(violet)
	5p → 4s	404.4 nm ⎭	

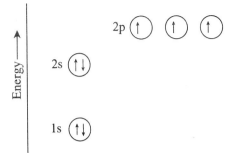

Fig. 12-6: *Population of the orbitals by electrons in the nitrogen atom. The orbitals are occupied by electrons in the order of increasing energy, but where a set of orbitals have the same energy, electrons will occupy these singly until they have to pair up. The three electrons in the 2p sub-shell in nitrogen are distributed one in each orbital; you can see from Fig. 11-14 that this keeps the negatively charged electrons as far from each other as possible.*

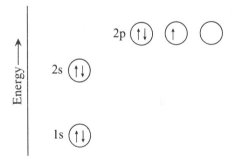

Fig. 12-7: *A less stable configuration of electrons in the nitrogen atom. The distribution of three electrons among the p orbitals as shown in Fig. 12-6 is more stable because it distributes the negative charge more uniformly. The distribution shown here is not forbidden and actually occurs in an excited state of the nitrogen atom.*

Important uses of the so-called inert gases depend on their chemical inertness. Here, during the welding of an aluminium beer barrel, the working area is being flooded with argon to prevent the oxygen of the air from reacting with the molten metal. (When it is viewed upside down, this is still a good picture, though somewhat cyclopean.)

The original statement of the law preceded by some decades the use of the term atomic number. Mendeléeff and Meyer arranged the elements in order of increasing atomic mass, but in that form the law involved some unexplainable exceptions. When atomic numbers were subsequently used as the basis of arrangement the embarrassing exceptions disappeared.

8. FAMILY GROUPS AMONG THE ELEMENTS. Long before all these elaborate details of the structure of atoms were worked out, and indeed almost before scientists were in full agreement about the reality of atoms, chemists had observed interesting similarities in properties among small groups of elements. We have already illustrated this with respect to the elements fluorine, chlorine, bromine, and iodine in Chapter 8. We drew attention in Sec. 9-7 to the similar behaviour toward atmospheric oxygen displayed by potassium and sodium, and subsequently to the similar, though more subdued, reactions of calcium and magnesium with oxygen. Earlier (Sec. 6-3), we described the similar, vigorous reaction of both potassium and sodium with water, in the course of which the similar alkaline substances KOH and NaOH are formed (Sec. 5-12). The more moderate reactions of calcium and magnesium with water (the latter actually requiring boiling water or steam to yield a reaction) were also described. Here again there were resemblances between the products formed.

Even from such a limited sample of elements and their reactions as we have described up to this point you can see evidence of some natural grouping. By 1869 a good deal of evidence of such family relationships among the elements had been accumulated, and in that year two scientists independently proposed a law that summarized (but did not explain) such recurring similarities. The more comprehensive demonstration of this law, which is known as the *Periodic Law*, was given by the Russian chemist, Dmitri Mendeléeff, but the German, Lothar Meyer, deserves honourable mention. The law states that the properties of the elements and their compounds exhibit recurring (or periodic) similarities when the elements are arranged in order of increasing atomic number.

9. THE PERIODIC TABLE. The recurring association of similar elements is made very apparent when the names of the elements are set down in tabular form serially by atomic number. Such an arrangement is known as the *Periodic Table*, and a portion of it, for the 20 elements of lowest atomic number, is shown in Table 12-2 and, in more abbreviated form, in Table 12-3.

TABLE 12-2

A PORTION OF THE PERIODIC TABLE OF THE ELEMENTS

1 Hydrogen							2 Helium
3 Lithium	4 Beryllium	5 Boron	6 Carbon	7 Nitrogen	8 Oxygen	9 Fluorine	10 Neon
11 Sodium	12 Magnesium	13 Aluminium	14 Silicon	15 Phosphorus	16 Sulphur	17 Chlorine	18 Argon
19 Potassium	20 Calcium						

TABLE 12-3

A "COMPACT" PERIODIC TABLE FOR ELEMENTS 1-20

1 H							2 He
3 Li	4 Be	5 B	6 C	7 N	8 O	9 F	10 Ne
11 Na	12 Mg	13 Al	14 Si	15 P	16 S	17 Cl	18 Ar
19 K	20 Ca						

This arrangement brings out some of the family relationships that we have mentioned, and perhaps some that wouldn't have occurred to you. You see that sodium and potassium and the less familiar, but similar, element lithium are now together in a column or Group; these are three of the so-called **alkali metals** (and you have enough information now to be able to account for that name). In the next Group we see calcium and magnesium together, along with beryllium, and they are part of a family known as the **alkaline earth elements** (Chapter 29). On the other side of the Table you will recognize two of the **halogen elements**, and from what was said in Chapter 8 you could add three other names to that Group. Another Group of elements, with three representatives in Table 12-2, is distinctive in quite a different way. These elements are all gases; when subjected to electrical discharge they glow with characteristic colours as a consequence of electron excitation; but otherwise they don't do much chemically. Prior to 1961 no member of this Group had been discovered to react with any other element; since then a few compounds of the elements xenon (Xe) and krypton (Kr) have been produced. Because of this unusual indifference to chemical reaction this family of elements is called the **inert gases**. Their lack of chemical activity caused them to remain undetected for many years. The three inert gases in Tables 12-2 and 12-3 are helium, neon, and argon.

10. The place of hydrogen in the Periodic Table has always been debatable. We have put it in the first column, but we caution you that it is not much related to the alkali metals on the basis of properties, and this is why we have set it slightly apart from them in Table 12-3. Chemists are agreed that because of the small size of its atoms and the simplicity of its atomic structure, hydrogen is unique among the elements.

11. The Periodic Law and the Periodic Table were developed by Mendeléeff and others on the basis of chemical and physical properties of the elements and their compounds, but there was available at the time no theory capable of explaining why such regularities should occur. From what has been said in this chapter it is obvious that a connection can now be found between the electron configurations of atoms and the occurrence of family groupings among the elements. This is

The term "earth" is a very ancient relic of chemistry's past, and was used to denote the residue left when a metal was heated in air. It is reasonably correct to think of earths (in this sense) as equivalent to metal oxides. The "earths" of calcium and to a lesser degree magnesium, react with water to produce an alkaline solution; beryllium oxide is too insoluble to show this reaction.

The first of these few compounds, $XePtF_6$, was made by Professor N. Bartlett, at the University of British Columbia, in 1961. In spite of many attempts in many different laboratories, no compound of helium or neon or argon has been prepared.

brought out by a detailed comparison of the information in Tables 12-1 and 12-2. The atoms of the elements in the first Group, for instance, H, Li, Na, and K all have a single electron in their outermost shell. The atoms of the inert gases, He, Ne, and Ar have, in succession, completely filled 1s, 2(s and p), 3(s and p) orbitals; though not shown in the Tables, the atoms of the inert gases krypton and xenon have completely filled 4(s and p) and 5(s and p) orbitals. In other words, the Group 1 elements share a common electron configuration ns^1; the inert gases (except helium) a common configuration ns^2np^6. And similar examples of common electron configurations exist for the members of each column or Group in the Periodic Table (though we again admit to a few small exceptions beyond element 20).

That much seems evident. What isn't evident yet is why the periodic recurrence of similar properties of the elements should be related to the electron configurations of their atoms. The fact is, there is a very direct relationship, and we shall be explaining this and giving examples throughout the chapters which follow.

QUESTIONS

1. How many electrons may occupy one orbital? What requirement must be met by the electrons in order to occupy an orbital fully?

2. Why are s orbitals lower in energy than p orbitals in the same shell?

3. What is the Pauli Exclusion Principle? Why is it of significance to the occupancy of orbitals in atoms?

4. For each of the five electrons in a boron atom write a complete set of four quantum numbers, and show that your answer is in accord with the Pauli Principle.

5. What is meant by the term "building-up principle"?

6. In the hydrogen atom all orbitals with the same value of n have the same energy, but in all other atoms s orbitals lie lower in energy than p orbitals. Why is that?

7. Explain what is meant by the term "shielding" of nuclear charge in atoms with two or more electrons.

8. In Fig. 12-4 there are no energy units shown for the vertical axis. Why? Would the 1s level be at the same energy in lithium as in helium, for instance? Explain.

9. Without referring to Table 12-1, write down electron configurations for the elements of atomic number 6, 13, 19. Then check your answer against Table 12-1, noting the names of these elements.

10. With the aid of Fig. 12-4 or 12-5, write down electron configurations for the elements of atomic number 25, 38, 47, and 54. From the information on the inside back cover determine which elements these are.

11. The electron configurations deduced from the building-up principle are all "ground-state" configurations. Explain what this means. Write down what might be an "excited-state" configuration for a neon atom. When might

a neon atom be in this configuration, and how would an electron have become thus altered?

12. Explain why the ground-state configuration for nitrogen is as shown in Fig. 12-6, rather than as shown in Fig. 12-7.

13. On a chart such as Fig. 12-4 mark in with small arrows the occupancy of the orbitals in the sub-shell of highest energy in the ground state of each of the following atoms: phosphorus, vanadium, and germanium. (For atomic numbers, see the inside back cover.) How many "unpaired" electrons are there in each of these atoms?

14. How is it that the N shell ($n = 4$) begins to be occupied before the M shell is filled?

15. Calculate the energy in joules per atom and in kilojoules per mole for the photons of light emitted, with wavelength 589.3 nm, by excited sodium atoms. Check your answer with Fig. 12-3, and satisfy yourself that this energy accords with the transition indicated in Sec. 12-7.

16. Give a statement of the Periodic Law.

17. How are similarities within Groups of elements explained by the structure of their atoms?

18. Explain the origin or significance of the group names:

(a) alkali metals   (c) halogens (Sec. 30-1)

(b) alkaline earth elements   (d) inert gases

19. To the extent that the chemistry of sulphur has been discussed so far, what grounds are there for associating oxygen and sulphur in the same Group of elements?

20. What common feature can be identified in the electron configuration of fluorine and chlorine atoms? Would you expect this to occur in the atoms of bromine and iodine? From the atomic numbers of these elements work out the electron configuration of their atoms to check your prediction.

Atoms Become Ions

1. IONIZATION IN A GAS. We mentioned in Sec. 11-2 that α and β particles from radioactive substances were capable of affecting a gas through which they passed so that it could conduct an electric current. An electric current is simply a movement of charged particles. You could imagine charged particles being formed in a gas in the following manner. The α or β particles must pass through a great many atoms as they traverse a gas, and occasionally they must collide with some of the atomic particles. Suppose such a collision resulted in knocking an electron out of one of the atoms of the gas. What would this produce? The answer is: an atom minus an electron. Such an incomplete atom would bear a net positive charge, since the positive charge on the nucleus would exceed the combined charges of the electrons by one unit. This new particle—a charged atom—is called an *ion*. It would move under the influence of an electrical potential difference toward a negatively charged body, and thereby create a very small electric current.

We could write an equation to represent the formation of an ion from an atom. Thus, for oxygen:

$$\underset{\text{oxygen atom}}{O} \;\longrightarrow\; \underset{\substack{\text{positive} \\ \text{oxygen ion}}}{O^+} \;+\; \underset{\text{electron}}{e^-}$$

The electron knocked out of an atom could itself move toward a positively charged body, and so carry a charge through the gas. More often, however, an isolated electron will be picked up by an atom, with the result that a negatively charged atom is produced. The positive charge on the nucleus is evidently sufficient to hold "in orbit" a small surplus of electrons. The negative charge of a surplus electron is added to the atom, and the resulting particle is also called an ion. Thus:

$$\underset{\text{oxygen atom}}{O} \;+\; \underset{\text{electron}}{e^-} \;\longrightarrow\; \underset{\substack{\text{negative} \\ \text{oxygen ion}}}{O^-}$$

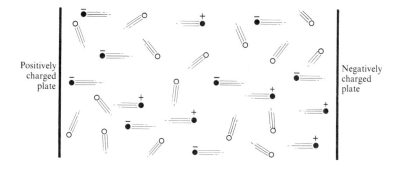

Fig. 13-1: *The atoms that have lost an electron and become positively charged ions move toward the negatively charged plate. The ions formed by an atom acquiring an extra electron, being negatively charged, move toward the positive plate. Neutral atoms will move only randomly. In this way a current passes through an ionized gas.*

A negatively charged ion will move toward a positive pole, and this adds to the current carried through the gas. The gas is said to be *ionized* by exposure to radioactivity. The movement of charge—which is an electric current—through the gas is illustrated by Fig. 13-1.

The ions we are talking about are called *gaseous ions*; later, in Chapter 27, we shall speak of *ions in solution*, which enable us to explain why, for instance, salt solution can conduct an electric current. But the two kinds of ions are somewhat different. For one thing, only a very small fraction of the atoms in a gas are ever ionized in this way, so that even at their best gases are very poor conductors compared to solutions. Also, the haphazard way in which gaseous ions are formed results in their having a variety of charges, for example, O^+, O^-, O^{2+}, or O^{2-}. (The symbols O^{2+} and O^{2-} describe oxygen atoms that have lost or gained two electrons, respectively.)

2. IONIZATION ENERGY. The amount of work required to remove an electron from a gaseous atom in its ground state (Sec. 11-17) is called its *ionization energy* or, less desirably, its ionization potential. For a single atom this is an exceedingly small amount of energy, but calculated on a molar basis it turns out to be a significant size; convenient units are kilojoules per mole (kJ/mol).

It is instructive to relate this amount of energy to the diagrams showing the energy levels of the orbitals in atoms, such as Fig. 11-16 or 12-3. When the electron in the ground state of the hydrogen atom is removed (that is, from the 1s orbital) the atom has become ionized to H^+; this is equivalent to raising the electron's energy to the level shown as "A" in Fig. 11-16. You will note that it is also at this level that the distinct energy states become closer and closer: they are said to converge. We explained in Sec. 11-17 that that level ("A" in Fig. 11-16) is assigned a value of zero energy, while the electron in any orbital is assigned a negative value of energy.

In hydrogen the electron in the 1s orbital has an energy of –1311 kJ/mol. To remove an electron from this orbital means that 1311 kJ of energy must be added per mole of atomic hydrogen, and that is the value of the ionization energy for hydrogen. In sodium (Fig. 12-3), the electron most easily removed from the atom is in the 3s orbital. The energy of this is – 495.8 kJ/mol, or, put another way, 495.8 kJ of energy must be put into a mole of atomic sodium to remove the 3s electrons and so convert the sodium atoms to sodium ions, Na$^+$. The quantity 495.8 kJ/mol is the ionization energy of sodium.

For an electron in the ground state the ionization energy is the same as the binding energy (Sec. 11-14). If, however, the electron being removed is in an orbital other than that corresponding to the ground state, the energy required to remove it—the binding energy—is less than the ionization energy.

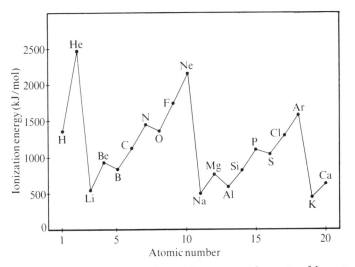

Fig. 13-2: *The ionization energies of the twenty elements of lowest atomic number are here plotted against atomic number. Such a plot is a beautiful illustration of the Periodic Law (Sec. 12-8). (The ionization energies so represented refer to the removal of one electron. This is only the first stage of ionization for most atoms, since under more drastic conditions two or more electrons can be removed.)*

3. PERIODICITY IN IONIZATION ENERGIES. In Fig. 13-2 values of the ionization energies are plotted against atomic number for the twenty elements of lowest atomic number. Observe how the peaks in this plot recur with members of the inert-gas family of elements (He, Ne, Ar), and the minima occur with members of the alkali metals (Li, Na, K). This plot shows some interesting correlations with the electron configurations given in Table 12-1.

In the atoms of both hydrogen and helium the electrons occupy 1s orbitals, yet helium has a distinctly greater ionization energy. This is accounted for by the greater nuclear charge in helium; that greater nuclear charge binds helium's electrons more strongly, and so makes more difficult the removal of an electron. Accordingly a greater input of energy is required to convert helium atoms to helium ions, He$^+$, than to convert hydrogen atoms to hydrogen ions, H$^+$.

The much smaller ionization energy for lithium (and later for sodium and potassium) corresponds to a configuration with a single (ns) electron in the outermost shell. It is evident from Fig. 12-4 that the energy of an ns orbital lies appreciably higher than that of the ($n - 1$)p orbitals, and therefore it is to be expected that an electron in an outermost s orbital should be more easily removed than electrons in the inner shell. To take a specific case, the 4s electron in potassium occupies an orbital considerably higher in energy than the 3p orbitals, which become filled with electrons when argon ($Z = 18$) is reached in the Periodic Table. Thus, even though the nuclear charge in potassium is one unit greater than that in argon (and that should cause a general increase in binding energy of all electrons), the 4s electron lies in an orbital so much higher in energy than the 3p orbitals that the former is relatively easily removed. The drop in ionization energy that occurs following each inert gas (Fig. 13-2) can be traced to this cause each time it happens. Then, in passing across the series of elements from lithium to neon, or from sodium to argon, etc., there is a gradual increase in ionization energy corresponding to the gradual increase in nuclear charge (which has the effect of binding the electrons more strongly).

4. There are some minor peaks and valleys in the plot of Fig. 13-2 within these sequences; can we account for these? For instance, although the nuclear charge of the boron atom (B) is greater than that of beryllium (Be), and likewise the same for aluminium (Al) compared with magnesium (Mg), the ionization energies of the first member in each pair is less than that of the second. You might expect that a nuclear charge would bind the electrons more strongly and therefore make it more difficult to remove an electron from the neutral atom—that is, with the greater nuclear charge you would expect a greater ionization energy. You must remember, however, that the 2p orbital (or the 3p) is higher in energy than the 2s (or 3s). It appears that the higher energy of the p orbitals outweighs the increase in binding due to the increase in nuclear charge, so that the net binding energy of an electron in boron or aluminium is lower than for an electron in the corresponding element that precedes it in atomic number.

Notice also that values of the ionization energies for oxygen, fluorine, and neon (and also for sulphur, chlorine, and argon) are displaced downward from values that would be expected from a simple continuation of the trend between boron and nitrogen (or between aluminium and phosphorus). To explain these discontinuities we assume, first, that the occupancy of the three p orbitals is by one electron at a time until each of the three has an electron; second, that when a fourth electron (or more) is added there is a repulsion between the two electrons occupying the same region of space, and this raises the energy of these, making them easier to remove from the atom—that is, the atoms have smaller ionization energies. These "occupancies" are illustrated in Fig. 13-3, in which you see how the pairing of electrons begins in p orbitals with oxygen (or sulphur); it is with these elements that the dip in the sequence of increasing ionization energies occurs (Fig. 13-2).

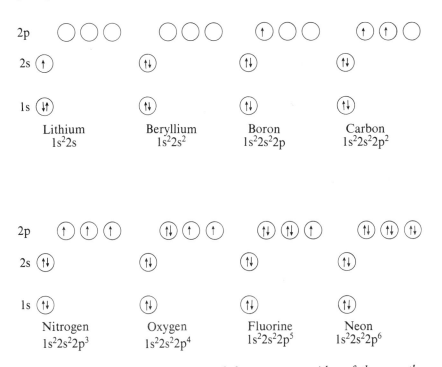

Fig. 13-3: *These diagrams are intended to convey an idea of the way the electrons are distributed among orbitals in the atoms of the elements lithium (Z = 3) to neon (Z = 10). Notice—in carbon and nitrogen—that although a p orbital can accommodate two electrons, it doesn't do so if an empty p orbital is available. Electrons don't share an orbital if they don't have to. (When an orbital has its full complement of two electrons, we depict this with arrows pointing in opposite directions to signify that the electrons have opposite spins.)*

5. IONIZATION AND REACTIVITY. The most distinctive feature of the alkali metals (Li, Na, K, Rb, Cs) is that they are chemically very reactive (Sec. 12-8). In contrast, we have mentioned (Sec. 12-9) the striking lack of reactivity on the part of the inert gases (He, Ne, Ar, Kr, Xe). You have just seen that the atoms of the alkali metals have relatively low values for their ionization energies, whereas the corresponding values for the inert gases mark the peaks in the plot of Fig. 13-2. Does this mean we can relate chemical reactivity to ionization energy?

The answer is no, not entirely. There are some elements, such as fluorine and chlorine (Chapter 30), that are exceedingly reactive and yet have rather large ionization energies. Now the ionization energy is a measure of the work required to remove an electron, thereby forming a positive ion. But, as we saw, negative ions may form when a neutral atom acquires one or more surplus electrons. When this happens, energy is often released to the surroundings. Thus to form a positive ion from *any* atom requires the input of some energy (like pushing a bicycle

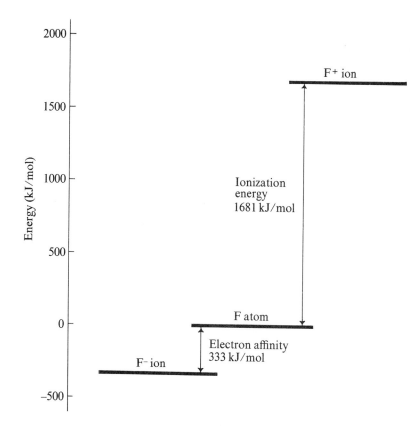

Fig. 13-4: *The energies of positive and negative fluorine ions are shown here relative to the energy of a neutral fluorine atom (which we have called zero on the scale). The figure will perhaps make clear why energy must be expended to form a positive ion, but in favourable cases (such as this) energy is given out when a negative ion is formed.*

uphill), while to form at least *some* negative ions the atoms experience a decrease in energy (like coasting downhill), passing the surplus energy to the surroundings. This is illustrated in Fig. 13-4 for fluorine atoms. The quantity of energy released when F⁻ is formed from the atom is called the *electron affinity* of fluorine. The energy relationship shown in Fig. 13-4 indicates that it is easy for an atom like fluorine to form a negative ion, but difficult for it to form a positive ion.

Elements such as fluorine, whose atoms easily form negative ions by picking up one or more electrons, are called **electronegative.** Those which can fairly easily lose one or more electrons, like the alkali metals, are called **electropositive.**

Metals are all electropositive in varying degrees. Non-metals are commonly, though not exclusively, electronegative. Thus one of the striking divisions of all chemical elements into metals and non-metals appears to be connected with the ease or difficulty of removing electrons from their atoms.

The clue to the connection between ionization and chemical reactivity which we mentioned a moment ago is this: *the most reactive elements are those whose atoms most easily form ions*—that is, those that are strongly electropositive (small ionization energy) or strongly electronegative (large electron affinity). The most unreactive elements are the inert gases, whose atoms have almost no tendency to form ions, either positive or negative.

6. THE ELECTRON STRUCTURE OF COMMON IONS. The alkali metals, as we have said, are strongly electropositive; their atoms have one electron more than an inert gas, and the small ionization energies of these elements show that this electron is relatively easily removed. Fluorine, chlorine, and the other halogens are among the most electronegative elements; their atoms have one electron fewer than an inert gas, and their electron affinities are among the highest of all the elements. Hence conditions are favourable for the conversion of the atoms of these two families of elements into ions having the same number of electrons as the atoms of the adjacent inert gases. Here are the sets of ions and atoms possessing the same numbers of electrons, together with the electron configuration characteristic of each set.

2 electrons		He	Li^+	$1s^2$
10 electrons	F^-	Ne	Na^+	$1s^2 2s^2 2p^6$
18 electrons	Cl^-	Ar	K^+	$1s^2 2s^2 2p^6 3s^2 3p^6$

With respect to ionization it is the outer-shell electrons that are of interest, and we note that once beyond helium, whose entire shell is $1s^2$, the inert gases have an outer-shell configuration that can be represented by $ns^2 np^6$, where n is the quantum number for the shell. This particular set of eight electrons is often called an **octet,** and it appears to be a very stable configuration; it is difficult to remove an electron from it or to add one to it. It is this electron stability that accounts for the characteristic lack of reactivity of the atoms of the inert gases. It also appears to account for the comparative ease with which the atoms of the the alkali metals or the halogens can form positive or negative ions respectively. The result of shedding an electron in the first case, or of acquiring one in the second, is the formation of an ion with this same stable grouping. The ions most easily, and therefore most commonly, formed by these atoms are those tabulated above (or ones like them from the remaining elements in each family), and they all have the electron arrangement typical of an atom of the inert gas adjacent to them in atomic number.

The metals beryllium, magnesium, and calcium are also reactive (Chapter 29). Their atoms possess two more electrons than an inert gas, and their reactivity can be traced to a marked tendency to form ions bearing a double positive charge. This can be seen for the case of magnesium in the equation:

$$Mg \rightarrow Mg^{2+} + 2e^-$$

atom   ion
12 electrons   10 electrons

Among the elements we have been considering are two, oxygen and sulphur, whose atoms are lacking two electrons from the complement of an inert gas. These elements are reactive and form many compounds because their atoms are converted to doubly charged negative ions:

$$2e^- \quad + \quad S \quad \rightarrow \quad S^{2-}$$

	atom	ion
	16 electrons	18 electrons

Here, then, are more ions having the electron arrangement of inert gas atoms. It is not impossible for ions such as Mg^+ or S^- to form, but under the conditions of chemical reactions the usual ion to be formed is that resembling an inert gas. We can extend the table of such ions begun near the start of this section, thus:

2 electrons			He	Li^+	Be^{2+}
10 electrons	O^{2-}	F^-	Ne	Na^+	Mg^{2+}
18 electrons	S^{2-}	Cl^-	Ar	K^+	Ca^{2+}

There are three series in these horizontal rows, the members of which all contain the same number of electrons. The atoms or ions in such a series are described as *isoelectronic*.

As we move further away from inert gases in the Periodic Table it becomes more difficult to remove an increasing number of electrons, or for a nucleus to "hold on" to an increasing surplus of electrons. Thus we shall encounter few ions bearing charges, positive or negative, that are greater than two, and whose electron configuration is that of an inert gas.

THE SIZES OF ATOMS AND IONS

7. In Sec. 10-5 we alluded to the size of the neon atom, and of atoms in general. Most atoms have diameters between 1×10^2 and 4×10^2 pm. The methods of measuring such diameters are too complicated to explain at this stage of our introduction to chemistry; you will have to take our word for it that they can be measured.

8. THE RELATIVE SIZES OF ATOMS. It isn't necessary to learn or remember the actual sizes of atoms or ions, but it is helpful to have some idea of their relative sizes one to another. For instance, for a family of elements such as the alkali metals, the size increases with increasing atomic number.

Element	Li	Na	K	Rb	Cs
Atomic Number	3	11	19	37	55
Diameter (pm)	245	314	405	432	470

As more shells of electrons are added the size of the atoms increases. Although the charge on the nucleus goes up in proportion to atomic number, and the electrons feel the pull of this increased nuclear charge, the electrons also repel one another and resist being crowded together.

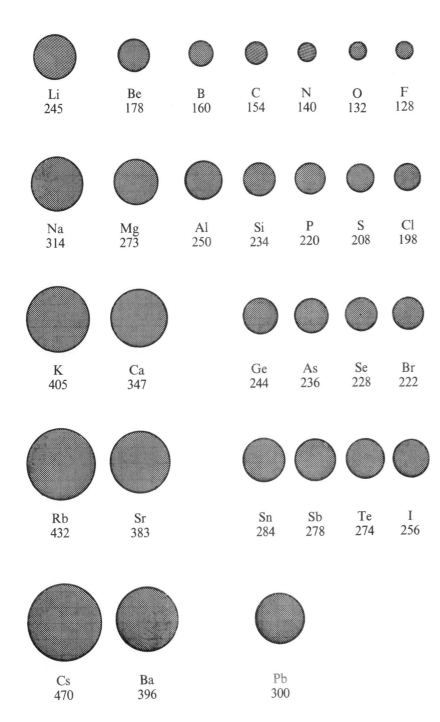

Fig. 13-5: *The shaded circles are drawn with diameters in proportion to the atomic diameters given below the symbol of each element. These are arranged according to their position in the Periodic Table. The trends discussed in Sec. 13-8 are all clearly recognizable. (Atomic diameters are given in picometres.)*

Hence the volume occupied by the electron shells goes up, and this is shown by the increase in atomic diameter.

That this trend is consistently found among families of elements is shown by Fig. 13-5. This depicts the relative sizes of the atoms of a number of common elements arranged in the same vertical and horizontal rows that they occupy in the Periodic Table. (See Table 12-2 and also Chapter 31.)

9. THE SIZES OF IONS COMPARED WITH ATOMS. When positive ions are formed by the removal of one or more electrons from atoms, a shrinkage of the electron shells occurs. This could happen for two reasons. First, the electrons removed originally occupied the outermost shell, and in many, though not all, cases this is left vacant when the ion is formed. Second, each electron in the ion will be subject to the same pull by the nucleus as in the atom, but will experience less repulsion by all the other electrons since there will be fewer electrons in the ion than in the atom. As a result, the whole set of electron shells can shrink somewhat toward the centre.

In any negative ion there will be more electrons than protons. Each electron will experience the same force of attraction by the protons in the nucleus as it would in the neutral atom containing the same nucleus. But each electron will undergo more repulsion from the other electrons in the ion, since there are more electrons, than in the atom. This will lead to an expansion of the electron shells, causing the ion to be larger than the corresponding atoms.

These principles are borne out by the observed values for atomic and ionic diameters of which values for the elements discussed in Sec. 13-6 are shown in Table 13-1.

TABLE 13-1

COMPARISON OF ATOMIC AND IONIC DIAMETERS*				
(ALL VALUES IN PICOMETRES)				
		Helium He	Lithium Li $= 245$ Li$^+$ $= 136$	Beryllium Be $= 178$ Be^{2+} $= 60$
Oxygen O $= 132$ O^{2-} $= 292$	Fluorine F $= 128$ F$^-$ $= 266$	Neon Ne	Sodium Na $= 314$ Na$^+$ $= 196$	Magnesium Mg $= 273$ Mg^{2+} $= 130$
Sulphur S $= 208$ S^{2-} $= 380$	Chlorine Cl $= 198$ Cl$^-$ $= 362$	Argon Ar	Potassium K $= 405$ K$^+$ $= 266$	Calcium Ca $= 347$ Ca^{2+} $= 188$

*The values used here and in Fig. 13-5 are based on crystal radii for the metals, the so-called tetrahedral covalent radii for the non-metals, and Zachariasen's values for ionic radii. No comparable values are available for the inert gas atoms.

QUESTIONS

1. Explain in your own words the meaning of:

(a) ionization

(b) ionization energy

(c) electron affinity

(d) electropositive

(e) electronegative

2. Write the electron configuration for each of the following: an oxide ion, O^{2-}; a fluoride ion, F^-; a neon atom, Ne; a sodium ion, Na^+; and a magnesium ion, Mg^{2+}. What name is given to species, such as these, that have a common electron configuration?

3. Why do atoms of the inert gases not easily form positive ions? Why do they not form negative ions?

4. Atoms of a certain element M have the electron configuration $1s^2 2s^2 2p^6 3s^2$. Which of the following would be the symbol of the ions formed from these atoms: M^+, M^{2+}, M^-, M^{2-}? Explain.

5. Explain how ionization energies furnish strong evidence concerning the filling of electron orbitals among the first twenty elements.

6. Although carbon forms innumerable compounds, in none of these does the element occur as simple ions, C^{4+} or C^{4-}. Account for this.

7. Explain how ionization energies show a general increase in passing across a row of elements such as lithium to neon, or sodium to argon. (You may ignore small discrepancies such as occur with boron or oxygen.)

8. Although the capacity of the M shell ($n = 3$) for electrons is 18, the N shell ($n = 4$) begins to fill after 8 electrons occupy the former. Show how the values of the ionization energies support this statement.

9. Why is it easier to remove an electron from an oxygen atom than from a nitrogen atom, in spite of the fact that oxygen atoms have the greater nuclear charge?

10. Why is it easier to remove an electron from an aluminium atom than from a magnesium atom, in spite of the fact that aluminium atoms have the greater nuclear charge?

11. Why is a sodium atom ($Z = 11$) larger than (a) a lithium atom ($Z = 3$); (b) a magnesium atom ($Z = 12$); (c) a sodium ion?

12. Would you expect a neon atom to be larger or smaller than a sodium atom; than a sodium ion? Explain.

13. From Fig. 13-2 it is evident that there is a progressive decrease in values of the ionization energies of the atoms of the alkali metals. If you consult a reference book, you will find that this trend continues with rubidium and caesium. Account for this trend among these five elements.

14. The values plotted in Fig. 13-2 refer to the removal of one electron from an atom, and are known as first-stage ionization energies. The energy required to remove a second electron is called the second-stage ionization energy, and so on. Can you suggest why second-stage ionization energies are always greater than first-stage ones?

*15. The first- and second-stage ionization energies of lithium and beryllium are given below. Can you suggest why beryllium has the higher first-stage ionization energy, but the lower value for the second stage?

IONIZATION ENERGY (kJ/mol)	LITHIUM	BERYLLIUM
First stage	520	899
Second stage	7297	1757

*16. Consider the following electron configurations for neutral atoms:

(a) $1s^2 2s^2 2p^6 3s^2$

(b) $1s^2 2s^2 2p^6 3s$

(c) $1s^2 2s^2 2p^6$

(d) $1s^2 2s^2 2p^5$

(e) $1s^2 2s^2 2p^3$

(a) Which of these would you expect to have the lowest ionization energy?

(b) Which would you expect to be an inert gas?

(c) List the five atoms in a predicted order of increasing first-stage ionization energy.

(d) Predict the atom that should have the highest second-stage ionization energy.

(e) Predict the atom that should have the lowest second-stage ionization energy.

14 Chemical Bonding

1. Although we have now devoted four chapters to a study of the structure of single atoms, we must keep in mind that individual atoms are not a common occurrence. You will recall that there are about one hundred chemical elements, and that means about one hundred different kinds of atoms, without counting isotopic variations. From this hundred we picked neon for discussion in Sec. 10-2 because "it is one of the relatively few elements whose atoms are not paired or clustered." You have, in contrast, been told of elements with formulas like H_2, Cl_2, P_4, or S_8; these consist of molecules, or small clusters of atoms. You might wonder what holds the atoms together in such structures.

Then there are hundreds of thousands of compounds, each consisting of two or more elements. In these compounds the different atoms of the elements are held together in some way; whatever way that is, it leads to each pure substance having a constant composition (Sec. 3-10). What holds the atoms together in this case, and why are they always in such fixed proportions?

2. ATOMIC AGGREGATES. In this chapter we shall describe what we call *aggregates* of atoms, by which we mean any cluster of two or more atoms held together with sufficient force that a significant amount of work must be done to separate the cluster into its constituent parts. We shall see that there are at least two apparently different ways in which atoms can join together. When atoms link together into various sorts of aggregates, it is customary to say that a *bond* has formed between the atoms. We shall try to convey the nature of chemical bonds.

Bonding between atoms occurs as a result of electrical forces which develop among the electrically charged particles in atoms. You have probably seen electrostatic forces demonstrated by placing charge on small pith or cork balls hanging by light threads, and you will remember that unlike charges give rise to forces of attraction whereas like charges repel each other. In these demonstrations you saw nothing between the pith balls, but the invisible forces you saw in operation are the same kind as those by which atoms are held together in clusters or aggregates.

THE IONIC BOND

3. In Chapter 13 we explained how atoms may become ions by the removal or addition of electrons. We stated that a number of these ions could survive with a deficiency or surplus of electrons provided the ions had configurations of electrons similar to those in inert gas atoms. Evidence points to the fact that these particular electron configurations are remarkably stable. Now imagine what would happen if two such ions, one positively charged and the other negatively charged (say, the sodium ion, Na^+, and the chloride ion, Cl^-), were brought close together. You might expect them to be attracted to each other, just like two oppositely charged pith balls. However, when they they get close enough, their respective "electron clouds" (Sec. 11-13) will begin to repel one another. On this account there is some minimum distance of closest approach at which there is a balance between attractive and repulsive forces. In Sec. 13-9 we gave actual diameters for several ions, and these quantities demonstrate that each ion (or atom) does occupy, because of its electron shells, a certain volume. Having got, in your mind's eye, two oppositely charged ions to their minimum distance of approach, you should realize that some work will then be required to pull them apart again. They are, in fact, linked or bonded together, and because the linkage is between ions it is called an **ionic bond.** The amount of work required to separate the ions again is known as the *bond energy.* The bonded sodium and chloride ions make up what is called an *ion pair.*

By means of Coulomb's Law, which describes the force between two charged bodies in relation to their distance of separation, it is possible to calculate the energy required to separate a sodium ion from a chloride ion. For this we need to know the charges, which are $+e$ and $-e$, and the distance of separation, which is the sum of their ionic radii, 279 pm (Table 13-1). The answer turns out to be 498 kJ/mol of ion pairs ($Na^+ + Cl^-$), which is a reasonable estimate of the bond energy. The conclusion is that sodium ions and chloride ions cling to each other with considerable strength when placed in contact. Another way to express this is to say that a strong ionic bond develops between the two.

It is actually too high because we made no allowance for the repulsion of the electron clouds of the two ions. The answer incorporating this correction is 442 kJ/mol.

4. CRYSTALS OF IONIC SUBSTANCES. This doesn't tell the whole story, however. We commented in Sec. 8-5 on the reaction between sodium and chlorine to form sodium chloride. If you have seen this reaction take place you could not fail to have observed that a good deal of heat, and usually some light, is given out to the surroundings as the elements combine. The sodium chloride formed in this way is a white fluffy mass, but under a microscope this may be seen to consist of tiny crystals and these are cubic in shape. Larger crystals, such as those found in natural

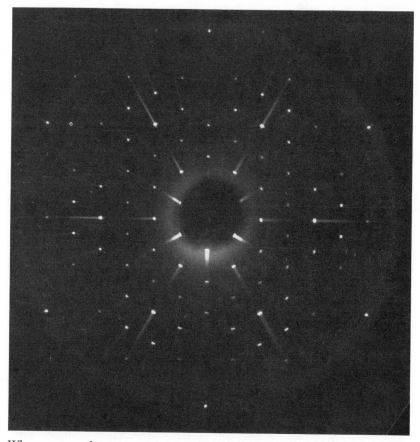

When x-rays of an appropriate wavelength impinge on a crystal, the rays are diffracted by the planes of atoms or ions in the crystal, and produce on a photographic film a diffraction pattern such as that reproduced here. The symmetry of this pattern is a consequence of the symmetry of the arrangement of the atoms or ions in the crystal. From the relative intensities and positioning of the spots, much can be deduced about the spacing and arrangement of the atoms or ions.

This diffraction pattern is from a crystal of the complex compound ammonium hexafluorotitanate dihydrate, $(NH_4)_2TiF_6 \cdot 2H_2O$, which consists of ammonium ions, NH_4^+, and fluorotitanate ions, TiF_6^{2-}, with water molecules regularly spaced among them.

deposits of sodium chloride in a salt mine, also have this shape as is evident in the photograph in Chapter 8.

The regular and recurrent shape of these crystals suggests that their outward forms may be due to an orderly arrangement of the atoms in them. The clue to the structure of crystals of sodium chloride and of crystals in general came from experiments in which beams of x-rays were diffracted in passing through them. Since x-rays have wavelengths about the same as the spacing between the atoms, the rays undergo diffraction in the same way that visible light does in passing through tiny slits. See the photograph.

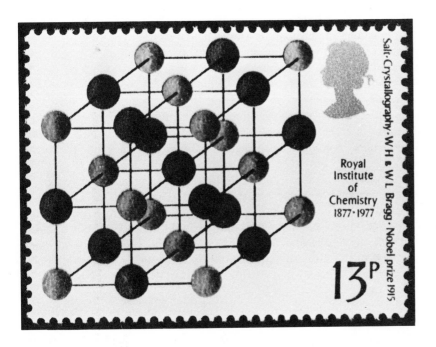

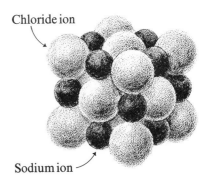

Fig. 14-1: *The arrangement indicated here in a small section of a sodium chloride crystal is repeated for millions of ions in each direction.*

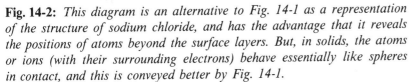

Fig. 14-2: *This diagram is an alternative to Fig. 14-1 as a representation of the structure of sodium chloride, and has the advantage that it reveals the positions of atoms beyond the surface layers. But, in solids, the atoms or ions (with their surrounding electrons) behave essentially like spheres in contact, and this is conveyed better by Fig. 14-1.*

This stamp, issued in 1977 by Great Britain, honours Sir William and Sir Lawrence Bragg, father and son, who were jointly awarded a Nobel Prize (1915) for their fundamental researches on the nature of crystals.

Scientists were able to interpret these observations in the case of sodium chloride by assuming a model for the crystal in which *ions* (not atoms) are laid out in a simple array in three dimensions. The nature of this arrangement is shown in Fig. 14-1; the ions are represented by spheres in contact, and each sphere can be thought of as the "electron cloud" of an ion. The spheres are of two sizes, but so are the ions (Sec. 13-9). Taken as a whole a grain or crystal of salt will be electrically neutral; therefore, there must be an equal number of positive and negative ions in a crystal.

The number of ions in even a tiny crystal is enormous. A calculation based on the masses of the sodium and chloride ions shows that in a single grain of salt, having a mass of 0.1 mg, there will be about 10^{21} of each kind of ion. Next time you talk about taking something with a grain of salt, think of all those ions! And in this tiny bit of salt the ions will be arranged in the same regular way as the comparatively few spheres in Fig. 14-1.

5. The electrons in these ions are very small and are moving swiftly around the nuclei. By comparison, the nuclei are relatively stationary and also make up practically all of the mass. If we want to show the relative positions of the ions in a crystal like sodium chloride it may be better to confine our attention to the location of the nuclei relative to one another. Such a representation is shown in Fig. 14-2. You should be able to relate the arrangement of the small spheres in this to that of the space-filling spheres in Fig. 14-1. In Fig. 14-2 straight lines have been added to show how the nuclei are arranged in lines and planes, and how in three dimensions the lines trace out a cubic shape. The straight lines trace out what is called the *lattice* of the solid; the nuclei occupy positions at regular points along the lattice.

As revealed by Fig. 14-2 and 14-4(a), the central small sphere has six nearest neighbours of the opposite kind around it: above and below, fore and aft, left and right. This is true of any sphere in the model. Translated into ions, this means that each chloride ion has six equidistant sodium ions closest to it; each sodium ion has six chloride ions around it in the same spatial relationship. *No one ion is the sole partner of any other ion.*

6. The account in Sec. 14-4 and 14-5 indicates that the product of a chemical reaction between sodium and chlorine is a crystalline solid made up of "zillions" of sodium and chloride ions laid out in an arrangement like a three-dimensional checker-board. Although we described in Sec. 14-3 a simple, stable ion pair formed from these ions, it appears that the normal state of sodium chloride is an aggregate of many, many ions rather than a large number of such separate ion pairs. Nevertheless, the multitudinous array of ions in the crystal is linked together in the same way as the two ions in the ion pair—that is, by the attraction of opposite charges.

7. We explained in Sec. 14-3 how the energy of the bond in a sodium chloride ion pair could be estimated. For a mole of sodium chloride in an ionic lattice arranged as in Fig. 14-1 or 14-2, the attractions and repulsions among all the ions lead to an energy that is about 75% greater than the value for ion pairs. That means that the ionic bonding in sodium chloride in the crystalline form is about 75% stronger than it would be if the same substance occurred as ion pairs. This is why under ordinary conditions we encounter sodium chloride as a solid rather than as a gas (of ion pairs). The energy associated with the bonding in the crystal is known as the *crystal lattice energy,* and for sodium chloride this amounts to 773 kJ/mol. That is the amount of work needed to dismantle the crystal lattice and separate all the ions from each other. We reaffirm the point made previously, that the ionic bonding in this crystal is strong, and gives to the substance its coherence and mechanical strength, which are great enough to hold the solid together up to its melting point of 800°C.

8. THE PRINCIPLE OF ELECTRICAL NEUTRALITY. It may be worth stressing a point that has already been mentioned, namely, that the proportions in which sodium atoms and chlorine atoms combine (or occur together in combination) are exactly one to one. This happens because of two factors: sodium chloride is electrically neutral, and both kinds of

At sufficiently elevated temperatures, for instance above 1465°C, the boiling point of sodium chloride, the vapour will contain these ion pairs. Fig. 14-3 suggests how the ion pairs could coalesce into the pattern adopted by the ions in the solid, as would happen when the vapour is cooled.

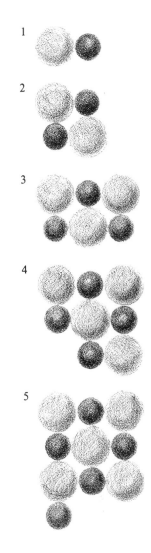

Fig. 14-3: *This sequence of drawings is intended to show in two dimensions how ion pairs might merge because of electrical attractions between unlike charges and in doing so might start the growth of an ionic crystal. The small circles represent a positive ion such as* Na+ *and the larger circles represent a negative ion such as* Cl-. *You might compare the fifth member of the sequence with one face of the model of the sodium chloride crystal shown in Fig. 14-1.*

In Chapter 2 we described the burning of magnesium in air to a white smoke of magnesium oxide, but nothing in that experiment would suggest that the magnesium oxide particles were crystalline. However, with the enormous magnification (here, 50 000 times) provided by the electron microscope, the smoke particles are seen to be crystals, and unmistakably cubic.

The shape of the crystal is a consequence of an arrangement of the ions (Mg²⁺ and O²⁻) similar to that in sodium chloride (Fig. 14-1 and 14-2).

ions that make up the crystal of sodium chloride are singly charged. The positive charges on a large number of sodium ions are exactly balanced by the negative charges on an equal number of chloride ions.

This is known as the electrical neutrality principle, and it governs the composition of ionic substances whether the ions involved are singly charged or otherwise.

9. MORE IONIC COMPOUNDS. There are many other compounds made up of two elements in which we believe the atoms are linked together in the same way. The essential requirement for bonding in these cases is that the elements that make up the compounds can readily form ions of opposite charge. That means that one element must be strongly electropositive, and that implies a metal of relatively small ionization energy (Sec. 13-6). The other element must be strongly electronegative, and that means a non-metal with an electron configuration one or two electrons short of that of an inert gas (three electrons short in the case of nitrogen). Suitable electronegative elements include the halogens, oxygen, and sulphur, and in some instances nitrogen. The following are examples of such ionic compounds:

potassium iodide	KI	=	$(K^+)(I^-)$
magnesium oxide	MgO	=	$(Mg^{2+})(O^{2-})$
calcium fluoride	CaF_2	=	$(Ca^{2+})(F^-)_2$
sodium sulphide	Na_2S	=	$(Na^+)_2(S^{2-})$
lithium nitride	Li_3N	=	$(Li^+)_3(N^{3-})$

In the next chapter (Sec. 15-10) we shall show how groups of atoms can form *compound ions*. These include ammonium, NH_4^+; nitrate, NO_3^-; sulphate, SO_4^{2-}; and carbonate, CO_3^{2-}. When we introduced them earlier (Sec. 5-12) we gave these groups of atoms an older name—radicals—but we may now add that in many compounds they occur as ions. Within such ions atoms are linked together by another kind of bonding which we shall describe shortly, but taken as a whole the compound ions behave just like simple ions in forming ionic compounds. Thus in the compound ammonium chloride the positive ion, NH_4^+, occupies sites in a crystal lattice equivalent to the caesium ion in caesium chloride, CsCl; the ammonium ions and chloride ions are held together in this crystal by ionic bonding. Additional examples of ionic substances incorporating compound ions are:

silver nitrate	$AgNO_3$	=	$(Ag^+)(NO_3^-)$
ammonium sulphate	$(NH_4)_2SO_4$	=	$(NH_4^+)_2(SO_4^{2-})$
lithium carbonate	Li_2CO_3	=	$(Li^+)_2(CO_3^{2-})$

You will notice in all of the foregoing examples that the principle of electrical neutrality governs the formula of the compound.

10. OTHER PACKINGS OF IONS. The simple packing of ions that applies to sodium chloride (Fig. 14-1 and 14-2) is found in a number of other compounds in which the ions combine one to one; for instance, potassium bromide, silver chloride, and magnesium oxide. But this is *not* the *only* way in which spherical ions may be packed together. The electrical forces between ions apply in all directions and are a maximum at the shortest possible distance. Accordingly the greatest lattice energy, and therefore the most stable arrangement of ions in a crystal lattice, will be achieved when the packing of the spherical ions is most efficient. Closest packing of the ions will lead to different arrangements accord-

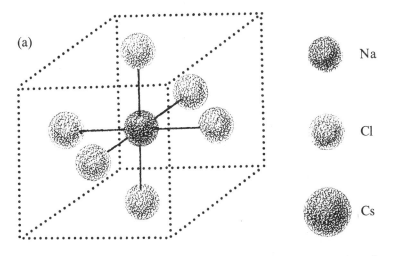

(a)

Na

Cl

Cs

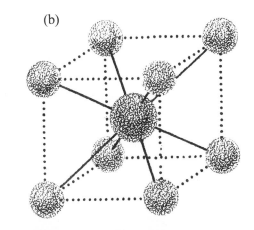

Fig. 14-4: *This illustrates a point made in the text concerning the packing of one kind of ion around another. In (a) we show the location of six chloride ions that are the nearest neighbours of a sodium ion in crystalline sodium chloride. This group of seven ions has been removed, so to speak, from the array shown in Fig. 14-2, but the cubic outline of that figure is here suggested by the dotted lines. Six, the number of nearest neighbours to the central ion, is called the coordination number for this packing.*

In (b) a different situation is shown, which arises when the positive ion becomes larger. The coordination number has now increased to eight. In caesium chloride the metal ion is at the centre of a cube of eight chloride ions.

Each of these structural units occurs repeatedly throughout the respective crystals.

ing to the relative sizes of the positive and negative ions. For instance, caesium chloride (or ammonium chloride) consists of a simple cubic array of chloride ions with one caesium (or ammonium) ion in the centre of each cube (Fig. 14-4(b)).

Naturally, for compounds with ions in ratios other than 1:1, such as CaF_2, other patterns of packing of the spherical ions will arise in order to achieve maximum stability of the crystal (Fig. 14-5). Some compound ions are not spherical; for instance, the nitrate and the carbonate ions are triangular. When non-spherical ions form part of a crystal lattice, the resulting crystal shape may be other than cubic. See the accompanying photograph of the mineral calcite.

Calcite is a naturally occurring form of calcium carbonate, $CaCO_3$. As grown slowly in ancient geologic times, these crystals reveal the faces, edges, and definite angles of single crystals. The packing of ion "spheres" often leads to crystal forms that are cubic (as with sodium chloride) but in calcite the packing of flat triangular carbonate ions alters the symmetry, and the crystals that develop are of a different shape. Here you see beautifully formed hexagonal prisms of calcite, up to 5 cm long.

THE COVALENT BOND

11. Not all links between atoms can be accounted for by the ionic bonding model just described. Many substances under ordinary conditions are not crystalline, nor do they have enormous numbers of atoms

Fig. 14-5: *The relationship in three dimensions of the ions in calcium fluoride. Solid lines have been drawn joining the ions only for the purpose of illustrating the spatial relationship of the ions one to another. The broken lines outline the crystalline shape that might be generated by these arrangements of ions. To make the relationship of the ions clearer, the relative sizes of the calcium and fluoride ions have been reversed.*

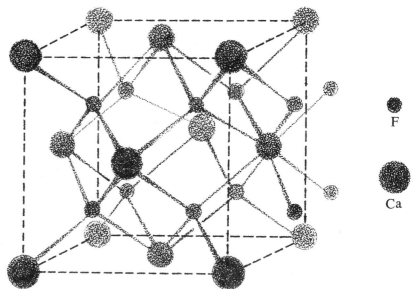

F

Ca

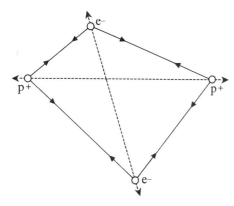

This drawing illustrates electrical forces of attraction and repulsion operating within a hydrogen molecule. This molecule consists of two protons (p⁺) at a fixed distance apart, and two electrons (e⁻) moving rapidly about but mainly in the space between the protons. The positions of the electrons in the figure are those occurring at a particular instant —as though in a very high-speed photograph. Forces of repulsion exist between the particles of like charge, along the broken lines in the drawing. Forces of attraction exist between the particles of unlike charge, along the solid lines in the drawing. The arrowheads indicate the directions in which these electrical forces would tend to move the particles. In the position depicted the attractive forces outweigh the repulsive forces, and this is how the shared pair of electrons hold the molecule together.

bonded together. We need to be able to account for small groupings of atoms into molecules, such as occur in gaseous or liquid substances. We have already mentioned a number of elements that occur as molecules at ordinary temperatures, for example, H_2, Cl_2, P_4, and S_8. In these molecules of elements the atoms are all alike, and that suggests that it is most unlikely that the bonds between atoms would be ionic. In that event we need another sort of bonding to account for aggregates of this type.

12. The ionic bond operates by virtue of electrical attraction between ions of opposite charge. There is another way by which electrical attraction of unlike charges could achieve bonding in a molecule. It will be easier to describe this by reference to a specific example, and for this we shall use the hydrogen molecule, H_2. This simple molecule consists of two protons and two electrons. The distance between the protons is known from certain measurements to be 76 pm. To interpret the binding of the hydrogen atoms into a molecule we shall regard the two electrons as shared between the two protons. Each proton exerts an attractive force on the electrons; conversely, the electrons must exert an attractive force on the protons. The protons appear to be bound together by the electrons they share. The pair of electrons have created another kind of bond by which the molecule is held together. To emphasize that the bonding electrons are the shared property of the two joined atoms the bond that they create is known as a *covalent bond.*

13. A MOLECULAR ORBITAL. Since we devoted some pages in Chapters 11 and 12 to a description of the hydrogen atom and other atoms in terms of wave mechanics, we shall now attempt an extension of these ideas in order to explain the covalent bond. We shall continue to refer to the bonding in the hydrogen molecule as we did in the preceding section. Imagine two hydrogen atoms, originally completely separate, being brought closer and closer together until they eventually reach the distance of separation corresponding to the hydrogen molecule. In each separate atom there will be a single electron which we shall assume to be in the 1s orbital (ground state). The atoms are represented in Fig. 14-6(a) by a dot and a circle. The dot conveys the location of

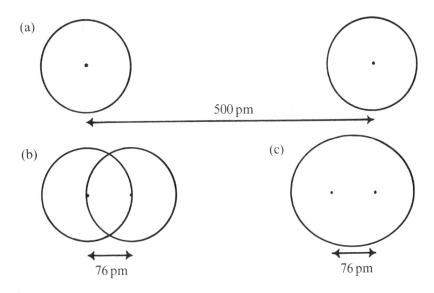

(a)

500 pm

(b)   (c)

76 pm   76 pm

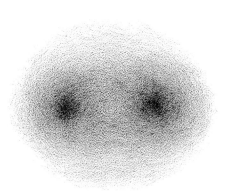

Fig. 14-6: *This series of drawings illustrates how the overlap of two 1s atomic orbitals of hydrogen can lead to an enhancement of electron density in the region between the nuclei. In (a) the nuclei are about 500 pm apart, at which distance one atom has little effect on the other, and the 95% boundary surfaces of the electron densities are separated by about 340 pm. In (b) the nuclei are separated by 76 pm, the same distance as in the hydrogen molecule. By now there is significant overlap of the zones of high electron probability. In (c) the same boundary surface for a molecular orbital is shown. The increased probability of the electron being in the middle region can be gauged from the broadening of the figure there and a reduction in the zone behind either nucleus.*

the nucleus, and the circle conveys a section (in one plane) through the spherical 1s orbital, showing the boundary within which the electron is found (with a 95% probability). When the nuclei are 76 pm apart, as represented in Fig. 14-6(b), you see that there is considerable overlap of the two atomic orbitals in the zone between the nuclei. These orbitals, you remember, are simply mathematical descriptions of the wave pattern of the electron in space around the nucleus. It has been proposed that if these mathematical descriptions are added together a *new* mathematical description emerges which describes a new wave pattern that is characteristic of the entire molecule, and is known as a *molecular orbital.* The probability distribution for the location of an electron in this combination orbital is shown in Fig. 14-6(c) and 14-7. Either of these drawings has to be imagined in three dimensions, so that the molecular orbital might be compared in shape to a football or an Easter egg.

The effect of combining the atomic orbitals in this way is to cause a greater probability for an electron to be in the zone between the nuclei—greater, that is, than the combined probabilities in the uncombined atoms at this distance apart. Why this should be so will not be apparent unless you examine the details of the calculation; we shall spare you that task, but invite you to take our word for the conclusion. The reinforcement of electron probability depends upon the amount of overlap of the separate atomic orbitals.

The act of combination of two hydrogen atoms to form a molecule amounts, therefore, to a merging of their separate electron orbitals into a new communal molecular orbital. The molecular orbital achieves a piling-up of electron density in the region between the nuclei greater than would occur from the separate atomic orbitals. The molecular orbital, like the atomic orbitals described earlier, can accommodate two electrons of opposite spin. The two electrons in the hydrogen molecule are thus assigned to this orbital, and there they create the electrical attraction necessary to hold the molecule together.

Fig. 14-7: *The dots in this drawing of a hydrogen molecule each represent a fixed small probability of finding an electron in that vicinity at a given time. The denser the dots, the higher the probability.*

(a)

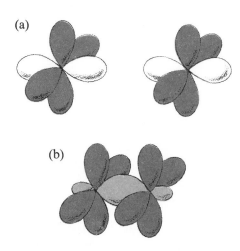

(b)

Fig. 14-8: *This drawing illustrates the formation of a bonding molecular orbital between two fluorine atoms. In (a) the two separate fluorine atoms are shown, and in each the two 2p orbitals containing paired electrons are shown shaded while the 2p orbital occupied by only one electron is shown unshaded. In (b), as a result of overlap and combination of the singly occupied orbitals at closer approach, a new combined molecular orbital has formed, and is shown shaded (differently) to indicate that in the molecule it is occupied by a pair of electrons.*

14. To complete this description of the hydrogen molecule we must add that the attraction created by the electrons in the region between the nuclei would pull the latter closer and closer together unless some opposing force kept them apart. There is such an opposing force provided by the repulsion of the positive charges of the nuclei. At a distance of 76 pm between nuclei in the hydrogen molecule there is a balance between the attractive and repulsive forces. This distance is known as the covalent *bond length*.

15. MOLECULES OTHER THAN HYDROGEN. The same principles apply to the formation of other molecules, but different orbitals are involved. For instance, in the fluorine molecule, F_2, a molecular orbital can be created by the suitable addition of p orbitals in the fluorine atoms. The ground-state electron configuration of the fluorine atom is $1s^2 2s^2 2p^5$ (Sec. 12-4); in the 2p sub-shell two of the three orbitals are occupied by a pair of electrons and one is occupied singly. Suppose this last orbital overlapped with the corresponding orbital in a second fluorine atom. A mathematical combination of these would lead to a new wave pattern with increased electron density in the region between the two nuclei. This new communal orbital can accommodate the two electrons which were unpaired in the atomic orbitals prior to combination (see Fig. 14-8). In a similar way, one hydrogen atom and one fluorine atom can unite with formation of a bonding molecular orbital by overlap of their 1s and 2p orbitals, respectively.

In general, we can account for formation of a covalent bond in this way whenever the atoms to be linked together each have half-empty orbitals which, at short internuclear distance, can overlap. A consequence of this overlap is the formation of a joint molecular orbital characterized by increased electron probability in the zone between the atoms. When a fairly great electron density is made possible between two atoms in this way, the conditions are favourable for bonding.

16. It is quite possible for one atom to form more than one such bond. The water molecule affords an example of this. The uncombined oxygen atom has two 2p orbitals occupied by single electrons, and one filled with a pair (Fig. 14-9(a)). The singly occupied p orbitals lie at right angles to one another. Each of these could be thought of as merging with 1s orbitals of different hydrogen atoms if the latter came close enough for overlap to occur. Thereby two new communal orbitals could be formed which could accommodate two electrons each, one provided by each atom, and in this way the requirements for two bonds could be satisfied (Fig. 14-9(b)).

This representation of the formation of bonds between the oxygen atom and two hydrogen atoms in the water molecule does not tell the whole story. For instance, it is known that the angle between the bonds is greater than 90°, and from that information we must infer that some additional rearrangements of electrons may occur when bonds are formed. We shall have more to say about shapes of molecules in the next chapter.

REPRESENTATION OF BONDS

17. We have described a little of the orbital theory of covalent bonding so that you might see how the sharing of electrons between atoms can be the means of linking the latter together, and also how the combination of atomic orbitals can lead to an increase in electron density in the region between the atoms being joined. Once you understand how such bonding arises we can resort to a much simpler notation for representing the covalent bond. One way is to show the bond by a line joining the symbols of the linked atoms, thus:

H—H   O—H   or, less desirably,
              | H—O—H
H—F   H

F—F

18. LEWIS DIAGRAMS. A better method, which gives much more insight about the number and nature of the chemical bonds formed, was suggested about 1916 by the American chemist G. N. Lewis. To illustrate this method we turn to the members of the row of elements with atomic numbers 3 to 10 which occur in the Periodic Table after helium (Sec. 12-9). These have in their atoms a filled K shell, and one to eight electrons in the L shell. Only the latter group of electrons are involved in forming bonds (ionic or covalent) with other atoms, and on this account this outer shell is called the **valence shell** in these atoms. For the present purpose only the electrons in the valence shell are represented in print by dots placed around the symbol of the element. The dots are shown, either singly or in pairs, above, below, and on either side of the symbol. A pair of dots is shown if it is known that an orbital is occupied by two electrons; a single dot conveys an unpaired electron. For the elements with atomic numbers three to ten this representation looks as follows:

Li .   Be :   . B :   . C :   . N :   . O :   . F :   : Ne :

As a result of the mechanism outlined in Sec. 14-13 to 14-16, unpaired electrons in the valence shell may become paired with single electrons from other atoms to form one or more covalent bonds. Neon, with a full complement of eight electrons in the valence shell, does not form covalent bonds; this tallies with the inert or unreactive character of the element, and the fact that its molecules are single atoms.

The molecules of fluorine and hydrogen fluoride, whose formation we explained by orbital theory in Sec. 14-15, can be represented as arising through the sharing of a pair of electrons between the bonded atoms:

: F : F :   H : F :

In either of these molecules the valence shell of a fluorine atom has been augmented by sharing an additional electron with another atom. The number of electrons around each fluorine atom is now seen to be eight, and this complete set of eight electrons, found in the atoms of the inert gases (except helium) and in many stable ions, is called an **octet.** The octet is also found in the valence shell of many atoms when these are covalently bonded to other atoms. Here are representations of several other molecules in which an octet appears in the valence shell of a second-row element:

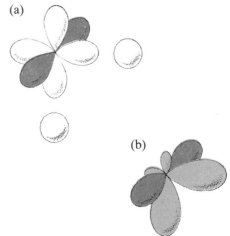

(a)

(b)

Fig. 14-9: *This drawing, like Fig. 14-8, illustrates orbitals before and after combination. In (a) are seen the 2p orbitals of an oxygen atom and the 1s orbitals of two hydrogen atoms. The one 2p orbital in oxygen which is occupied by a pair of electrons is shown shaded. The atoms should be imagined as separated enough so that no significant interaction has occurred. In (b) the nuclei are shown at their distance of separation in the water molecule. Each of the unfilled oxygen 2p orbitals has overlapped and combined with the orbital of a hydrogen atom. The new molecular orbitals are shown shaded (differently) to convey, as before, that in the molecule they will each be occupied by a pair of electrons.*

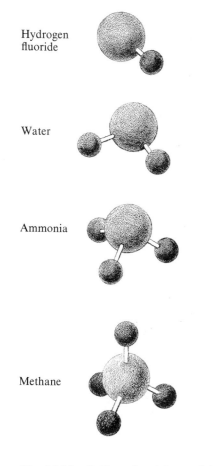

Hydrogen fluoride

Water

Ammonia

Methane

Fig. 14-10: *Ball and stick models of molecules*

$$H : \overset{\cdot\cdot}{O} :$$
$$H$$
water
$$H_2O$$

$$: \overset{\cdot\cdot}{F} : \overset{\cdot\cdot}{O} :$$
$$: \overset{\cdot\cdot}{F} :$$
oxygen fluoride
$$OF_2$$

$$H : \overset{\cdot\cdot}{N} : H$$
$$H$$
ammonia
$$NH_3$$

$$H$$
$$H : \overset{\cdot\cdot}{C} : H$$
$$H$$
methane
$$CH_4$$

In each case where a hydrogen atom is bonded the number of electrons assigned to its valence shell is two. This can be related to the electron complement of the neighbouring inert gas, helium. You will notice that in arriving at the number of electrons in these covalently bonded atoms we have counted the shared electrons as belonging to both of the atoms joined by the bond.

In developing this way of thinking about and representing bond formation, G. N. Lewis placed considerable emphasis on the fact that the valence shells of the bonded atoms did contain, in the majority of cases, the complement of electrons typical of an inert gas. These "electron-dot" representations of molecules and bonds are often called *Lewis diagrams*. In the next chapter we shall describe structures for a number of other substances in which covalent bonding occurs, and we shall encounter cases where the octet principle does not apply.

19. MOLECULAR MODELS. It is often helpful to represent the arrangement of atoms in molecules by simple models. One way to do this is to use balls to represent atoms and thin sticks or stiff wire to represent the bonds between them. Models of this kind are illustrated in Fig. 14-10. When atoms are linked together they are actually much closer together in relation to their own size than these models suggest. A truer representation is given by models of the type shown in Fig. 14-11; in these the atoms are represented by sections of spheres fastened together.

20. VALENCE. After the formulas of many compounds had been established in the nineteenth century by careful experiments, it was noticed that atoms of the various elements often showed regularity in the numbers of atoms of other elements with which they combined. For instance, consider the following compounds and their formulas:

sodium fluoride	NaF	*sodium oxide*	Na_2O
magnesium fluoride	MgF_2	*magnesium oxide*	MgO
aluminium fluoride	AlF_3	*aluminium oxide*	Al_2O_3
silicon tetrafluoride	SiF_4	*silicon dioxide*	SiO_2
phosphorus pentafluoride	PF_5	*phosphorus pentoxide*	P_4O_{10}
sulphur hexafluoride	SF_6	*sulphur trioxide*	SO_3
*	*	*chlorine heptoxide*	Cl_2O_7

*It would be nice to include chlorine heptafluoride, ClF_7, in this space, but at the time of writing there is no evidence for the existence of such a compound. However, iodine (another halogen) does form a heptafluoride, IF_7.

The atoms of the elements sodium, magnesium, etc., in this list show a progressive increase in the number of fluorine or oxygen atoms with which they are combined. This is summed up by saying that if we assign to fluorine a valence of unity, the valence of sodium is one, that of magnesium is two, aluminium three, etc. The choice of one for the valence of fluorine rests on the fact that no compound has been found in which one fluorine atom is combined with more than one atom of another element. The compound oxygen fluoride, mentioned in Sec. 14-18, indicates a valence of two for oxygen. From this value for oxygen, the valence of the elements whose oxides are listed in the second column above can be worked out. For example, one sulphur atom in sulphur trioxide is combined with three 2-valent oxygen atoms, and that gives sulphur a valence of six, just as in the fluoride (SF_6).

Some elements show more than one characteristic valence, while others are fairly consistent in their combining capacity.

This basic idea of valence, developed in the 1860s, has undergone some modifications as our understanding of the nature of chemical bonding has increased. For one thing, when chemists speak about valence now they have in mind not only the capacity of one atom to combine with some number of atoms of another element, but also the forces by which they are linked. In this chapter we have shown that some compounds owe their stability and structure to the fact that the basic building blocks are ions of the combined elements, held together by electrical forces of attraction, and in such proportions as to ensure electrical neutrality. The bonding in such compounds is described as **ionic.** Other substances, elements or compounds, have their constituent atoms linked together by electron pairs shared by the joined atoms. In this kind of structure the bonding is called **covalent.**

In the former of these categories of compounds the valence of each element is determined by the charge on its ions. Because of this the charge on the ions is often called the *ionic valence* or *electrovalence* of the element. Magnesium is thus said to have an ionic valence or electrovalence of +2; nitrogen, in the nitride ion (N^{3-}), has an ionic valence of –3. On the other hand, when we speak of the valence of an element in some kind of aggregate where the atoms are linked by covalent bonding, we call the number of such bonds formed by the element in question the *covalence* of that element. Thus, in the molecules represented by Lewis diagrams in Sec. 14-18, oxygen has a covalence of two in water and in oxygen fluoride; nitrogen has a covalence of three in ammonia; and carbon has a covalence of four in methane.

21. Before concluding this chapter we should stress that the distinction between ionic bonding and covalent bonding is not always as clear-cut as in the examples we have given. There are many compounds whose properties do not clearly reveal which of these two types of bonding is responsible for their structure. The ionic bond and the covalent bond should be regarded as two extreme types of valence forces, but the situation in a number of compounds may lie somewhere between these extremes. The sharing of electrons between two like atoms (as in H_2 or F_2) is equal between the bond partners, but in bonds between atoms which differ appreciably in ionization energy or electron affinity, the sharing of electrons will not be equal. Instead, the "shared" electrons will lie closer to the more electronegative atom. To take hydrogen fluoride as an example, the electron distribution will be unequal,

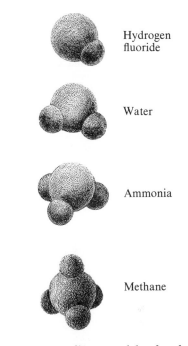

Hydrogen fluoride

Water

Ammonia

Methane

Fig. 14-11: *Space-filling models of molecules. Isolated atoms are probably spherical. The flattening of the spheres where they are in contact in these space-filling models conveys the idea that between two atoms joined by shared-electron-pair bonds the electron shells are merged.*

It is often helpful to put objects (or even people) into categories for purposes of classification and comparison. But nearly always with such schemes of classification there will be examples that are hard to accommodate. There are many breeds of dogs, but it is often difficult to classify a mongrel.

the fluorine atom getting the greater share of the electron density. The H—F bond is, on this account, described as "polar," with one end slightly positive (the hydrogen end) and the other end (fluorine) slightly negative. Although the bonding in hydrogen fluoride is still regarded as predominantly covalent, it is said to have "some ionic character." Conversely, there are compounds (for instance, zinc sulphide, whose formation we described in Chapter 2) in which the bonding is regarded as principally ionic but with a "degree of covalent character."

QUESTIONS

1. Make clear in your own words the meaning of:
(a) ionic bond
(b) ion pair
(c) ionic crystal
(d) bond energy
(e) crystal lattice
(f) crystal lattice energy

2. Explain clearly why it is not appropriate to speak of molecules of a substance such as sodium chloride.

3. In general, what properties of the participating atoms favour the formation of an ionic compound?

4. List as many characteristics as you can that are associated with the term crystalline.

5. What is meant by the principle of electrical neutrality?

6. Why does it require the expenditure of energy to separate the individual ions from their positions in an ionic crystal?

7. Why is the energy of an ion pair, such as Na^+Cl^-, different when buried within a crystal than when isolated from all neighbouring ions?

8. Sodium fluoride and magnesium oxide are typical ionic compounds, and they share the additional feature that their ions are all isoelectronic. What differences in properties between these compounds do you think might result from the ions in the second compound having double the charge of those in the first? Consult chemistry books in your library to see if these differences are observed.

9. Making use as necessary of the table on the inside back cover of the book, name the following compounds, and state the ionic valence of each element in them:

　　(a) Sc_2O_3　　(d) HfF_4　　(g) CoO
　　(b) RbI　　　(e) Ca_3N_2　　(h) TiO_2
　　(c) Cs_2S　　(f) $NiBr_2$　　(i) FeF_3

10. Examine your answer to Question 9 to see which of the ions in that list of compounds do not possess an inert-gas electron structure. (You may need to make use of Table 29-3.)

*11. A focussed beam of x-rays, in passing through a crystal of salt, undergoes diffraction. What does this mean? What conclusions can be drawn from the observation?

12. Make clear in your own words the meaning of:

(a) covalent bond
(b) atomic orbital
(c) molecular orbital
(d) orbital overlap
(e) covalent bond length
(f) bond angle

13. Explain clearly what is meant by the *valence shell* in an atom. Make clear in your explanation that the valence shell is a valid concept for an atom whether separate or in a molecule.

14. Draw Lewis diagrams to illustrate the bonding in the following compounds: silane (silicon hydride), SiH_4; silicon tetrachloride, $SiCl_4$; phosphine, PH_3; phosphorus trichloride, PCl_3; hydrogen sulphide, H_2S; sulphur dichloride, SCl_2; hydrogen chloride, HCl; chlorine monoxide, Cl_2O. Identify the valence shell of the central atom in each of these compounds. How many electrons are in the valence shells of the atoms in these molecules? What is the covalence of the elements in each compound?

15. Describe in detail the formation of a molecule of hydrogen chloride from atoms of the constituent elements. State clearly which orbitals are involved in bond formation.

16. It is possible to represent hydrogen chloride by either an ionic model or a covalent molecular model. Why is the latter preferred?

17. Describe and compare the two ways, electron transfer and electron sharing, in which an atom can attain the stable configuration of an inert gas. Show that a fluorine atom can use either way.

18. Distinguish between an ionic bond and a covalent bond. Why is it that metals like sodium or magnesium rarely exhibit covalence?

19. In general, what conditions favour the formation of (a) an ionic bond, (b) a covalent bond between two atoms.

20. Explain how there are two ideas implied by *covalence*; a force, and a number.

21. Show with the aid of diagrams how oxygen can have a covalence of two in some compounds and an ionic valence of minus two in others.

22. Why is an ionic structure considered highly improbable for a diatomic molecule of an element such as oxygen?

Chemical Structure

1. In the last chapter we explained how atoms could link together into simple aggregates. Since atoms consist of smaller particles of which some are negatively and others positively charged, it is not surprising that the basis of the forces involved in chemical bonding is electrical. We have seen that there are two different ways in which bonding may be described. One is by large arrays of ions clinging together to form stable and compact solids. The formation of the ions in the first instance implies that electrons are readily lost by some elements and readily acquired by others, so that compound formation between elements of these opposed tendencies really entails *electron transfer* to form stable ions. Such compounds owe their stability to ionic bonding.

Another basis for chemical bonding involves *electron sharing* between atoms, and in contrast to the previous case it is understandable that such bonding will most readily occur between atoms whose electropositive or electronegative character is more alike. In fact among the examples of covalent bonding we saw cases of bonding between atoms of a single element.

Although we perceive that these extreme bond types occur in a number of compounds, it is also evident from a study of many compounds that a sharp boundary cannot always be drawn between ionic and covalent bonding. Thus in many compounds the bonding may be regarded as ionic with some covalent character, or as covalent with some ionic character.

We made it clear that the nature of ionic bonding leads to arrays which contain enormous numbers of ions. These are crystalline solids, and since the electrical forces between ions at close range are very strong, these solids are not easily dismantled. They are usually mechanically fairly strong, and usually high temperatures are required to melt them, thereby destroying the regularity of their packing. In this chapter we pursue further the matter of structure in relation to the bonding between atoms, and we shall see that for covalent substances the possibilities are more varied.

MOLECULAR SUBSTANCES

2. When John Dalton introduced his atomic theory of chemical combination (Sec. 4-2), he pictured the linking of atoms of one element with those of another (or others) to form what he called "compound atoms." What he meant by this term is undoubtedly what we mean by the term molecule. Historically, however, the ideas embodied in the words atom and molecule developed in different ways. Dalton introduced the idea of atoms to explain the proportions by mass in which elements combine. The word molecule (meaning "little mass") was introduced by Amadeo Avogadro in 1811, and it was then as a rule applied by physicists to the tiny particles that make up a gas. The two ideas did not become generally related until 1860 (see Sec. 20-6). The nature of a gas will be described in detail in Chapter 18, but from what was said about neon in Sec. 10-2 you will realize that it is the distances between their molecules that give to gases their distinctive properties. This discrete, separate existence of molecules causes any substance having molecules as its basic structural unit to have characteristics very different from substances such as ionic crystals and network solids. In this chapter we hope to make this relationship between structure and properties clearer.

3. HOW MANY ATOMS IN A MOLECULE? We have already mentioned that neon and other members of the family of inert gases have molecules each consisting of a single atom. Such molecules are called *monatomic*; we say that neon is a monatomic gas. So also is mercury vapour.

In Chapter 14 we explained how two or more atoms could link together to form stable molecules. We have already encountered several substances whose molecules under ordinary conditions consist of two atoms joined by a covalent bond. These molecules and substances (which are mainly gaseous) are called *diatomic*. Molecules consisting of three atoms are called *triatomic*. As the number of atoms increases to four or more we rarely bother to use special words to indicate how many atoms per molecule. The word *polyatomic*, meaning *many*-atomic, applies in these cases.

There is no set upper limit to the number of atoms in a molecule. Some substances found in nature possess molecules of considerably greater complexity than those just mentioned. Sugar is made up of molecules containing forty-five atoms of three elements, in proportions conveyed by the formula, $C_{12}H_{22}O_{11}$. Chlorophyll, the important green colouring matter in plants, consists of two pure substances with slightly different molecules, represented by the formulas $C_{55}H_{72}O_5N_4Mg$ and $C_{55}H_{70}O_6N_4Mg$. Proteins, nucleic acids, and many of the substances occurring in living cells, have enormously complicated molecules with thousands of atoms.

4. MOLECULES IN LIQUIDS AND SOLIDS TOO. As we said previously, the word molecule entered the vocabulary of science to describe the tiny particles that make up a gas. But at low enough temperatures any gaseous substance can be liquefied, and ultimately solidified. In the liquid or solid there is no fundamental change in the molecules; they merely

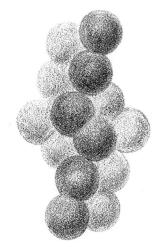

Fig. 15-1: *The arrangement of iodine molecules, I_2, in solid iodine*

become packed together into a small volume. Thus we can have molecular liquids and solids, as well as gases. Many liquids and solids are made up of molecules, for instance, water and sulphur. These substances may evaporate, especially if the temperature is raised, and their molecules become distributed in the vapour in precisely the same way as molecules in a gas.

In Sec. 8-11 and 8-12 we briefly described and gave properties of the halogen family of elements: fluorine, chlorine, bromine, and iodine. At room temperature the first two of these are pale yellow gases; the third is a dark red liquid; and the last is a very dark, almost black solid. But if you examine a stoppered bottle of bromine you will observe a good deal of red vapour above the liquid; liquid and vapour consist of the same kind of molecules, represented by Br_2. Similarly, above the crystals in a bottle of iodine you will see a purple-coloured vapour; crystals and vapour are both made up of the molecules I_2.

Substances that are gases or liquids under ordinary conditions are invariably made up of molecules. The molecules are more or less independent of each other and can move around, and consequently neither gases nor liquids have any special shape of their own. In crystalline solids, of which we gave some examples in Chapter 14, the particles are arranged in an ordered way. This ordered arrangement gives rise to the regular external shapes by which we recognize crystals. It is easy to see that iodine is a crystalline solid, and we may infer from this that the molecules are arranged in some regular way. The method of x-ray diffraction has shown the arrangement of iodine molecules to be that shown in Fig. 15-1.

Another solid element that we have mentioned in previous chapters, and whose structure is based on molecules, is sulphur. The molecule of sulphur consists of eight atoms arranged in a puckered ring, with each sulphur atom linked to two others (Fig. 15-2).

5. MULTIPLE BONDS. In some molecules atoms are linked by more than one shared-electron-pair bond. By assuming two or three such bonds between certain atoms we manage to retain the common covalence that they normally exhibit. For instance, in carbon dioxide, CO_2, the formula $O=C=O$ shows carbon to be 4-covalent and oxygen 2-covalent. The carbon and oxygen atoms are said to be linked by *double bonds*, and these are represented in print by two lines between the atoms. A double bond utilizes two pairs of electrons shared between the linked atoms. In carbon dioxide all three atoms have octets of electrons in the valence shell (Sec. 14-8), as the following representation shows:

$$\ddot{\overset{..}{O}} :: C :: \ddot{\overset{..}{O}}$$

The explanation given in Sec. 14-13 for formation of molecular orbitals, which build up electron density between the contributing atoms and thereby create conditions favourable to bonding, can be extended to include multiple bonding. However, a description of this would be beyond the needs of this book.

You must keep the bottle of bromine stoppered unless you have a well ventilated fume cupboard. The vapour is exceedingly unpleasant and injurious to the tissue of the eyes, nose, throat, and lungs.

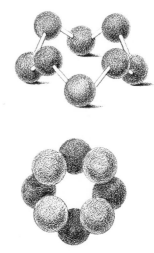

Fig. 15-2: *Models of the sulphur molecule*

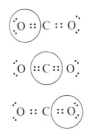

This simple sketch may help to make clearer how the sharing of two pairs of electrons—which we call a double bond—can lead to octets in the valence shells of the bonded atoms. The three atoms in a molecule of carbon dioxide are individually circled to show the octets of electrons.

$$\overset{\cdot\cdot}{\underset{\cdot\cdot}{O}} :: \overset{\cdot\cdot}{\underset{\cdot\cdot}{O}}$$

oxygen, O_2

This representation of the oxygen molecule oversimplifies the way the electrons are distributed in the molecule. It is not far from the truth, however, and we shall use it; but we caution you that if you go further in the study of chemistry you will have to learn a different interpretation of the bonding in this molecule.

$$: N ::: N :$$

nitrogen, N_2

$$\overset{H}{\underset{H}{\cdot}} C :: C \overset{\cdot H}{\underset{H}{}}$$

ethylene, C_2H_4

$$H : C ::: C : H$$

acetylene, C_2H_2

Fig. 15-3: *Lewis diagrams for molecules with multiple bonds*

Some other molecules incorporating multiple bonds are represented in Fig. 15-3. In order for two atoms to share four or six electrons it is necessary that there be considerable overlap of the orbitals in their valence shells. This seems to be possible only for some small atoms in the second row of the Periodic Table; multiple bonding is restricted chiefly to carbon, nitrogen, and oxygen. The last Lewis diagram shown, for acetylene, involves a *triple bond* between carbon atoms, and this is represented in print as H—C≡C—H.

6. PROMOTION OF ELECTRONS IN THE VALENCE SHELL. There is a problem which we didn't mention in Chapter 14 about covalent bonding of some atoms. We can illustrate this with three examples from the second-row elements.

ELEMENT	GROUND-STATE CONFIGURATION (omitting 1s)		TYPICAL COVALENT MOLECULES
	2s	2p	
Beryllium	(↑↓)	( )( )( )	$BeCl_2$
Boron	(↑↓)	(↑)( )( )	BCl_3
Carbon	(↑↓)	(↑)(↑)( )	CCl_4

In each case the 2s orbital is occupied by a pair of electrons, and that seems to put that orbital and those electrons out of action for forming shared-electron-pair bonds. In fact, if beryllium, with outer shell configuration $2s^2$, behaved like helium ($1s^2$), it wouldn't form covalent bonds at all. Yet each of these elements does form molecules with covalent bonds, as indicated.

The electron configurations shown above (and also in Fig. 13-3) are the *ground-state* configurations, that is, those of lowest energy in the individual gaseous atoms. But the atoms *can* assume other electron configurations which place the atoms in a higher energy state which we call excited. If the necessary energy is supplied, each of the atoms of the above elements could be excited to what is often called a *valence state*, shown as follows:

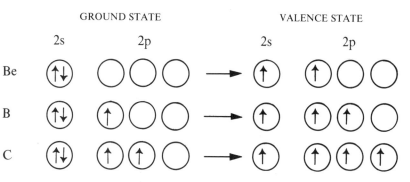

Since in the formation of a covalent bond the energy of the electrons is lowered, the surplus energy passes to the surroundings, and there is available in the total process a source of energy for converting atoms to the valence state. It is customary to speak of this transformation to the valence state as a *promotion* of electrons.

It is clear that *in the valence states shown each atom has that number of singly occupied orbitals which corresponds to its covalence.*

7. OCTETS NOT ALWAYS FORMED. When the theory of the shared-electron-pair bond was developed by G. N. Lewis considerable emphasis was put on the fact that the valence shell of the bonded atoms had been augmented to an octet as a result of bond formation (Sec. 14-18). Although this is commonly the case it is not invariably so. We have just described two molecules, $BeCl_2$ and BCl_3, in which there are fewer than eight electrons in the valence shell of the central atom. A similar situation is to be expected whenever an atom initially possessing fewer than four valence electrons forms a molecule with covalent bonds to other atoms.

The possibility also arises for the valence shell to contain more than eight electrons. The capacities of the K and L shells are two and eight electrons respectively, but the M shell and all others subsequently added have capacities greater than this (Sec. 11-16). Thus it is feasible for elements in the third row of the Periodic Table or beyond to have an expansion of the valence shell beyond an octet. This would require incorporation of d orbitals, as well as s and p, in the bonding. The presence of more than eight electrons in the valence shell indicates that the atom so possessed will have a covalence greater than four. Two examples of this are phosphorus pentafluoride, PF_5, and sulphur hexafluoride, SF_6, for which the central atoms have respectively ten and twelve electrons in the valence shell. They are represented as follows:

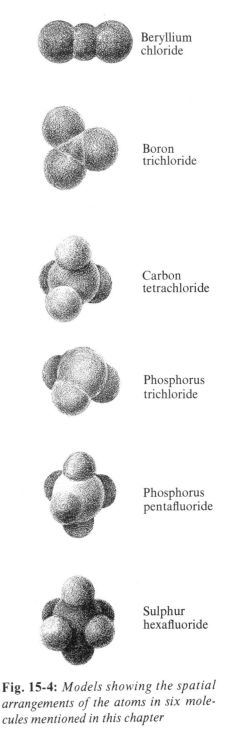

Beryllium chloride

Boron trichloride

Carbon tetrachloride

Phosphorus trichloride

Phosphorus pentafluoride

Sulphur hexafluoride

Fig. 15-4: *Models showing the spatial arrangements of the atoms in six molecules mentioned in this chapter*

8. THE SHAPE OF MOLECULES. When we examine models, such as those shown in Fig. 15-4 for molecular compounds described in this chapter, and in Fig. 14-11 of the previous chapter, certain general features about the shapes of molecules become apparent. Many of these molecules can be represented by a general formula AX_n in which n may have any value from 1 to 6. When $n = 1$ we are dealing with a diatomic molecule which will be elongated in the direction joining the atomic centres, but otherwise will have no special shape—for example, hydrogen fluoride (Fig. 14-11).

When $n = 2$, we may have either a linear molecule X—A—X, for example, beryllium chloride, or a bent molecule   for example, water (Fig. 14-11). The angle formed by the X atoms at A (angle XAX) is called the *bond angle,* and for a particular molecule has a fixed value. The covalent bond is said to be directional; the average positions of the shared electron pairs lead to preferred directions for the covalent bonds, and hence to certain molecular shapes.

When $n = 3$ we may have either a planar triangular molecule like that of boron trichloride (Fig. 15-4) or a triangular pyramidal molecule like that of phosphorus trichloride (Fig. 15-4) or of ammonia (Fig. 14-11).

When $n = 4$ the X atoms are arranged at the corners of a tetrahedron with the A atom at the centre, as in the molecules of methane (Fig. 14-11) or carbon tetrachloride (Fig. 15-4).

When $n = 5$ the X atoms occupy the corners of a geometric figure known as a triangular bipyramid (two triangular pyramids base to base), and when $n = 6$ the X atoms occupy the corners of a figure called an octahedron (8 sides, 6 corners, 12 edges). These figures are observed in the molecules of phosphorus pentafluoride and sulphur hexafluoride (Fig. 15-4).

This variety of shapes, and more particularly the choice of shape when $n = 2$ or 3, have been found to follow a very simple principle. It is that the electron pairs in the valence shell of the central atom will repel each other as far as possible. The average position then assumed by each electron pair in the valence shell will be as far as possible away from the other electron pairs in that shell. This is known as the principle of *valence-shell electron-pair repulsion* (VSEPR).

The position to be adopted by each electron pair in the valence shell becomes equivalent to the placing of ink spots at the maximum distances removed from each other on the surface of a tennis ball. If you wish to put two spots as far apart as possible they must go at opposite poles. Three spots must go around the equator spaced out at one third of the circumference. And so on. The directional properties corresponding to various numbers of electron pairs are given in Table 15-1.

TABLE 15-1

FACTORS GOVERNING THE SHAPES OF MOLECULES		
NUMBER OF PAIRS OF ELECTRONS	ARRANGEMENT OF ELECTRON PAIRS AROUND NUCLEUS	ANGLE SUBTENDED AT NUCLEUS BY ADJACENT ELECTRON PAIRS
2	linear	180°
3	triangular planar	120°
4	tetrahedral	109°28'
5	trigonal bipyramidal	120° & 90°
6	octahedral	90°

Finally it must be added that the electron pairs repel one another whether they form bonds or not. In water, the oxygen atom has an octet in the valence shell, but only two pair of these electrons are bonding; the other two pair are non-bonding. Because of the mutual repulsion of the non-bonding pairs of electrons the bonds are directed much as they would be in a tetrahedron; so the water molecule is bent, with a bond angle of 104.5°. In the same way the ammonia molecule (NH_3) is not flat because the non-bonding pair of electrons in the valence shell pushes the bonding electrons away to the other side of the nitrogen atom. In more advanced courses in chemistry these ideas are developed further.

9. TOO MANY FORMULAS. A situation arises in connection with certain covalent molecules whereby more than one Lewis diagram can be drawn to represent the arrangement of the electrons in the valence shell. A case in point is sulphur dioxide, SO_2. Sulphur atoms and oxygen atoms each have six valence electrons; the molecule therefore has eighteen such electrons. In order to show each atom in the molecule with an octet of electrons in the valence shell we

The term "valence electrons" is used to designate the electrons which are involved in bond formation. Magnesium is said to have two valence electrons; they are in the 3s orbital of the atom, and are the ones by whose removal magnesium can form ionic bonds. Sulphur has six valence electrons (two 3s and four 3p) in the free atom but, by sharing electrons to form covalent bonds with other atoms, or by accepting electrons to form a negative ion (S^{2-}), sulphur may acquire more than six electrons in the valence shell of its atom in a compound.

need to formulate one of the sulphur-oxygen bonds as double, the other single, thus:

$$: \ddot{O} : \ddot{S} :: \ddot{O} :$$

But there are two things wrong with this. First, there is no reason why the double bond should be shown on the right of the sulphur atom; it could just as well be on the left, thus:

$$: \ddot{O} :: \ddot{S} : \ddot{O} :$$

Secondly, since double bonds are known to be stronger and shorter than single bonds, the structures shown imply that the bond lengths in this molecule are unequal. In fact, however, the bond lengths can be shown from certain experimental measurements to be equal. Hence these two Lewis structures are not altogether satisfactory.

One way to get around this difficulty is to remember that electrons are very light compared with atomic nuclei, and to guess that they can oscillate very rapidly—much too fast to be detected by measuring bond lengths or other properties—between the two alternative arrangements shown.

$$: \ddot{O} : \ddot{S} :: \ddot{O} : \longleftrightarrow : \ddot{O} :: \ddot{S} : \ddot{O} :$$

The effect of this oscillation is to cause the bonds on average to be about midway in strength and length between a single and a double bond. The true state of the molecule is a sort of hybrid between the structures shown.

That is not, frankly, a very satisfactory explanation, though it has been used to account for this molecule, and others for which more than one equivalent Lewis diagram can be drawn, for as long as Lewis diagrams have been around. There is a far better description of the situation in terms of molecular orbitals, but it is beyond the level of this book. For that matter so is the nature of the double bond, which we have really rather glossed over in Sec. 15-5.

10. COMPOUND IONS. Before leaving this account of molecules we would like to review and extend our account of some of the ions that contain two or more atoms which we mentioned in Sec. 14-9. These consist of groups of atoms linked together by covalent bonds but with either a surplus or a deficiency of electrons compared to the number required for a neutral molecule. As a result these compound ions bear an over-all charge, positive or negative.

For the present we shall merely give the name, formula, and Lewis diagram for several of the common ions of this sort. You have already encountered several of them in substances described thus far, and you will see more examples in the forthcoming chapters. In salts and certain acids and alkalis these ions will be paired with some ion of opposite charge in accordance with the principle of electrical neutrality (Sec. 14-8).

The compound ions with which you should be familiar are illustrated in Fig. 15-5 and 15-6.

(a) $\quad : \ddot{O} \cdot \quad \cdot \ddot{S} \cdot \quad \cdot \ddot{O} :$

(b) $\quad : \ddot{O} : \ddot{S} : \ddot{O} :$

(c) $\quad : \ddot{O} : \ddot{S} : \ddot{O} :$

(d) $\quad : \ddot{O} : \ddot{S} :: \ddot{O} :$

When we try to draw a Lewis diagram for sulphur dioxide, SO_2, we run into some problems. In (a) are shown the valence electrons in the separate atoms. In (b) the three atoms have been brought together as in the molecule, and electron pairing can be shown so as to indicate bonding between the atoms. But there are seven electrons in the valence shell of each oxygen atom —a situation which experience shows to be very unlikely. In (c) we try again by putting an octet of electrons on one oxygen atom, but that leaves only six (a sextet) on the other. If we want to have octets on all atoms, we must show one double bond (that is, two shared pairs of electrons) between one oxygen atom and the sulphur atom, as in (d). But which oxygen gets the double bond?

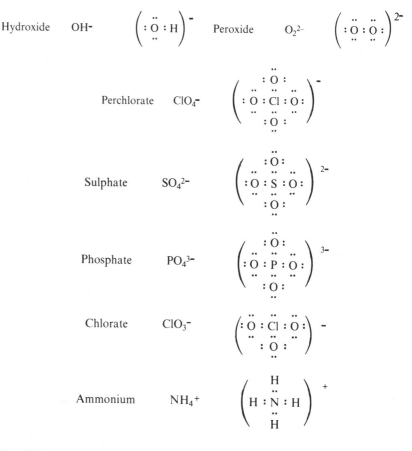

Fig. 15-5: *Lewis diagrams for common compound ions*

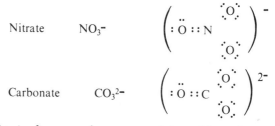

Fig. 15-6: *Lewis diagrams for compound ions. More than one such diagram can be drawn for each.*

NETWORK SOLIDS

11. In Chapter 14 we described ionic bonding, and showed how this normally results in crystalline solids consisting of very large numbers of ions held together by forces of electrical attraction. Then we described the covalent bond, and showed how it can link two atoms together. Since many atoms are capable of forming more than one such covalent bond, it follows that simple aggregates, called molecules and containing

Those are fingers, not porpoises, holding a diamond that has been made from graphite. The process involves temperatures of about 1400°C and a pressure about sixty thousand times greater than the pressure of the atmosphere.

This gem-quality diamond, about three-quarters of a carat (or about 150 mg) in mass, has been polished slightly but it has not been cut; it retains the shape in which it was "grown."

two or more atoms, can readily be explained. We now turn to another kind of atomic aggregate in which covalent bonds hold enormous numbers of atoms together.

12. DIAMOND AND GRAPHITE: TWO FORMS OF CARBON. The element carbon occurs pure in two strikingly different forms. One is diamond, the hard, crystalline mineral, sometimes used in jewellery and sometimes in the cutting heads of special drills. The other form is graphite, a soft, flaky, black material often used as a special lubricant, and also in pencil "leads." The ability of an element to exist in two or more crystalline or molecular forms is called *allotropy*: diamond and graphite are two *allotropes* or allotropic forms of carbon. A few selected properties of these are given in Table 15-2.

TABLE 15-2

SOME PROPERTIES OF THE ALLOTROPES OF CARBON

PROPERTY	DIAMOND	GRAPHITE
Appearance	colourless	grey-black
Hardness	very hard	soft
Density (g/cm³ at 20°C)	3.51	2.22
Electrical Conductivity	very poor	fair

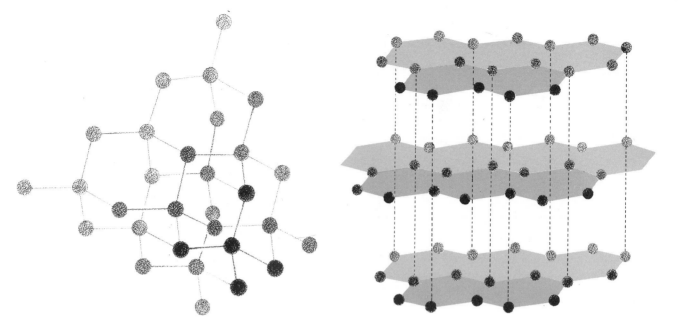

Fig. 15-7: *The arrangement of carbon atoms in diamond*   **Fig. 15-8:** *The arrangement of carbon atoms in graphite*

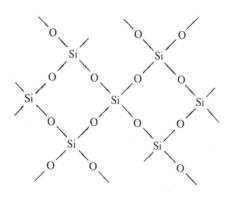

Fig. 15-9: *This conveys the linking together of atoms in silicon dioxide without trying to represent their relative positions in three dimensions. The oxygen atoms are actually arranged around the silicon atoms in the form of a tetrahedron. This is the expected arrangement for four covalently bonded atoms when the valence shell of the silicon atom is an octet.*

The method of x-ray diffraction enables the relative positions of the carbon atoms in these allotropes to be determined, and from this information we can see how differences in properties can be related to differences in structure. A representation of the structure of diamond is shown in Fig. 15-7. In this figure five of the circles representing carbon atoms are shown dark. The appearance of this group of five atoms should remind you of the model of the methane (CH_4) molecule shown in Fig. 14-10. The bonds formed by each carbon atom in diamond occupy directions in space just like those in methane or carbon tetrachloride. The nearest neighbours of a carbon atom in the diamond crystal are four other carbon atoms arranged at the corners of a tetrahedron surrounding the first atom. The three-dimensional network of carbon atoms in diamond accounts for the great hardness of this substance; the carbon atoms are very small and strongly bonded together, so that the whole structure is very strong and rigid. You must remember that the drawing shows only 30 atoms linked in this way; a one-carat diamond contains about 10^{22} atoms, and in that stone that is the extent of the network.

A representation of the structure of graphite is given in Fig. 15-8. In this the atoms are arranged in layers. In each layer the atoms are closely bound in a repeating six-sided structure (like the pattern made by six-sided bathroom floor tiles). The distance between layers is much greater than that between the atoms in a layer, and this leads to weaker bonding between layers. In consequence of this weaker bonding the layers can slide over one another easily; this helps to explain why graphite is a flaky substance and a good lubricant.

13. NETWORK SOLIDS. This description of diamond and graphite makes clear the fact that for these substances there are no characteristic molecules, but there *is* a characteristic *structure*. Substances (elements or compounds) consisting of vast arrays of atoms linked together by covalent bonds are described by such terms as *network solids, covalent crystals,* or *giant molecules.*

The first of these terms conjures up a picture of a vast network of covalent bonds holding an equally vast number of atoms in some, usually rigid, arrangement in space. The second term lays more stress on the word crystal than we might wish; there are some non-crystalline substances (for example, glass) which have the network of bonds but lack the orderly array of a crystal. The problem with the term "giant molecule" is that it equally well applies to substances that we might prefer to regard as molecular, even though the molecule is large (for example, a protein).

Because the atoms in network solids are bonded together in all directions, they are not, as a rule, easily able to evaporate or to form solutions. The solids usually require high temperatures to melt or to evaporate; this is understandable when it is realized that evaporation in this case means breaking covalent chemical bonds to set the individual atoms free.

14. TWO NETWORK SOLIDS CONTAINING SILICON. Silicon, immediately below carbon in the Periodic Table, shows similarities and differences with carbon in the properties of the elements and compounds.

There is a compound, properly called silicon carbide, but more often known as *carborundum,* which contains equal numbers of carbon and silicon atoms. Carborundum is used to make grindstones and grinding wheels because it is very hard, though not as hard as diamond. The clue to its hardness is that the silicon and carbon atoms are arranged alternately in a network, just like that of diamond. To be more specific, every carbon atom is bonded to four silicon atoms as nearest neighbours, and every silicon atom is similarly bonded to four carbon atoms. The atoms of silicon are larger than those of carbon; therefore, the greater interatomic distances do not permit as much overlap of the atomic orbitals, and accordingly the bonds between atoms are somewhat weaker than in diamond. This appears to explain the fact that carborundum is not quite as hard as diamond.

The formula for carborundum is written SiC. You cannot tell from the formula whether this compound is made up of diatomic molecules, or is a network solid containing equal numbers of the two kinds of atoms. From the hardness, the high melting point, and lack of volatility or solubility, you might guess that carborundum is the latter.

One of the most common and abundant minerals is *quartz,* which consists almost entirely of silicon dioxide, SiO_2, often called *silica.* This too is a network solid. Each silicon atom in the mineral is bonded to four oxygen atoms, and each oxygen atom to two silicon atoms. The arrangement in three dimensions is not easy to portray in a diagram, but the linking of atoms (without regard to their positions in space) is conveyed by Fig. 15-9. If you examine a larger array than that shown in

The flat representation in Fig. 15-9 of the network of bonded silicon and oxygen atoms in silicon dioxide fails to convey the three-dimensional character and the regular shape of the crystals that result from this regular array of atoms. These qualities are evident in this cluster of naturally occurring quartz crystals from Bonsecours, Quebec.

Incidentally, the semi-precious gemstone amethyst, which is the official mineral emblem of Ontario, is a variety of quartz that owes its purple colour to the inclusion of minute amounts of iron.

this figure you will see that the number of oxygen atoms is twice the number of silicon atoms. Thus the formula SiO_2 conveys the relative numbers of atoms, but fails to convey the enormous numbers of these in the network.

15. Carbon dioxide and silicon dioxide provide a striking example of the contrast between a molecular compound and a network solid. The former is gaseous at room temperature and pressure, but will solidify at temperatures below –78°C to the material known as "Dry Ice." The solid evaporates without melting at this temperature. The readiness with which this occurs indicates that the individual molecules are not strongly attracted or bonded to one another. Carbon dioxide will also dissolve to some extent in water as molecules of CO_2: soda water is a solution of this gas. On the other hand, quartz is a hard solid with a high melting point and with practically no tendency to evaporate or to form solutions. There is no evidence in this case of individual molecules like SiO_2.

16. AMORPHOUS AND NON-CRYSTALLINE SOLIDS. In this chapter and the last we placed considerable emphasis on the regularity with which ions or atoms are arranged in solids, and how this sub-microscopic regularity was often revealed in the external shape and symmetry of crystals. However, we have all encountered solids in the form of fine powders which exhibit none of the regular geometry of crystals and we might wonder whether or not crystallinity was a required feature of all solids. Some powdered solids, when examined with a microscope, reveal crystalline characteristics too small to be seen with the naked eye. But even if no regularity in external shape can be detected under magnification, the ordered arrangements of atoms in solids can still be revealed by their ability to diffract a beam of x-rays (Sec. 14-4). Thus lampblack, sometimes called amorphous carbon, has been shown by x-ray diffraction to be a microcrystalline form of graphite; and many other solids, in spite of having been finely ground, have been shown to retain the organized pattern of their atoms just the same as they would have in a larger crystal.

There are, however, truly non-crystalline solids. Probably the commonest example is glass. If you break a piece of glass with a sharp blow the fragments do not have straight edges or plane surfaces such as you would find with a crystalline material like quartz or calcite. Glass is said to break with a conchoidal fracture, and this unusual word sums up the lack of any crystalline faces on a freshly broken surface. When glass is examined for an x-ray diffraction pattern, no clear evidence of a well-ordered arrangement of the atoms is observed.

Glass, and glass-like materials such as slags, which are often not pure substances, are invariably formed by cooling from a melt. The arrangement of atoms or molecules in a liquid, as we shall explain in Chapter 17, is much more random than in a solid. But this does not mean that there is no linking between the particles. Glasses are formed from substances, especially silica, which have a tendency to form network structures in the solid state, and even in molten glass it is believed that considerable linking of atoms occurs, though less extensive and less rigid than in the solid. Such linking is believed to be the cause of high viscosity when it occurs in liquids, and molten glass is often quite viscous. As the temperature is lowered, more and more such linking oc-

Amphorous means "without form."

A crystalline mineral like quartz, when freshly fractured, forms fragments with plane surfaces and with definite angles at the edges of these surfaces. You have never seen a piece of glass break this way.

The strong covalent bonds that link atoms in network solids sometimes fail to provide for growth of the network equally in all directions. In the mineral from which asbestos comes, the silicon and oxygen atoms are bonded in long straight parallel chains; these are held together by weaker ionic bonds (to magnesium ions). The long fibres arise from this chain-like development of the —Si—O— network and the fact that the ionic bonds can more easily be broken.

The properties of what is commonly called mica can also be related to the way silicon and oxygen atoms are linked. In this, the covalent network is developed strongly in two dimensions, and the layers of atoms so formed are held together (as in asbestos) by weaker ionic bonds. Cleavage of these separates the layers into thin sheets familiar to anyone who has handled mica.

curs, but without much opportunity (because of the tangled way the molecular fragments have joined up) for an orderly crystal pattern to grow. Eventually the whole melt can solidify, with much of the structure linked together by chemical bonds but lacking the geometrical layout characteristic of a crystalline solid.

Many plastic materials, such as Lucite, polyvinyl cholride, polystyrene, and so forth, are non-crystalline. They too are produced by setting from a melt, and like glass these are disordered solids.

METALS

17. METALLIC CRYSTALS. We devoted Chapter 9 to a discussion of metals, but one of the things we didn't mention there is what holds their atoms together. The bonding of atoms in metals was probably the last to be understood in terms of the structure of atoms, and because it is more complicated than the cases discussed so far it may be difficult to explain in a way that can be visualized.

It should first be stated that in metals the atoms are in a regular ar-

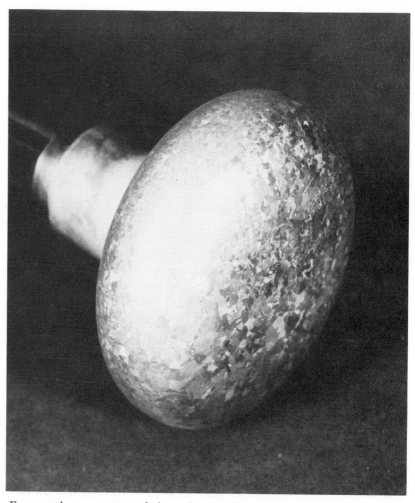

Few people are aware of the polycrystalline structure of metals and alloys. Sometimes, as this doorknob shows, cast brass becomes etched by sweat over the years, to reveal the arrangement of the component crystals.

Granite and various other rocks that were formed in antiquity by crystallization from melts present a similar appearance, A polished granite tombstone is a good specimen in which to see polycrystalline structure.

rangement as they are in other crystalline solids. Only rarely, however, do metals reveal an outward crystalline shape, and so their crystallinity is not as obvious as it is with substances like common salt or calcite. If smooth metal surfaces are etched with suitable acids and then examined under magnification, it can often be seen that the compact metal is made up of many crystals in close contact. Such a material is described as *polycrystalline*, and it grew this way during crystallization from a melt. By careful, slow cooling, large single crystals of many metals have been prepared. Diffraction of x-rays by these has shown that the atoms are arranged in a simple pattern characteristic of the metal in question.

Given that metals can occur or be produced as crystals, how can we explain their cohesion and their orderly structure?

18. BONDING IN METALS. When we attempt to explain the bonding of atoms in metals, we must take into account the following facts:

(i) In a metallic element the atoms are all alike; their bonding must involve some kind of covalence.

(ii) Metals are all electropositive; that is, the atoms readily part with electrons to form ions in compounds.

(iii) Some electrons in the metal are evidently able to move under the influence of a potential difference; these are the carriers of charge when a metal conducts an electric current.

(iv) The presence of "foreign" atoms, as in an alloy, does not destroy these characteristics.

(v) With very few exceptions the arrangement of atoms in metals is simple, like the close packing of spheres. (This can be simulated with cork or Styrofoam spheres or ping-pong balls, and models of the three commonest ways in which atoms are arranged in metals are shown in Fig. 15-10.)

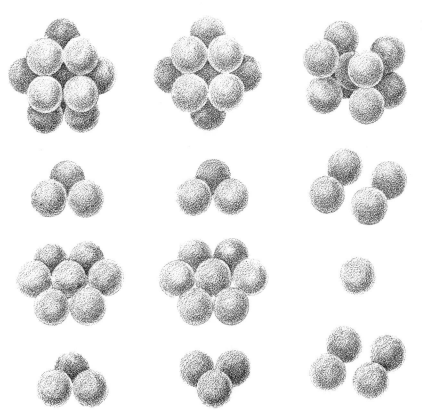

Fig. 15-10: *The atoms in metals behave like tiny spheres, and in most metals these are packed in one of the three arrangements illustrated in the top row. Representative metals in which these arrangements occur are (from left to right) magnesium, copper, and sodium. Observe that the packing in the right-hand case is more open than in the other two; this is predisposing to lower density. The lower three rows are simply "expanded" diagrams to help you visualize the packing arrangements shown in the top row.*

The atoms in metals are believed to share their valence electrons for purposes of bonding. But, since there are often one or two (occasionally three and rarely four) valence electrons per atom, and since the atoms are usually packed with 8 or 12 nearest neighbours, there aren't enough electrons to make shared-electron-pair bonds between atoms in all directions. The result of this is that the electrons, needing, as it were, to be in several places all at once, may move about from place to place among the atoms that share them in the crystal. This is very different from the situation in a molecule.

We described the methane molecule, CH_4, in Sec. 14-18 and 14-19. The valence shell of the carbon atom in this molecule contains eight electrons. These are in four pairs, spaced well apart, so that the hydrogen-carbon bonds become spread out and the molecule assumes a shape like a tetrahedron. The bonding electron pairs are concentrated or *localized* in certain directions in space so that the bonds in the molecule are directed as though to the corners of a tetrahedron. In a metal, however, the electrons do not remain in fixed regions; they are said to be *delocalized*. It is the freedom of their electrons to move around that results in metals being good conductors of electricity and of heat. The positions the atoms take up in a metallic crystal are not governed by special directions assumed by the bonding electrons; rather, the arrangement seems determined mainly by efficiency in packing of the atoms. In other words the metallic bond is *non-directional*.

A metallic crystal thus consists of a regular, closely packed array of ions held together by a mobile sea of electrons. The close packing is probably significant. There are fewer valence electrons in metals than the number required for a fully covalent network; provided the ions are packed together closely, however, the electrons can bind them strongly. Thus, the majority of metals are hard and strong, and have high melting points. You will notice, too, that this free and easy sharing of electrons would make it possible for one kind of metal atom to substitute for another in a metallic crystal, especially if the atoms were alike in size. In this way it is possible to account for the existence of alloys of variable composition, and for the fact that these continue to exhibit the general metallic characteristics of their component elements.

"In a metal some electrons are so loosely bound to their parent atoms that they can wander through the metal. Metals conduct electricity well for that reason; a current of electricity through a metal is a flow of its loosely bound electrons, which thread their way among the atoms." (Holden and Singer, 1960)

OTHER STRUCTURAL TYPES

19. MOLECULAR SOLIDS. Molecular substances occur in any of the three states—solid, liquid, or gaseous—at ordinary temperatures. At low enough temperatures, sometimes with the aid of pressure, liquids and gases solidify. In the solid, the molecules are arranged in some orderly pattern, for instance that shown for iodine in Fig. 15-1. But, while the iodine atoms are linked into pairs by covalent bonds, it is not evident what forces hold the molecules together in a crystal like iodine. Similarly, in "Dry Ice" the atoms in individual molecules of carbon dioxide are held together by *intra*molecular forces. But to account for the rigidity of the solid and the regular pattern of the molecules in it, we must look for some attractive force between molecules—*inter*molecular forces.

The precise nature of such forces is not yet fully understood, but they do have a name. They are called ***Van der Waals' forces*** after the celebrated Dutch physicist, Johannes Van der Waals (1837-1927) who devoted a scientific lifetime to the study of attractions between molecules. We shall not attempt to describe the theory of these forces, but it is known that they are stronger the more protons and electrons there are in a molecule—so they must involve some kind of electrical attraction between opposite charges.

"Dry Ice" evaporates at −78°C; iodine vaporizes enough that one can always see the purple vapour above the crystals in a stoppered bottle. We must conclude from these observations that the Van der Waals' forces are comparatively weak. The molecules become separated from each other much more easily than do atoms in the various kinds of bonded aggregates described in this chapter and the last.

QUESTIONS

1. Explain the meaning of monatomic, diatomic, triatomic, and polyatomic, as applied to molecules, and give one example of each.

2. Show that the individual atoms in the sulphur molecule possess octets of electrons. What is the covalence of sulphur in this structure?

3. Explain how Gay-Lussac's Law of Combining Gas Volumes enables the chemist to deduce that the halogen elements are diatomic.

4. There are three well-known hydrocarbons each of whose molecules contain two carbon atoms. These are ethane, C_2H_6, ethylene, C_2H_4, and acetylene, C_2H_2. Show how these may be represented in two ways: one with solid lines representing electron-pair bonds between the symbols of the atoms (a bond diagram) and the other by Lewis diagrams.

5. There are ways of determining bond lengths in most molecules. The distances between the carbon atoms in ethane, ethylene, and acetylene (Question 4) have been found to be 154 pm, 134 pm, and 120 pm, respectively. Can you suggest why this trend occurs?

6. Prussic acid, the deadly poison of countless detective stories, is properly called hydrocyanic acid, with formula HCN. Represent this by a bond diagram and by a Lewis diagram.

7. Explain, with examples, the *promotion* of electrons in some atoms from the ground state to a valence state. Does such promotion require the input of energy from the surroundings, or does it result in energy passing to the surroundings? Why is promotion of importance in chemical bonding?

8. Compare the electron configuration of helium with that of beryllium. Can you suggest any reasons why beryllium doesn't behave like helium, that is, as an inert gas? Or, to look at it the other way around, why doesn't helium resemble beryllium?

9. Write Lewis diagrams descriptive of the bonding in:

(a) iodine monochloride, ICl (e) disulphur dichloride, S_2Cl_2

(b) carbon tetrafluoride, CF_4 (f) chloroform, $CHCl_3$

(c) hydrogen peroxide, H_2O_2 (g) stannic chloride, $SnCl_4$

(d) nitrogen trichloride, NCl_3 (h) silane, SiH_4

10. We mentioned in Chapter 13 the idea of *isoelectronic* species. The idea may be extended to molecules. Show that within each of the following sets of molecules the structures are isoelectronic:

(a) methane, ammonia, water, hydrogen fluoride, neon

(b) nitrogen, acetylene, hydrogen cyanide, carbon monoxide (CO)

(c) fluorine, hydrogen peroxide (H_2O_2), hydrazine (N_2H_4), ethane (C_2H_6).

11. Using straight lines to represent covalent bonds, draw representations of molecules of the type AX_n for values of n from 1 to 6, to show each of the following molecular shapes: linear diatomic, linear triatomic, bent triatomic, triangular planar, triangular pyramidal, tetrahedral, square planar, trigonal bipyramidal, octahedral.

12. Write Lewis diagrams for the molecules of:

(a) stannous chloride, $SnCl_2$ (d) antimony pentachloride $SbCl_5$

(b) iodine trichloride, ICl_3 (e) sulphur dioxide, SO_2

(c) boric acid, $B(OH)_3$ (f) xenon tetrafluoride, XeF_4

13. Apply the principles described in Sec. 15-8 to deduce the shape of the molecules listed in Questions 9 and 12.

14. Show three different, but equivalent, Lewis diagrams for the nitrate ion. Show that the nitrate ion and carbonate ion are isoelectronic, but that neither is isoelectronic with the chlorate ion.

15. Nitrous oxide, N_2O, which was described briefly in Chapter 7, unexpectedly turns out to be an unsymmetrical molecule, in which the oxygen atom is not between the two nitrogen atoms. Show that two different Lewis diagrams can be drawn for this molecule, in each of which the valence shells of all atoms contain octets.

16. What are the principal differences between network solids and molecular solids? How are these differences illustrated by carbon dioxide and silicon dioxide?

17. How are the physical properties of graphite and diamond related to the network structures of carbon atoms in each?

18. Compare and contrast the structure and properties of: covalent crystals, ionic crystals, and metallic crystals.

19. Make clear the distinction between intermolecular forces and intramolecular forces.

20. Beryllium oxide (BeO, molar mass = 25 g) has a melting point of 2530°C. Carbon monoxide (CO, molar mass = 28 g) has a melting point of –215°C. What inferences can be drawn from that evidence?

21. More than one kind of bonding or attractive force exists within the structure of each of ammonium chloride and solid iodine. Explain how and where each kind of bonding applies.

22. Explain what is meant by localized electrons and delocalized electrons, and how the former give rise to directional covalent bonds, the latter to non-directional bonds.

23. Would you say that the ionic bond described in Chapter 14 is directional or non-directional? Give reasons.

∗24. Give a description of the structure of a non-crystalline solid such as polyvinyl chloride —— $(CH_2—CHCl)_n$.——

*25. Electrical conductance in metals is accounted for by delocalized electrons that are free to move when a difference in potential is applied to two places in the metal. Can you devise an explanation for the electrical conductance of graphite? (*Hint*: By examination of Fig. 15-8 decide how many covalent bonds are formed by each carbon atom in the plane in which it is located. Will these account for all the electrons in the system?)

*26. Boron trifluoride, BF_3, has three pairs of electrons (a sextet) in the valence shell of the boron atom. An octet could be achieved for the boron atom if one of the boron-fluorine bonds were double. Show that three equivalent representations are then possible for the bonds in this molecule.

Chemical Reactions

1. Earlier we pointed out that changes in substances can be classified into *physical changes* and *chemical changes* (Sec. 2-2).

The essential characteristic of a chemical change, or (chemical) reaction, is the formation of one or more new substances. The substances that undergo reaction, or that interact, are called the **reactants**; any new substance formed by the reaction is called a **product**. In a chemical reaction the atoms of the substance or substances that are reactants rearrange into different groupings, thereby forming molecules or crystals of new substances.

For instance, the reaction between hydrogen and oxygen, which was described in Sec. 6-7, involves diatomic oxygen molecules and diatomic hydrogen molecules interacting to form triatomic water molecules. Each oxygen molecule requires two hydrogen molecules, and two water molecules are formed:

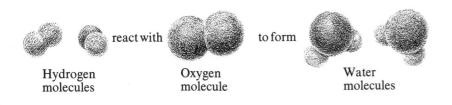

Hydrogen molecules   react with   Oxygen molecule   to form   Water molecules

A little thought should convince you, however, that in passing from reactants to product some things not illustrated must have occurred. The oxygen atoms must have parted company in order to form two separate water molecules, so the bond in the oxygen molecule must have been broken. Similarly the hydrogen atoms are no longer bonded together in the product, and thus must have become uncoupled. The product molecule includes new hydrogen-oxygen bonds.

2. Notice that in the rearrangement of the *atoms* of hydrogen and the *atoms* of oxygen to form molecules of water, no atoms are lost and no new atoms are formed. The four atoms that comprise the two molecules of hydrogen are present in the two molecules of water, and the two atoms of the molecule of oxygen are in the two molecules of water. *In a chemical reaction, atoms are always conserved.* This is a way of expressing the **Law of Conservation of Mass.** You should compare this with the statement given earlier (Sec. 3-5), and satisfy yourself that the two statements are merely different ways of saying the same thing.

3. From what has been said previously you will realize that in any detectable chemical reaction the numbers of atoms or molecules involved is enormous. Thus we should be thinking of reactions such as that between hydrogen and oxygen as between billions of molecules at a time, but always with exactly twice as many hydrogen molecules consumed as oxygen molecules.

What happens, then, if we mix one billion molecules of each of hydrogen and oxygen, and apply a spark to the mixture? A reaction will occur, but not all the oxygen will be consumed. Half a billion oxygen molecules will react with one billion molecules of hydrogen, and another half billion oxygen molecules will be left over, unreacted. No matter in what proportions these two gases are mixed, if a reaction occurs between them it will only be in the proportion of two molecules of hydrogen to one molecule of oxygen, and the reaction will cease when one or other of the reactants is used up.

4. EQUATIONS AND STOICHIOMETRY. In Sec. 4-12 we introduced the chemical equation as a concise statement of a chemical reaction. In some of the subsequent chapters we have given numerous examples of the use of equations to accompany descriptions of the reactions of elements and compounds. In Sec. 10-25 we pointed out that balanced equations could provide information about the masses of substances formed or consumed in reactions. This is possible because of the dual significance that chemists attach to the symbol or formula of a pure substance. The symbol of an element, for instance O for oxygen, conveys on the one hand an atom of oxygen, and on the other hand a mole of atomic oxygen. The mass of a mole of any substance, as we have seen (Sec. 10-25), can be looked up in, or worked out from, a table of relative atomic masses such as that on the inside back cover of this book. Accordingly, the chemical equation also conveys the existence of relationships among the masses of the reactants and products. These relationships are frequently referred to as *stoichiometric* relationships, and the term *stoichiometry* is applied to the various proportions by mass in which substances react or are produced in chemical reactions. Here are some examples of stoichiometric calculations.

Problem 16-1: What is the maximum mass of chlorine that can be produced by treatment of 1.000 kg of sodium chloride by excess of sulphuric acid and manganese dioxide? (See Sec. 8-3.)

Here the product of a chemical reaction is being recovered. The chemist will already have calculated, from the equation for the reaction, what the yield should be under ideal conditions.

Solution: We start with the balanced equation for the reaction:

$$MnO_2 + 2NaCl + 3H_2SO_4 \rightarrow$$
$$2NaHSO_4 + MnSO_4 + 2H_2O + Cl_2$$

This tells us that 2 mol of sodium chloride produces 1 mol of chlorine.

(It tells us a good deal more than that, but we have selected the significant information for our purpose.)

The mass of the reactant sodium chloride (NaCl) = 1.000 kg
= 1000 g

The molar mass for sodium chloride = (23.0 + 35.5) g/mol
= 58.5 g/mol

∴ 1000 g of sodium chloride = $\dfrac{1000 \text{ g}}{58.5 \text{ g/mol}}$ = 17.1 mol

The number of moles of chlorine will be half this number
= 8.55 mol

The molar mass for chlorine (Cl_2) = 2 × 35.5 g/mol = 71.0 g/mol

∴ 8.55 mol of chlorine = 8.55 mol × 71.0 g/mol = 607 g

And hence the maximum mass of chlorine = 607 g

Notice that you are asked to calculate the *maximum* mass of chlorine; if for any reason there were losses in the process you might not recover all of the chlorine predicted. Notice, too, that the problem states that an excess of the other reagents was present; if there were a deficiency of either of these the yield of chlorine would have been less. (Why?)

Problem 16-2: If you were planning to produce chlorine under the conditions in the previous problem, you would need to know how much of each of the other reactants is required to ensure an excess. Calculate how much sulphuric acid, containing 95.0% hydrogen sulphate by mass, would be required to react with 1.000 kg of sodium chloride. (A slightly greater amount of this acid would provide the necessary excess.)

Solution: The equation for the reaction is given above. It tells us that 2 mol of sodium chloride requires 3 mol of hydrogen sulphate for complete reaction; in other words, 1.5 mol of hydrogen sulphate is required for each mole of sodium chloride.

We saw before that 1.000 kg of sodium chloride = 17.1 mol

∴ the required amount of hydrogen sulphate
= 1.5 × 17.1 mol = 25.6 mol

The molar mass for hydrogen sulphate (H_2SO_4)
= (2.0 + 32.1 + 64.0) g/mol = 98.1 g/mol

∴ the mass of hydrogen sulphate required
= 25.6 mol × 98.1 g/mol = 2511 g

Because the sulphuric acid contains 95.0% hydrogen sulphate, 95 g of hydrogen sulphate is available in 100 g of acid.

Therefore, 2511 g of hydrogen sulphate is available in

$\dfrac{100 \times 2511}{95}$ g = 2643 g of acid = 2.64 kg of acid

5. WRITING BALANCED CHEMICAL EQUATIONS. Before stoichiometric calculations such as the foregoing can be done, a properly balanced equation must be written for the reaction involved. Although you have by now encountered a number of equations, they were presented to you in balanced form. You will need to develop some skill in writing such equations yourself.

We list the following requirements for writing the correct equation for a chemical reaction:

(1) The reactants and the products of the reaction must be known.

(2) The formulas for all reactants and products must be known.

(3) Coefficients must be added before symbols and formulas in such a way as to show the same numbers of each kind of atoms on both sides of the equation; this is called "balancing the equation."

(4) The equation should be written with whole-number coefficients, the smallest possible.

It is not particularly easy to predict the products of some reactions; for others it is not too difficult, especially as you expand your experience in chemistry. At this stage you will have to learn the outcome of many reactions as you encounter them; for reactions that you have not yet encountered you will be told what the products are. You will have to manage writing formulas correctly; this is a matter of learning common valences of the elements, and the formulas and valences of some radicals. By the end of step (2) you will have what is called an unbalanced equation. Step (3) can usually be achieved by inspection.

Problem 16-3. Propane (a common "bottled gas" for cooking) has the formula C_3H_8. It reacts with oxygen on burning, to form water and carbon dioxide only. Write the equation for the reaction.

Solution: The unbalanced equation is

$$C_3H_8 + O_2 \rightarrow H_2O + CO_2$$

There should be 3 C's and 8 H's on the right, as on the left:

$$C_3H_8 + O_2 \rightarrow 4H_2O + 3CO_2$$

There are 10 O's on the right, so we must change the left:

$$C_3H_8 + 5O_2 \rightarrow 4H_2O + 3CO_2$$

This is the balanced equation.
(Check: 3 C's, 8 H's, 10 O's on each side.)

Problem 16-4: Large amounts of ammonia (Sec. 7-8) mixed with air are converted to nitric oxide (Table 7-2) and water vapour as a first stage in the manufacture of nitric acid (Sec. 7-11). The air furnishes oxygen as a reactant. Write the equation for the oxidation of ammonia in this way.

Solution: The unbalanced equation is

$$NH_3 + O_2 \rightarrow NO + H_2O$$

To balance the H's there must be at least $2NH_3$ and $3H_2O$:

$$2NH_3 + O_2 \rightarrow NO + 3H_2O$$

To balance the N's there must be 2NO on the right:

$$2NH_3 + O_2 \rightarrow 2NO + 3H_2O$$

To balance the O's there must be $2\frac{1}{2}O_2$ on the left:

$$2NH_3 + 2\frac{1}{2}O_2 \rightarrow 2NO + 3H_2O$$

This is balanced. Now clear the equation of fractions:

$$4NH_3 + 5O_2 \rightarrow 4NO + 6H_2O$$

(Check: 4 N's, 10 O's and 12 H's on each side.)

6. TYPES OF CHEMICAL REACTIONS. Many of the reactions that have been described in this and previous chapters can be placed into a few categories according to the way the atoms or molecules form new groupings. These categories form part of a scheme of classifying chemical reactions.

Combinations are reactions in which two (or perhaps more) substances combine to form a single new substance. These are illustrated by:

$$Zn + S \rightarrow ZnS \quad \text{(Sec. 2-8)}$$
$$2H_2 + O_2 \rightarrow 2H_2O \quad \text{(Sec. 6-7)}$$
$$NH_3 + HCl \rightarrow NH_4Cl \quad \text{(Sec. 7-9)}$$
$$P_4 + 6Cl_2 \rightarrow 4PCl_3 \quad \text{(Sec. 8-5)}$$

Decompositions are reactions in which a single substance is converted to two or more new substances. For example:

$$2HgO \rightarrow 2Hg + O_2 \quad \text{(Sec. 3-13)}$$
$$2KClO_3 \rightarrow 2KCl + 3O_2 \quad \text{(Sec. 5-5)}$$
$$NH_4NO_2 \rightarrow N_2 + 2H_2O \quad \text{(Sec. 7-3)}$$

Double decompositions are reactions in which atoms or groups of atoms are exchanged between two reactants, and two new products are thereby formed:

$$NH_4Cl + NaNO_2 \rightarrow NH_4NO_2 + NaCl \quad \text{(Sec. 7-3)}$$
$$2HNO_3 + CaO \rightarrow Ca(NO_3)_2 + H_2O \quad \text{(Sec. 7-14)}$$
$$H_2SO_4 + NaCl \rightarrow NaHSO_4 + HCl \quad \text{(Sec. 8-9)}$$

Displacements are reactions in which one element displaces another from a compound:

$$Zn + H_2SO_4 \rightarrow H_2 + ZnSO_4 \quad (Sec. 6-3)$$

$$2K + 2H_2O \rightarrow H_2 + 2KOH \quad (Sec. 6-3)$$

$$H_2 + CuO \rightarrow Cu + H_2O \quad (Sec. 6-7)$$

You will easily find other reactions in earlier chapters that do not fit into any of these categories. Don't worry; there are still some types of reactions that have to be mentioned, but we need to develop some other ideas first.

ENERGY AND CHEMICAL REACTIONS

7. THE HYDROGEN-OXYGEN REACTION AGAIN. When hydrogen burns with oxygen the reaction produces heat (Sec. 6-7). This is of practical interest, for instance in oxy-hydrogen welding and rocket propulsion, but it is also of theoretical interest to account for the production of heat in this way.

For a given amount of hydrogen reacting, the amount of heat produced is always the same. For instance, when one mole of molecular hydrogen reacts with oxygen, one mole of water is produced, and 286 kJ of heat is given out. If only half a mole of hydrogen reacts, only half the amount of energy, 143 kJ, is produced, and so on. Thus a more complete equation for the reaction of hydrogen and oxygen is

$$2H_2 + O_2 \rightarrow 2H_2O + 572 \text{ kJ}$$

Now 572 kJ is the amount of heat evolved when two *moles* of molecular hydrogen react with one *mole* of molecular oxygen—not when a mere two *molecules* of hydrogen react with one *molecule* of oxygen. So, in expressing the heat effect this way we are "reading" the equation in terms of moles, not molecules, and this practice will be followed consistently.

8. The evolution of heat in a chemical reaction is very common. In fact, in every chemical reaction, energy is either absorbed or produced. If energy is absorbed, the reaction is said to be **endothermic**; if energy is produced, the reaction is said to be **exothermic** (Sec. 5-8).

The energy, whether absorbed or evolved, may be in the form of light energy or electrical energy, but commonly is in the form of heat.

When hydrogen and oxygen react to form water the energy evolved is ordinarily in the form of heat, but there is some light (and by now we know that that, too, represents energy), and also some energy is expended in rapidly pushing back the atmosphere if the gases explode (and that accounts for the "pop" you heard in the laboratory experiment (Sec. 6-7)). The same reaction can be made to occur in such a way that most of the energy produced is electrical. This is what happens, for example, in "fuel cells" that provide electricity for spacecraft.

Explosions are sudden expansions of gases, caused by exothermic reactions that produce gaseous products rapidly, at high temperature, in a confined space. The gases get more space by bursting the walls of their "container."

Here, an underground explosion has been set off in the Northwest Territories during "seismographic prospecting." Measurements of the time and nature of the "echo" of the shock wave from deep-down rock strata indicate whether or not the structures are of a kind that may contain oil or natural gas.

9. Where does the energy that is produced in an exothermic reaction come from? And where does the energy that is absorbed in an endothermic reaction go to?

The source of the energy from an exothermic reaction must be the reactants themselves (hydrogen and oxygen in our example), because no energy was supplied to them (except the trifling amount to initiate the reaction). Molecules of hydrogen and of oxygen have energy stored in them, energy we can call *chemical energy.*

We stated in Sec. 14-3 that, once atoms have united to produce molecules by the formation of chemical bonds, it would require the expenditure of energy to separate the atoms again. If it takes energy to break a chemical bond, then this amount of energy must be released by the molecule when its bonds are formed; the molecule thus contains less energy than the atoms of which it is composed. The chemical reaction mentioned above must involve the breaking of bonds in hydrogen and oxygen molecules, and the forming of new bonds in water molecules, as represented in the following scheme:

$$H—H + H—H + O=O \rightarrow H—O—H + H—O—H$$

The breaking of these bonds
requires an *input* of energy

The formation of these bonds
results in an *output* of energy

Since this particular reaction is exothermic we may conclude that more energy is produced in the formation of the bonds indicated "on the right" than is consumed in the breaking of the bonds indicated "on the left." The water molecules contain less energy than the hydrogen and oxygen molecules from which they can be produced. Thus, compared with water molecules, the molecules of hydrogen and oxygen have more stored energy. In general, *the product or products of an exothermic reaction have less chemical energy than the reactants.*

The reverse is true of an endothermic reaction: the product or products of an endothermic reaction contain *more* chemical energy than the reactants, more by the amount of energy that was absorbed in the reaction.

We have implied that it is the breaking and formation of bonds that account for the net energy produced or consumed in a chemical reaction. This is certainly true for most of the energy, but if we got down to the "nitty gritties" and tried to do an exact energy balance for most chemical reactions we would have to take into account a few minor factors that influence the result. We have already mentioned a couple of these in the marginal note with Sec. 16-8. Also with respect to the hydrogen-oxygen reaction, for example, it makes some difference in the amount of energy produced (a difference you should be able to explain after reading the following chapter) whether the water formed is a liquid or a vapour.

10. Energy can be changed from one form to another, but in *any ordinary physical or chemical change the total amount of energy is the same after the change as before it.* This is the **Law of Conservation of Energy.** *Other ways of expressing it are: energy can neither be created nor destroyed* and *energy is always conserved.*

This "law," like the Law of Conservation of Mass, is a generalization that has been made from a great many careful experiments involving many forms of energy: energy of motion (kinetic energy), energy of position (potential energy), mechanical work, electrical energy, chemical energy, and heat.

Problem 16-5: Write the equation for the burning of molecular sulphur in oxygen (Sec. 5-9). The heat evolved in the reaction so written is 2375 kJ. Calculate the amount of heat evolved for the formation of 1 mol of sulphur dioxide.

Solution: The required equation is

$$S_8 + 8O_2 \rightarrow 8SO_2 + 2375 \text{ kJ}$$

This produces 8 mol of sulphur dioxide, and so the formation of 1 mol of sulphur dioxide would produce 2375 kJ ÷ 8 = 297 kJ.

This, incidentally, is known as the *heat of formation* (per mole) for this compound.

Problem 16-6: By means of an electric current, water can be decomposed into hydrogen and oxygen. (The process is called the electrolysis of water.)

How much electrical energy is required to produce 0.5 mol of molecular hydrogen by the electrolysis of water?

Solution: Water is formed from hydrogen and oxygen according to the equation:

$$2H_2 + O_2 \rightarrow 2H_2O + 572 \text{ kJ}$$

Thus when 2 mol of hydrogen (H_2) reacts to form water, 572 kJ of energy is given out. Accordingly, to get 2 mol of hydrogen from water, this amount of energy must be supplied from some external source. To get 0.5 mol of hydrogen the energy required would be

$$\frac{572 \text{ kJ} \times 0.5 \text{ mol}}{2 \text{ mol}} = 143 \text{ kJ}$$

11. ENERGY RELEASED IN COMBUSTION OF FUELS. In Sec. 5-10 we described the role of oxygen in supporting the combustion of several substances used as fuels. At that time we mentioned that the chemical reactions involved were accompanied by the evolution of heat. We can now make this more quantitative by listing what are often called the *heats of combustion* of several substances used as sources of energy. These are given in Table 16-1. The values refer to the energy produced by the complete combustion of one mole of the named substance to carbon dioxide and water. (Heats of combustion are experimentally found by burning a known mass of the substance in a calorimeter containing a known amount of water, and observing by how much the temperature of the apparatus is raised.)

TABLE 16-1

HEATS OF COMBUSTION OF SOME SUBSTANCES

SUBSTANCE	FORMULA	HEAT EVOLVED (kJ/mol)
Methane	CH_4	882
Acetylene	C_2H_2	1305
Ethylene	C_2H_4	1411
Ethane	C_2H_6	1550
Propane	C_3H_8	2202
Methanol	CH_3OH	715
Ethanol	C_2H_5OH	1371
Glucose	$C_6H_{12}O_6$	2816
Sucrose	$C_{12}H_{22}O_{11}$	5644

Problem 16-7: The heat of combustion of methane, the principal substance in natural gas, is 882 kJ/mol. (a) Write an equation for the reaction involved, in which the products are carbon dioxide and water, and show the energy as part of the equation. (b) Calculate what mass of methane would produce on combustion the energy equivalent to one kilowatt-hour (the units in which we purchase electrical energy).

Solution: (a) The unbalanced chemical equation is

$$CH_4 + O_2 \rightarrow CO_2 + H_2O$$

The balanced equation can easily be seen to be:

$$CH_4 + 2O_2 \rightarrow CO_2 + 2H_2O$$

Then we show the heat energy as a product of the reaction:

$$CH_4 + 2O_2 \rightarrow CO_2 + 2H_2O + 882 \text{ kJ}$$

(b) In physics you learned that one watt × one second = one joule

$\therefore$ 1 kW·h = 1000 W × 3600 s = 3600 kJ

882 kJ are produced by combustion of 1 mol of methane

Therefore, 3600 kJ are produced by combustion of

$$\frac{1 \text{ mol} \times 3600 \text{ kJ}}{882 \text{ kJ}} = 4.08 \text{ mol of methane}$$

(What significance can you see in this problem?)

12. ENERGY TO INITIATE REACTIONS. Some substances, such as sodium metal, react with oxygen as soon as they are exposed to air, thereby producing oxides and evolving heat. Indeed some, such as white phosphorus (Sec. 5-9), react with the oxygen of the air so readily that they catch fire spontaneously. Other substances, such as sulphur and carbon (for example, charcoal) can react vigorously with oxygen to yield oxides and evolve heat, but do not ordinarily do so to any appreciable extent unless they are "set" afire.

A substance that does not of its own accord react with oxygen, but which can be made to do so, say, by applying to it a burning match or a blowtorch, is obviously capable of exothermic combustion. But to get the reaction going it needs to be "primed" with some energy. Once started, however, the reaction may continue by itself. For example, a fire propagates itself because the energy that is released in the combustion can start the burning of adjacent material, and so on. Thus the energy provided by a single spark or match can set afire a frame house or even a city block of such houses.

If you go back to the hydrogen-oxygen reaction with which we began this chapter, you might picture the energy supplied by a spark setting in motion a chain of events as follows. The energy provided is sufficient to break the bonds in a few hydrogen or oxygen molecules. The atoms formed in this way combine to form water molecules, and in doing so release energy. This new energy disrupts more hydrogen and oxygen molecules, and the cycle is repeated until either the hydrogen molecules or the oxygen molecules are used up.

13. You have heard of fires being caused by "spontaneous combustion." Often this results from a heap of oily rags left in some room where there is little movement of air. The oil in the rags slowly reacts with the oxygen of the air, producing heat. If the rags were spread out, and the air around them were moving, this heat would be carried away by the air, and no harm would result. But if the rags are in a heap and the air is still, the heat raises the temperature of the oil, which then combines with oxygen faster, producing still more heat. After a time, the oil reaches its kindling temperature, and the rags burst into flame. This whole process is called **spontaneous combustion.** In much the same way, large piles of coal sometimes catch on fire, particularly if they contain a lot of coal "dust"—fine particles of coal that offer a lot of surface to the oxygen of the air and so oxidize readily.

QUESTIONS

1. Explain in your own words what is meant by *stoichiometry*.

2. In most important zinc ores the zinc is present in the form of sulphide, ZnS. This is separated from useless rock and then "roasted" in air to convert zinc sulphide to zinc oxide. The sulphur is converted to sulphur dioxide gas. Write an equation for the reaction. Then calculate the mass of zinc oxide that can be produced from one tonne of pure zinc sulphide.

*3. Compounds of the elements carbon and hydrogen, often containing oxygen or nitrogen and sometimes one or more other elements are called "organic" compounds. Among all known chemical substances organic compounds are more numerous than "inorganic" compounds. The composition of many organic compounds can be determined by burning them in an excess of oxygen, and trapping and finding the mass of the water and carbon dioxide thereby formed. When 0.555 g of a compound, known to contain only carbon, hydrogen, and oxygen, was so burned, 0.675 g of water and 1.320 g of carbon dioxide

were formed. Calculate the percentage composition of the compound.

4. Saltpeter, KNO_3, also known as "nitre," is an ingredient of gunpowder. It provides oxygen for the combustion of charcoal and sulphur (the other ingredients). Calculate what mass of potassium nitrate is the stoichiometric amount for the burning of one gram of each of carbon and sulphur. (The decomposition of potassium nitrate was described in an earlier chapter.)

5. Without referring to the textbook, write down the four requirements for writing the correct equation for a chemical reaction.

6. Balance equations for the following reactions:

(a) $Li + H_2O \rightarrow H_2 + LiOH$

(b) $Cu + S_8 \rightarrow Cu_2S$

(c) $P_4 + O_2 \rightarrow P_4O_{10}$

(d) $C_2H_6 + O_2 \rightarrow CO_2 + H_2O$

(e) $CS_2 + O_2 \rightarrow CO_2 + SO_2$

Name each reactant and product.

7. Identify each of the following reactions by type (Sec. 16-6):

(a) $6Li + N_2 \rightarrow 2Li_3N$

(b) $BaCl_2 + H_2SO_4 \rightarrow BaSO_4 + 2HCl$

(c) $Ag_2S + H_2 \rightarrow 2Ag + H_2S$

(d) $CaCO_3 \rightarrow CaO + CO_2$

(e) $Fe + 2HClO_4 \rightarrow Fe(ClO_4)_2 + H_2$

8. Explain clearly the meaning of:

(a) exothermic
(c) heat of combustion

(b) endothermic
(d) chemical energy

9. Why do we use paper, sticks of wood, and finally coal in starting a fire?

10. How could a fire start in a pile of oily rags if they were kept in a cupboard?

11. As it is normally used coal burns slowly, but the fine coal dust in mines sometimes will burn so rapidly as to cause an explosion. Account for the difference in rates.

12. From the data in Table 16-1 calculate:

(a) Which produces more heat per atom of carbon burned, methane or propane?

(b) Which produces more heat per gram of gas burned, methane or propane?

(c) Which produces more heat per litre of gas burned, methane or propane? (Densities at STP: methane 0.714 g/L; propane 1.96 g/L.)

13. Suggest an explanation in terms of atoms, molecules, and bonds, why a certain kindling temperature must be attained before a combustible substance will burn.

14. The burning of sulphur in oxygen is represented by the equation:

$$S_8 + 8O_2 \rightarrow 8SO_2 + 2375 \text{ kJ}$$

(a) Make sketches of each molecule taking part in this reaction, and show in these which bonds must be broken and which must be formed.

(b) How much heat is evolved per mole of sulphur dioxide formed?

(c) Where is more chemical energy stored: in 8 mol of sulphur dioxide molecules or in 1 mol of sulphur molecules + 8 mol of molecular oxygen?

*15. When one mole of water is formed from the constituent elements 286 kJ of energy is evolved. Suppose that Q_1 represents the energy evolved when one mole of molecular hydrogen is formed from the individual atoms (bond energy), and Q_2 the corresponding bond energy for a mole of molecular oxygen, and Q_3 is the energy evolved when a mole of water is formed *from the atoms*. Show how Q_1, Q_2, and Q_3 must be combined to yield the value 286 kJ.

*16. The synthesis of ammonia is represented by the equation:

$$N_2 + 3H_2 \rightarrow 2NH_3 + 92 \text{ kJ}$$

(a) How much heat is evolved in the formation of 5 mol of ammonia?

(b) Draw representations of the various molecules participating in this reaction. Show which of these must be decomposed to atoms and which require the combining of atoms during this reaction.

(c) If Q_1 is the energy evolved with the formation of one mole of molecular hydrogen, Q_2 with the formation of one mole of molecular nitrogen, and Q_3 with the formation of one mole of ammonia (from atoms in all cases), show how these energy quantities relate to 92 kJ.

17. Show that the combination of various quantities of energy, such as was done in the two previous questions, is justifiable on the basis of the Law of Conservation of Energy.

18. With respect to Questions 15 and 16, the following are recorded bond energies:

H_2	436 kJ/mol	O_2	497 kJ/mol
Cl_2	244 kJ/mol	N_2	946 kJ/mol

(a) Draw bond diagrams or Lewis diagrams for each molecule, and note how many electron-pair bonds must be broken to convert the molecules to atoms.

(b) Suggest an explanation for the trend in values from $Cl_2 \rightarrow O_2 \rightarrow N_2$.

(c) Nitrogen was described in Chapter 7 as a "lazy" element; do the above values give any hint why?

(d) Can you suggest an explanation why the bond energy in hydrogen is so much greater than that in chlorine?

19. Many diet-conscious people are familiar with the calorie content of food. In this connection the Calorie is actually a kilocalorie (= 4.18 kJ). When substances like glucose and alcohol are consumed in the body they are transformed ultimately to the same products as if they had been oxidized in the laboratory. Can you relate the following information, taken from a Calorie chart, to the data in Table 16-1?

Corn syrup (a solution of glucose)	75 Cal/tbsp
Scotch whisky	110 Cal/1.5 oz

20. For the reaction in which iron oxide (Fe_3O_4) is reduced by hydrogen (Chapter 6):

(a) What is the amount of iron (in moles) produced by one mole of molecular hydrogen?

(b) What is the total number of atoms in one mole of Fe_3O_4?

(c) What is the amount of water vapour (in moles) produced per mole of iron atoms reduced?

21. Consider the reaction by which hydrogen is prepared in the laboratory from zinc and sulphuric acid (Chapter 6):

(a) What is the amount of molecular hydrogen (in moles) produced by one mole of zinc?

(b) What is the molar mass of molecular hydrogen?

(c) Given that the density of hydrogen gas at STP is 0.090

g/L, what is the volume (measured at STP) of the hydrogen produced by one mole of zinc?

(d) What amount of zinc (in moles) would produce one litre of hydrogen at STP?

* **22.** One litre each of hydrogen and oxygen are put in a two-litre container which is then closed tightly and maintained at STP. A spark is generated in the container, causing hydrogen and oxygen to react.

(a) From the densities given in Table 6-1, what masses of hydrogen and oxygen were taken?

(b) Which element was added in excess of the amount required for the reaction?

(c) What mass of liquid water would be formed as a result of the reaction?

(d) What mass of oxygen remains unreacted?

(e) Neglecting the vapour pressure of the water (Sec. 19-11), what pressure would be exerted inside the container after the reaction?

23. The ore from which iron is commonly obtained consists mainly of ferric oxide, Fe_2O_3, in the form of the mineral hematite. In what is called a blast furnace, this reacts with carbon monoxide (CO) which has been made from coke. The complete process is more complicated than this, but as an approximation we can describe the reaction by the equation:

$$Fe_2O_3 + 3CO \rightarrow 2Fe + 3CO_2$$

Calculate (a) what mass of iron might be obtained from one tonne (1000 kg) of pure hematite; (b) what mass of coke (assuming it to be pure carbon) would be required to generate the amount of carbon monoxide needed to reduce one tonne of hematite.

17 Changes of State

1. **THE THREE STATES OF MATTER.** Substances can exist in three different states: solid, liquid, and gaseous. Although you are probably familiar with the characteristics of these, it will be useful to summarize them briefly here.

A sample of a substance in the **solid state** (a solid) has a definite volume and a definite shape. Its volume depends on the mass of the sample and, very slightly, on the temperature and the pressure. Its shape is its own, and it keeps this shape because it flows only when subjected to considerable stress (squeezing, pulling, and so on). When any of these stresses is applied suddenly, a solid does not flow but instead breaks or shatters into smaller pieces.

A sample of a substance in the **liquid state** (a liquid) has a definite volume but no definite shape. Its volume, like that of the solid sample, depends on the mass of the sample and very slightly on the temperature and pressure; it does *not* depend on the size or shape of the containing vessel. Its shape, however, does depend on that of the vessel; its shape is in fact the shape of that part of the vessel that it fills, but with a flat upper surface. This is because a liquid flows readily.

A sample of a substance in the **gaseous state** (a gas) has neither a definite volume nor a definite shape. Like a liquid (but unlike a solid) it takes the shape of the containing vessel; but unlike a liquid it expands to occupy uniformly the whole of the container. Its volume therefore is the volume of the container.

2. By this time you should have a fairly good idea how the three states of matter can be explained in terms of particles. Fig. 17-1 may help to make the idea clearer. A solid is shown as made up of particles arranged in some regular pattern, and although the drawing doesn't show it we realize the pattern must extend in three dimensions. In a liquid the particles are no longer arranged in a regular way, although they are shown clinging together. In both solids and liquids the particles are

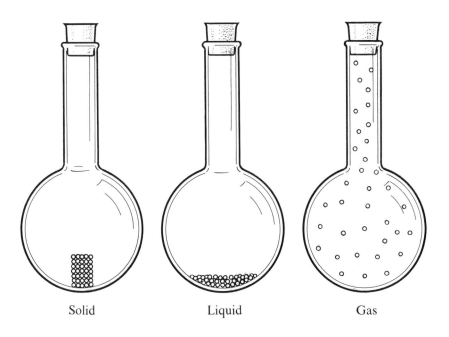

Solid   Liquid   Gas

Fig. 17-1: *A substance in the solid state pays no attention to the shape or size of the container. A substance in the liquid state retains its own volume but adapts itself to the shape of the container. A substance in the gaseous state has no mind of its own.*

bunched together so that they make up most of the volume of the material; there isn't much space left for compression. The pattern assumed by the particles in solids often results in outward regularities in shape which we describe by the word *crystalline* (Sec. 14-4). Even if the crystalline features are lacking, the regularly arranged or "ordered" rows of molecules in most solids ensure that they do have a fixed shape. In a liquid the arrangement of particles is best described by the word disordered, so a liquid has no shape of its own.

The special feature about gases is that the particles are relatively far apart—with great empty spaces between them. Such an assemblage of particles can have neither characteristic shape nor volume. The 35 particles shown in the flask on the right-hand side of Fig. 17-1 could have been accommodated in a flask twice as large (or half as large, for that matter), and this would have represented the same mass of gas expanded (or contracted) into a different volume.

"We can form a rough human picture of what is going on in the following way. In a solid, the molecules can be pictured as a crowd of men all doing physical exercises—"the daily dozen"—without moving from the spot where they stand. If they have taken up their positions at random, we have a so-called amorphous or non-crystalline solid, such as glass or glue: if they are neatly drawn up in rows by a drill instructor, we have a crystalline substance, such as quartz or rock-salt or washing soda. In a liquid the molecules can be pictured as a swarm of men gathered together in a hall at a crowded reception; they are tightly wedged, but each one works his way through the others, with many a push and apology, and we cannot expect the same two men to be near each other all through the evening. (If we want two kinds of atoms, we may take men and women; if dancing starts we have chemical combination, two atoms combining to form a molecule.) For a gas we have to think of a large open space on which men are walking without looking where they are going; each man continues in a straight line until he bumps into someone else, when he abruptly starts off again in a different direction. In each case, the hotter the substance the more rapid the motion. If a cinematograph picture could be taken of the molecules of the air in a room all we should have to do to represent the air in an oven would be to run the film more quickly." (Andrade, 1927)

3. MOLECULAR MOTION. What these simple drawings fail to convey is that the molecules, or even the atoms that make up the molecules, in these materials are in constant motion. The molecules of a gas move about in the empty space that separates them, dashing about at high speed like a swarm of gnats, from time to time colliding with each other or with the container walls. This kind of straight-line motion of the molecules is called *translation*.

But this is not all that happens; the molecules may undergo various internal motions as well. For instance, a molecule may *rotate* about one or more axes, or it may *vibrate* internally in various ways. These kinds of motion are illustrated for a water molecule in Fig. 17-2.

"Translation" sounds like something that happens to a foreign language. But this usage of the word "translate" (which is given first place by the Oxford English Dictionary) is quite in keeping with the Latin roots from which it stems: *trans* = across; *latus* = borne or carried. *Latus* is a past participle of *ferre*, to bear or carry; you will see that transfer and translate (in this sense) mean about the same thing.

Molecules in the gaseous state have the greatest freedom to move in these ways because the spaces between them are usually large compared to the sizes of the molecules themselves. But molecules in liquids also move about, though more slowly than in gases. (This is scarcely surprising: you cannot move as quickly through a dense crowd of people as you can in an open field.)

The movement of molecules in a liquid can be inferred from the following simple observation. Drop a crystal of iodine into a beaker containing 500 mL or so of cyclohexane, and leave the vessel undisturbed while watching what happens. A purple colour develops in the solution around the crystal, and in time this purple colour will become uniformly distributed throughout the liquid. This could happen only if the molecules of iodine were free to move through the liquid.

Caution: Cyclohexane is flammable.

Atoms or molecules can also move through solids, but here the process is very slow and harder to observe (though mercury will penetrate into a solid metal like gold quickly enough to be detectable within a day or so).

4. STRUCTURAL UNITS IN SOLIDS. In Chapters 14 and 15 we described various kinds of atomic aggregates that occur in pure substances. A number of the examples given there were solids. In order to understand the properties of different solids it is important that you know for any particular substance:

(i) what are the structural units that make up the solid?
(ii) what are the bonding forces that hold these units together?

Translation: motion from one position to another

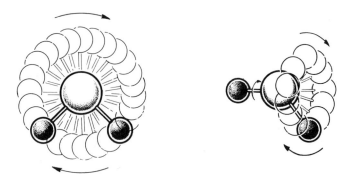

Rotation: two axes of rotation are shown.

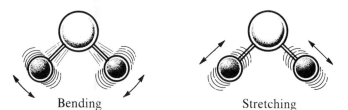

Bending   Stretching

Vibration: the movement of the atoms is shown by the double-headed arrows.

Fig. 17-2: *This illustrates molecules in motion: at the top, translation; in the middle, rotation (in two directions); at the bottom, vibration (bending and stretching).*

Solids may be classified on the basis of these two criteria as illustrated in Table 17-1. The examples selected in this table are typical of the structural units and bonds given. You should re-read Sec. 14-21, however, as a reminder that it is sometimes difficult to classify a bond as purely ionic or covalent.

5. VIBRATIONAL ENERGY AND TEMPERATURE. The structural units mentioned in the last section occupy regular positions in a crystal lattice (Sec. 14-5). Descriptions and diagrams of several of these spatial arrangements were given in the previous two chapters. There is good evidence, however, that the particles are not static in these places, but rather that they vibrate back and forth about these relative positions in the solid. In Sec. 19-4 we shall be discussing the relationship between molecular energy and temperature, but we may anticipate what is to be

TABLE 17-1

CLASSIFICATION OF SOLIDS BY STRUCTURAL UNITS

TYPE OF STRUCTURAL UNIT	MODE OF LINKING OF THESE UNITS	EXAMPLES
Like atoms	Covalent bonds	Diamond, graphite (C)
	Metallic bonds	Pure metals
Unlike atoms	Covalent bonds	Carborundum (SiC)
		Quartz (SiO_2)
	Metallic bonds	Alloys
Molecules	Van der Waals' forces	Iodine (I_2)
		"Dry Ice" (CO_2)
		Sulphur (S_8)
Ions	Electrostatic attraction of unlike charges (Ionic bonding)	Sodium chloride (NaCl)
		Calcium fluoride (CaF_2)

said there by stating that the kinetic energy (energy of motion) of molecules or other particles is believed to increase as temperature increases. Thus the vibrations of particles about their central positions in solids will be greater or less as the temperature is higher or lower.

You will already be familiar with the idea that to increase the temperature of a body you must add heat energy to it. The heat energy goes to increase the motion (and hence the kinetic energy) of the atoms or molecules. The amount of energy required to raise the temperature of a body by one Celsius degree is called its *heat capacity*. In chemistry, heat capacity of a substance is often expressed on a molar basis; thus, the *molar heat capacity* of a substance is the amount of energy required to raise the temperature of one mole of the substance by one Celsius degree. An interesting observation was made about 150 years ago by the French scientists P. L. Dulong and A. T. Petit: expressed in modern terms, what they noted was that the molar heat capacity of nearly all metals lies within the range 25 to 27 J/(mol·°C).

You also know that nearly all materials expand on heating. If we picture the molecules in a solid or liquid vibrating more vigorously as the temperature is raised, we expect them to require more space in which to move. To make room they nudge their neighbours away a little; if all the molecules do this the solid or liquid will undergo a measurable expansion.

6. MELTING OF A SOLID. When their temperature is raised sufficiently most solids melt. At some characteristic temperature a crystal or chunk of solid slumps into a pool of liquid. Moreover, as we pointed out in Sec. 1-7, pure substances as a rule melt all at one characteristic temperature, called the *melting point*. Now if we accept that there is a connection between temperature and kinetic energy of particles (atoms or molecules, as appropriate), and also that there are forces of some sort

Heat capacity may also be expressed on the basis of unit mass, in which case it is called *specific heat capacity*. For instance, it requires 389 J of energy to raise the temperature of 1.00 kg of copper by 1°C. The specific heat capacity of copper, therefore, is 389 J/(kg·°C) or 0.389 J/(g·°C).

(chemical bonds or van der Waals' forces) between the particles in a solid which hold them in an ordered array, melting and a characteristic temperature for melting can be explained. There must be some temperature at which the particles acquire sufficient vibrational energy to overcome the forces binding them in an ordered structure.

The reverse process, called freezing, occurs at that temperature when the particles are slowed down enough by cooling that the forces that may bind them into a regular pattern just exceed the disruptive forces of vibration. This temperature is called the *freezing point*. The freezing point and melting point for a pure substance are ordinarily the same temperature. A liquid and solid may remain together at this temperature indefinitely in a state of balance between crystals disintegrating and reforming. We say the liquid and solid, when so balanced, are in a condition of *equilibrium*.

When cooled slowly and without agitation many liquids can be brought to temperatures below their freezing point without crystals of solid appearing. The liquid is then said to be *supercooled*. On stirring or jarring the liquid, it then rather quickly freezes. It is almost as if the particles "forgot" to line up in the required pattern to form a solid. The reverse phenomenon, raising a solid above its melting point without melting, is never observed.

7. HEAT OF FUSION. For a solid to be melted heat energy must always be supplied. For instance, to melt 1.00 g of ice at 0°C requires an input of 333 J. But since the resulting water is still at 0°C, none of the added energy went to increase the kinetic energy of its molecules. This quantity of heat is sometimes called the *latent heat of fusion*, the word latent conveying "hidden" or "concealed." It was called latent because when it was first observed and measured there was no explanation available why the added heat failed to raise the temperature of the substance as it melted. It is now understood that the heat of fusion is the amount of work required to rupture the bonds or to overcome whatever forces exist between the particles when they are arranged in the regular three-dimensional pattern of the solid. It measures, if you like, the difference in energy between the particles in the ordered, close-packed array of the solid state and in the disordered, but still close-packed, array of the liquid state (Fig. 17-3).

The total amount of energy required to melt a solid will obviously depend on how many atoms or molecules have to be separated from their ordered structure. The value quoted above, 333 J, applies to the melting of one gram of ice; two grams, containing twice as many molecules, would require 666 J, and so on. For our purposes it will be more interesting to compare the amounts of energy required to melt *one mole* of different substances. Since a mole is the amount of substance containing 6.02×10^{23} particles (Sec. 10-23), the *molar heat of fusion* really measures the work required to overcome the intermolecular or interatomic forces holding this number of particles in shape in the solid state. Some representative values are shown in Table 17-2.

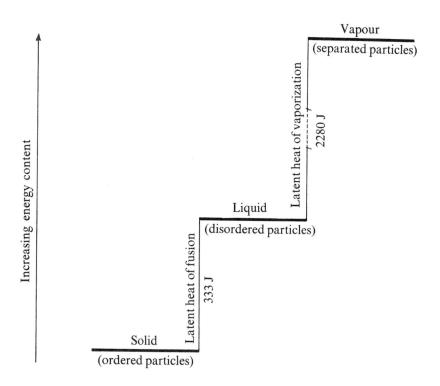

Fig. 17-3: *Relative energy content of one gram of the three states of water: ice, liquid, and vapour*

TABLE 17-2

THE LATENT HEAT OF FUSION OF SEVERAL SUBSTANCES

SUBSTANCE	FORMULA	LATENT HEAT OF FUSION (J/g)	MOLAR MASS (g/mol)	MOLAR HEAT OF FUSION (kJ/mol)
Water	H_2O	333	18.0	6.0
Sulphur	S_8	52	256.5	13.4
Iodine	I_2	62	253.8	15.8
Copper	Cu	205	63.5	13.0

8. SUBLIMATION. Some substances pass directly from the solid to the vapour state without ever becoming liquid. Solid carbon dioxide—"Dry Ice"—is a particularly good example because at ordinary pressure it cannot be liquefied. One of its great virtues as a refrigerant is that it is always dry: the dry solid changes directly into a gas. There are also some solids used as moth-repellents in the home; one is naphthalene ($C_{10}H_8$) in common moth balls, and another paradichlorobenzene ($C_6H_4Cl_2$). These both evaporate, giving off vapours with odours easily detected by humans and evidently offensive to moths; given sufficient time both will disappear completely by evaporation.

Actually, all solids vaporize to some extent, but with many the extent is small enough to be negligible. The tendency to evaporate increases with increasing temperature, and sometimes becomes appreciable before the solid melts. A solid that behaves in this way, when heated to just below its melting point, will vaporize readily. This vapour, when cooled, will condense to the solid again. The double process is known as *sublimation*. Iodine, for example, sublimes readily (Fig. 17-4), and this property is used to separate it from impurities which do not sublime.

9. EVAPORATION OF LIQUIDS. We have described a liquid as a disordered, close-packed assemblage of particles in incessant motion. The particles in a liquid are usually molecules, although one can think of exceptions: for instance, in molten salt at high temperatures the particles are ions, and in the liquid metal mercury the particles are atoms. Because the molecules are packed closely together liquids are shrunk very little by comparison; for example, at the enormous pressure of 10^9 Pa water undergoes only a 20% shrinkage.

We have once or twice previously mentioned in this book the attractive forces between molecules which become appreciable when they get close together. Clear evidence of the existence and extent of these forces is provided by the amount of energy required to separate the molecules when a liquid is evaporated. Thus, to evaporate 1.00 g of water at 100°C requires the input of 2.28 kJ. When 1.00 g of water, with a volume of about 1 mL, evaporates at 100°C the volume of water vapour produced is about 1700 mL. This corresponds to a considerable separation of the molecules from one another. The fact that so much energy has to be supplied when this separation occurs clearly indicates that a substantial force of attraction exists between the molecules in the liquid state.

The energy required to cause a mass of a liquid to evaporate is called the *latent heat of vaporization,* and the amount of this energy is proportional to the amount of substance evaporated. As before, we shall regard the *molar heat of vaporization* a useful measure of intermolecular or interatomic attraction since this amount of energy applies to a fixed number of particles. Representative values for a few liquids are shown in Table 17-3.

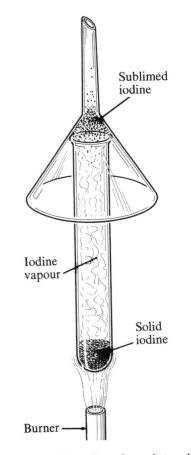

Fig. 17-4: *Solid iodine, heated in the test tube, vaporizes to a violet vapour which solidifies into crystals on the cold under-surface of the funnel.*

TABLE 17-3

THE LATENT HEAT OF VAPORIZATION OF SEVERAL SUBSTANCES

SUBSTANCE	FORMULA	LATENT HEAT OF VAPORIZATION (J/g)	MOLAR MASS (g/mol)	MOLAR HEAT OF VAPORIZATION (kJ/mol)
Water	H_2O	2280	18.0	41.1
Bromine	Br_2	191	159.8	30.5
Carbon tetrachloride	CCl_4	214	153.8	33.0
Mercury	Hg	294	200.6	59.1
Oxygen	O_2	212	32.0	6.8

The last substance named in Table 17-3 is normally a gas, but it can be liquefied at low temperature. From the value in the last column you can see that the intermolecular forces are much weaker in liquid oxygen than they are in the four substances that are normally liquid. This is presumably why oxygen doesn't occur as a liquid at ordinary temperatures.

10. EVAPORATION AND MOLECULAR ENERGY. There is another way of thinking about the evaporation of a liquid, and the heat effect accompanying it. When a liquid turns to vapour the surface from which the evaporation takes place is cooled. The human body is cooled in warm weather by the evaporation of perspiration from the skin. Water evaporates so slowly that the cooling that takes place is not noticeable, but if you place a drop or two of a volatile liquid such as ether or acetone on the back of your hand it evaporates very quickly and the skin from which the liquid evaporates is left quite cool. Since volatilization requires the input of latent heat, this must be abstracted from the surroundings; and in the simple case described the heat is removed from an area of skin, thereby lowering the skin's temperature and causing it to feel cold.

Now we said previously (Sec. 17-5) that there was a connection between molecular speed and temperature such that the higher the temperature the greater the average molecular speed or kinetic energy. We must put the word *average* into this statement because it is perfectly obvious that in a large population of molecules darting about, colliding and rebounding, some molecules are bound at any given instant to be travelling faster or slower than others. We must assume there is a distribution of molecular speeds (and individual kinetic energies) throughout the population.

Molecules are clustered together in a liquid, and essentially independent of each other in a gas or vapour. For an individual molecule to break away from the cluster in a liquid and become separate, that is, to evaporate, it must momentarily have enough kinetic energy to overcome the attractive forces that we have assumed to exist in the liquid. The molecules most likely to escape, therefore, are those with kinetic energy higher than the average. We sometimes colloquially speak of these as "hot" molecules, and this is a good reminder of the connection between kinetic energy and temperature. Given that the "hot" molecules, because of their greater-than-average speed, break away from the bulk of the liquid, it will be the slower, "cool" molecules that remain behind. The average kinetic energy of the molecules in the residual liquid will be less, because of the escape of the faster molecules, than it was prior to any evaporation. Therefore the temperature of the remaining liquid will have been lowered because of some vaporization.

The foregoing provides an explanation of the cooling that accompa-

Molecular speed refers to translational motion.

nies evaporation in terms of the molecular model, with the added assumption, of course, that attractive forces operate between molecules when they are close together as in a liquid.

11. CONDENSATION. When the vapour of a substance that is normally liquid is caused to return to the liquid state, for example, by cooling, we speak of the process as *condensation.* Thus we say water vapour will condense on a cold surface, and so on. On the other hand we are more apt to describe the process when a substance that is normally gaseous is converted to a liquid as *liquefaction,* We say, for instance, that ammonia is liquefied under pressure.

Since it requires the input of energy to evaporate any liquid, we should expect that the reverse process of condensation or liquefaction will be accompanied by a heat output. This is indeed observed, and the amount of heat per gram given out on condensation is exactly the same as the amount absorbed on evaporation.

12. DISTILLATION. Evaporation and subsequent condensation is often used to purify or separate liquids. The combined process is then called *distillation.* Fig. 17-5 illustrates a device, usually called a *still,* by which this can be done in the laboratory.

This is "Smokey" of the R.C.M.P. enjoying the cooling effect of the latent heat of vaporization by evaporating water from his tongue. The greater the surface of liquid exposed to the air, the greater the cooling effect—so he exposes all the tongue he has. The more rapidly the moisture-laden air is removed from his tongue's surface and replaced, the greater the cooling effect —so he pants.

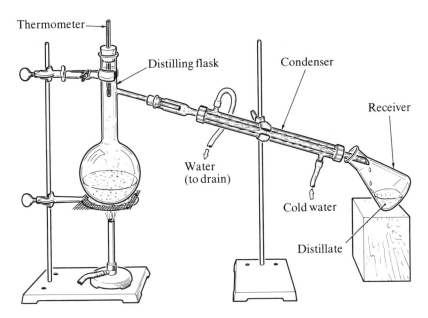

Fig. 17-5: *The vapour formed in the distilling flask is condensed in the (Liebig) condenser, and the liquid so formed is collected in the receiver. In this way a volatile liquid may be separated from a non-volatile solid or liquid with which it is mixed or dissolved.*

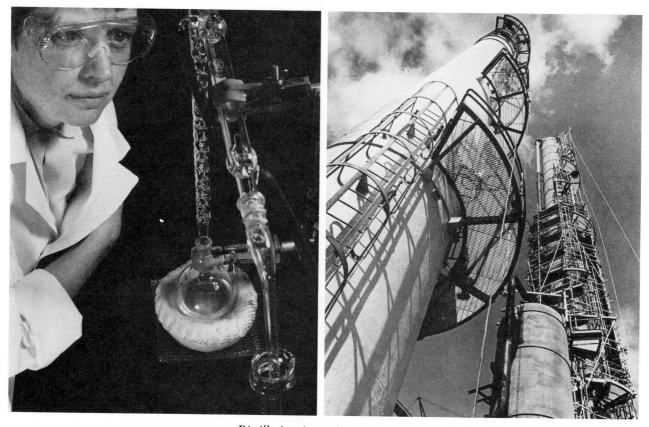

Distillation is an important process in both the laboratory and industry. The equipment looks different and is certainly different in size, but the "stills" in these pictures are doing the same job: separating substances by taking advantage of differences in their boiling points.

A simple application of distillation is for the purification of water. Ordinary water from wells or lakes or rivers contains dissolved compounds, and may as well contain suspended matter, visible or invisible, so that it scarcely qualifies under our description of a "pure substance" (Sec. 1-4). To prepare water largely free of such impurities one may subject it to distillation. The dissolved substances, bugs, and other unwanted matter remain in the distilling flask, since these do not evaporate to any extent at 100°C; and the condensed vapour that drops into the receiver, known then as "distilled water," is largely rid of the impurities in the raw water.

The purification of water is only one of many applications of distillation. A solution of two or more liquids may usually be separated into its separate components by distillation. What is required is that each liquid in the mixture must boil at a different temperature, and then if the temperature is carefully raised the different liquids evaporate successively. In practice the situation is a bit more complicated than that because the second liquid doesn't wait until the first has all evaporated before it too begins to distil. Nevertheless, very efficient separations can be made by suitable design of the "still."

As early as the twelfth century men discovered that a substance that we now call alcohol could be separated by distillation from the water and fermented grains or grapes in which it had been produced. This was the beginning of what is now a major industry to produce distilled alcoholic beverages. We mentioned in Sec. 5-6 and 7-6 that oxygen and nitrogen could be produced in large amounts by the distillation of liquefied air, taking advantage of an almost thirteen degree difference in boiling points. In this century, enormous amounts of petroleum are treated by distillation to separate various hydrocarbons (compounds of hydrogen and carbon, of which there are a great many) into different "fractions" to be used as fuels, gasoline, lubricating oils, and asphalt, as well as a host of compounds used as starting materials for the manufacture of plastics, synthetic rubber, and many other petroleum chemicals (petrochemicals).

QUESTIONS

In some of the numerical questions in this chapter units appear that are not part of the International System (SI). These examples are included to give an opportunity to recognize and handle units outside SI that are still in widespread use.

1. Make clear in your own words the meaning of:

(a) translation
(b) average molecular speed
(c) crystalline solid
(d) supercooled liquid
(e) evaporation
(f) condensation
(g) sublimation
(h) liquefaction
(i) distillation
(j) heat capacity
(k) heat of fusion
(l) heat of vaporization

2. What are the characteristics that distinguish solids, liquids, and gases from each other?

3. Why would all molecules in a gas (or liquid) at constant temperature not be travelling at the same speed?

4. Explain in terms of molecules each of the following:

(a) Solids and liquids are almost incompressible; gases are very compressible.

(b) Solids melt when heated.

(c) Liquids evaporate when heated.

(d) Liquids exert a cooling effect on evaporation.

(e) Gases diffuse very readily.

(f) Changes of state are physical changes.

(g) Liquids and solids expand only slightly on heating, whereas gases expand markedly on heating.

5. Explain what you understand by *ordered arrangement* and *disordered arrangement* as applied to the particles in matter.

6. Make sketches to illustrate the motions of translation, rotation, and vibration in a molecule of hydrogen chloride (HCl).

7. A block of aluminium with a mass of 120 g had its temperature raised 10°C by the input of 1088 J. What is the heat capacity of the block of aluminium? What is the specific heat capacity of aluminium? What is the molar heat capacity of aluminium? (Check the last value with Dulong and Petit's Law.)

8. Explain why solids and liquids almost always expand when heated.

9. Compare the volumes of one gram of ice, of water, and of water vapour. Are the relationships here typical of substances in general?

10. An energy unit not included in SI is the calorie. It is defined as the quantity of energy required to raise the temperature of one gram of water by one Celsius degree. Which is the larger unit: the joule or the calorie? What is the value of the factor that converts calories to joules? What would be the range of values of the nearly constant product of gram-atomic mass × specific heat capacity (Dulong and Petit's Law) if specific heat capacities are expressed in calories per gram per degree (Celsius)? What are the values of the latent heats of fusion and evaporation of water in kilocalories per mole?

11. Why is it a more serious injury to be scalded by steam than by boiling water?

12. Referring to Table 17-2, in which element, sulphur or iodine, do you think the intermolecular forces binding the crystals together are greater?

13. Is the function of the latent heat of evaporation to increase the kinetic energy of the evaporating molecules or to overcome the intermolecular attractions among these? Explain.

14. Show the operation of Dulong and Petit's Law with the following data:

ELEMENT	SPECIFIC HEAT CAPACITY $J/(g \cdot °C)$
Iron	0.46
Silver	0.23
Copper	0.39
Calcium	0.63

18 The Behaviour of Gases

1. As we stated at the beginning of Chapter 17, gases differ from liquids, and especially solids, because they have no true volume of their own. They expand and occupy completely the volume of their container. Moreover, they shrink considerably if compressed, whereas solids and liquids are relatively incompressible.

We commonly say that gases are light, but what we ought to say is that they have *low density*. Density is mass per unit volume. The SI unit for density is kilograms per cubic metre; at the scale of laboratory operations it may be easier to visualize density of gases in units of grams per litre; the numerical value of density is the same in either unit. Table 18-1 lists the densities of a few common gases, and for comparison the values of some common liquids and solids. The latter are about a thousand times denser than the common gases.

TABLE 18-1

DENSITIES OF SOME COMMON SUBSTANCES			
GASES		LIQUIDS	
SUBSTANCE	DENSITY (kg/m³ or g/L, at STP)	SUBSTANCE	DENSITY (kg/m³ at 0°C)
Ammonia	0.771	*Carbon disulphide*	1.292×10^3
Carbon dioxide	1.977	*Carbon tetrachloride*	1.595×10^3
Chlorine	3.214	*Mercury*	13.595×10^3
Hydrogen	0.0899	*Water*	1.00×10^3
Hydrogen sulphide	1.538	SOLIDS	
Methane	0.717	*Aluminium*	2.70×10^3
Nitrogen	1.250	*Copper*	8.96×10^3
Oxygen	1.429	*Ice*	0.92×10^3
Sulphur dioxide	2.927	*Quartz*	2.66×10^3

Gases also *diffuse* through the air or through other gases, or even through porous solids. If a little ammonia or hydrogen sulphide (both of which have pronounced odours) is released in a room, in a very short time the odour permeates the entire space. This observation could simply be due to drafts or air currents; but even when great care is taken to exclude these, odours still spread. We explained diffusion in liquids by the movement of molecules, and the same explanation applies here. Diffusion in gases is much faster because the spaces between molecules are so much greater than in liquids or solids.

The changes in the volume of a gas brought about by changes in temperature or pressure have been studied for a long time. The volume of a gas varies in rather simple mathematical ways with the pressure or the temperature to which it is subjected. These simple mathematical relationships, which will be described in succeeding sections, have led to a useful theoretical model for gases, by means of which their properties can be explained. The purpose of this chapter is to help you become familiar with the laws that describe the behaviour of gases. In the next chapter we shall describe a theory that accounts for these laws.

2. VOLUME OF A GAS. It is important that you appreciate how much more sensitive to the prevailing temperature and pressure the volume of a gas is, compared to that of a solid or liquid. To illustrate this we give the results of some calculations based on published physical constants. Let us consider the consequence of transferring one litre of water and one litre of air from a place where the temperature is 10°C to where it is 25°C (from outdoors to indoors on a spring day). The water would increase in volume by 2.7 mL, or 0.27%, while the air would expand by 53 mL, or 5.3%. The effect of pressure change is even more dramatic. In passing from an initial pressure of 100 kPa to double that value, the water would decrease by 0.046 mL, or 0.0046%, whereas the air would decrease to half its initial volume, or by 50%. In this behaviour water is typical of liquids and solids, and air is typical of all gases.

On this account, *a statement of the volume of a gas is meaningless unless the temperature and pressure are specified.*

3. PRESSURE OF A GAS. *Pressure* is the force applied per unit area. The SI unit of pressure is the *pascal* (symbol Pa); one pascal is equivalent to one newton per square metre. Other units, to be mentioned shortly, are also widely used to describe gas pressures, although they are not part of the International System of units.

One of the characteristics of a gas is that any pressure that is applied to it is transmitted equally in all directions. A corollary of this is that any enclosed sample of gas exerts a pressure on the walls of the container, and that pressure is the same in all directions. So we can properly speak of *the* pressure of the gas, and we can measure it by measuring the force exerted by the gas on some known area. One way to do this is with a pressure gauge such as you might see on a compressed air tank. Sometimes when we speak of the pressure *of* a gas we actually measure a balancing pressure *on* a gas, as with a manometer (Fig. 18-1).

Because a gas has a much greater volume than an equal mass of the same substance in the liquid or solid states, the storage of gaseous chemicals is a problem to chemical manufacturers. Shown here is the preferred type of storage tank—a huge hollow metal sphere, in which an appropriate gas may be stored under a pressure sufficient to liquefy it.

This picture was taken in Canada's "chemical valley," in Sarnia, Ontario, a region that at night is rather like a fairyland.

The "pascal" is named after Blaise Pascal who, in a short life (1623-1662), made a lasting impression on mathematics, physics, computing science, and French literature. Before he was 16 years old, he made a brilliant discovery in geometry and, at age 18, he invented one of the first calculating machines. Later, he formulated "Pascal's Principle" (the basis of the hydraulic press) and, with another mathematician, created the theory of probability.

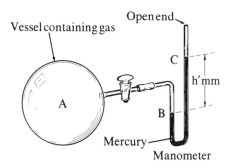

Fig. 18-1: *The gas in A has a pressure greater than that of the atmosphere: in a state of balance, the gas presses harder on the mercury at B than the atmosphere does at C. The difference in level between B and C, namely h' mm, is a measure of how great the pressure difference is. If the atmospheric pressure is h mm of mercury, the pressure of a gas in A is therefore (h + h') mm of mercury.*

Evangelista Torricelli (1608-1647) was the first to recognize that we live at the bottom of a "sea of air."

In the interest of strict accuracy, it should be stated that because of the way it is defined, one torr differs from one millimetre of mercury, but by less than one part per million.

4. THE PRESSURE OF THE ATMOSPHERE. The air of the atmosphere, having mass, is subject to a force because of gravity, and therefore exerts a pressure. The magnitude of this is greatest at sea level and decreases gradually above the earth's surface. Atmospheric pressure is measured by means of a barometer, a device invented by the Italian physicist Torricelli in 1644.

In the simple mercury barometer (Fig. 18-2) the pressure of the atmosphere is *balanced* by the force of gravity on a column of mercury. (There is no air pressure on the mercury surface inside the tube because pains were taken to ensure that there would be no air in the enclosed space.) The force of gravity on the mercury can be found by multiplying together:

the area of cross-section of the tube (a)

the length of the mercury column (h)

the density of mercury (ρ)

the acceleration due to gravity (g)

That is, the force of gravity = $a{\cdot}h{\cdot}\rho{\cdot}g$. The *pressure* at the base of the column will be this product (force) divided by the cross-sectional area, that is, $a{\cdot}h{\cdot}\rho{\cdot}g/a$, or $h{\cdot}\rho{\cdot}g$. Since ρ for mercury is a fixed value (at a specified temperature) and g is constant (at a particular place on the earth's surface), it follows that variations in atmospheric pressure will be reflected by variations in h. This means that we can use the length of a column of mercury in a barometer to measure the pressure of the atmosphere.

This is how it comes about that *barometric pressures* have for a long time been measured in units of length; this is the length of a column of mercury balanced by the force of the atmosphere. Barometers for the home do not employ a column of mercury, but retain this unit of calibration. Most barometers show pressure in inches or *millimetres of mercury* (or both). In recent years the millimetre of mercury has in large part been replaced by the unit the *torr* (symbol Torr) named after Torricelli. It is intended as part of conversion to SI that these units of pressure be phased out and they will in time become obsolete.

Returning to the mercury barometer discussed just above, we can add that, provided h, ρ, and g are put in the proper units, the product $h{\cdot}\rho{\cdot}g$ will give the pressure of the atmosphere in pascals, the correct SI unit.

Since many vacuum and pressure gauges and barometers are at present calibrated in millimetres of mercury or torr, and since so much of the information in the scientific literature is expressed in these units, it will clearly be necessary for some time to be able to convert them into pascals or the reverse. For these purposes you should note that:

1 mm of mercury = 1 Torr = 133.3 Pa

1 kPa = 7.50 Torr = 7.50 mm of mercury

Atmospheric pressure changes continually, as anyone acquainted with weather forecasts is aware. Typical values range from 96 kPa to 104 kPa (730 Torr to 790 Torr). In scientific work it has been found convenient to select one particular pressure at which to compare volumes of gases and other properties. This pressure is 101.3 kPa (760 Torr). This pressure is also known as *one standard atmosphere,* or commonly *one atmosphere* (symbol atm). Though not an SI unit, the atmosphere too is used widely in chemistry, and in fact it is the standard pressure for comparing densities and other properties of gases.

1.000 atm = 101.3 kPa = 760 Torr

Problem 18-1: A gas is confined in a bulb equipped with a mercury manometer, as illustrated in Fig. 18-1. The difference in the two mercury levels, h' in the diagram, is 74 mm. The barometric pressure was read at 756 mm of mercury. Find the pressure of the gas in the bulb in kilopascals.

Solution: The pressure of the atmosphere on the mercury in the open-ended arm of the manometer is the barometric pressure.

The pressure of the gas in the bulb must be greater than atmospheric pressure in order to push the mercury up in the outer arm of the manometer. The pressure of the gas is thus balanced against the pressure of the atmosphere *plus* the additional pressure due to a mercury column 74 mm in length.

∴ pressure of gas in bulb = 756 mm of mercury + 74 mm of mercury
= 830 mm of mercury, or 830 Torr

Converting to kilopascals: 1 Torr = 133.3 Pa

Therefore, 830 Torr = 830 Torr × 133.3 Pa/Torr
= 1.106×10^5 Pa = 110.6 kPa

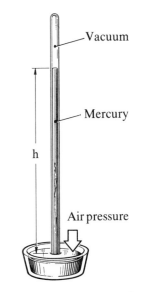

Fig. 18-2: *To construct a simple barometer, a tube, at first completely filled with mercury, is inverted with the open end under mercury in the bowl. The mercury in the tube falls until the column of mercury is just the height, h, that can be supported by the pressure of the atmosphere.*

5. TEMPERATURE OF A GAS. A body's temperature is a measure of how hot it is. Since temperature—hotness—is a relative thing we must choose some reproducible temperature as a standard or basis of comparison. The freezing point and the boiling point of water (at standard atmospheric pressure, 101.3 kPa) are reference points for the common scale of temperature. They are taken as 0 and 100 on the **Celsius scale**. A thermometer is marked off with 100 equal divisions between these temperatures, and each division is called one degree on that scale.

We have emphasized (Sec. 1-6 and Sec. 17-6) that when a pure substance changes state it does so all at one temperature. The phase changes for the common, purifiable substance water provide two easily reproducible temperatures with which to define a temperature scale and check the calibration of thermometers.

6. BOYLE'S LAW. A RELATIONSHIP BETWEEN VOLUME OF A GAS AND ITS PRESSURE. Just as the length of a coiled metal spring can be increased or decreased by altering the force on it, so the volume of a gas can be increased or decreased by changing the pressure on it. The analogy between a spring and a gas caught the imagination of the Irish peer, Robert Boyle, as early as 1660. He made measurements of the effect of

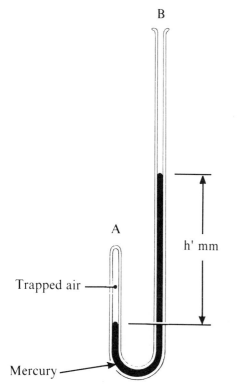

B

A

h' mm

Trapped air ———

Mercury ———

Fig. 18-3: *Boyle's apparatus for measuring the effect on the volume of a gas sample of changing the pressure on it.*

changes in pressure on the volume of a gas, using the simple apparatus shown diagrammatically in Fig. 18-3. A bent tube closed at one end A and open at the other was partially filled with mercury so as to trap a quantity of air in the shorter tube. When the level of mercury was the same in the two tubes the pressure of the entrapped air was the same as the atmospheric pressure, say h mm of mercury. Then by pouring more and more mercury into arm B the pressure on the air in A could be increased in steps. When the difference in level of the mercury columns was h' mm as shown in the diagram, the pressure on the air in A was the original atmospheric pressure, h mm of mercury, *plus* the pressure exerted by the column of mercury h' mm high. The pressure of the trapped air was $(h + h')$ mm of mercury. Boyle observed that with each increase in pressure the volume of the air in A decreased further, and in such a way that the product of the pressure and the volume remained constant. He had therefore discovered a law—a law that has since been proved to apply to all gases. In mathematical language, **Boyle's Law** can be very simply stated:

$$\text{pressure} \times \text{volume} = \text{constant}$$

$$\text{or} \quad pV = \text{constant}$$

$$\text{or} \quad V = \frac{\text{constant}}{p}$$

$$\text{or} \quad p = \frac{\text{constant}}{V}$$

Stated precisely in words, the law is as follows: *The volume of a fixed mass of a gas is inversely proportional to its pressure, provided the temperature remains constant.* (Notice that the simple relationship between p and V holds only for a fixed mass of gas and at a fixed temperature.) Thus if the pressure on a sample of gas is doubled, its volume will be halved (provided the temperature remains constant). Conversely, if a given mass of gas is allowed to expand at constant temperature to three times its original volume, its pressure will decrease to one-third its original value.

A useful way to write Boyle's Law is this:

$$p_1 V_1 = p_2 V_2$$

where p_1 and V_1, p_2 and V_2 are any two different sets of values of the pressure and volume. (The temperature and mass of gas must remain the same.) Hence

$$V_2 = V_1 \frac{p_1}{p_2} \tag{1}$$

Thus, if the pressure of a given mass of a gas is changed, the volume will change in such a way that the new volume will equal the former volume multiplied by a ratio of pressures—the initial pressure divided by the final pressure. We can illustrate the use of this relationship by solving two problems.

Problem 18-2: A quantity of gas occupies 200 mL at a pressure of 100 kPa. What will be its volume at a pressure of 75 kPa?

Solution: The new volume will be the old volume multiplied by a ratio of pressures. Since the pressure has decreased, the volume will increase; hence the ratio of pressures must be greater than one, that is

$$100 \text{ kPa}/75 \text{ kPa} \ (\textit{not} \ 75 \text{ kPa}/100 \text{ kPa})$$

$$\text{Therefore the new volume} = 200 \text{ mL} \times \frac{100 \text{ kPa}}{75 \text{ kPa}} = 267 \text{ mL}$$

(The problem could, of course, have been solved by substituting the appropriate values in Equation (1), but it is more valuable in mastering Boyle's Law to *reason* out the answer.)

Problem 18-3: A sample of gas which has a volume of 40 mL at a pressure of 500 kPa is allowed to expand until its volume is 100 mL. What will the pressure of the gas be then?

Solution 1: Let us call the new pressure p_2 kPa. The new volume equals the original volume multiplied by a ratio of pressures (the initial pressure divided by the final pressure).

$$100 \text{ mL} = 40.0 \text{ mL} \times \frac{500 \text{ kPa}}{p_2 \text{ kPa}}$$

So

$$p_2 \text{ kPa} = \frac{40.0 \text{ mL}}{100.0 \text{ mL}} \times 500 \text{ kPa} = 200 \text{ kPa}$$

The pressure after expansion will, therefore, be 200 kPa.

Notice that if you had put the ratio of pressures the wrong way up (p_2 kPa/500 kPa) the calculated pressure—p_2 kPa—would have turned out to be greater than the initial pressure, and this, you should realize immediately, is impossible; when a gas expands its pressure *decreases*. It is a very good idea to examine answers to problems of this sort to see if they make sense in relation to the process involved.

Solution 2: The problem can be solved simply by substituting in Equation (1):

$$100 \text{ mL} = 40.0 \text{ mL} \times \frac{500 \text{ kPa}}{p_2 \text{ kPa}}$$

and solving. But there is a danger in using a memorized formula: your memory may give you the wrong formula! So don't use formulas for solving problems unless you know what you are doing.

7. THE RELATIONSHIP BETWEEN VOLUME OF A GAS AND TEMPERATURE. A sample of any gas expands when heated and contracts when cooled. The more the gas is heated the more its volume increases. Late in the eighteenth century the French scientist J.-L. Gay-Lussac measured the effect of temperature changes on volume for several different gases. He found that, if the pressure of a given mass of gas were kept constant, the increase in its volume caused by an increase of one degree (Celsius) was always the same fraction, 1/273, of its volume at 0°C. This was true of each of the gases he tested.

It was later shown that *all* gases behave in this way. If a sample of a gas—any gas—had a volume V_0 at 0°C, its volume at 1°C would be $(V_0 + (1/273)V_0) = V_0 (1 + 1/273)$, as long as the pressure was unchanged. At 2°C the volume would be $V_0 (1 + 2/273)$; at 20°C, $V_0 (1 + 20/273)$; and so on. This can be expressed generally by a mathematical equation:

$$V_t = V_0 (1 + (1/273)t)$$
$$= V_0 (1 + t/273) \quad \text{(pressure and mass of gas constant)} \quad (2)$$

In this equation V_t represents the volume at t°C. This can be rearranged:

$$V_t = V_0\left(\frac{273 + t}{273}\right) = \frac{V_0}{273}\left(273 + t\right)$$

For a given mass of gas at a fixed pressure, V_0 will have a fixed value, and therefore for that sample:

$$V_t = \text{constant} (273 + t) \quad (3)$$

8. THE ABSOLUTE TEMPERATURE SCALE. Those with a mathematical turn of mind will recognize that Equation (3), as a statement of the way in which the volume of a sample of gas varies with temperature, can be represented graphically by a straight line. The equation for that line is

$$V_t = \frac{V_0}{273}\left(273 + t\right) \quad \text{or} \quad V_t = \frac{V_0}{273}t + V_0$$

Two such straight lines are plotted in Fig. 18-4. In each case the intercept on the V_t axis is V_0, so the two lines represent samples of different masses of the gas. The slope of each line is $V_0/273$, and the plots show that the line with greater V_0 also has the greater slope. Each line can be extended to the left of the V_t axis (where the values of t are negative). These extensions, shown as broken lines in Fig. 18-4, converge and have a common intercept on the t axis where $t = -273$. This corresponds to the solution of Equation (3): $V_t = 0$ when $t = -273$.

This is quite straightforward when viewed as a mathematical exercise, but it doesn't altogether make sense when applied to the physical situation that Equation (3) is supposed to represent. The significance of the mathematical exercise is that if we could somehow cool a gas down to –273°C, its volume would become zero; presumably the gas would disappear. In reality, however, every known gas turns into a liquid before a temperature as low as –273°C is reached, and all those liquefied gases

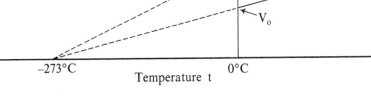

Fig. 18-4: *A plot of the volume of gas against Celsius temperature yields a straight line, and this is represented for temperatures above 0°C by a solid sloping line. Two sloping lines are shown, corresponding to two different masses of the gas. The intercept of these on the V_t axis is the volume at 0°C, designated V_o for one mass of gas and V'_o for another mass. Both these lines, when extended to negative values of t, intersect the t axis at −273°C.*

will have some measurable volume that is not much reduced by further cooling.

There is a lesson to be learned here. Equation (3) and those that preceded it in Sec. 18-7 are concise mathematical statements of a law based on observations made with gases. It is tidy and convenient to express a generalization about natural events in the form of a mathematical relationship. You have to realize that the equation or expression so formulated may extend the generalization into regions where the events it is intended to describe no longer have physical reality. When you come to apply some mathematical statement of a scientific law in a particular situation, you should be certain that the conditions are appropriate for the application of the law.

Boyle's Law, for example, was reduced to the simple mathematical statement: pV = constant. But you can be fooled by the simplicity of this. There are many gases, for instance ammonia and carbon dioxide, that turn to liquids when compressed sufficiently. If you were testing Boyle's Law experimentally with one of these gases you might get some surprising results if part of the gas being studied turned to liquid; there could be a sudden shrinkage that would cause pV to be far from constant.

Notwithstanding all we have just said, there are some good, sound reasons for regarding −273°C as a significant temperature. In fact, scientists have developed another temperature scale on which the zero point is set at this special temperature (−273.15°C to be precise). This is known as the **Kelvin scale** or **Absolute scale**, and the temperature

There is a second problem here. Although they have come fairly close, scientists have never succeeded in reaching the temperature −273°C.

The scale was named after Lord Kelvin (1824-1907), the British scientist who pointed out some of its advantages.

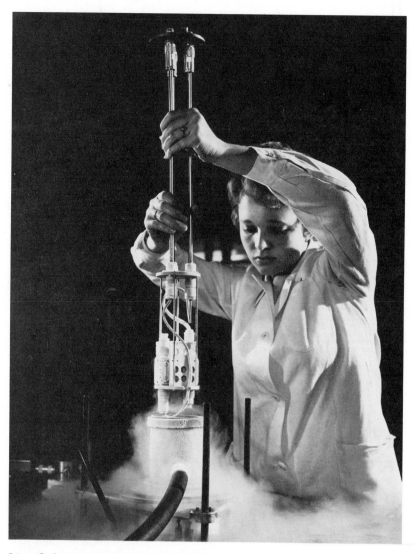

Liquefied gases are commonly used in scientific work done at very low temperatures. Here a device is being lowered into a kind of thermos bottle that contains liquid nitrogen at a temperature of about –200°C.

The cloud consists of tiny ice crystals formed from the moisture in the air when chilled by the very cold nitrogen gas escaping from the container.

–273.15°C is called the **Absolute zero** of temperature. A degree on the Kelvin scale is the same size as a degree on the Celsius scale, and thus a temperature on the Kelvin scale will be 273 degrees higher than the same temperature on the Celsius scale. It is customary to represent a temperature on the Kelvin or Absolute scale by the capital letter T, and since we have used t previously to represent temperature on the Celsius scale, the relationship between the two can be given simply as:

$$T = t + 273$$

Degrees on the Kelvin scale are called kelvins (symbol K), and a temperature is written as a number followed by the symbol, but no degree sign (°) is used. The freezing point of water, for instance, is 273 K, and is read: 273 kelvins. The Kelvin and Celsius scales of temperature are compared visually in Fig. 18-5.

9. GAY-LUSSAC'S LAW. Equation (3) stated that, for a given mass of gas at fixed pressure, $V_t = $ constant $(273 + t)$. Immediately we see an advantage of the Kelvin temperature scale, for we can now rewrite this as:

$$V_T = \text{constant} \times T \qquad (4)$$

This gives us a very concise statement of the effect of temperature on the volume of a sample of gas measured at constant pressure. *If the pressure is kept constant, the volume of a fixed mass of a gas is directly proportional to its temperature in kelvins.* This is a modern statement of **Gay-Lussac's Law.**

Rearranging Equation (4), and omitting the subscript on V, gives:

$$\frac{V}{T} = \text{constant}$$

Hence $$\frac{V_1}{T_1} = \frac{V_2}{T_2}$$

or $$V_2 = V_1 \left(\frac{T_2}{T_1}\right)$$

where V_1 and V_2 are the volumes at the two temperatures T_1 and T_2. If the temperature of a certain mass of gas changes from T_1 to T_2, the volume will change proportionately: the final volume, V_2, will be the initial volume multiplied by a ratio of Kelvin temperatures. This ratio must be such that if the temperature goes up ($T_2 > T_1$), V_2 will be greater than V_1.

Problem 18-4: A sample of hydrogen gas has a volume of 10.0 L at 20°C. What will be its volume at 200°C (the pressure remaining constant)?

Solution: $V_1 = 10.0$ L $\qquad T_1 = (273 + 20)$ K $= 293$ K
$V_2 = ?$ $\qquad T_2 = (273 + 200)$ K $= 473$ K
(Don't forget these conversions from the Celsius to the Kelvin scale!)

The final volume, V_2, will be the initial volume corrected for the change in temperature, that is, multiplied by the appropriate ratio of temperatures. Since the temperature increases, the volume must increase. Therefore

$$V_2 = 10.0\,\text{L} \times \frac{473\ \text{K}}{293\ \text{K}} = 16.1\ \text{L}$$

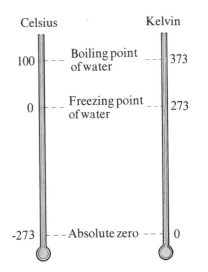

Fig. 18-5: *On the Kelvin scale a temperature interval of one degree (called one kelvin) is identical with a one-degree interval on the Celsius scale; that is, one kelvin equals one Celsius degree. In effect, then, the Kelvin scale is the Celsius scale with the zero shifted downwards by 273 degrees.*

In many textbooks, including the first edition of this book, what we are calling Gay-Lussac's Law is known as Charles' Law. There is relatively little known about the contribution of J. A. C. Charles to the discovery of the law, but he appears never to have published anything about it. Gay-Lussac published a full account of his own experimental work that led to the law; in this account he mentions that the law had earlier been known to Charles. We are following the practice in many countries of attributing the law to Gay-Lussac. About the same time John Dalton also discovered the same relationship.

10. WHEN BOTH PRESSURE AND TEMPERATURE VARY. So far we have discussed the effect on the volume of a sample of gas of changing either its pressure or its temperature, while keeping the other constant. It is a simple matter to calculate the effect of changing both pressure and temperature if we consider the change as being made up of two steps, in each of which one of pressure or temperature is kept constant.

Suppose, for example, that a sample of gas whose volume is 525 mL at 200 kPa and 27°C is compressed and heated to 600 kPa and 327°C. We can calculate the new volume in two ways:

(a) Assume that the gas is *first heated* at 200 kPa to 327°C, and *then compressed* at 327°C to 600 kPa.

In the first step the volume *increases* to, let us say, V' (a gas expands when heated).

Then $V' = 525 \text{ mL} \times \dfrac{600 \text{ K}}{300 \text{ K}}$ (keeping the pressure constant)

In the second step the volume *decreases* to V_2 (a gas contracts when compressed).

$$V_2 = V' \times \frac{200 \text{ kPa}}{600 \text{ kPa}} \quad \text{(keeping the temperature constant)}$$

$$= 525 \text{ mL} \times \frac{600 \text{ K}}{300 \text{ K}} \times \frac{200 \text{ kPa}}{600 \text{ kPa}} = 350 \text{ mL}$$

or (b) Assume that the gas is *first compressed* at 27°C to 600 kPa, and *then heated* at 600 kPa to 327°C.

In the first step the volume *decreases* to, say, V''

Then $V'' = 525 \text{ mL} \times \dfrac{200 \text{ kPa}}{600 \text{ kPa}}$ (keeping the temperature constant)

In the second step the volume *increases* to V_2

$$V_2 = V'' \times \frac{600 \text{ K}}{300 \text{ K}} \quad \text{(keeping the pressure constant)}$$

$$= 525 \text{ mL} \times \frac{200 \text{ kPa}}{600 \text{ kPa}} \times \frac{600 \text{ K}}{300 \text{ K}} = 350 \text{ mL}$$

These volume changes are shown diagrammatically in Fig. 18-6.

Problem 18-5: A sample of a gas occupies a volume of 350 mL at 7°C and 303.9 kPa. What volume would it occupy at 47°C and 152.0 kPa?

Solution: Step 1. Correct for the change in temperature, assuming (for the moment) that the pressure stays constant 303.9 kPa.

$$T_1 = (273 + 7) \text{ K} = 280 \text{ K} \qquad T_2 = (273 + 47) \text{ K} = 320 \text{ K}$$

Let the new volume be V_1

Then $V_1 = 350\,\text{mL} \times \dfrac{320\,\text{K}}{280\,\text{K}}$ (The volume should be greater than

the original volume since the temperature of the gas has increased.)

Step 2. Correct now for the change in pressure, assuming that the temperature stays constant at the new value, 320 K.

Let the final volume be V_2 (V_2 will be greater than V_1 because the pressure has decreased.)

Then $V_2 = V_1 \times \dfrac{303.9\,\text{kPa}}{152.0\,\text{kPa}}$

$\qquad = 350\,\text{mL} \times \dfrac{320\,\text{K}}{280\,\text{K}} \times \dfrac{303.9\,\text{kPa}}{152.0\,\text{kPa}} = 800\,\text{mL}$

The volume at 47°C and 152.0 kPa would be 800 mL.

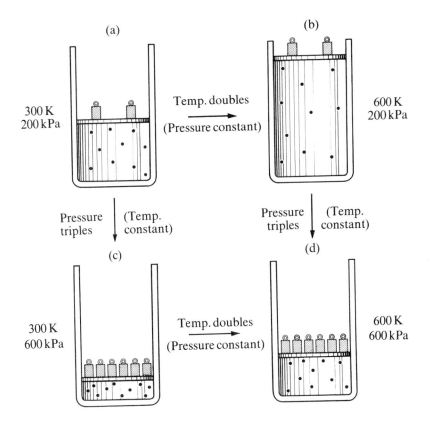

Fig. 18-6: *The effect on volume of changing both temperature and pressure is demonstrated here. Doubling the Kelvin temperature doubles the volume: (a) to (b), or (c) to (d), in accordance with Gay-Lussac's Law. Tripling the pressure reduces the volume to one-third: (a) to (c), or (b) to (d), in accordance with Boyle's Law. It does not matter in what order the two changes are made; the final volume is the same either way.*

The essence of an explosion is a very rapid expansion of very hot gases, produced by very rapid reactions that preferably are very exothermic.

Here a rock plug in a water tunnel is being blasted out of existence by several tonnes of a water-resistant explosive.

If we use the symbols p_1, V_1, T_1 and p_2, V_2, T_2 to represent, respectively, the initial and final pressures, volumes, and temperatures, and if we carry out the same steps we arrive at the combined expression:

$$V_2 = V_1 \times \frac{p_1}{p_2} \times \frac{T_2}{T_1}$$

This may also be written:

$$\frac{p_1 V_1}{T_1} = \frac{p_2 V_2}{T_2} \tag{5}$$

or, more generally for a fixed mass of gas:

$$\frac{pV}{T} = \text{constant} \tag{6}$$

Equation (5) is useful for the solution of problems in which volumes of gases are altered by simultaneous changes in pressure and temperature.

Problem 18-6: A 20.0 mL sample of gas, initially at 17°C and 100 kPa, was heated to 307°C, and at this temperature its volume was observed to be 75.0 mL. What was the pressure of the gas at the new temperature?

Solution: The answer can be obtained by substituting in Equation (5), thus:

$p_1 = 100\,\text{kPa}$ $V_1 = 20.0\,\text{mL}$ $T_1 = 290\,\text{K}$

$p_2 = ?$ $V_2 = 75.0\,\text{mL}$ $T_2 = 580\,\text{K}$

Thus $\dfrac{100 \times 20.0}{290} = \dfrac{p_2 \times 75.0}{580}$

and accordingly, $p_2 = 53.3\,\text{kPa}$

Therefore, the new pressure was 53.3 kPa.

11. Boyle's Law deals with the change in volume of a gas when pressure changes at constant temperature; Gay-Lussac's Law with change in volume due to change in temperature at constant pressure. From Equation (6) we can discern a third relationship among these quantities. Suppose we had a certain amount of a gas in a container of fixed volume, and then the temperature increased. Equation (6) shows that the pressure of the gas will increase in accordance with the relationship.

$$p = \text{constant} \times T \quad \text{(at constant mass and volume)}$$

A common example of change in gaseous pressure resulting from change in temperature occurs in automobile tires. A tire may be inflated to the recommended pressure on a summer morning, but as it rolls along on a hot pavement in the middle of the day, the air inside may become a good deal hotter. The tire casing cannot expand much, and the result of this heating is that the pressure inside the tire increases. The manufacturers of tires sometimes recommend underinflating them before long trips in summer.

12. STANDARD TEMPERATURE AND PRESSURE. Since the volume of a gas depends so markedly on temperature and pressure, there is no point in a comparison of volumes unless the temperature and pressure at which each of the volumes was measured are stated. It is better to compare volumes that have been measured at the same temperature and pressure. If the volumes have, through necessity, been measured under different conditions, one can calculate what the volumes would have been at some common temperature and pressure. Scientists have agreed on a *standard temperature* and a *standard pressure* for such comparisons.

Standard Temperature = 0°C or 273 K
Standard Pressure = 101.3 kPa or 1.00 atm or 760 Torr

To be precise, 273.15 K and 101.325 kPa.

Volumes of gases are therefore very frequently measured at, or corrected to, *standard temperature and pressure* (STP). The densities of gases, given in Table 18-1 and elsewhere, all refer to these conditions.

The volume of a gas measured under conditions other than standard can be corrected to STP by means of Boyle's and Gay-Lussac's Laws.

Problem 18-7: A sample of oxygen occupies 2.00 L at 27°C and 100 kPa. What would its volume be at STP?

Solution: 27°C = 300 K; 0°C = 273 K

Correct the volume in two stages as in Problem 18-5. The two steps may be combined as in Problem 18-6, but only when you are familiar with the separate steps.

$$V_2 = 2.00 \text{ L} \times \frac{273 \text{ K}}{300 \text{ K}} \times \frac{100 \text{ kPa}}{101.3 \text{ kPa}} = 1.80 \text{ L}$$

13.' VARIATION IN DENSITY OF A GAS WITH CHANGES IN CONDITIONS. The density of a body is the ratio: mass/volume. Since the volumes of gases are so greatly affected by changes in temperature and pressure, in comparison with liquids and solids, it is clear that their densities will be comparably affected. The change in density of a gas when the pressure or temperature changes will be in the opposite sense to the corresponding changes in volume. That is, the density of a gas increases when the pressure increases, but decreases when the temperature increases. It is sometimes necessary to calculate the density of a gas at a particular temperature and pressure given a value at some other conditions, for instance a value at STP (Table 18-1). You can in this case show by reasoning such as that developed in Sec. 18-10 that

$$\rho_2 = \rho_1 \times \frac{p_2}{p_1} \times \frac{T_1}{T_2}$$

where ρ_1 is the given density and ρ_2 is the value sought.

QUESTIONS

In some of the numerical questions in this chapter units appear that are not part of the International System (SI). These examples are included to give an opportunity to recognize and handle units outside SI that are still in widespread use.

1. Why are the densities of gases so much lower than those of liquids and solids?

2. What is meant by *diffusion* of a gas? Why do gases diffuse so much more rapidly than liquids or solids?

3. (a) Make a labelled diagram of a mercury barometer. Mark precisely the positions between which the height of the mercury column is measured.

(b) For a height of mercury column = 74.0 cm, state the pressure of the atmosphere in kilopascals, standard atmospheres, and torr.

4. The density of mercury is 13.6 g/cm^3 (= 13.6 × 10^3 kg/m^3), and the acceleration due to gravity (at sea level) is 9.8 m/s^2. From these data calculate the pressure (in kilopascals) equivalent to a column of mercury 760 mm in length. Note that this is how one standard atmosphere is defined. (To be precise, the density is 13.595 g/cm^3 for 0°C, and *g* is 9.806 m/s^2.)

5. Make the following conversions of pressure from one unit to another:

(a) 700 Torr to kPa

(b) 95.9 kPa to atm

(c) 3.00 atm to Torr

(d) 1.00 Pa to Torr

(e) 300 atm to MPa (megapascals)

(f) 19 Torr to atm

6. Convert the following melting points, given in kelvins, to degrees Celsius: oxygen 54, chlorine 172, mercury 234, sulphur 392, zinc 692.6, copper 1356, iron 1809, molybdenum 2893.

7. Convert the following boiling points, given in degrees Celsius, to kelvins: helium −268.9, neon −246.1, argon −185.9, krypton −153.4, xenon −108.1, radon −62.1.

*8. Plot boiling points of the inert gases, in kelvins, against atomic number of the element. Does the relationship so revealed suggest any connection between Van der Waals' forces, which the molecules must overcome in order to evaporate, and atomic number? (See Sec. 15-19.)

9. From the data in the following table calculate the missing quantity (assuming constant temperature).

INITIAL		FINAL	
VOLUME	PRESSURE	PRESSURE	VOLUME
200 L	700 Torr	350 Torr	— L
22.4 L	1 atm	— atm	2.8 L
60 mL	— kPa	101.3 kPa	16 mL
— m^3	40 Pa	100 kPa	1.0 L
2.50 L	7.5 atm	— atm	100 mL

10. A cylinder of compressed oxygen, with a capacity of 40 L, was equipped with a pressure gauge that read 1910

lb/in². How much oxygen, measured at 1.0 atm (14.7 lb/in²) will this cylinder provide?

11. Why was zero on the Kelvin temperature scale set at −273°C rather than at some convenient value such as −300°C?

12. To what temperature on the Celsius scale must a gas be cooled at constant pressure so that it will occupy half the volume it occupies at 25°C?

13. Why is it advantageous to express temperatures on the Kelvin scale when dealing with gaseous volumes?

14. From the data in the following table calculate the missing quantity (assuming constant pressure).

INITIAL		FINAL	
VOL.	TEMP.	TEMP.	VOL.
22.4 L	0°C	91°C	— L
125 mL	—°C	25°C	100 mL
— L	400 K	175 K	6.20 L
250 mL	298 K	— K	273 mL

15. It is a common saying that "hot air rises." A better description is to say that the density of air is decreased by heating, and that the colder, more dense air descends and displaces upward the warm, less dense air. To show this, calculate the density of air at 50°C and 1 atm, given that the density at STP is 1.293 g/L.

16. From the data in the following table calculate the missing quantity.

INITIAL			FINAL		
VOL.	PRESS.	TEMP.	TEMP.	PRESS.	VOL.
20.0 L	101.3 kPa	250 K	400 K	50.6 kpa	— L
400 mL	2.00 atm	27°C	—°C	3.00 atm	356 mL
1.00 L	109 Torr	50°C	100°C	— Torr	1.25 L
820 mL	87.5 kPa	— K	270 K	1.00 atm	1010 mL
7.2 L	— kPa	800°C	300°C	120 kPa	6.9 L

17. Explain why it is more important with a gas than with a liquid to specify the temperature and the pressure when stating the volume or density.

18. One litre of ammonia gas, measured at 27°C and 93.3 kPa was found to have a mass of 0.646 g. Calculate the density at STP.

19. The pressure gauge on a tank of compressed helium gas was observed in the laboratory at 25°C to be reading 2000 lb/in². The tank was then taken out to an unheated shed for storage, and on a cold day the temperature fell to −10°C. What would the pressure gauge then have read? What would this reading be, converted to kilopascals?

20. When an automobile tire is inflated to a gauge pressure of, say, 26 lb/in², this means that the pressure inside the tire is the indicated value greater than atmospheric pressure. Given the conversion factor: 1 atm = 14.7 lb/in², calculate the pressure inside a tire that has been inflated to 26 lb/in². Give your answer in pounds per square inch, atmospheres, and kilopascals.

21. Suppose the tire in the preceding problem had been inflated at 20°C, but after running on hot pavement its temperature had risen to 50°C. If the tire casing allowed for negligible expansion, what would the pressure inside the tire then be?

22. The volume of a sample of oxygen was measured at several temperatures, but at constant pressure, with the following results:

t (°C)	–25	0	25	50	75
V (mL)	250	276	300	326	350

Show that the sample obeyed Gay-Lussac's Law.

19 A Theory of the Gaseous State

In fact, "gas" is derived from the Greek word for "chaos." This appropriate choice was made by J. B. van Helmont (1577-1644) some two hundred and fifty years before the chaotic nature of a gas was established.

1. Early in Chapter 17 we gave a brief description of a gas in terms of molecules, widely separated from each other, and in endless chaotic motion. This model permits us to explain why a gas is so compressible compared to solids or liquids, and why gases diffuse or mingle so readily. We should like to go further in this chapter, and show how the model can be extended to account for Boyle's and Gay-Lussac's Laws.

THE KINETIC-MOLECULAR THEORY OF GASES

2. MOLECULAR COLLISIONS. The motion of the molecules leads to frequent collisions one with another or with the container walls. We can account for the pressure exerted by a gas as the result of the continual bombardment by the fast-moving molecules on the walls of the container. The pressure applies uniformly on the entire inner surface of the container; we may deduce from this that the motion of the molecules is completely *random*. The pressure also remains constant at constant temperature. This leads us to believe that the collisions must all be perfectly *elastic*, for otherwise the pressure would gradually diminish as the molecules dissipated their kinetic energy through inelastic collisions.

When objects collide and rebound, some kinetic energy is usually lost because of the work required to deform the surfaces of the objects where they come in contact. Ideally one could imagine this happening with no such loss in energy; such an idealized collision would be described as perfectly *elastic*. The collision of two billiard balls is fairly elastic, but that of two tennis balls is less so, while that of two balls of putty is highly inelastic.

3. THE PRESSURE FORMULA. Assuming gaseous pressure to be caused by a rain of molecules on the container walls, we next try to establish what factors influence how great or how small the pressure will be. There appear to be four such factors:

(a) **The number of molecules in the sample of gas** (*n*). Obviously the more gas molecules are present in a container, the heavier will be the bombardment on the container walls, assuming the other factors to be kept constant.

Pressure is greater the greater is n.

(b) **The mass of the molecules** (*m*). Other things being equal, a heavy molecule will strike a harder blow on the container wall than a light one.

Pressure is greater the greater is m.

(c) **The speed of the molecules** (*u*). The speed of the molecules will affect the pressure in two ways. For one thing, the faster a molecule strikes a surface the more force it exerts, and this contributes more to the pressure. But also, the faster a molecule is moving about in a container the more often it will get to a wall and add its small blow to the total force.

Pressure is greater (for two reasons) the greater is u.

(d) **The volume of the container** (*V*). The larger the container, the greater the distance the molecules will have to travel from one collision to the next. Fewer collisions per second mean less force.

Pressure is less the greater is V.

Compare yourself running in straight lines from wall to wall in your bedroom and in the school gymnasium: you will register more blows on the bedroom walls in one minute than you can possibly manage in the gymnasium.

The exact effect of each of these factors can be worked out for a model gas by the straightforward application of mechanics. The result shows that the various factors can be combined in one relationship. For *n* molecules, each of mass *m* and average speed $\bar{u}$, the relationship is

$$p = \frac{\frac{1}{3}nm\bar{u}^2}{V}$$

or

$$pV = \tfrac{1}{3}nm\bar{u}^2 \tag{1}$$

The right-hand side of this equation can be related to the kinetic energy of the molecules. The kinetic energy of a single molecule of mass *m* and speed *u* will be $\frac{1}{2}mu^2$; for *n* molecules with various speeds, u_1, u_2, u_3, etc., the total kinetic energy will be

$$\tfrac{1}{2}m(u_1^2 + u_2^2 + u_3^2 + \ldots u_n^2)$$

and the average kinetic energy per molecule will be $\frac{1}{2}m\bar{u}^2$, where $\bar{u}$ represents a kind of average speed of the molecules.

In the interest of precision it should be stated that $\bar{u}$ is not just the simple average or mean of the speeds: it is, rather, the square root of the average of the squares of the individual speeds. This is often called the *root-mean-square* speed.

4. THE SIGNIFICANCE OF ABSOLUTE TEMPERATURE. From Equation (1) we therefore conclude that

pV is proportional to the average kinetic energy of the molecules in a gas.

But we previously saw, by combining Boyle's and Gay-Lussac's Laws in Equation (6) of Chapter 18, that

pV is proportional to the temperature of a gas on the Kelvin scale.

These two relationships suggest a remarkable conclusion. There appears to be some connection between the Kelvin scale of temperature (which we introduced as a convenient device for expressing Gay-Lussac's Law in Sec. 18-9) and the average kinetic energy of the molecules in a gas. This certainly gives the Kelvin temperature scale a much greater significance than a mere aid in formulating Gay-Lussac's Law. From the sort of evidence very briefly developed here, and much more besides, scientists have come to regard this conclusion as valid, and applicable to molecules in all states of matter, not just in gases. Thus we may state: *the Kelvin temperature of a body is a measure of the average kinetic energy of its molecules.*

The molecular model of matter is one of the great theories of physical science. To give emphasis to the motion of the molecules, and to the energy associated with this motion, we usually refer to this model or description of matter as the *kinetic-molecular theory.*

5. SOME CONSEQUENCES OF THE PRESSURE FORMULA. If we have n molecules, each of mass m, their total mass is nm; a gas consisting of these molecules would have a mass of nm units. Equation (1) may be rearranged to read

$$\bar{u}^2 = \frac{3\,pV}{nm} = \frac{3 \times \text{pressure} \times \text{volume}}{\text{mass}}$$

$$= \frac{3 \times \text{pressure}}{\text{density}}$$

By expressing pressure in the proper units one can solve this equation for $\bar{u}$, the average molecular speed. The answer is rather surprising. For common gases like oxygen or nitrogen the average speed of the molecules is about 1700 km/h—comparable to the speed of a rifle bullet.

Boyle's Law is seen as a consequence of the pressure formula provided we assume that at constant temperature the average molecular speed remains constant. We put Equation (1) in the form:

$$pV = \tfrac{1}{3} \times \text{mass} \times \bar{u}^2$$

This shows clearly that if $\bar{u}$, the average speed of the molecules, remains constant, pV for a given mass of gas also remains constant—which is Boyle's Law.

You see also, by the way, that if the mass, nm, of a gas is doubled without changing the pressure or temperature, the volume is doubled.

As we have just noted, Gay-Lussac's Law can be related to the pressure formula if we make the assumption that the average kinetic energy of the molecules is proportional to the Kelvin temperature.

To repeat, the pressure formula states

$$pV = \tfrac{1}{3}\,nm\bar{u}^2$$

A given sample of gas will contain a fixed number, n, of molecules. If the pressure, p, of this gas is constant, the volume, V, is proportional to $m\bar{u}^2$, which by this last assumption is proportional to the Kelvin temperature, T. So volume varies as the Kelvin temperature—which is Gay-Lussac's Law.

Also, at constant volume, the pressure varies directly as the Kelvin temperature. This relationship was mentioned in Sec. 18-11.

There is another consequence of the pressure formula which is of sufficient importance to merit the following section to itself.

6. AVOGADRO'S PRINCIPLE. Suppose we have two different gases in separate containers. We shall write the pressure formula for each, using subscripts *1* and *2* to indicate the various characteristics of each.

$$p_1 V_1 = \tfrac{1}{3} n_1 m_1 \bar{u}_1^2 \quad \text{and} \quad p_2 V_2 = \tfrac{1}{3} n_2 m_2 \bar{u}_2^2$$

Now suppose the gases are at the same pressure: $p_1 = p_2$. Also suppose they are at the same temperature: then $m_1 \bar{u}_1^2 = m_2 \bar{u}_2^2$. Finally, let us suppose the volumes of the two containers are equal: $V_1 = V_2$. When all these equalities are cancelled out we are left with the relationship that $n_1 = n_2$. That means that under these conditions there are the same number of molecules in each container.

This relationship is known as **Avogadro's Principle**, and it may be stated in words as follows. *Equal volumes of gases, measured at the same temperature and pressure, contain equal numbers of molecules.*

Avogadro came to this conclusion in 1811 by an entirely different chain of reasoning. (Indeed, the pressure formula was not derived until 1848, by Joule.) In 1808 the same Gay-Lussac noted that in many chemical reactions in which gases participate a simple relationship exists among the volumes of the gases, provided these are all measured at the same temperature and pressure. Here are a few examples of such reactions:

Water $\longrightarrow$ Hydrogen gas + Oxygen gas
2 volumes   1 volume

Carbon monoxide + Oxygen $\longrightarrow$ Carbon dioxide
2 volumes   1 volume   2 volumes

Hydrogen + Chlorine $\longrightarrow$ Hydrogen chloride
1 volume   1 volume   2 volumes

What is often known as **Gay-Lussac's Law of Combining Gas Volumes** can be expressed in this way: *In any chemical reaction involving gaseous substances, the volumes of the various gases reacting or produced are in the ratio of simple whole numbers* (provided that all volumes are measured at the same temperature and pressure).

Avogadro in Italy conceived the idea of *molecules* as the ultimate particles in gases, and suggested that the simple volume relationships such as the foregoing could be explained by the assumption that a fixed volume of any gas contained the same number of these particles (under the same conditions of temperature and pressure), and that the particles combined or rearranged in integral proportions.

7. AVOGADRO'S PRINCIPLE AND GAS DENSITY. There is a very important deduction to be made from Avogadro's Principle. Table 18-1 lists densities of several gases. These are the masses of one litre of gas at STP. But one litre of any gas at STP contains the same number of molecules as one litre of any other at the same temperature and pressure. So if we compare the densities of two gases, we are really comparing the masses of equal numbers of molecules. Then if one gas should happen to be twice as dense as another, we could deduce that

The heavier of the two kinds of gas molecules will travel on the average more slowly, so that $\bar{u}_1/\bar{u}_2 = \sqrt{m_2/m_1}$.

Joseph-Louis Gay-Lussac (1778-1850) was a meteorologist, geologist, physicist, chemist, professor, superintendent of the government powder factory, chief assayer at the Mint and, later, parliamentarian.

The year 1808 was perhaps his greatest year: it was then that he enunciated what is now called his Law of Combining Gas Volumes, isolated the element boron, and married Joséphine who, as a seventeen-year old, had attracted his attention by reading a chemistry textbook in her spare time. In those days textbooks were far from common, and seventeen-year-old girls who read them were even more rare.

its molecules must be twice as heavy as those of the other gas. To take a specific example, the density of oxygen (1.429 g/L) is about twice as great as that of methane (0.717 g/L). We may conclude from Avogadro's Principle that 1.429 g and 0.717 g are the masses of the same number of molecules of oxygen and methane respectively. Therefore we deduce that oxygen molecules are about twice as heavy as methane molecules. We cannot tell from this anything about the mass of a single molecule of either gas, but we can compare their relative masses. We are left in much the same position as we found ourselves in discussing the relative masses of atoms in Sec. 4-3. We shall deal with this problem again in Chapter 20.

8. REAL GASES AND THE IDEAL GAS. Boyle's and Gay-Lussac's Laws and certain other laws describing the behaviour of gases have been known for a very long time. With the development of physical science, studies of the behaviour of gases were extended to many different substances, and to more extreme conditions than had been tried in the earliest experiments; also the techniques of handling and measuring gases were improved. As more and more data were collected it became apparent that the various gas laws were not always rigorously adhered to. Departures from Boyle's Law were found at high pressures, and from Gay-Lussac's Law at low temperatures; and, as a rule, gases like ammonia or chlorine that could easily be liquefied behaved worse than gases like hydrogen or oxygen with low boiling points.

The conclusion has been reached that Boyle's and Gay-Lussac's Laws and some other gas laws really apply rigorously only to a *model* gas in which the size of the molecules and the forces between the molecules are assumed to be negligible. No actual or real gas has quite the properties of such a model gas (although some gases come close to achieving this). For this reason we speak of the gas laws as describing the behaviour of an "ideal" or "perfect" gas. Insofar as real gases approximate the properties of this ideal gas, the gas laws will describe their behaviour too. Real gases become more like the ideal gas the higher their temperature and the lower their pressure. Departures from ideal behaviour are most noticeable as a gas approaches liquefaction.

Real gases fail to behave just like the model or ideal gas for two reasons. One reason is that in real gases there *are* intermolecular forces between the molecules, and these become more significant the closer the molecules are to one another and the slower their speed. That is why the behaviour of real gases deviates more and more from ideal behaviour as the pressure increases (thereby bringing the molecules into closer proximity) and as the temperature decreases (thereby slowing down the molecules). The second reason for the non-ideal behaviour of real gases is that their individual molecules are not insignificant in size: they *do* occupy some volume. As you might predict, the effect of this becomes increasingly important as the volume of the gas as a whole decreases, that is, as the pressure increases. On both counts, then, we would expect what we said in the final sentence of the preceding paragraph.

VAPOUR PRESSURE

9. SATURATED VAPOUR. Now that we have devoted some discussion to the origin and measurement of pressure in gases we are in a better position to consider a property associated with the evaporation of liquids (and solids, too, though to a much lesser extent).

If you place a few millilitres of water in a flat dish like a saucer, and leave the dish undisturbed for some hours, all the water will evaporate. There are some liquids like ether and acetone which will evaporate in the open quickly enough that you can watch them disappear within a minute or so. We gave a molecular interpretation of evaporation in Sec. 17-10. Suppose you next put a few millilitres of water into a litre bottle and then close the bottle with a stopper. This time, no matter how long you wait, most of the water will remain in the bottle without evaporating. You might notice, though, that droplets of water accumulate around the shoulder of the bottle on prolonged standing; and this suggests that some of the water may have evaporated from the pool at the bottom of the bottle and condensed near the top. This is the only evidence you are apt to see that anything has happened.

By much more elaborate experiments it is possible to show that:

(a) a small amount of water does evaporate into the bottle;

(b) there is a limit to the amount of this evaporation;

(c) this limit depends on the temperature of the water, so that more water *vapour* can accumulate in the bottle the higher the temperature.

The space in the bottle is said to become *saturated* with water vapour, or we say that at the limit of evaporation we have a saturated vapour in the bottle. As a rule, to produce a saturated vapour, we allow a liquid (or a solid, perhaps) to evaporate in a closed container, so that the vapour accumulates. Moreover, we must take a surplus of the liquid—more than enough to produce saturation in the container—because it is only when we see some of the liquid remaining that we know we have really saturated the vapour.

10. EQUILIBRIUM IN A SATURATED VAPOUR. When we have a liquid and a saturated vapour together in a closed container nothing outwardly seems to be happening. However, there are reasons for believing that at the molecular level much is still going on. The "hot" molecules continue to break away from their less energetic companions in the liquid. But by this time there are a lot of molecules in the vapour phase, and among these there will be some that suffer some adverse collisions and get slowed down. These "cooler" molecules in the vapour will, if they come near the surface of the liquid, suffer capture into the pool of liquid because of intermolecular attractions. Hence some molecules will be evaporating and others condensing. In the closed container, where liquid and vapour are together, these two processes are going on at the same rate, so that there is no net gain or loss to either phase. Chemistry has a special word to describe this situation, which has many parallels in physical and chemical changes. The liquid and its saturated vapour are said to be in **equilibrium.** The equilibrium represents a state of balance between two opposing processes: in this case evaporation and con-

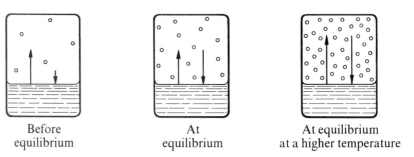

Before equilibrium   At equilibrium   At equilibrium at a higher temperature

Fig. 19-1: *The relative rates of evaporating and condensing are indicated by the relative lengths of the arrows. The number of molecules per unit volume of vapour, and hence its pressure, is at a maximum at equilibrium, when the two rates are equal. At a higher temperature, this number of molecules is higher and hence the vapour pressure is higher.*

densation. And if we wish to remind ourselves of the activity still going on at the molecular level we add a word implying motion, and call the condition *dynamic equilibrium*.

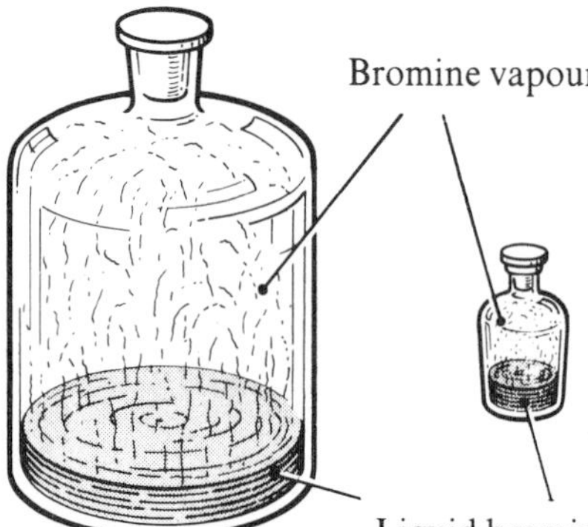

11. PRESSURE OF THE SATURATED VAPOUR: VAPOUR PRESSURE. The amount of a substance required to produce a saturated vapour depends on the volume of the closed container. To illustrate this, we make the following simple experimental comparison. We select two glass-stoppered bottles of widely different capacity (say 2L and 50 mL). Into each we put a small amount of liquid bromine, sufficient in each case to produce a saturated vapour. (Bromine, though unpleasant to work with, has the advantage that its vapour is easily seen.) When we are satisfied that equilibrium has been established, we compare the colour of the vapour in the two bottles (Fig. 19-2). It will be obvious that there is much more bromine in the vapour in the larger bottle. But we might guess by visual inspection that if we could extract from each bottle *samples* of the vapour which were the *same size* they would contain the same amount of bromine. Our guess would be confirmed by a careful experiment.

We can sum up the state of affairs in the two bottles of saturated bromine vapour by saying that *there are in each the same number of bromine molecules per unit of volume.* But Equation (1), the pressure formula, shows that at a fixed temperature the pressure, p, is proportional to the ratio n/V, the number of molecules per unit volume. So we may conclude that the pressure due to bromine molecules is the same in each bottle. The pressure due to the molecules of a particular substance in a saturated vapour is called the *vapour pressure* of that substance.

It is important to understand that the (equilibrium) vapour pressure is a *maximum* pressure of the vapour. In the space above a water surface, the pressure of water vapour can have any value all the way from zero (before evaporation has begun) up to the equilibrium vapour pressure.

For bromine, for water, or for any volatile substance, there is a particular vapour pressure at a specified temperature. In the case of substances like ether or acetone, which show a pronounced tendency to evaporate, a considerable amount of vapour can accumulate in a closed space above the liquid before equilibrium is attained. These substances thus have relatively large vapour pressures even at room temperature. Water or turpentine, by comparison with the foregoing examples, are less volatile; a lower pressure of their vapours will

Bromine vapour

Liquid bromine

Fig. 19-2: *The amount of bromine in the vapour phase in the large bottle is much greater than that in the small bottle when both vapours are saturated. However, the amount of bromine per millilitre of the vapour in each bottle is the same.*

To be precise about terms here, we remind you that because of the way this simple experiment was performed there would also have been air in the bottles, and that the air molecules would also contribute to the pressure inside the bottles. We are interested in the pressure contributed by the bromine molecules only. The proper term to describe this pressure is the *partial pressure of the bromine vapour.* This partial pressure is the pressure the bromine vapour would have exerted if it alone occupied the volume of the container.

TABLE 19-1

VAPOUR PRESSURES OF SOME
COMMON SUBSTANCES AT 25°C

SUBSTANCE	VAPOUR PRESSURE
	(kPa)
Ether	71.6
Acetone	30.6
Bromine	28.5
Carbon tetrachloride	15.3
Ethyl alcohol	7.86
Water	3.17
Turpentine	0.73
*Paradichlorobenzene**	0.088
*Iodine**	0.041
*Naphthalene**	0.012
Mercury	0.000 24

*A solid. Paradichlorobenzene and naphthalene are used as moth repellents.

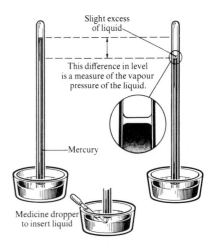

Fig. 19-3: *To measure the vapour pressure of a liquid, a small excess of the liquid is introduced above the mercury in a barometer tube. The vapour pressure of the liquid (in torr) is the difference (in millimetres) between the mercury level after equilibrium is reached and that before the liquid was introduced. The vapour pressure can be converted to a value in kilopascals (Sec. 18-4).*

be sufficient to balance the evaporation of the liquids. A substance like mineral oil scarcely evaporates at all, and so has a negligibly small vapour pressure. We can compare the volatility of liquids by comparing their vapour pressures at any given temperature. Table 19-1 lists the vapour pressures of a number of common substances at 25°C (that is, about room temperature); and as these are arranged in descending order of vapour pressure, this is the order of decreasing volatility.

Vapour pressure is a characteristic and quantitative property of a solid or liquid (though its values are very sensitive to changes in temperature, as outlined in Sec. 19-14). Some people have found it puzzling that the pressure (or partial pressure) of a *vapour*, observed and measured in a different phase, should be used as a measure of the volatility of a *solid* or *liquid*. You may find it helpful, therefore, to think of vapour pressure as the number of vapour molecules per unit volume just sufficient to balance the *escaping tendency* of the molecules from the solid or liquid.

12. By this time you should have acquired enough information about the connection between structure and properties to realize that the substances most likely to form vapours are those existing as molecules. The attractive forces between molecules are much smaller than those residing in the bonds that join atoms within molecules or crystals. Some molecules can therefore escape from a congregation of other molecules in the manner suggested in Sec. 17-10. It is much more difficult for an atom in a crystal of, say, a metal to acquire sufficient kinetic energy to overcome the attraction of its fellows. Hence for substances such as metals, network solids, or ionic solids no appreciable vapour pressure is detected at moderate temperatures.

13. EXPERIMENTAL DETERMINATION OF VAPOUR PRESSURE. The simplest and most direct—though not the most accurate—method of measuring a vapour pressure of a liquid is illustrated in Fig. 19-3. The liquid is introduced drop by drop into a barometer tube. It rises to the top of the mercury and evaporates into the vacuum. Enough is added to saturate the space with vapour. The pres-

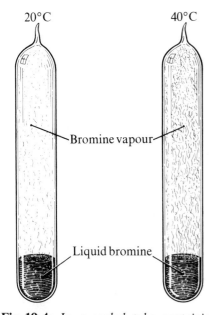

20°C   40°C

Bromine vapour

Liquid bromine

Fig. 19-4: *In a sealed tube containing bromine and its vapour, the intensity of colour above the liquid is higher at the higher temperature, indicating a higher concentration of bromine vapour.*

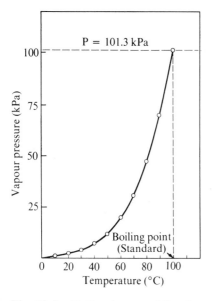

Fig. 19-5: *Notice how rapidly the vapour pressure of water increases as the temperature increases. The standard boiling point—the temperature at which the vapour pressure is 101.3 kPa—is 100°C.*

sure of the vapour depresses the mercury. When the mercury stops falling, the equilibrium pressure has been reached. This is the vapour pressure of the liquid at the temperature of measurement. (It is very important that both the tube and the mercury used in making the barometer be clean and *dry*.) Measurements of vapour pressure at temperatures other than room temperature can be made by surrounding the barometer tube with a water jacket and circulating water at the desired temperature through it.

The pressure of water vapour that develops at the top of a barometer tube in this way proves to be practically identical with the partial pressure of water vapour that develops when water evaporates into a closed space already containing some other molecules, for instance, a space already filled with air. We may deduce from this that the equilibrium between a liquid and its vapour is not significantly affected by the presence in the vapour phase of other molecules that play no role in the equilibrium.

14. EFFECT OF TEMPERATURE ON VAPOUR PRESSURE. Without exception, vapour pressures are considerably increased by increase in temperature. This fact is consistent with the kinetic-molecular theory. At a higher temperature a larger fraction of the molecules in a liquid (or solid) will have energy sufficient to escape at any instant, and hence the rate of evaporation will increase. To balance this increased rate of evaporation would require an increased rate of condensation, and to achieve this we would require more molecules per unit volume (that is, a greater concentration of molecules) in the vapour (Fig. 19-1).

By selecting bromine again, with its easily visible vapour, we can demonstrate the higher concentration of vapour when the temperature is raised. Two identical sealed tubes, each containing some liquid bromine, are maintained at different temperatures for some time in order to establish equilibrium in each. This is illustrated in Fig 19-4, where the temperatures 20°C and 40°C are suggested for comparison. The intensity of the red colour of the bromine vapour will be noticeably greater in the tube kept at 40°C.

The way in which the vapour pressure of a liquid changes with temperature is shown in Fig. 19-5. Values of the vapour pressure of water at a number of different temperatures are plotted at these temperatures and a smooth curve is drawn through the resulting points.

15. VAPOUR PRESSURE AND BOILING POINT. Ordinarily, evaporation is slow because the air immediately above the liquid surface becomes saturated with vapour. Then further (net) evaporation must wait until some of this vapour diffuses away. If the temperature is raised till the vapour pressure of the liquid is equal to the atmospheric pressure, then the vapour can "push the atmosphere back" and so escape, and evaporation can proceed rapidly. This is the temperature at which the liquid *boils,* that is, the temperature at which bubbles of vapour, formed in the liquid, grow rapidly in size (because the pressure exerted by the vapour can now push back the liquid) and rise to the surface. *The temperature at which a liquid boils,* then, *is that at which the vapour pressure of the liquid is equal to the atmospheric pressure.* Owing to the daily variations in the atmospheric pressure, the actual temperature at which a liquid boils is subject to some variation. For purposes of comparison and tabulation, therefore, we define the **boiling point** of a liquid as *the temperature at which its vapour pressure equals standard atmospheric pressure, 101.3 kPa.* This is sometimes called the *standard* or *normal boiling point.*

If the prevailing atmospheric pressure is less than this standard, the liquid will boil below its normal boiling point; if the pressure is greater, the liquid will boil above its normal boiling point. The normal boiling point of water is 100°C. But water can be made to boil at any desired temperature (between 0°C and 374°C) by adjusting the atmospheric pressure on it to the vapour pressure of water at that temperature. On a mountain top, where the atmospheric pressure is low, water boils well below 100°C; deep in a mine it boils above 100°C.

When a boiling point is given without a pressure being stated, it is understood that the pressure is standard atmospheric pressure — that is, the boiling point as ordinarily listed is the *normal* boiling point.

QUESTIONS

In some of the numerical questions in this chapter units appear that are not part of the International System (SI). These examples are included to give an opportunity to recognize and handle units outside SI that are still in widespread use.

1. Explain clearly how the kinetic-molecular theory can account for Boyle's Law.

2. Explain clearly how the kinetic-molecular theory can account for Gay-Lussac's Law. What additional assumption, not required to answer Question 1, has to be built into the theory to provide this explanation?

3. List briefly the characteristics of the model gas for which the pressure formula can be derived.

4. Show that it is a direct consequence of Avogadro's Principle that relative molecular masses of different gases are proportional to their densities, measured under comparable conditions.

5. The densities at STP of gaseous ammonia and hydrogen sulphide are 0.771 and 1.538 g/L respectively. What conclusion can be drawn about the relative masses of their molecules?

*6. Show that Equation (1) in this chapter can also be written in the form $p = \frac{1}{3}\rho\bar{u}^2$, where ρ is the density of the gas in question.

7. The relative molecular masses of hydrogen and oxygen are, respectively, 2 and 32. On the average does each molecule in a "mixture" of hydrogen and oxygen at 0°C have the same or different values of: (a) mass, (b) momentum, (c) velocity, (d) kinetic energy?

*8. In a gaseous mixture containing equal masses of hydrogen and oxygen at STP state for which element (hydrogen, oxygen, or neither) on the average: (a) the molecules have the greater velocity, (b) the molecules have the greater momentum, (c) there are a greater number of molecules per millilitre, (d) the individual molecules strike the container wall with greater force, (e) the kinetic energy of the molecules is greater, (f) the partial pressure is the greater. (For the meaning of partial pressure see Question 19.)

*9. Suppose you had two closed glass containers of the same volume. One is filled with hydrogen, the other with oxygen, both at STP. How do the number of molecules compare in the two containers? How do the masses of the two gases compare? If the temperature of the hydrogen container is now increased, how do the two gases now

compare in (a) pressure, (b) volume, (c) number of molecules, (d) average molecular kinetic energy, (e) average speed?

10. Why do some gases show significant deviations from Boyle's and Gay-Lussac's Laws? Which of the following pairs of gases would you expect to show greater departures from these gas laws?

(a) Carbon monoxide (CO)	Boiling point	–192°C
Carbon dioxide (CO_2)	Sublimes	–78°C
(b) Nitrogen (N_2)	Boiling point	–195.8°C
Nitrous oxide (N_2O)	Boiling point	–89.8°C

11. (a) What is meant by the statement that there is a "dynamic equilibrium" between a liquid and its vapour?

(b) Explain (i) the increase in the vapour pressure of a liquid as the temperature rises, (ii) the difference between a saturated and an unsaturated vapour.

12. A few crystals of paradichlorobenzene (a moth repellent) will gradually disappear by evaporation if left in an open place. If placed in a stoppered bottle, however, the crystals will remain indefinitely. Explain.

13. Explain how at a given temperature there can be many different pressures of water vapour in the air, but only one vapour pressure.

14. Explain how damp washing will dry on a line outdoors even in winter when the temperature is below freezing. Why is the drying faster in summer? Why is the drying faster on a breezy day?

15. Why does a bottle of milk or other cold object, when removed from a refrigerator on a summer day, frequently become coated with droplets of moisture? Why does this occur less commonly in winter?

16. Vegetables may be cooked in a pressure cooker in very much shorter time than in an ordinary saucepan. Account for this.

17. The curve shown in Fig. 19-5 is typical of the changes in vapour pressure of a substance that occur with changes in temperature. Contrast the effect of increasing temperature on the vapour pressure of a substance and on the pressure of a gas maintained at constant volume.

*18. A pressure gauge on a cylinder of compressed ammonia read 62 lb/in² at 0°C and 169 lb/in² at 30°C. Do you think the ammonia in the tank was all gaseous, all liquid, or liquid and gas together? Explain your reasoning.

19. Explain in terms of the kinetic-molecular theory how two gases can occupy the same volume at the same time. Show that each gas in this case will contribute to the total pressure an amount (called its partial pressure) equal to the pressure it would exert if it alone occupied the volume of the gaseous solution. (This is known as the Law of Partial Pressures—discovered by John Dalton in 1801; this antedated his atomic theory.)

20. A certain sample of air was found to contain water vapour at a partial pressure of 15.0 Torr (2.00 kPa). The temperature of the air was 25°C; at this temperature the vapour pressure of water is 23.8 Torr (3.17 kPa). Express the partial pressure of water vapour as a percentage of the vapour pressure. (This percentage is called the *relative humidity*.)

21. A one-litre bottle contains air saturated with water vapour at 25°C. The barometric pressure is 100.00 kPa, and the vapour pressure of water at 25°C is 3.17 kPa. A few crystals of a substance that absorbs water vapour practically completely are dropped into the bottle which is then tightly stoppered. What happens inside the bottle, and what will be the pressure inside the bottle when a steady condition is reached?

22. Explain why the boiling point of water is lower in Banff, Alberta (elevation 1500 m above sea level) than in Halifax, Nova Scotia.

23. A flask contains enough oxygen molecules to exert a pressure of 1 atm on the walls. If the same number of hydrogen molecules and double the number of nitrogen molecules are introduced, all at the same temperature, what will be the pressure on the walls?

24. The vapour pressure of water is 733.2 Torr at 99°C, and 787.5 Torr at 101°C. Estimate the boiling temperature for water when the atmospheric pressure is 740 Torr, and also when it is 770 Torr.

25. In general, the higher the vapour pressure of a liquid at room temperature, the lower is the liquid's boiling point. Why should this be so?

26. Which member of each of the following pairs of liquids has the higher vapour pressure at room temperature: (a) water and glycerine, (b) gasoline and motor oil, (c) corn syrup and corn oil?

27. Define vapour pressure of a solid, and also vapour pressure of a liquid. Can you suggest a reason why these two vapour pressures should be equal at the melting temperature?

28. Ammonia is formed from nitrogen and hydrogen at elevated temperature and pressure. Reactants and product are all gaseous, and the following relationship applies to their volumes when measured at the same temperature and pressure:

1 volume of nitrogen + 3 volumes of hydrogen → 2 volumes of ammonia

What conclusion may be drawn concerning the number of nitrogen atoms per molecule?

*29. When you use a hand pump to inflate a bicycle tire, you often notice that the barrel of the pump becomes warm. Can you suggest any reason why a gas, being compressed gradually by a moving piston, should increase in temperature?

Quantitative Relationships

1. In earlier chapters we have introduced and used the terms *relative atomic mass* and *molar mass*. But, if you have been reading the book critically, you will know that we have not explained how values are assigned to them. In this chapter we shall bring together ideas that have now been developed, so that we may describe where relative atomic masses and molar masses really come from.

Although a scale of relative atomic masses was attempted first by John Dalton in 1808, chemists were unable until 1860 to agree on a method (or methods) for determining values on this scale. A great deal had to be learned by the scientists of that era before they could confidently make the correct choice of these quantities. In a comparable way, you have had to learn a good deal about chemistry in order to have the background to read this chapter with understanding.

2. THE PROBLEM. Soon after Dalton introduced his atomic theory to account for the proportions by mass in which elements combine, the great Swedish chemist J. J. Berzelius (1779-1848) saw the need to develop better methods for finding accurately the characteristic masses in which each element reacted. He greatly improved methods for the quantitative analysis of substances, and used his results to draw up tables of relative masses of atoms which were a great improvement over Dalton's original table. But even the best analytical information in the world could not solve the problem confronting Berzelius and his contemporaries.

The problem was that nobody could see atoms, and therefore no one could interpret information about *masses of elements* that combined in terms of *numbers of atoms* that combined. Any competent experimenter could establish that 100 parts of water consisted of 11.2 parts of hydrogen (by mass) and 88.8 parts of oxygen (roughly 1:8). Dalton was convinced that atoms of hydrogen and of oxygen should combine one to one; that assumption leads to the conclusion that oxygen atoms are eight times heavier than hydrogen atoms. Berzelius, on the other hand, knowing that when water is decomposed it yields two volumes of hydrogen gas for each volume of oxygen gas, believed that two atoms of hydrogen are combined with one of oxygen; from that assumption oxygen atoms appear to be sixteen times heavier than hydrogen atoms. Who could tell which of these inferences was correct or, for that matter, if either was?

Berzelius started with O = 100 for his standard, then switched to O = 16.00. The latter standard continued in use until 1961.

3. Berzelius used oxygen (not carbon) as the reference element for setting relative atomic masses. He was able to study oxides of many elements and, for many of these, the simplest guess concerning the ratio of atoms, namely one to one, would correspond to the formula MO (where M is the symbol of the other element). He was fortunate that many of the metal oxides he worked with did have this atom ratio, so he got the correct relative mass in these cases. But by no means always!

4. DULONG AND PETIT: ATOMIC HEATS. In 1819 P. L. Dulong and A. T. Petit, working with an early table of Berzelius' atomic masses, hit upon a relationship that was to prove helpful in solving the problem just outlined. They noted that the product of relative atomic mass × specific heat capacity was reasonably constant for a group of elements. Expressed in today's units, this product lay in the range 25-27 J/(mol·K) (Sec. 17-5). They called this quantity the *atomic heat;* today it is called the *molar heat capacity.*

These men noted that the product they obtained was occasionally double the expected value, so for these they promptly halved Berzelius' value for the atomic mass. They believed in their law sufficiently to advocate its use in establishing or correcting relative atomic masses, and for this purpose it proved useful, though with some limitations. For one thing, molar heat capacities which conform to the "law" are constant only within about 10%; for another, there are some elements for which the "law" doesn't work even that well.

Problem 20-1: The element platinum has a specific heat capacity of 0.136 J/(g·K). Estimate the relative atomic mass for platinum.

Solution: In what follows, the mole refers to platinum atoms.

According to the Dulong and Petit Law, the molar mass for platinum × the specific heat capacity lies in the range 25-27 (J/(mol·K).

Lower estimate for molar mass for platinum

$$= \frac{25 \text{ J/(mol·K)}}{0.136 \text{ J/(g·K)}} = 184 \text{ g/mol}$$

Upper estimate $= \dfrac{27 \text{ J/(mol·K)}}{0.136 \text{ J/(g·K)}} = 199 \text{ g/mol}$

Therefore, the expected relative atomic mass for platinum lies between 184 and 199 (no units).

Compare this estimate with the value on the back cover.

The next problem shows how the information gained from Problem 20-1 can be utilized together with some analytical information to determine the relative atomic mass of platinum.

Problem 20-2: A chloride of platinum, having a mass of 1.000 g, was heated strongly in order to decompose it to the metal (which remains in the heating vessel) and chlorine (which escapes). The residue of platinum had a mass of 0.579 g. Combine this information, that derived from Problem 20-1, and the relative atomic mass of chlorine (35.45), to calculate the relative atomic mass of platinum.

Solution: There is no information concerning the formula of the platinum chloride. We represent it as $PtCl_x$, where x is an integer.

We calculate the mass of platinum combined with 35.45 g of chlorine.

Since 0.579 g of platinum combined with $(1.000-0.579)$ g $= 0.421$ g of chlorine, therefore the mass of platinum combined with 35.45 g of chlorine

$$= 35.45 \text{ g} \times \frac{0.579 \text{ g}}{0.421 \text{ g}} = 48.75 \text{ g}$$

Since the formula of the chloride of platinum is $PtCl_x$, and 48.75 g is the mass of platinum combined with the molar mass of atomic chlorine, it follows that 48.75 g is the mass of $1/x$ mol of atomic platinum. We assume x is an integer, so what integer will yield a molar mass in the range 184 to 199 (Problem 20-1)?

By inspection, x $= 4$. Therefore the molar mass of atomic platinum $= 4 \times 48.75$ g $= 195.0$ g

Hence the relative atomic mass of platinum $= 195.0$ (no units).

Incidentally, this shows that the formula of the platinum chloride taken was $PtCl_4$.

Before continuing with our account of the determination of relative atomic masses of the elements, we must make a brief excursion into the determination of molar masses of substances that occur or are obtainable in the gaseous state.

5. MOLAR VOLUMES OF GASEOUS AND VOLATILE SUBSTANCES. Avogadro's Principle states that equal volumes of gases, measured at the same temperature and pressure, contain equal numbers of molecules. The converse of this is that equal numbers of molecules of different gaseous substances should occupy the same volume at constant temperature and pressure. Applying this to a mole of any gaseous substance (which contains 6.02×10^{23} molecules; Sec. 10-21), we conclude that *a mole of any gas will occupy the same volume at a fixed temperature and pressure.* This is known as the *molar volume of a gas.*

We shall calculate the molar volume of oxygen, but first we must decide upon the *molar mass* of gaseous oxygen. As we said in a marginal note with Sec. 20-3, the relative atomic mass scale was for many years based on O = 16.00. Although the reference standard for these masses changed to ^{12}C = 12.00, this had little effect on the value for oxygen. The fact that in the gaseous state at ordinary temperatures oxygen consists of diatomic molecules has been mentioned several times already. There are several reasons for believing this to be the case, but the earliest (and probably the easiest to understand) is based on volume relationships in chemical reactions involving gases during which oxygen is consumed or produced. Consider the following two reactions:

hydrogen gas   +   oxygen gas $\rightarrow$ water vapour
2 volumes   1 volume   2 volumes

carbon monoxide gas + oxygen gas $\rightarrow$ carbon dioxide gas
2 volumes   1 volume   2 volumes

(The volumes in each reaction refer to the same temperature and pressure.) According to Avogadro's Principle *one* volume of oxygen contains some particular number of molecules, and *two* volumes of water vapour or carbon dioxide implies *double* that number of molecules. But part of the gaseous oxygen is built into each of the molecules of each product, and this is possible only if the oxygen molecules contain two (or at least an even number of) atoms.

For a diatomic oxygen molecule the relative molecular mass will be 32.00, and the molar mass will be 32.00 g/mol. The density of oxygen gas at STP = 1.429 g/L (Table 18-1). The volume occupied by the molar mass of oxygen

$$= \frac{32.00 \text{ g/mol}}{1.429 \text{ g/L}} = 22.4 \text{ L/mol at STP}$$

This is the *molar volume at STP.*

But from what was said in the first paragraph of this section this volume at STP will contain one mole of *any* gas. It is a useful quantity to remember.

The molar volume for any gas is 22.4 L/mol at STP.

The molar volume will be different at other temperatures and pressures, but it can be calculated by means of Boyle's and Gay-Lussac's Law. For instance, at 100°C and 101.3 kPa the molar volume of a gas is 30.6 L/mol. (Satisfy yourself that this is true.)

Problem 20-3: Calculate the molar mass for cyanogen gas, given that its density at STP is 2.337 g/L.

Solution: You have probably never heard of cyanogen, much less know its formula or composition. Nevertheless, its molar mass can be determined. The molar volume at STP for cyanogen (or any gas) is 22.4 L/mol.

The molar mass, therefore, is 22.4 L/mol × 2.337 g/L = 52.3 g/mol.

This is the mass of one mole of cyanogen.

Problem 20-4: A sample of cooking gas, taken from a cylinder, was collected and its density measured at 27°C and 100 kPa pressure. The density under these conditions was 1.768 g/L. What was the molar mass of the cooking gas?

Solution 1: Since the density was measured under other than standard conditions, we first calculate what the density would be at STP. (See Sec. 18-13.)

$$\rho_2 \;=\; \rho_1 \times \frac{p_2}{p_1} \times \frac{T_1}{T_2}$$

$$=\; 1.768 \text{ g/L} \times \frac{101.3 \text{ kPa}}{100 \text{ kPa}} \times \frac{300 \text{ K}}{273 \text{ K}} = 1.968 \text{ g/L at STP}$$

Therefore the molar mass = 22.4 L/mol × 1.968 g/L = 44.1 g/mol

This is the molar mass of the unknown cooking gas.

Solution 2: An alternative method is to calculate the molar volume at 27°C and 100 kPa, then multiply it by the density found under these conditions.

The molar volume at STP = 22.4 L/mol

At 27°C and 100 kPa this would be

$$22.4 \text{ L/mol} \times \frac{300 \text{ K}}{273 \text{ K}} \times \frac{101.3 \text{ kPa}}{100 \text{ kPa}} = 24.9 \text{ L/mol}$$

Therefore the molar mass = 24.9 L/mol × 1.768 g/L = 44.1 g/mol

Both approaches must and do lead to the same answer.

Many substances that are liquids at STP can be vaporized, and the density of their vapours measured at conditions other than standard. In this way their molar masses can be determined.

Problem 20-5: Calculate the molar mass of chloroform from the information that its vapour, measured at 100°C and 98.6 kPa, has a density of 3.80 g/L.

Solution: We could calculate the density of chloroform vapour at STP in exactly the same way as in Problem 20-4. We should realize, however, that the value obtained in this way is an entirely imaginary quantity because chloroform cannot exist as vapour at STP. Instead, we prefer to tackle this problem by the second method given in Problem 20-4.

The molar volume at 100°C and 98.6 kPa is

$$22.4 \text{ L/mol} \times \frac{373 \text{ K}}{273 \text{ K}} \times \frac{101.3 \text{ kPa}}{98.6 \text{ kPa}} = 31.4 \text{ L/mol}$$

The molar mass will be 31.4 L/mol × 3.80 g/L = 119 g/mol

Hence this is the molar mass of chloroform. The formula of this substance is $CHCl_3$. How does the molar mass obtained experimentally compare with that obtained by adding up the relative atomic masses (Sec. 10-22)?

6. CANNIZZARO'S ASSIGNMENT OF RELATIVE ATOMIC MASSES. We now return to the problem outlined in Sec. 20-2, namely, how to relate combining proportions by mass to combining proportions by atoms. The method based on Dulong and Petit's Law, which worked well for some elements, failed for a number of common elements, and therefore wasn't altogether trusted. As we indicated in Sec. 4-8, the situation with respect to relative atomic masses was unsettled and confusing prior to 1860. In that year a group of European chemists met in Karlsruhe, Germany, to discuss the problem, and at that meeting an Italian professor named Stanislao Cannizzaro outlined a simple system of picking atomic masses based on the principle suggested long before by his countryman Avogadro.

We can explain Cannizzaro's proposal by reference to Tables 20-1 and 20-2. In the first of these we show the percentage composition (by mass) of thirteen substances, all but one of which are gaseous at room temperature; the thirteenth is a volatile liquid. Analysis of compounds like this in the laboratory is generally straightforward, and doesn't depend on any knowledge of the numbers of atoms in the molecule. In the first column of the second table we give the molar masses of each substance; these can be determined by measurement of the density of the gas or vaporized substance, as we explained in the previous section. This assignment of molar mass also does not depend on any knowledge of the composition of the molecules. In the remaining columns of Table 20-2 we have calculated the masses of the constituent elements in one mole of each substance. For example:

In fact we have deliberately included something called "cooking gas" in the list to emphasize that the information in these tables does not require us to know what the particular substance is, provided only that it is a pure substance.

The molar mass of carbon monoxide is 28.0 g/mol

Of this, 57.1% is oxygen, 42.9% is carbon.

The mass of oxygen in one mole of carbon monoxide

$$= 28.0 \text{ g} \times \frac{57.1}{100}$$
$$= 16.0 \text{ g}$$

The mass of carbon in one mole of carbon monoxide

$$= 28.0 \text{ g} \times \frac{42.9}{100}$$
$$= 12.0 \text{ g}$$

When you examine the numbers in Table 20-2 it is evident that the masses of hydrogen per mole of each substance are approximately whole numbers; those of oxygen are 16.0 g or 32.0 g; of carbon, 12.0 g, 24.0 g, or 36.0 g; and so on. There is a very simple relationship among the numbers in any one column; in each case there is a characteristic number and multiples of it. From these observations and many others like them it has been possible to draw the following conclusions:

(1) In one mole of any gaseous or volatile substance containing the element, there is never less than:

> 1.0 g hydrogen
>
> 16.0 g oxygen
>
> 12.0 g carbon
>
> 14.0 g nitrogen
>
> 32.1 g sulphur

(2) If more than these characteristic masses of the elements are present in one mole of a substance containing them, the amount is a multiple of the masses given in (1).

(3) The characteristic masses given in (1) are the gram-atomic masses, or molar masses of the elements in the atomic state. If a multiple of this mass occurs in a mole of a substance, an integral number of atoms are present in the molecule of the substance.

It is only necessary to add two comments. First, Cannizzaro's ideas were quickly accepted by chemists everywhere, and after about 1860 everyone began using the same numbers for relative atomic masses and the same formulas for compounds. This in turn paved the way for many other developments, including the periodic classification of the elements which we mentioned in Chapter 12. Secondly, because gases and vapours do not always adhere exactly to Boyle's and Gay-Lussac's Laws

TABLE 20-1

PERCENTAGE COMPOSITION BY MASS OF SOME GASEOUS OR
VOLATILE SUBSTANCES

	HYDROGEN (%)	OXYGEN (%)	CARBON (%)	NITROGEN (%)	SULPHUR (%)
Carbon monoxide		57.1	42.9		
Oxygen		100.0			
Carbon dioxide		72.7	27.3		
Water	11.2	88.8			
Methane	25.1		74.9		
Acetylene	7.8		92.2		
"Cooking gas"	18.3		81.7		
Hydrogen sulphide	5.9				94.1
Ammonia	17.8			82.2	
Hydrogen cyanide	3.7		44.4	51.8	
Sulphur dioxide		50.0			50.0
Carbon disulphide			15.8		84.2
Cyanogen			46.2	53.8	

TABLE 20-2

MOLAR MASSES OF THE SUBSTANCES IN TABLE 20-1,
AND MASSES OF THE CONSTITUENT ELEMENTS
PER MOLE OF THE SUBSTANCES

	MOLAR MASS (g)	HYDROGEN (g)	OXYGEN (g)	CARBON (g)	NITROGEN (g)	SULPHUR (g)
Carbon monoxide	28.0		16.0	12.0		
Oxygen	32.0		32.0			
Carbon dioxide	44.0		32.0	12.0		
Water	18.0	2.0	16.0			
Methane	16.0	4.0		12.0		
Acetylene	26.0	2.0		24.0		
"Cooking gas"	44.1	8.1		36.0		
Hydrogen sulphide	34.1	2.0				32.1
Ammonia	17.0	3.0			14.0	
Hydrogen cyanide	27.0	1.0		12.0	14.0	
Sulphur dioxide	64.1		32.0			32.1
Carbon disulphide	76.1			12.0		64.1
Cyanogen	52.0			24.0	28.0	

(Sec. 19-8), molar masses determined by gas densities are not always exactly the value predicted from the formula of a substance. In consequence, the numbers in the columns of Table 20-2 may show small discrepancies from the relative atomic masses listed on the back cover. The latter have been settled only after consideration of several careful determinations.

7. A NEWER APPROACH TO COMPARING ATOMIC MASSES. In Sec. 13-1 we described how gaseous ions could be formed by removing one or more electrons from neutral atoms, or in some instances by adding one or more electrons to atoms. We stated that these ions would move under the influence of a difference in electrical potential, and thereby permit a gas to become a conductor when so ionized (Fig. 13-1).

The movement of electrons or of gaseous ions through space from which air has been removed to *very* low pressure has been studied in some detail. Although the electrons or ions cannot be seen individually, the path of a beam of them can be revealed by their effect when they strike:

(a) a photographic film, which they darken;

(b) a fluorescent screen, which glows (like a TV screen);

(c) a sensitive charge detector, such as an electron-multiplier tube, which generates a tiny electric current.

For the purposes of this discussion the particles of interest are positive ions, making up a beam of *positive rays*. When these pass between the poles of a magnet they are deflected from their course. The charged particles experience in the magnetic field a sideways "push" similar to that experienced by a wire carrying an electric current. The amount of deflection suffered by an individual particle depends on its mass, its charge, its speed, and on the strength of the magnetic field.

> This "push" is the basis on which electric motors and galvanometers operate.

Formulas are given in more advanced books on physics, showing the effect of each of these variables on the path of a charged particle passing through a magnetic field. Qualitatively, the effects can be described by reference to Fig. 20-1. A single beam of positive ions passing from left to right enters a magnetic field at A. Because of the lateral force on the particle within the magnetic field, its path becomes an arc of a circle as shown. Emerging from the magnetic field at B, the beam resumes its straight-line flight; it can be located at C and its intensity measured by any of the detectors listed in the previous paragraph. The curvature of the circle in which the beam is deflected is greater the greater the magnetic field strength, the slower the particles are moving, and the greater the charge borne by the particles. The curvature is less the heavier are the particles. With suitably designed equipment it is possible to produce a focussed beam of positive ions all travelling at the same speed. Electromagnets with regulated power supplies can produce a fixed or controllable magnetic field of moderate area.

It can be proven that, for a fixed speed of particles and constant magnetic field, all ions in a ray emerging at B must have the same ratio of mass/charge, m/e. From the deflection of the beam caused by the magnetic field it is possible to calculate m/e, and if e is assumed to be the charge borne by a proton, m can be found. Thus it is that the mass of a single ion (or an electron, or a molecule) can be determined. In practice, m is not directly calculated this way, but instead the value of m sought is compared with the mass of a standard such as carbon-12 atoms.

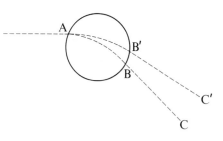

Fig. 20-1: *A beam of ions is deflected from its course as it passes through a magnetic field, represented here by the circle.*

Should it happen that the positive-ray beam contains ions of two different masses, these will be sorted out during the curved flight through the magnetic field. The heavier ions will be less deflected, and will emerge from the field at B' and pass on to be detected at C'. This is, in fact, how isotopes (Sec. 10-14) were discovered. In a classic experiment by J. J. Thomson (in England in 1913) a beam of ionized neon (Ne$^+$) was split by a combination of magnetic and electric deflections into two beams. The only possible explanation was that the neon atoms were an assortment of particles of two different masses.

Instruments have been developed in which a beam of positive ions, each carrying the same charge and moving at the same speed, is fed into a uniform magnetic field. The beam is deflected by the magnetic field and then passes on to a detector and its intensity is measured. The amount by which the positive-ray beam is bent by the magnetic field in this case depends only on the mass of the particles in the beam and the strength of the magnetic field. Such an instrument is called a **mass spectrometer** or **mass spectrograph**. The latter name is usually applied to an instrument in which the magnetic field strength is maintained con-

A modern mass spectrometer is a much more complicated instrument than the schematic diagram of Fig. 20-2 suggests. You should be able to locate the electromagnet in this photograph, as well as the curved tube in which the positive ions are deflected in the arc of a circle. Inside the large cabinet is a carefully regulated power supply to control the magnetic field, pumping equipment to maintain a high vacuum in the ion chamber, and an amplifier to magnify and record the signal of the ion beam striking the detector. An instrument such as this is easily capable of distinguishing particles whose masses differ by only one part in one hundred thousand parts.

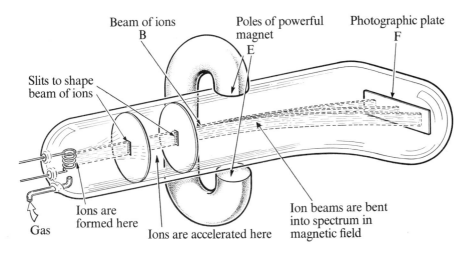

Fig. 20-2: *This diagram illustrates the essential principles of a mass spectrograph. A beam of positive ions, B, containing ions of identical charge but differing masses, is bent on passing between magnetic poles, E, into separate beams, the lighter ions being deflected most. When the separated beams strike a photographic plate, F, a spectrum is recorded. (This is not a diagram of an actual mass spectrograph but of a highly simplified version of one.)*

stant, and particles of different mass are detected at different positions on a photographic film (Fig. 20-2). The more common practice today is to use a single detector (electron-multiplier) and variable magnetic field; referring back to Fig. 20-1, the beam at C' can be brought to focus at C by increasing the magnetic field strength.

8. THE DETERMINATION OF RELATIVE ATOMIC MASSES. If an element has only one kind of atom, as sodium or fluorine has, the mass spectrometer will detect only one mass in the positive-ray beam. If, however, the element has isotopes, the detector will reveal particles of different masses. Since isotopes occur in nature in essentially constant ratios, the relative atomic mass of an element, as determined from chemical composition, appears to be constant. But the atomic mass is an average of the isotopic masses, weighted according to their naturally occurring proportions (Sec. 10-20). The mass spectrometer is capable of revealing (i) the mass of each isotope, as revealed by the position of marks on a photographic film or by peaks on a recorder chart; and (ii) the relative abundance of each isotope as revealed by the intensity of the film darkening or by peak heights (Fig. 20-3). From these two bits of evidence it is a straightforward matter to calculate atomic masses from measurements with a mass spectrometer. Since the mass spectrometer is capable of *very* accurate comparisons of masses of two or more ions, it is now acknowledged as furnishing more precise (with more decimal places, if you like) atomic masses than chemical analysis. The most recent and most authoritative atomic-mass determinations have been made with mass spectrometers.

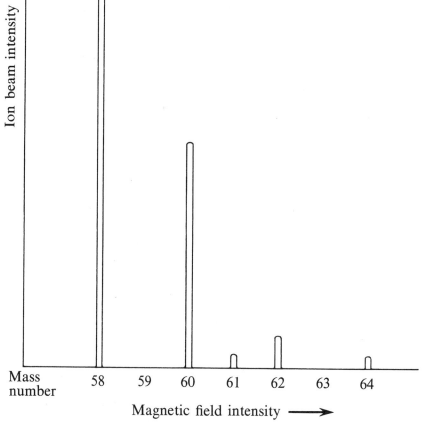

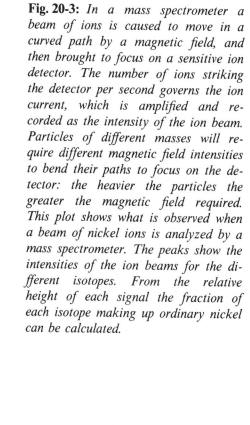

Fig. 20-3: *In a mass spectrometer a beam of ions is caused to move in a curved path by a magnetic field, and then brought to focus on a sensitive ion detector. The number of ions striking the detector per second governs the ion current, which is amplified and recorded as the intensity of the ion beam. Particles of different masses will require different magnetic field intensities to bend their paths to focus on the detector: the heavier the particles the greater the magnetic field required. This plot shows what is observed when a beam of nickel ions is analyzed by a mass spectrometer. The peaks show the intensities of the ion beams for the different isotopes. From the relative height of each signal the fraction of each isotope making up ordinary nickel can be calculated.*

It may be helpful to explain how a value for the relative atomic mass of hydrogen can be determined in this way. Neglecting for a moment the minor isotopes, deuterium and carbon-13, the significant peaks observed for methane (CH_4) and carbon correspond to masses related as 1.335 93 to 1.000 00. The atomic mass for carbon-12 is defined as 12.0000 u, so the corresponding quantity for methane (molecular mass) is 16.0312 u (that is, 12.0000 u $\times$ 1.335 93). This leads to a value for the mass of the common hydrogen isotope = (16.0312 – 12.0000) u $\div$ 4 = 1.0078 u.

However, because a very small fraction of the hydrogen atoms have a mass number 2, being the isotope of hydrogen known as deuterium (symbol D), a few of the methane molecules will have a formula that we can represent as CH_3D. These molecules, when ionized, will cause a very small peak in the mass spectrometer. The mass corresponding to that peak can be determined in just the same way as that for CH_4, and when this is found, a value for the mass of deuterium can be worked out. The value so found is 2.0141 u.

These isotopes of hydrogen occur in the ratio 99.985 to 0.015. The weighted average mass is then calculated as follows:

$$99.985 \times 1.0078 \text{ u} = 100.765 \text{ u}$$

$$\frac{0.015 \times 2.0141 \text{ u} =}{100.000 \text{ atoms}} \quad \frac{0.030 \text{ u}}{100.795 \text{ u}}$$

The average mass per atom is 1.00795 u. The internationally accepted value of the relative atomic mass for hydrogen is 1.0079.

WHAT'S IN A FORMULA?

9. FORMULAS AND COMPOSITION. As early in this book as Section 4-12 we indicated that "the formula of a substance indirectly expresses its composition by implying the relative amounts of the elements in it." In this section we shall illustrate by some worked-out examples how the percentage composition (by mass) of the elements in a compound relates to the formula of that compound.

Problem 20-6: Calculate the percentage (by mass) of aluminium in the mineral *corundum*, of which the formula is Al_2O_3.

Solution: The molar mass of corundum is
(2 $\times$ 27.0 + 3 $\times$ 16.0) g/mol = 102.0 g/mol.

Each mole of corundum contains 2 mol of atomic aluminium.

The mass of 2 mol of aluminium = 2 mol $\times$ 27.0 g/mol = 54.0 g

Since 102.0 g of corundum contains 54.0 g aluminium, 100 g of

corundum contains $\dfrac{54.0 \text{ g}}{102.0 \text{ g}} \times 100.0$ g = 52.9 g of aluminium

Therefore the percentage of aluminium in corundum is 52.9%

Problem 20-7: Calculate the percentage composition of sodium sulphate, Na_2SO_4.

Solution: The molar mass of sodium sulphate is

$$(2 \times 23.0 + 32.1 + 4 \times 16.0) \text{ g/mol} = 142.1 \text{ g/mol}$$

Each mole of sodium sulphate contains:

2 mol of atomic sodium = (2×23.0) g = 46.0 g

1 mol of atomic sulphur = 32.1 g

4 mol of atomic oxygen = (4×16.0) g = 64.0 g

(Notice the importance of specifying the form of the sulphur and the oxygen. Atomic sulphur (S) has a different molar mass than molecular sulphur (S_8); likewise atomic oxygen (O) differs in molar mass from molecular oxygen (O_2).)

One hundred grams of sodium sulphate contains:

$$\frac{46.0 \text{ g}}{142.1 \text{ g}} \times 100.0 \text{ g} = 32.4 \text{ g of sodium}$$

$$\frac{32.1 \text{ g}}{142.1 \text{ g}} \times 100.0 \text{ g} = 22.6 \text{ g of sulphur}$$

$$\frac{64.0 \text{ g}}{142.0 \text{ g}} \times 100.0 \text{ g} = 45.0 \text{ g of oxygen}$$

Therefore the percentage composition of sodium sulphate is 32.4% sodium, 22.6% sulphur, and 45.0% oxygen

10. A chemical formula for a compound must convey the following information:

    (a) the elements that are combined in the compound;

    (b) the numerical ratio in which the atoms of these elements are combined;

    (c) the proportions by mass in which these elements are combined.

For any compound there are an infinite number of formulas that will do these things. For cyanogen, as an example, such formulas are CN, C_2N_2, C_3N_3, C_4N_4. . . . If, however, the compound is molecular, and its molar mass is known from some investigation, the formula should show, in addition:

    (d) the number of atoms of each kind in the molecule;

    (e) the molar mass of the compound.

Such a formula is known as a **molecular formula**.

For many compounds a molecular formula cannot be written because the substance in its normal state does not exist as molecules. This would be the case with ionic compounds, such as sodium chloride or potassium nitrate. It would also be the case with network solids such as diamond or silicon dioxide, and likewise for metals. In such cases we must be content with the **simplest formula** that conveys the information (a), (b), and (c). (The simplest formula is often called the *empirical formula*.)

Problem 20-8: Treatment of metallic copper with excess of chlorine results in a yellow solid compound which contains 47.2% copper, and 52.8% chlorine. What is the simplest formula of the compound?

Solution: In 100.0 g of compound there are 47.2 g of copper and 52.8 g of chlorine.

We convert these *masses* of the elements to *amounts* of each element (moles).

Number of moles of atomic copper

$$= \frac{47.2 \text{ g}}{63.5 \text{ g/mol}} = 0.743 \text{ mol}$$

Number of moles of atomic chlorine

$$= \frac{52.8 \text{ g}}{35.5 \text{ g/mol}} = 1.49 \text{ mol}$$

By inspection, the number of moles of (atomic) chlorine is twice the number of moles of copper.

Therefore, the simplest formula of the compound is $CuCl_2$.

Problem 20-9: Calculate the simplest formula of a compound whose percentage composition is: carbon 81.8%; hydrogen, 18.2%.

Solution: We proceed exactly as in Problem 20-8.

In 100.0 g of compound, the number of moles of carbon

$$= \frac{81.8 \text{ g}}{12.0 \text{ g/mol}} = 6.82 \text{ mol}$$

and the number of moles of (atomic) hydrogen =

$$\frac{18.2 \text{ g}}{1.0 \text{ g/mol}} = 18.2 \text{ mol}$$

Here the ratio of the numbers of moles is not so evident by inspection. We must work it out.

$$\frac{\text{Number of moles of (atomic) hydrogen}}{\text{Number of moles of carbon}} = \frac{18.2 \text{ mol}}{6.82 \text{ mol}} = 2.67$$

We don't normally write a formula $CH_{2.67}$, but instead, express the molar ratio 2.67 as a ratio of integers. If we note that 2.67 is equivalent to 2⅔, then the ratio 2⅔:1 can, by multiplying through by three, be changed to 8:3. $C_1H_{2.67}$ thus becomes C_3H_8.

Therefore, the simplest formula of the compound is C_3H_8.

Over the years the authors have watched many students make a very simple but deadly mistake in solving problems of this sort. The error is frequently made of "rounding off" the numbers of moles obtained at this stage without proper justification. If in dividing 18.2 by 6.82 you round off your answer to 3, or to 2.5 (and lazy people are often prone to do this) you will be misled into thinking that the simplest formula is CH_3 or C_2H_5.

11. MOLECULAR FORMULA FROM SIMPLEST FORMULA AND MOLAR MASS. In Problem 20-9 the simplest formula of the compound was C_3H_8, but with only the information given there is no way of telling whether the molecule of this substance is properly represented by this formula. The same percentage composition can just as well be represented as C_6H_{16} or C_9H_{24}, or any other formula in which the ratio of carbon atoms to hydrogen atoms is 3:8.

The molecular formula is either the simplest formula or a simple multiple of it. The substance benzene has for its simplest formula CH. If that were the molecular formula it would imply that the relative mass of a benzene molecule was $(12.0 + 1.0) = 13$. Actually the molar mass of benzene can be found from the density of its vapour, and turns out to be 78 g/mol. As 78 is six times as great as 13, it must be concluded that the molecular formula of benzene is $(CH)_6$ or, as we prefer to write it, C_6H_6.

In Table 20-3 are shown a few comparisons of simplest formulas and molecular formulas. These examples show that the simplest formula may not be enough to identify a compound. Two or more different compounds may have the same simplest formula (for instance, acetylene and benzene).

TABLE 20-3

SOME SIMPLEST FORMULAS
AND MOLECULAR FORMULAS COMPARED

	SIMPLEST FORMULA	MOLECULAR FORMULA
Hydrogen chloride	HCl	HCl
Hydrogen peroxide	HO	H_2O_2
Methane	CH_4	CH_4
Acetylene	CH	C_2H_2
Benzene	CH	C_6H_6
Cyanogen	CN	C_2N_2
Carbon dioxide	CO_2	CO_2
Acetic acid	CH_2O	$C_2H_4O_2$
Glucose	CH_2O	$C_6H_{12}O_6$

The correct molecular formula is that which represents a molar mass corresponding to an experimentally determined molar mass. It can readily be established from the simplest formula by inspection.

Problem 20-10: The simplest formula for the gas ethylene is CH_2; its molar mass is 28.0 g/mol. What is its molecular formula?

Solution: For CH_2 the molar mass would be $(12.0 + 2 \times 1.0)$ g/mol
$$= 14.0 \text{ g/mol}$$

The observed molar mass is twice this value.
Therefore, the molecular formula is C_2H_4.

Problem 20-11: The composition of cyanogen is: carbon, 46.2%; nitrogen, 53.8%. Combine this information with that given in Problem 20-3 to find the molecular formula of this compound.

Solution 1: Find the simplest formula. For 100 g of cyanogen there are:

$$\frac{46.2\,\text{g}}{12.0\,\text{g/mol}} = 3.85\,\text{mol (atomic) carbon}$$

and

$$\frac{53.8\,\text{g}}{14.0\,\text{g/mol}} = 3.84\,\text{mol (atomic) nitrogen}$$

By inspection the simplest formula is CN.

For CN the molar mass is (12.0 + 14.0) g/mol = 26 g/mol

In Problem 20-3 we found the molar mass of cyanogen from the gaseous density to be 52.3 g/mol.

Accordingly, the molecular formula must be C_2N_2.

Solution 2: Find the number of moles of carbon and of atomic nitrogen in one mole of cyanogen.

The mass of one mole of cyanogen = 52.3 g

$$\text{The mass of carbon in this} = \left(52.3 \times \frac{46.2}{100}\right)\text{g} = 24.2\,\text{g}$$

$$\text{The mass of nitrogen in this} = \left(52.3 \times \frac{53.8}{100}\right)\text{g} = 28.1\,\text{g}$$

$$\text{The amount of carbon in moles} = \frac{24.2\,\text{g}}{12.0\,\text{g/mol}} = 2.02\,\text{mol}$$

$$\text{The amount of atomic nitrogen} = \frac{28.1\,\text{g}}{14.0\,\text{g/mol}} = 2.01\,\text{mol}$$

In one mole of cyanogen there are two moles each of carbon and (atomic) nitrogen.

Therefore, the molecular formula is C_2N_2.

Given sufficient scientific curiosity, you might wonder why these numbers of moles do not work out to be perfect integers, or why the molar mass found in Problem 20-3 was not precisely the sum of the molar masses of the atoms in cyanogen molecules. The answer is that cyanogen does not behave perfectly as an ideal gas (Sec. 19-8).

Problem 20-12: A hydrocarbon (Sec. 5-10) of industrial importance, called butylene, has the composition: carbon, 85.7%; hydrogen, 14.3%. The density of butylene at 100°C and a pressure of 100 kPa is 1.805 g/L. Find the molecular formula for butylene.

Solution 1: First, find the simplest formula for butylene.

$$\text{For 100 g of butylene there are 85.7 g of carbon} = \frac{85.7\,\text{g}}{12.0\,\text{g/mol}}$$

$$= 7.14\,\text{mol of carbon}$$

There are also 14.3 g of hydrogen $= \dfrac{14.3 \text{ g}}{1.0 \text{ g/mol}}$

$$= 14.3 \text{ mol of atomic hydrogen}$$

By inspection, the number of moles of atomic hydrogen is twice the number of moles of atomic carbon.

Therefore, the simplest formula for butylene is CH_2.

The molar mass corresponding to this formula
$= (12.0 + 2 \times 1.0) \text{ g/mol} = 14.0 \text{ g/mol}$

Then, find the molar mass for butylene from the experimental data.

The molar volume of any gas at STP $= 22.4$ L

At $100°C = 373$ K, this becomes $22.4 \text{ L} \times \dfrac{373 \text{ K}}{273 \text{ K}} = 30.6 \text{ L}$

At 100 kPa, this becomes $30.6 \text{ L} \times \dfrac{101.3}{100.0} = 31.0 \text{ L}$

The mass corresponding to this volume $= 31.0 \text{ L} \times 1.805 \text{ g/L}$
$$= 56.0 \text{ g}$$

Therefore the molar mass of butylene $= 56.0 \text{ g/mol}$

The molecular formula is that multiple of CH_2 which has a molar mass of 56.0 g/mol, and therefore is C_4H_8.

Therefore, the molecular formula of butylene is C_4H_8.

Solution 2: First, find the molar mass of the substance. This was done in Solution 1, and proved to be 56.0 g/mol.

Second, find the amounts (in moles) of carbon and of atomic hydrogen in one mole of butylene.

The number of grams of carbon in one mole of butylene

$$= 56.0 \text{ g/mol} \times 1.00 \text{ mol} \times \frac{85.7}{100} = 48.0 \text{ g}$$

The number of moles of atomic carbon per mole of butylene

$$= \frac{48.0 \text{ g}}{12.0 \text{ g/mol}} = 4.00 \text{ mol}$$

The number of grams of hydrogen in one mole of butylene

$$= 56.0 \text{ g/mol} \times 1.00 \text{ mol} \times \frac{14.3}{100} = 8.01 \text{ g}$$

The number of moles of atomic hydrogen per mole of butylene

$$= \frac{8.01 \text{ g}}{1.0 \text{ g/mol}} = 8.01 \text{ mol}$$

This shows that the molecular formula must be C_4H_8.

12. THE IDEAL GAS LAW. In Sec. 18-10 (Equation (6)) we established for a fixed mass of a gas the relationship:

$$\frac{pV}{T} = \text{constant}$$

where p is the pressure of the gas, V its volume, and T the temperature in kelvins. From the notion of molar volume of a gas (Sec. 20-5) we also know that at constant temperature and pressure the volume of a gas is proportional to the number of moles (n) of substance (or substances) in it. The above equation can therefore be written:

$$\frac{pV}{T} = nR$$

where R is the constant of proportionality. This is usually written:

$$pV = nRT \tag{1}$$

Equation (1) is known as the **ideal gas equation**; it is a concise summary of Boyle's and Gay-Lussac's Laws and Avogadro's Principle.

We can readily evaluate R, which is known as "the gas constant," as follows:

at STP, when $p = 101.3$ kPa and $T = 273$ K,　$V = 22.4$ L for $n = 1$ mol

$$\text{Therefore } R = \frac{101.3 \text{ kPa} \times 22.4 \text{ L}}{1 \text{ mol} \times 273 \text{ K}}$$

The numerical value of R is 8.31, and, to assign it a unit we must draw attention to the fact that the product of a pressure in kilopascals and a volume in litres will be a number of *joules*.

The unit of R is therefore J/(mol·K)

$$\mathbf{R = 8.31 \text{ J/(mol·K)}}$$

In applying the ideal gas equation with this value of the gas constant, remember to express pressure and volume in appropriate units (kilopascal and litre, or pascal and cubic metre).

The amount of substance in moles (n) of a gas is related to the mass of gas (m) and its molar mass (M)

$$n = \frac{m}{M}$$

We can transform Equation (1) into

$$pV = \frac{m}{M}RT$$

$$M = \frac{mRT}{pV} \tag{2}$$

One pascal (N/m²) multiplied by one cubic metre (m³) is one of a quantity having the dimensions N·m — and is therefore one joule. Likewise 1 kPa (= 10³ Pa) x 1 L (10⁻³ m³) = 1 J.

Equation (2), which applies strictly to an "ideal gas" (Sec. 19-8) can be used for the calculation of M, the molar mass, provided the values of the other physical quantities are known. Also, since the density (ρ) of a gas is the mass per unit volume,

$$\rho = \frac{m}{V}$$

We can transform Equation (2) into

$$M = \frac{\rho RT}{p} \qquad (3)$$

Equation (3) is very useful for solving problems like Problem 20-12. Try it!

The ideal gas law permeates the whole structure of theoretical chemistry, as you will discover if you study the subject further, and so Equation (1) must be regarded as an important relationship.

QUESTIONS

In some of the numerical questions in this chapter units appear that are not part of the International System (SI). These examples are included to give an opportunity to recognize and handle units outside SI that are still in widespread use.

1. Careful analysis of an oxide of tin shows it to contain 78.8% tin and the remainder oxygen. With this, but no other information, what can be said concerning the relative mass of tin atoms? If, in addition, the relative mass of oxygen atoms is taken as 16.00, what then may be said about the tin atoms?

2. The specific heat capacity of tin metal is known to be 0.22 J/(g·°C). Show how this information may be applied to an estimate of the molar mass of tin. From this estimate and the data of Question 1 calculate an accurate atomic mass for tin. What was the formula of the tin oxide in Question 1?

3. Why does the molar mass of any gaseous pure substance occupy the same volume as a mole of molecular oxygen, provided the volumes are measured at the same temperature and pressure?

4. Explain one method by which it can be deduced that oxygen molecules are diatomic. If it is known that oxygen molecules are diatomic, what can be said of the molar mass of molecular oxygen?

5. Calculate the molar volume of a gas under the following conditions:

(a) 25°C and 1 atm
(b) 100°C and 100 kPa
(c) –78°C and 110 kPa
(d) 77 K and 4.0 Torr

6. Calculate the molar volume of water vapour at its own vapour pressure: (a) 25°C and 3.17 kPa; (b) 0°C and 0.61 kPa.

7. Calculate the molar mass of a substance from the information that the density of its vapour, measured at 0.985 atm and 50°C, is 2.678 g/L.

8. A compound called dioxane, which is a liquid at room temperature, was evaporated at a higher temperature and 1.00 L of its vapour, measured at 150°C and 100 kPa, was found to have a mass of 2.506 g. Calculate the molar mass for dioxane.

9. A sample of a certain compound had a mass of 0.082 g. It was evaporated and produced 20.6 mL of a vapour at 20°C and 780 Torr. What is the molar mass of the compound?

10. Calculate the molar masses of the pure substances to which the following sets of data apply:

	VOLUME	TEMPERATURE	PRESSURE	MASS
(a)	150 cm³	100°C	100 kPa	0.25 g
(b)	426 cm³	300 K	85.3 kPa	0.49 g
(c)	1.00 dm³	91°C	2.00 atm	6.13 g
(d)	380 cm³	300 K	106.6 kPa	0.728 g
(e)	1.00 dm³	273°C	50.6 kPa	0.53 g

11. From the density of the vapour of six volatile substances containing phosphorus, their molar masses were determined. By other experiments the percentage of phosphorus in each was determined. From these data determine the molar mass of atomic phosphorus.

SUBSTANCE	MOLAR MASS (g/mol)	% PHOSPHORUS
A	137	22.6
B	126	24.6
C	284	43.6
D	34	91.1
E	66	93.9
F	124	100.0

12. What are the factors that determine the amount of deflection experienced by a moving charged particle as it passes through a uniform magnetic field?

13. Explain how the presence of isotopes, and the relative abundance of isotopes, can be determined by a mass spectrograph.

14. Calculate an atomic mass for boron given the following information about its isotopes:

MASS NUMBER	EXACT MASS	ABUNDANCE
10	10.012 939 u	19.6%
11	11.009 305 u	80.4%

Compare your answer with the internationally accepted value given on the inside back cover of the book.

15. Repeat the calculation shown in Sec. 10-20 for the atomic mass of lithium but using the following more exact data for the masses of the nuclides:

MASS NUMBER	EXACT MASS	ABUNDANCE
6	6.015 126 u	7.42%
7	7.016 931 u	92.58%

Check your answer against the accepted value of the atomic mass.

*__16.__ Some details were omitted from the description of the determination of the relative atomic mass of hydrogen, given in Sec. 20-8. One detail that was glossed over is that there are two isotopes of carbon, so that in the methane there will be $^{12}CH_4$ molecules, but also a few of $^{13}CH_4$. The other detail is that in addition to CH_3D molecules there will be a smaller number of CH_2D_2, a still smaller number of CHD_3, and so on. (D = deuterium.) In a high-resolution mass spectrometer it may be possible to detect peaks for all such species, though some peaks may be very weak. Find the total number of different species that may be found in methane; work out the mass number of each, and decide how many different mass numbers there will be.

Given the relative abundances of each carbon and hydrogen isotope (Table 10-2), try to predict which mass numbers would give strong, weak, or very weak signals in a mass spectrometer.

17. In the laboratory preparation of oxygen from potassium chlorate:

(a) What amount of molecular oxygen (in moles) is produced from each mole of potassium chlorate?

(b) What amount of potassium chlorate (in moles) is equivalent to 10 g of this substance?

(c) What amount of oxygen (in moles) can be produced from 10 g of potassium chlorate?

(d) What is the mass of this amount of oxygen?

(e) What is the volume at STP of this amount of oxygen?

18. Write an equation for the burning of carbon disulphide in air, forming carbon dioxide and sulphur dioxide.

(a) What amount of oxygen (in moles) is required for the burning of one mole of carbon disulphide?

(b) What amount of each product of the burning is formed per mole of carbon disulphide?

(c) What volume of oxygen at STP would be required for the burning of one mole of carbon disulphide? Approximately what volume of air?

(d) What total volume of gaseous products would be formed from this burning?

19. Comment on the following statements. Correct them where necessary.

(a) The mass of a carbon atom is 12.01 g.

(b) The molar mass of hydrogen is 2.016.

(c) There are always two atoms in a molecule.

(d) A mole is an abbreviation for a molecule.

(e) Equal volumes of all gases at the same temperature and pressure have the same mass.

(f) The molar mass of potassium chloride is 74.6 g.

(g) The number of atoms in a mole of a substance is 6.02×10^{23}.

(h) A single fluorine atom has a mass of 19.0 u.

(i) A molecular formula may represent a mass and a volume of a substance.

(j) The formula NaCl for salt conveys that salt contains sodium and chlorine in equal proportions by mass.

20. The following is a list of substances that are all gaseous at room temperature: carbon dioxide, nitrogen dioxide, sulphur hexafluoride, krypton, ethane (C_2H_6), silane (SiH_4), stibine (SbH_3), bromine fluoride (BrF). Arrange them in order of increasing gaseous density.

21. Why are we reluctant to speak of the properties of water vapour at STP?

22. Table 18-1 lists the densities of several gases at STP. For each gas listed, calculate the molar mass indicated by the density. Also calculate the molar masses from the sum of the atomic masses. Compare your results in each case. Can you suggest any explanation why the two values do not exactly agree in some cases?

23. At 800°C approximately 10% of the molecules in a sample of iodine break down to single atoms. Calculate the number of moles of molecular iodine equivalent to one gram of this element at ordinary temperatures. Then calculate the number of moles (as molecules and atoms) when this one gram is heated to 800°C.

24. Make clear the distinction between *simplest formula* and *molecular formula*. Of the various structural types discussed in Chapters 14 and 15, for which types of substances are simplest formulas applicable, and for which are molecular formulas appropriate?

25. The formula for hydrazine is N_2H_4. Summarize all the information about hydrazine suggested by this formula.

26. Calculate the percentage composition of each of the substances represented by the following formulas: (a) SiH_4, (b) Mg_3N_2, (c) $C_{10}H_8$, (d) $CaCO_3$, (e) $Ca(HCO_3)_2$, (f) $FeSO_4$, (g) $Fe_2(SO_4)_3$, (h) $C_6H_4Cl_2$, (i) $CHCl_3$, (j) SiD_4 (D = deuterium).

27. Calculate the percentage by mass of each element in the antibiotics (a) sulphanilamide, $C_6H_8N_2O_2S$; (b) chloromycetin, $C_{11}H_{12}N_2O_5Cl_2$.

28. Calculate the simplest formulas for the compounds whose composition is listed below:

(a) carbon, 15.8%; sulphur, 84.2%

(b) sulphur, 47.5%; chlorine, 52.5%

(c) chlorine, 81.6%; oxygen, 18.4%

(d) silver, 70.1%; nitrogen, 9.1%; oxygen, 20.8%

(e) potassium, 40.2%; chromium, 26.9%; oxygen, 32.9%

(f) sodium, 29.1%; sulphur, 40.5%; oxygen, 30.4%

(g) potassium, 26.6%; chromium, 35.4%; oxygen, 38.0%

29. Calculate the simplest formulas of the oxides of phosphorus which contain 43.6% and 56.6% of oxygen.

30. For each of the following, calculate the simplest formula of the corresponding compound:

(a) 29.5% calcium, 23.5% sulphur, 47.0% oxygen

(b) 19.2% sodium, 0.8% hydrogen, 26.1% sulphur, 53.3% oxygen

(c) 65.0% carbon, 13.5% hydrogen, 21.5% oxygen

(d) 52.2% carbon, 13.0% hydrogen, 34.8% oxygen

(e) 27.4% sodium, 1.2% hydrogen, 14.3% carbon, 57.1% oxygen

(f) 14.0% potassium, 9.7% aluminium, 30.2% silicon, 46.1% oxygen

31. Chemicals should *never* be left in unlabelled bottles; however, on occasion mistakes are made and this happens. A bottle of a blue compound, evidently a copper salt, was found unlabelled. On analysis the salt showed a copper content of 47.3%. The only copper salts purchased for the storeroom, and therefore the only choices for this material, were listed as $CuCl_2$, $CuBr_2$, $CuSO_4$, and $Cu(NO_3)_2$. Which of these was the unknown?

32. The simplest formula for glucose is CH_2O; its molar mass is 180 g/mol. What is its molecular formula?

33. Determine the molecular formula from the information listed for each of the compounds below.

	SUBSTANCE	SIMPLEST FORMULA	MOLAR MASS (g/mol)
(a)	octane	C_4H_9	114
(b)	ethanol	C_2H_6O	46
(c)	naphthalene	C_5H_4	128
(d)	carotene	C_5H_7	536
(e)	melamine	CH_2N_2	126

34. The percentage compositions and approximate molar masses (M in grams per mole) of some compounds are listed below. Calculate the molecular formula of each.

		M
(a)	64.9% carbon, 13.5% hydrogen, 21.6% oxygen	74
(b)	52.2% carbon, 13.0% hydrogen, 34.8% oxygen	46
(c)	39.9% carbon, 6.7% hydrogen, 53.4% oxygen	60
(d)	26.7% carbon, 2.2% hydrogen, 71.1% oxygen	90
(e)	12.1% carbon, 16.2% oxygen, 71.7% chlorine	99
(f)	20.2% aluminium, 79.8% chlorine	267
(g)	40.3% boron, 52.2% nitrogen, 7.5% hydrogen	80

35. Two substances, one a gas and the other a volatile liquid, have the same percentage composition, 92.3% carbon and 7.7% hydrogen. The molar mass of the gas is 26 and that of the liquid is 78. Determine the molecular formula of each compound.

36. A compound was found to contain 58.5% carbon, 4.1% hydrogen, 11.4% nitrogen, and 26.0% oxygen. Its molar mass was found to be approximately 125. Calculate (a) the molecular formula of the compound, and (b) the exact molar mass of the compound.

37. One litre of a gas at STP has a mass of 1.26 g, and its composition is 14.3% hydrogen and 85.7% carbon. Calculate the molecular formula for the gaseous substance.

38. The composition of a gaseous compound is 92.3% carbon and 7.7% hydrogen. The mass of 300 cm³ of this gas, measured at STP, is 0.351 g. Calculate (a) its molar mass, (b) its molecular formula.

39. The composition of a compound is 30.5% nitrogen and 69.5% oxygen. Calculate its molecular formula, given that 1.00 L of the gas, measured at 91°C and 2.00 atm, has a mass of 6.13 g.

40. Calculate the mass of carbon in one litre of acetylene (C_2H_2) at STP.

41. A liquid which boils at 80°C has a vapour which, when measured at 100 kPa pressure and 100°C, has a density of 2.52 g/L. What is the molar mass of the substance?

42. A compound was found to contain 54.5% carbon,

9.1% hydrogen, and 36.4% oxygen. The vapour from 0.082 g of the compound occupied 21.6 mL at 20°C and 104.0 kPa. Calculate the simplest formula and the molecular formula for this compound.

43. Benzene is composed of carbon, 92.3%, and hydrogen, 7.7%. At 100°C and 96.0 kPa pressure it is a vapour, and 2.00 g of it, under these conditions occupy a volume of 828 cm³. What is the molecular formula of benzene?

44. From the information given in Tables 20-1 and 20-2, state the formula for the "cooking gas" listed in the tables.

45. A gas has the molecular formula C_3H_8. What volume will be occupied by 2.00 g of this gas at 27°C and 750 Torr pressure?

46. What mass of argon would be required to fill an electric light bulb having a capacity of 200 cm³ when the pressure is 1.0 atm and the temperature 20°C?

47. What mass of nitrogen can be compressed into a 10 L cylinder at a pressure of 100 atm when the temperature is 15°C?

48. From the following properties of benzene, C_6H_6, calculate the volume occupied by 10 g of this substance at a pressure of 101.3 kPa and a temperature of: (a) 0°C, (b) 100°C. (Boiling point, 80°C; density (at 0°C) 0.88 g/mL.)

49. Calculate the volume occupied by 1.00 g of ethyl alcohol at 25°C, given that its density is 0.79 g/mL. Calculate the volume occupied by 1.00 g of ethyl alcohol vapour at 25°C and at its vapour pressure, 7.87 kPa. (The formula for ethyl alcohol, also known as ethanol, is C_2H_5OH.)

50. From the density of air, 1.293 g/L at STP, calculate a "molar mass" for air. What is the significance of the result?

51. Calculate the density of benzene vapour (C_6H_6) at a pressure of 102.6 kPa and a temperature of 80°C (its boiling point).

52. "Dry ice" is solid carbon dioxide, and it has a density of 1.53 g/cm³. At room temperature it turns into gas spontaneously. Calculate the volume of gas at 20°C and 1 atm which would be produced by 1 cm³ of "Dry ice."

53. The vapour pressure of water at 25°C is 3.17 kPa. Calculate the mass of water vapour in an 18-L bottle containing air saturated with water vapour at this temperature.

54. Calculate the partial pressure of water vapour in air of which 8.0 L was found to contain 0.060 g of water vapour at 25°C.

55. How many molecules are present in a litre of a gas at STP? Is it necessary to specify what gas?

56. Vacuum pumps can exhaust a piece of apparatus to a pressure of about 10^{-6} Torr without difficulty. What is that pressure in pascals? How many molecules of gas remain in each millilitre at this pressure and at 0°C?

57. How many molecules are present altogether in one litre of air at STP? How many oxygen molecules are there? How many nitrogen molecules? (See Table 5-1.) How many of each of these molecules are there per millilitre? What percentage of the molecules in air are oxygen molecules?

58. The average carbon dioxide content of the atmosphere is 0.03% by volume. Calculate how many molecules of carbon dioxide there would be in 1 cm³ of "average" air at STP. Very minor constituents are often reported in parts per million (ppm), and for gases these refer to parts by volume. Calculate the number of ppm of carbon dioxide in "average" air.

59. Assuming the radius of the helium atom to be 10^{-8} cm, calculate the volume of 6.02×10^{23} helium atoms, and compare this with the molar volume of helium.

*60. Calculate the density of dry air at 760 Torr and 25°C, given that the density at STP is 1.293 g/L. Also calculate the density of air saturated with water vapour at 25°C; in this, the partial pressure of water vapour is 23.8 Torr and that of dry air is 736.2 Torr, for a total pressure of 760 Torr. Can you see any significance in your result?

*61. Show that the ideal gas equation can be rearranged to give expressions for (a) the density of a gas, (b) the molar mass of a gas, (c) the number of moles of a gas per litre.

*62. Given that 1.00 mol of a gas occupies 22.4 L at 273 K and 101.3 kPa, calculate the volume occupied by n mol at T K and p kPa. Rearrange your result into the ideal gas equation.

21 The Language of Chemistry

1. In *Through the Looking-Glass,* Alice asked Humpty Dumpty "*Must* a name mean something?" Well, it must mean something if we are using words to tell somebody something—and this is the primary function of words. And if an idea is to be conveyed correctly, then the words that are used must have the same meaning for the reader (or hearer) as for the writer (or speaker). You cannot hope to understand chemistry unless you clearly understand what chemists mean by the words and symbols they use. This is why we devote this chapter to some of the kinds of "shorthand" that chemists find useful.

2. NAMING OF BINARY COMPOUNDS. A *binary compound* is one that is composed of two elements only; several examples are given in Table 21-1.

The practice in naming binary compounds is to name the more electropositive constituent first and give the name of the more electronegative constituent the termination "ide." Accordingly, we speak of sodium chloride, not chlorine sodide (and write the formula NaCl, not ClNa).

It is perhaps well to point out that, although all binary compounds have names ending in *-ide*, not all compounds with names ending in *-ide* are binary compounds. For example, ammonium chlor*ide*, NH₄Cl, and sodium hydrox*ide*, NaOH, are not binary compounds.

TABLE 21-1

SOME BINARY COMPOUNDS

FORMULA	NAME
$ZnCl_2$	Zinc chlor**ide**
Ag_2S	Silver sulph**ide**
NaF	Sodium fluor**ide**
KBr	Potassium brom**ide**
CaH_2	Calcium hyd**ride**
Fe_3C	Iron carb**ide**
Mg_3N_2	Magnesium nit**ride**
Al_2O_3	Aluminium ox**ide**

Sometimes—but by no means always—Greek prefixes are used to indicate the relative proportions of the two kinds of atoms in a binary compound, for example, P_4S_3 is called *tetra*phosphorus *tri*sulphide. Such prefixes are particularly useful for distinguishing between two different binary compounds of the same elements:

carbon *mon*oxide (CO) and carbon *di*oxide (CO_2)
sulphur *di*oxide (SO_2) and sulphur *tri*oxide (SO_3)
phosphorus *tri*bromide (PBr_3) and phosphorus *penta*bromide (PBr_5)

There are some binary compounds of hydrogen, like HCl and HBr, that dissolve in water to form acidic solutions. When not dissolved in water, these substances should be called by their proper binary names (first column of Table 21-2), whether existing as gases (as they do at room temperature) or condensed to the liquid or solid states. The aqueous solutions, but *only* the aqueous solutions, should be given the names in the last column of Table 21-2, for reasons that will be apparent later (Sec. 26-8 and 27-3).

TABLE 21-2

ACID-FORMING BINARY COMPOUNDS

NAME OF COMPOUND	FORMULA	NAME OF AQUEOUS SOLUTION
Hydrogen fluoride	HF	Hydrofluoric acid
Hydrogen chloride	HCl	Hydrochloric acid
Hydrogen bromide	HBr	Hydrobromic acid
Hydrogen iodide	HI	Hydriodic acid

3. VALENCES OF SOME COMMON IONS. Earlier in this book (Sec. 13-6) you learned that sodium and potassium form singly charged positive ions, Na^+ and K^+; magnesium and calcium form doubly charged positive ions, Mg^{2+} and Ca^{2+}; fluorine and chlorine form singly charged negative ions, F^- and Cl^-; and oxygen and sulphur form doubly charged negative ions, O^{2-} and S^{2-}. And you learned how the electron arrangements in those ions are similar to the electron arrangements in the atoms of inert gases. We have pointed out (Sec. 14-9) that the combining capacity or *valence* of elements that form ionic compounds is determined by the charge on their ions. The *ionic valence* or *electrovalence* exhibited by some common elements is given in Table 21-3 by listing the ions that these elements form.

Later (Sec. 28-8) we shall see that the word "valence" has more than one meaning.

You will notice from Table 21-3 that some elements can have more than one valence. This is true of iron, for example. It forms two "sets" of compounds, such as $FeCl_2$ and $FeCl_3$, $Fe(OH)_2$ and $Fe(OH)_3$. The situation is more complicated with some other elements: titanium (Ti) has three different valences, and manganese (Mn) has five! Which of its possible valences an element has in a given compound can be deduced from the formula of the compound, as we shall see (Sec. 21-11). But first let us consider the naming of such compounds.

TABLE 21-3

SOME IONIC VALENCES (ELECTROVALENCES)

ALKALI METAL IONS	Sodium	Na^+	Fluoride	F^-	HALIDE IONS
	Potassium	K^+	Chloride	Cl^-	(IONS OF
			Bromide	Br^-	HALOGEN
ALKALINE EARTH METAL IONS	Magnesium	Mg^{2+}	Iodide	I^-	ELEMENTS)
	Calcium	Ca^{2+}			
	Aluminium	Al^{3+}	Oxide	O^{2-}	
	Iron	Fe^{2+}, Fe^{3+}	Sulphide	S^{2-}	
	Copper	Cu^+, Cu^{2+}	Nitride	N^{3-}	
	Silver	Ag^+			

An older system, now falling into disuse, was to append the word endings (or suffixes) "-ous" and "-ic" to the English or the Latin root of the name of the element, the "-ous" ending indicating the lower of two valences. Thus $Fe(OH)_2$ was ferrous hydroxide and $Fe(OH)_3$ was ferric hydroxide; CuCl was cuprous chloride and $CuCl_2$ was cupric chloride. These examples illustrate the confusion this system can engender: the "-ous" suffix in "ferrous" signifies a valence of 2 but in "cuprous" it signifies a valence of 1. Moreover, this system cannot cope with compounds of an element that has more than two different valences.

4. THE DISTINGUISHING OF VALENCES. The modern system for distinguishing the valence of an element that can form two or more "sets" of compounds is to cite the valence of the element in Roman numerals (in brackets) after the English name of the element. Thus:

$$Fe(OH)_2 \text{ is iron(II) hydroxide, and}$$
$$Fe(OH)_3 \text{ is iron(III) hydroxide}$$

$$CuCl \text{ is copper(I) chloride, and}$$
$$CuCl_2 \text{ is copper(II) chloride}$$

$$SnO \text{ is tin(II) oxide, and}$$
$$SnO_2 \text{ is tin(IV) oxide}$$

The properties of metal compounds that are composed of the same elements (such as each of the pairs cited above) depend very much on the valence of the metal. A name such as "mercury chloride" is ambiguous, and its use can lead to trouble.

There are two "mercury chlorides." Mercury(II) chloride, $HgCl_2$, is a soluble and very poisonous salt sometimes called *corrosive sublimate*; mercury(I) chloride, Hg_2Cl_2, has a very low solubility and, under the name *calomel*, has applications in medicine.

Auntie Jane gave baby Nell
What she thought was calomel;
But, alas, what baby ate
Was corrosive sublimate.
Not much difference, I confess
One atom (and one baby) less.

5. COMPOUND IONS OR RADICALS. Some ions, like chloride ion (Cl^-), bromide ion (Br^-), and sulphide ion (S^{2-}), contain only one element. Others, like hydroxide ion (OH^-), nitrate ion (NO_3^-), sulphate ion (SO_4^{2-}), and acetate ion $(C_2H_3O_2^-)$, contain two or more elements. These assemblages, and others listed in Table 21-4, are known as *compound ions* or *radicals*. Compound ions can be decomposed by

TABLE 21-4

SOME NEGATIVELY CHARGED COMPOUND IONS OR RADICALS

FORMULA	NAME	FORMULA	NAME
CO_3^{2-}	Carbonate	ClO_4^-	Perchlorate
SO_4^{2-}	Sulphate	ClO_3^-	Chlorate
SO_3^{2-}	Sulphite	ClO_2^-	Chlorite
NO_3^-	Nitrate	ClO^-	Hypochlorite
NO_2^-	Nitrite	$C_2H_3O_2^-$	Acetate
PO_4^{3-}	Phosphate	MnO_4^-	Permanganate

suitable reactions, but because they remain intact in many reactions it is convenient to give them distinctive names (Table 21-4).

Almost all the compound ions that you will meet in this book are negatively charged, that is, are negative ions. An important positively charged compound ion, however, is the ammonium ion, NH_4^+, which in many ways resembles a metal ion, such as Na^+ or Ca^{2+}.

Substances containing compound ions are named in a fashion similar to binary compounds. For example, $KClO_3$ is potassium chlorate and $(NH_4)_2S$ is ammonium sulphide.

ACIDS, BASES, AND SALTS

6. ACIDS AND BASES. We shall have more to say about *acids* and *bases* later (Sec. 27-3), but here we must extend the little we have said about them (Sec. 5-12), so that we may describe the naming of salts.

Acids and bases may each be defined by a characteristic set of properties.

An **acid**:

   (1) *has a sour taste;*

   (2) *changes the colour of certain dyes* (for example, blue litmus);

   (3) *liberates the gas carbon dioxide from carbonates* (for example, calcium carbonate);

   (4) *loses these properties on reaction with a "base."*

The definition of an "acid," then, in part depends on that of a "base."

A **base**:

   (1) *has a slippery feel when in aqueous solution* (if sufficiently concentrated);

   (2) *changes the colour of certain dyes* (the change is the reverse of that caused by acids; a base turns red litmus blue, whereas an acid turns blue litmus red);

   (3) *loses these properties on reaction with an acid.*

These definitions are in terms of experimentally observable phenomena. Acids and bases can also be defined in terms of their structure. It is found that *all* **bases** *either contain hydroxide ions, OH^-, or yield hydroxide ions when dissolved in water.* (All bases are therefore, at least in solution, hydroxides.) On the other hand, *all* **acids** *contain hydrogen ions, H^+, or yield hydrogen ions when dissolved in water.* This does *not* mean that all substances that contain hydrogen are acids—hydrogen *ions*, not hydrogen atoms, are responsible for acidic properties.

There is good evidence that it is not really simple hydrogen ions but hydrated hydrogen ions, or **hydronium ions**, H_3O^+, that are responsible for the characteristic behaviour of acids. The formation of this ion is discussed in Sec. 26-8 and 27-3.

7. NEUTRALIZATION: FORMATION OF SALTS. Acids and bases react with one another, and the process of interaction is called **neutralization.** Acids are said to neutralize bases, and bases are said to neutralize acids. Neutralization involves the formation of two products: water and a **salt.** Thus if potassium hydroxide and hydrobromic acid are brought together, the reaction may be represented by the equation:

$$\underset{\text{base}}{KOH} + \underset{\text{acid}}{HBr} \rightarrow \underset{\text{water}}{H_2O} + \underset{\text{salt}}{KBr}$$

In this example the salt is potassium bromide. It can be obtained in solid form by evaporating the water.

TABLE 21-5

SOME COMMON ACIDS AND BASES

ACIDS		BASES	
NAME	FORMULA	NAME	FORMULA
Nitric acid	HNO_3	Sodium hydroxide	$NaOH$
Hydrochloric acid	HCl	Potassium hydroxide	KOH
Sulphuric acid	H_2SO_4	Calcium hydroxide	$Ca(OH)_2$
Phosphoric acid	H_3PO_4	Magnesium hydroxide	$Mg(OH)_2$

Salts, however prepared, can always be thought of as being *derived* from a base and an acid. Sodium sulphate, Na_2SO_4, is derived from sodium hydroxide and sulphuric acid; calcium nitrate, $Ca(NO_3)_2$, is derived from calcium hydroxide and nitric acid, and so on.

8. NAMING OF ACIDS AND SALTS. All of the compound ions or radicals listed in Table 21-4 are constituents of acids as well as of salts. Thus the carbonate grouping is in carbonic acid, H_2CO_3, as well as in calcium carbonate, $CaCO_3$; the sulphate grouping is in sulphuric acid, H_2SO_4, as well as in sodium sulphate, Na_2SO_4; and so on. There is a consistent relationship between the names of these radical-containing acids and the salts which can be made from them (by reaction with a base). The nature of the relationship is indicated by the letters in bold face type in Table 21-6.

You will observe that

(1) *a salt that has a name ending in "ate" corresponds to an acid with a name ending in "ic";* and

(2) *a salt that has a name ending in "ite" corresponds to an acid with a name ending in "ous."*

Thus the neutralization of chlor**ic** acid yields a salt known as a chlor**ate**; chlor**ous** acid yields a chlor**ite**, hypochlor**ous** acid yields a hypochlor**ite**; and so on.

TABLE 21-6

SOME ACIDS AND CORRESPONDING SALTS

ACIDS		CORRESPONDING SALTS	
NAME	FORMULA	NAME	EXAMPLE
Carbonic acid	H_2CO_3	Carbonate	Zinc carbonate, $ZnCO_3$
Sulphuric acid	H_2SO_4	Sulphate	Copper sulphate, $CuSO_4$
Sulphurous acid	H_2SO_3	Sulphite	Calcium sulphite, $CaSO_3$
Nitric acid	HNO_3	Nitrate	Aluminium nitrate, $Al(NO_3)_3$
Nitrous acid	HNO_2	Nitrite	Ammonium nitrite, NH_4NO_2
Perchloric acid	$HClO_4$	Perchlorate	Magnesium perchlorate, $Mg(ClO_4)_2$
Chloric acid	$HClO_3$	Chlorate	Potassium chlorate, $KClO_3$
Chlorous acid	$HClO_2$	Chlorite	Sodium chlorite, $NaClO_2$
Hypochlorous acid	$HClO$	Hypochlorite	Calcium hypochlorite, $Ca(ClO)_2$
Acetic acid	$HC_2H_3O_2$	Acetate	Silver acetate, $AgC_2H_3O_2$
Phosphoric acid	H_3PO_4	Phosphate	Sodium phosphate, Na_3PO_4

Another aspect of systematic nomenclature indicated in Table 21-6 is the way in which two or more acids differing in their oxygen content are named. The acid having in its molecule one less atom of oxygen than an "-ic" acid is an "-ous" acid. Thus:

H_2SO_4 is sulphur**ic** acid H_2SO_3 is sulphur**ous** acid

HNO_3 is nitr**ic** acid HNO_2 is nitr**ous** acid

The acid having in its molecule one less atom of oxygen than an "-ous" acid is a "hypo . . . ous" acid, and the acid having in its molecule one more oxygen atom than a simple "-ic" acid is a "per . . . ic" acid. Thus:

$HClO_4$ is **per**chlor**ic** acid $HClO_3$ is chlor**ic** acid

$HClO_2$ is chlor**ous** acid $HClO$ is **hypo**chlor**ous** acid

SUMMARIZING:

Hypo . . . ous Acid	. . . ous Acid	. . . ic Acid	Per . . . ic Acid
$HClO$	$HClO_2$	$HClO_3$	$HClO_4$
	HNO_2	HNO_3	
	H_2SO_3	H_2SO_4	
		H_2CO_3	
H_3PO_2	H_3PO_3	H_3PO_4	

9. SALTS OF BINARY ACIDS. The acids we have just been considering are *ternary acids* (composed of three different elements) and the "-ic" → "-ate" and "-ous" → "-ite" rules for the naming of salts applies to such acids very regularly. But in the naming of the salts of *binary acids* (Table 21-2), such as hydrochloric acid and hydrobromic acid, the "hydro" prefix is dropped and the "-ic" ending becomes "-ide." Thus the salts of hydrochloric acid are chlorides (sodium chloride, calcium chloride, etc.), and the salts of hydrobromic acid are bromides (potassium bromide, silver bromide, etc.). This is because binary compounds should have names ending in "-ide."

DEDUCING FORMULAS, NAMES AND VALENCES

10. FORMULAS FROM NAMES AND VICE VERSA. For ionic compounds at least, the writing of a formula corresponding to a systematic name is easy enough, provided you know the symbols and valences of the constituent parts of the compound. For example, what is the formula of magnesium sulphide? Magnesium has an ionic valence of positive two, Mg^{2+}, and sulphur in the sulphide ion has an ionic valence of negative two, S^{2-} (Table 21-3). Hence, for the compound magnesium sulphide to be electrically neutral there must be one magnesium ion for each sulphide ion; so the formula is MgS. The formula for magnesium nitrate? Since the nitrate ion is singly negatively charged, NO_3^- (Table 21-4), in magnesium nitrate there must be two nitrate ions for every magnesium ion; the formula is thus $Mg(NO_3)_2$.

What about iron(III) sulphate? The Roman numeral tells us that iron is present as Fe^{3+}; the sulphate ion is doubly negatively charged, SO_4^{2-} (Table 21-4). So, for an assemblage of these ions to be electrically neutral, there must be two Fe^{3+} ions for every three SO_4^{2-} ions; accordingly, the formula is $Fe_2(SO_4)_3$.

The reverse operation—the writing of a systematic name from a given formula—is just as easy (provided you know the names that correspond to the given symbols). What is the name of the compound of formula $Mg(NO_2)_2$? Clearly, it is magnesium nitrite—clearly, that is, if you don't confuse nitrite (NO_2^-) with nitrate (NO_3^-). What about $Fe(NO_3)_3$? Obviously, it's *an* iron nitrate, but which valence of iron is the relevant one? Since a nitrate ion is singly charged, and there are three of them for each iron ion, then the iron is present as Fe^{3+}; the compound is iron(III) nitrate.

At this point you may ask why, when we named $Mg(NO_2)_2$, we didn't call it magnesium(II) nitrite rather than just magnesium nitrite? In fact, it can perfectly properly be called magnesium(II) nitrite; but there is no need to, because the only valence that magnesium exhibits is +2. A Roman numeral is required only when there may be doubt as to which of two or more valences is being exhibited by the element in question.

11. DEDUCING VALENCES FROM FORMULAS. We have already illustrated this in the preceding section when we deduced that the iron in $Fe(NO_3)_3$ has a valence of $+3$. In fact, one can deduce the valence of an element in an ionic compound without even knowing the name of the element, provided the valence of the other constituent part of the compound is known. For example, what is the valence of Sn in SnF_2? Since the fluoride ion, F^-, is singly charged (negatively) and there are two fluoride ions for every Sn ion, the latter must have a valence of $+2$, and so be Sn^{2+}. (The compound is tin(II) fluoride or stannous fluoride, a name you may have seen in toothpaste advertisements.)

12. What's in a name?

SHAKESPEARE

If names be not correct, language is

not in accord with the truth of things.

CONFUCIUS

"What's in a name?" asked Juliet and then, without waiting for an answer, she went on:

that which we call a rose

By any other name would smell as sweet.

Juliet very properly stressed that qualities or properties are more important than names, but we could wish that she had some of the respect for names that Confucius had. Certainly in chemistry names are important, and a student of chemistry is continually learning either the special meaning of a word, or the meaning of a special word.

QUESTIONS

1. Make clear, with the help of examples, the meaning of:

(a) binary compound   (f) acid
(b) ternary compound   (g) base
(c) radical   (h) salt
(d) compound ion   (i) neutralization
(e) valence   (j) hydronium ion

2. Name the Greek prefixes signifying one to five. (These are used frequently in the names of binary compounds.)

3. Write formulas for the chlorides, oxides, and sulphides of sodium, magnesium, aluminium, and silicon. Name each compound whose formula is given.

4. Write formulas for the following: hydrochloric acid, nitrous acid, sulphuric acid, chloric acid, hydriodic acid, hypochlorous acid.

5. Write the formula of each of the following compound ions: sulphite, acetate, hydroxide, nitrate, hypochlorite, phosphate, perchlorate, carbonate. Show the valence in each case.

6. Name four metallic elements that have more than one common valence.

7. Write the formula for each of:

1. sodium carbonate
2. nitrogen trihydride
3. calcium sulphate
4. phosphorus pentabromide
5. ammonium phosphate
6. copper(II) chloride
7. barium acetate
8. mercury(II) iodide
9. sodium chlorate
10. phosphorus(V) oxide
11. iron(III) sulphate
12. dinitrogen oxide
13. sodium hypochlorite
14. barium bromide
15. nitrogen trifluoride
16. calcium nitride
17. arsenic(III) sulphide
18. boron trifluoride
19. copper(I) oxide
20. aluminium phosphate
21. silicon tetraiodide
22. sulphur dioxide
23. carbon monoxide
24. mercury(I) sulphate
25. silver sulphide
26. di-iodine pentoxide
27. beryllium carbonate
28. tin(IV) chloride
29. ammonium chlorite
30. potassium permanganate

8. Give the correct chemical name for each compound whose formula is given in the following list, and state the valence of each element or radical in each:

(a) Na_3PO_4, (b) $Mg(ClO_4)_2$, (c) $HgCl_2$, (d) CaH_2, (e) SnS_2, (f) $Al(OH)_3$, (g) $ZnCO_3$, (h) NH_4NO_3, (i) CF_4, (j) $Ca(OCl)_2$, (k) $AsCl_5$, (l) Mg_3N_2, (m) $FeSO_3$, (n) $Cu(C_2H_3O_2)_2$, (o) BrF_3, (p) TiO_2, (q) $Fe_2(SO_4)_3$, (r) H_2Se, (s) $Ba(ClO_3)_2$, (t) Ag_3PO_4, (u) $CuCl$, (v) $CsNO_3$, (w) Sb_2S_3, (x) ZnI_2, (y) $Sc(NO_2)_3$.

9. Write equations for the sixteen neutralization reactions involving the following acids and bases (one acid and one base at a time!):

$$NaOH, KOH, NH_3, Ca(OH)_2$$
$$HCl, H_2SO_4, H_3PO_4, HNO_2$$

An aqueous solution of ammonia, NH_3, acts as a base although it is obvious that this compound is not a hydroxide. Show by an equation that an ammonia molecule can react with a water molecule to produce an ammonium ion and a hydroxide ion in the solution.

10. Give reasons why dinitrogen oxide is preferable to nitrous oxide as a name for N_2O; and why mercury(I) sulphate is preferred to mercurous sulphate as a name for Hg_2SO_4. In general, what advantages can be claimed for this nomenclature, advocated by the International Union of Pure and Applied Chemistry, over older forms of nomenclature?

11. Given that H_3PO_4 is phosphoric acid, what names would you propose for the acids whose formulas are H_3PO_3 and H_3PO_2?

12. Many acids are formed by a reaction between an oxide, usually of a non-metal, with water; for example, $SO_2 + H_2O \rightarrow H_2SO_3$ (sulphurous acid). The acid-forming oxide is known as an *anhydride* of the acid. Deduce from the formulas of the following acids what are the corresponding anhydrides, write their formulas, and give their proper chemical names: carbonic acid, sulphuric acid, perchloric acid, hypochlorous acid, nitric acid, pyrophosphoric acid ($H_4P_2O_7$), tetraboric acid ($H_2B_4O_7$), orthosilicic acid (H_4SiO_4).

13. Copy the following table and then deduce and fill in the proper formula in each of the blank spaces. (All the information required is in the table.)

	PHOSPHATE	CHLORATE	SULPHATE	CARBONATE	NITRATE	HYDROXIDE
Ammonium			$(NH_4)_2SO_4$		NH_4NO_3	
Hydrogen	H_3PO_4				HNO_3	HOH
Calcium	$Ca_3(PO_4)_2$			$CaCO_3$		
Aluminium		$Al(ClO_3)_3$				
Magnesium				$MgCO_3$		
Potassium		$KClO_3$				KOH
Iron(III)						

Phosphorus – an Essential Element

1. Late in the seventeenth century a physician in Hamburg named Hennig Brand subjected 50 and more pails-full of human urine to a variety of treatments. He undertook distillations, precipitations, roastings, and other operations—all in the hope of finding a liquid that would convert silver into gold. He didn't find that, but he did isolate a waxy white solid that glowed in the dark and that, unless kept under water, could spontaneously burst into flame. This was the discovery of the element phosphorus, in 1674 or thereabouts. (An irony of history is that, almost three centuries later, phosphorus was returned to Hamburg in a frightfully unwelcome way. The city was devastated in 1943, during World War II, by huge fires caused by the dropping of phosphorus incendiary bombs in four large-scale air raids.)

The word "phosphorus" comes from the Greek meaning "light bringing."

Treacherous though phosphorus itself can be, many compounds of phosphorus are valuable and some are vitally important. For example, certain phosphorus compounds have an essential role in chemical reactions that go on in our bodies, and other phosphorus compounds are major ingredients of our bones and teeth—and even our genes. The phosphorus we need comes from our food, that is, from plants (or from animals that have eaten these). The plants grow in soil that contains compounds of phosphorus, either naturally or thanks to the foresight of the farmer.

The vapour of phosphorus causes bone decay, particularly in the jaw. Years ago, when matches were made from white phosphorus (a practice now outlawed), many workers suffered, and some died, from phosphorus poisoning. Skin burns from white phosphorus are very unpleasant, and heal very slowly.

2. OCCURRENCE AND PRODUCTION. Phosphorus occurs in nature mainly as $Ca_3(PO_4)_2$, a salt that is properly called calcium orthophosphate but which more often is known, more simply, as calcium phosphate. It exists in this form in *phosphate rock* and in the mineral *apatite,* and also in our bones and teeth.

The artist who painted this picture about 100 years after Brand's discovery described it as: "The Alchymist in search of the philosophers' stone discovers phosphorus and prays for the successful conclusion of his operation, as was the custom of the ancient chymical astrologers."

The "philosophers' stone," sought for centuries by the alchemists, was something that was thought capable of transforming other metals into gold.

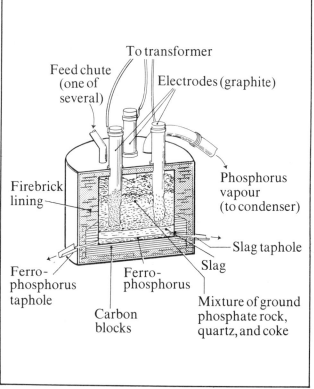

Fig. 22-1: *An electric furnace for the production of phosphorus. The phosphate is converted to phosphorus by hot carbon (as coke). The reaction mixture offers such resistance to the flow of electricity between the electrodes that most of the electrical energy is dissipated as heat, the heat being produced right where it's needed.*

Phosphorus itself is made nowadays by heating a mixture of ground phosphate rock and quartz (which is mainly silicon dioxide, SiO_2) and coke (which is mainly carbon). The reaction requires a very high temperature (about 1200°C) that is best achieved in an electric furnace (Fig. 22-1). The equation for the reaction is

$$2Ca_3(PO_4)_2 + 6SiO_2 + 10C \rightarrow 6CaSiO_3 + 10CO\uparrow + P_4\uparrow$$

The silica converts calcium compounds to a "slag" consisting mainly of calcium metasilicate ($CaSiO_3$) which, at the temperature of the furnace, is a liquid. The phosphorus distils off as a vapour and is collected in water as a solid waxy substance known as **white phosphorus**.

Iron compounds in the phosphate rock are decomposed in the furnace to iron; this combines with some of the phosphorus to give the alloy *ferrophosphorus,* which is used in steelmaking. Molten ferrophosphorus and molten slag settle to the bottom of the furnace in separate layers, which are "tapped" from time to time. Phosphorus and ferrophosphorus are produced in this way at Varennes, Quebec, and Long Harbour, Newfoundland.

Because the vapour of white phosphorus is spontaneously flammable a few degrees above room temperature, and is exceedingly poisonous, this form of phosphorus is a very hazardous chemical, and is stored under water. It is a soft substance that gradually turns yellow on exposure to light; hence it is often called *yellow phosphorus.* The yellowing is due to the gradual formation of *red phosphorus,* which is another form of the element, a more stable and less active form.

Red phosphorus is made by heating white phosphorus to about 260°C, out of contact with air. Red phosphorus is the essential constituent of the reddish-brown striking surface of a "match-book" of safety matches.

3. THE ALLOTROPY OF PHOSPHORUS. The phenomenon of an element occurring in more than one form with different properties is known as *allotropy* or allotropism (Sec. 15-12). White and red phosphorus are two **allotropes,** or allotropic forms, of this element. Although each is made up solely of phosphorus atoms, they exhibit striking differences in properties, as is illustrated in Table 22-1. These differences stem from differences in the way the phosphorus atoms are arranged and bonded in the crystals of the two forms.

TABLE 22-1

A COMPARISON OF WHITE AND RED PHOSPHORUS

PROPERTY	WHITE PHOSPHORUS	RED PHOSPHORUS
Appearance	white, waxy, translucent solid	reddish-violet powder
Toxicity	vapour is very poisonous	non-poisonous
Reaction with air	reacts at room temp.	none at room temp.
Kindling temperature	30 - 40°C	about 240°C
Solubility in:		
water	almost insoluble	almost insoluble
carbon disulphide (CS_2)	very soluble	almost insoluble
Melting Point (°C)	44	590
Density (g/cm³ at 20°C)	1.8	2.3

In the molecule of white phosphorus each atom is linked to three others as shown in Fig. 22-2. The valence forces of each atom are satisfied by this arrangement, so that one molecule shows little or no tendency to form bonds with another molecule that might be adjacent to it. Each molecule of white phosphorus is virtually independent of all others (but not quite; see Sec. 15-19) and so may move off into a vapour or into a solution with a suitable liquid like carbon disulphide. The relatively low melting point and easy evaporation

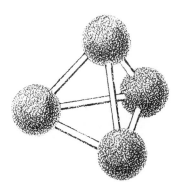

Fig. 22-2: *Models of the molecule of white phosphorus*

of white phosphorus, and its solubility in certain liquids are all consistent with its structure, namely, a small molecule, linked together internally, but with little tendency to attract other molecules.

Red phosphorus possesses a structure in which each atom is linked to three neighbouring phosphorus atoms as illustrated in Fig. 22-3. It is clearly very

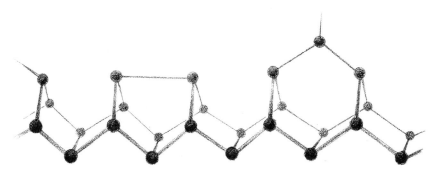

Fig. 22-3: *In the crystalline form of red phosphorus, the atoms of phosphorus are linked together by covalent bonds into a vast network, a portion of which is shown here.*

different from the tetrahedral molecule of white phosphorus; and the term molecule no longer seems appropriate because it is not evident where this structure comes to an end. It would, in fact, terminate at the faces of a crystal of this substance, so that if we were thinking about a molecule in this case it would extend just as far as the crystal. And since we might find big crystals and little crystals of red phosphorus in the same bottle, we would have to conclude that there was no specially characteristic molecule for this substance. There *is* a characteristic *structure*, but no characteristic molecule.

Red phosphorus has a kind of structure that is characteristic of a *network solid.* If you examine the properties of red phosphorus in the light of what we said earlier (Sec. 15-13) about network solids, you should have no trouble in accounting for most of the differences between the allotropes of this element shown in Table 22-1.

4. SOME OTHER PROPERTIES OF PHOSPHORUS. Phosphorus unites readily with the halogen elements. For example, with a restricted supply of chlorine the reaction is

$$P_4 + 6Cl_2 \rightarrow 4PCl_3$$
**phosphorus trichloride
or phosphorus(III)
chloride**

With an excess of chlorine the reaction goes further:

$$PCl_3 + Cl_2 \rightarrow PCl_5$$
**phosphorus pentachloride
or phosphorus(V)
chloride**

These phosphorus halides react vigorously with water to yield hydrogen chloride:

$$PCl_3 + 3H_2O \rightarrow H_3PO_3 + 3HCl$$

$$PCl_5 + 4H_2O \rightarrow H_3PO_4 + 5HCl$$

Hydrogen bromide and hydrogen iodide can be made by analogous reactions (Sec. 30-12).

When phosphorus burns in air or oxygen, a dense white smoke of what is called *phosphorus pentoxide* or *phosphorus(V) oxide* is produced (Sec. 5-9):

$$P_4 + 5O_2 \rightarrow P_4O_{10}$$

With a restricted supply of air, *phosphorus trioxide* or *phosphorus(III) oxide* is the main product:

$$P_4 + 3O_2 \rightarrow P_4O_6$$

5. ACIDS OF PHOSPHORUS. When phosphorus trioxide is treated with water it yields phosphorous acid:

$$P_4O_6 + 6H_2O \rightarrow 4H_3PO_3$$

Phosphorus trioxide is called the *anhydride* of phosphorous acid; hence this oxide is called *phosphorous anhydride.*

When water is added to phosphorus pentoxide, metaphosphoric acid, HPO_3, is formed:

$$P_4O_{10} + 2H_2O \rightarrow 4HPO_3$$

If excess water is present and the solution is heated, metaphosphoric acid is converted to orthophosphoric acid, H_3PO_4:

$$HPO_3 + H_2O \rightarrow H_3PO_4$$

Since the addition of water to phosphorus pentoxide yields a phosphoric acid (meta- or ortho-), this oxide is often called *phosphoric anhydride.* It is a very useful laboratory reagent; its avidity for water makes it a powerful drying (dehydrating) agent for many gases.

Reactions such as those cited in this section, in which water reacts directly with a substance, are often called *hydrations.*

In a marginal note with Sec. 5-9 it was explained why P_4O_{10} is called phosphorus pentoxide. Similarly, phosphorus trioxide is an old but firmly established name for P_4O_6, a name that originated when it was thought that the molecule contained only three atoms of oxygen (P_2O_3). In the molecules of P_4O_6 and P_4O_{10}, as in the molecule of white phosphorus (P_4), the four phosphorus atoms are in a tetrahedral arrangement (Fig. 22-2).

"Anhydrous" means "without water." An acid anhydride is an anhydrous compound that, on the addition of water, yields an acid.

TABLE 22-2

SOME ACIDS OF PHOSPHORUS	
NAME	FORMULA
Phosphorous acid	H_3PO_3
Metaphosphoric acid	HPO_3
(Ortho)phosphoric acid	H_3PO_4
Pyrophosphoric acid	$H_4P_2O_7$

Orthophosphoric acid (H_3PO_4) is the commonest acid of phosphorus; its name usually is shortened to *phosphoric acid.* Similarly, a salt of this acid, such as $Ca_3(PO_4)_2$ or Na_3PO_4, is commonly called simply a phosphate rather than an orthophosphate, which it properly is.

Salt hydrates such as $CaSO_4 \cdot 2H_2O$ are discussed in Sec. 24-11.

6. PHOSPHORIC ACID, H_3PO_4. This is made from phosphate rock, chiefly $Ca_3(PO_4)_2$, by two methods:

(1) Ground phosphate rock is treated with sulphuric acid (as at Warfield, British Columbia):

$$Ca_3(PO_4)_2 + 3H_2SO_4 + 6H_2O \rightarrow 3CaSO_4 \cdot 2H_2O\downarrow + 2H_3PO_4$$

The calcium sulphate dihydrate is filtered off, leaving an aqueous solution of phosphoric acid.

(2) Phosphorus is made from phosphate rock (Sec. 22-2); the phosphorus is burned to the pentoxide (Sec. 22-4), and then the oxide is hydrated (Sec. 22-5) to phosphoric acid (as at Buckingham, Quebec). This method yields purer phosphoric acid than method (1). Can you explain why?

An acid such as H_3PO_4, which has more than one hydrogen atom in its molecule, may react with a base in "stages." Depending on the proportions of the reactants, NH_3 and H_3PO_4 can yield $NH_4H_2PO_4$, $(NH_4)_2HPO_4$, or $(NH_4)_3PO_4$. The first two of these are known as acid salts (Sec. 27-8).

Salts of phosphoric acid are made by reacting it with a basic substance, for example:

$$H_3PO_4 + NH_3 \rightarrow NH_4H_2PO_4$$
$$H_3PO_4 + 3KOH \rightarrow K_3PO_4 + 3H_2O$$
$$2H_3PO_4 + 3Na_2CO_3 \rightarrow 2Na_3PO_4 + 3CO_2 + 3H_2O$$

The salt formed in the reaction represented by the third of these equations, Na_3PO_4, sodium orthophosphate, is also known as sodium phosphate, tertiary sodium phosphate, or trisodium phosphate; the last of these is commonly abbreviated to T.S.P. By whatever name, this salt gives a basic reaction in water; its value as a household and industrial cleaning agent, particularly for "cutting" or removing greasy substances, depends on this property.

7. PHOSPHATE FERTILIZERS. Phosphorus, like nitrogen, is essential for the nutrition of plants. The reaping of crops removes phosphorus from the soil, and no natural process restores it; accordingly, a farm will sooner or later become relatively unproductive unless fertilizer containing phosphorus in usable form is applied to the soil.

Calcium phosphate, $Ca_3(PO_4)_2$, the form in which phosphorus occurs in phosphate rock, is almost insoluble in water. This compound is therefore of little use as a fertilizer, because plants can absorb from the soil only substances that are dissolved in water.

More soluble phosphates, together with nitrogenous compounds, occur in very large amounts on some islands off the coast of Peru and elsewhere as guano, which is the accumulated excrement of untold millions of sea birds, notably cormorants, pelicans, and gannets. This is a valuable fertilizer that is "mined" as such.

The phosphate of phosphate rock can be converted into a more soluble compound, $Ca(H_2PO_4)_2$, by treating it with sulphuric acid (though not with as much as is needed to form phosphoric acid (Sec. 22-6)):

$$Ca_3(PO_4)_2 + 2H_2SO_4 + 4H_2O \rightarrow 2CaSO_4 \cdot 2H_2O + Ca(H_2PO_4)_2$$

The resulting mixture of calcium sulphate dihydrate and calcium dihydrogen phosphate is sold as a fertilizer under the name **superphosphate of lime.**

If phosphate rock is treated with phosphoric acid instead of sulphuric acid, calcium dihydrogen phosphate alone is obtained:

$$Ca_3(PO_4)_2 + 4H_3PO_4 \rightarrow 3Ca(H_2PO_4)_2$$

This fertilizer, richer in phosphorus, is called **triple superphosphate** or triple phosphate.

These fertilizers furnish both phosphorus and calcium (another important plant nutrient) to the soil. **Ammonium dihydrogen phosphate,** $NH_4H_2PO_4$, and **diammonium hydrogen phosphate,** $(NH_4)_2HPO_4$, are valuable fertilizers, providing both phosphorus and nitrogen in soluble form. Other fertilizers were discussed in Sec. 7-16.

Fig. 22-4 illustrates the way in which these and other phosphorus compounds referred to in this chapter are obtained from phosphate rock.

8. PHOSPHATES IN THE HOME. Household baking powder always contains sodium hydrogen carbonate, $NaHCO_3$, together with a substance that when moist and warmed, will act as an acid. (Baking powder also contains corn starch, which is to keep the mixture free-flowing.) If the acidic substance is $Ca(H_2PO_4)_2 \cdot H_2O$ as it commonly is, the reaction during baking can be represented by the equation:

$$2NaHCO_3 + Ca(H_2PO_4)_2 \cdot H_2O \rightarrow Na_2HPO_4 + CaHPO_4 + 3H_2O + 2CO_2\uparrow$$

The carbon dioxide that is evolved causes the cake or biscuit dough to "rise," so that the confection may be porous and "light."

$NaHCO_3$ is known in the kitchen as "baking soda." It should not be confused with another kitchen chemical called "washing soda." The latter is sodium carbonate decahydrate, $Na_2CO_3 \cdot 10H_2O$, a substance that is useful as a cleaning agent because of its alkalinity when dissolved in water.

TABLE 22-3

SOME IMPORTANT PHOSPHORUS COMPOUNDS

FORMULA	NAME	USE
$Ca_3(PO_4)_2$	calcium (ortho)phosphate	source of phosphorus and fertilizers
Na_3PO_4	sodium (ortho)phosphate trisodium phosphate (T.S.P.)	cleaning agent
$NH_4H_2PO_4$	ammonium dihydrogen phosphate	fertilizers; flame retardants
$(NH_4)_2HPO_4$	diammonium hydrogen phosphate	
$Ca(H_2PO_4)_2 \cdot H_2O$	calcium dihydrogen phosphate monohydrate	fertilizer; in baking powder
$Na_5P_3O_{10}$	sodium tripolyphosphate	water softener; in synthetic detergents
P_4O_{10}	phosphorus pentoxide	drying agent for gases
P_4S_3	tetraphosphorus trisulphide	in "strike-anywhere" matches

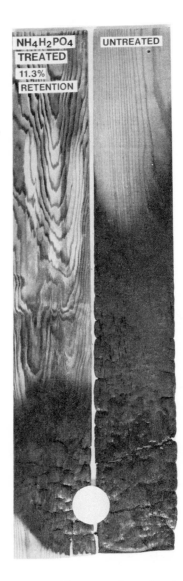

Treatment with ammonium dihydrogen phosphate does not make wood fireproof, but it does retard its burning. Here you see this effect.

Both these specimens of Douglas fir were subjected to a flame (of temperature 1150°C) which impinged on them at the spot indicated by the white circle. Flames spread very rapidly over most of the untreated specimen but over a much smaller area of the one impregnated with this phosphate. This picture shows their condition after being in this very hot flame for three minutes.

Among the functions of sodium tripolyphosphate are: forming water-soluble complex compounds with the calcium and magnesium in the water, and so preventing the deposition of insoluble substances that would discolour clothing and "spot" dishes and glassware; dispersing loosened soil particles and holding them in suspension; and furnishing alkalinity that aids the removal of oils and greases.

We have already mentioned (Sec. 22-6) the use of sodium phosphate ("T.S.P.") as a cleaning agent. Until recent years a more complex phosphate, sodium tripolyphosphate, $Na_5P_3O_{10}$, was widely and extensively used as a component of household detergents. The proportion of a detergent product that may be phosphate is now regulated by law in Canada, and in some jurisdictions in the United States the inclusion of phosphates in detergents is banned. These restrictive measures have been introduced because of evidence that the discharge of massive amounts of phosphates into the Great Lakes through sewage systems is threatening the life of the Lakes, by nourishing the growth of algae and other vegetation. This leads to a depletion of dissolved oxygen in the water and, in turn, to curtailment of fish life. But phosphate may not be the only, or even the major cause of this phenomenon. In any event, detergents are only one source of phosphate. Appreciable amounts reach the Lakes through human sewage and through streams that carry "run-off" from farms that use phosphate fertilizers.

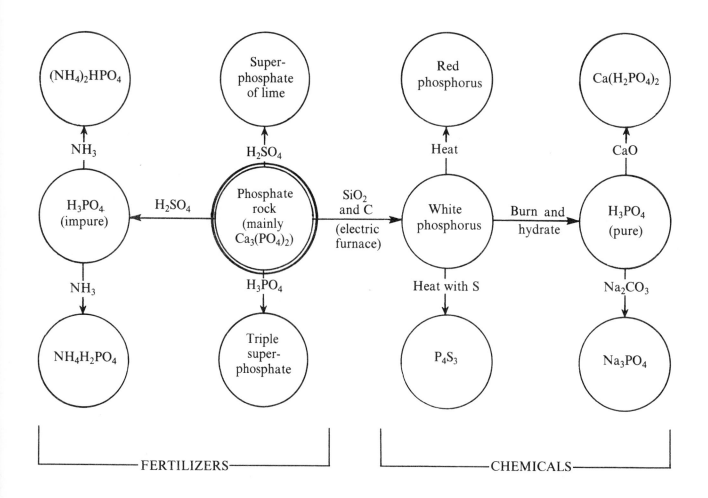

Fig. 22-4: *Phosphate rock as a source of phosphorus chemicals. All these products are made in Canada by the processes indicated.*

9. EUTROPHICATION. It is not generally recognized that a lake will die even if human beings never interfere with it nor add anything to it. For example, in the remote interior of Alaska, where there has been no human activity, there are dead lakes that once contained water but now are essentially swamp deposits of sediment from decomposed aquatic life. Other dying lakes are slowly but steadily approaching that fate.

As a new lake ages, nutrients and bottom sediment from natural drainage lead to an increase in aquatic plant and animal life. This process of aging with nutrient enrichment is called *eutrophication.* As living matter increases, and deposits pile up at the bottom, they take up more space and use up more oxygen. Eventually—and this may take thousands of years—the lake becomes a marsh, is overrun with vegetation, and disappears. Thus all lakes are born to die.

Agricultural development, urbanization, and industrial growth have vastly increased the flow of nutrients and sediments into the Great Lakes, and so have accelerated their aging process. Lake Erie, particularly, is in an advanced state of eutrophication.

7 N	TABLE 22–5
15 P	Atomic Numbers of Elements of the Nitrogen Family
33 As	
51 Sb	
83 Bi	

PHOSPHORUS IN ITS FAMILY

10. Phosphorus is a member of a family of elements the atoms of which all have five electrons in their outermost shell. This family—often called the *nitrogen family*—comprises nitrogen, phosphorus, arsenic (As), antimony (Sb), and bismuth (Bi).

These elements and their compounds exhibit interesting gradations in properties. For example, the hydrogen compounds have similar formulas (Table 22-4), but the ease with which these compounds can be decomposed to their constituent elements increases from ammonia through bismuthine. Ammonia forms ammonium compounds, such as ammonium chloride, NH_4Cl, and phosphine (a poisonous gas) forms analogous compounds, such as phosphonium chloride, PH_4Cl—but the other members of the family do not form such compounds.

Neither nitrogen nor phosphorus conducts electricity, and both have oxides that are acidic. These are properties of a non-metal. But the oxides of arsenic and antimony yield progressively less acidic solutions than the oxides of phosphorus, and Bi_2O_3 has no acidic properties at all (in fact, it is a basic substance, albeit weakly basic). Arsenic, antimony, and bismuth conduct electricity moderately well and have some of the lustre associated with metals.

The oxides of phosphorus are less acidic than the corresponding oxides of nitrogen (for example, HPO_3 is not as strong an acid as HNO_3).

So, in this family there is a steady progression from a true non-metal, nitrogen, to an almost true metal, bismuth. Can you explain this gradation in the properties of these elements? (Hint: the size of the atoms increases with increasing atomic number.)

TABLE 22-4

HYDROGEN COMPOUNDS OF ELEMENTS OF THE NITROGEN FAMILY

NH_3	Ammonia
PH_3	Phosphine
AsH_3	Arsine
SbH_3	Stibine
BiH_3	Bismuthine

The so-called Marsh test for very small amounts of arsenic depends on the ease with which arsine can be decomposed by heat to the elements arsenic and hydrogen. If ever you have a friend who is thinking of murdering someone by arsenical poisoning, you might explain to him or her that, although the method is reasonably sure, it is rather slow and, more particularly, that arsenic is very readily detected in organs of the *corpus delicti*, as several murderers have learned to their surprise and dismay.

QUESTIONS

1. Show that the individual atoms in the molecule of white phosphorus, and in the network structure of red phosphorus, possess octets of electrons in their valence shells. Which electron shell is the valence shell in the phosphorus atom?

2. Why does white phosphorus have a melting point more than 500 degrees below that of red phosphorus?

3. Why can white phophorus be dissolved in carbon disulphide, whereas red phosphorus is insoluble in the same liquid?

4. What is meant by the term *allotropy*? Name another element, dealt with in a previous chapter, that displayed the same phenomenon. How can allotropy be explained in these two instances?

5. Show that the two allotropic forms, white and red phosphorus, illustrate the typical differences between molecular solids and network solids.

6. Phosphorus(III) oxide has the molecular formula P_4O_6. The structure of this molecule can be related to that of the P_4 molecule illustrated in Fig. 22-2. In P_4 the atoms are at the corners of a geometrical figure called a tetrahedron. If, instead of the six P—P bonds along the edges of the tetrahedron, these atoms are linked through an oxygen, as

P ⌒ O ⌒ P, the P_4O_6 structure is obtained. (You might try this with gum drops and toothpicks, as a project.) Now see if you can propose a plausible structure for P_4O_{10}.

7. Draw a Lewis diagram for the phosphate ion, PO_4^{3-}. How many electron pairs are in the valence shell of the phosphorus atom in this ion? Apply the principles outlined in Sec. 15-8 to predict the shape of the phosphate ion.

8. Draw a Lewis diagram for the molecule of PCl_3. How many electron pairs are in the valence shell of the phosphorus atom in this molecule? Predict the shape of the molecule.

9. By analogy with the reactions described in this chapter predict the outcome of the reaction between phosphorus and bromine, and between the product of that reaction and water.

10. Show that phosphorus(V) oxide can react with water in different proportions to produce orthophosphoric acid, metaphosphoric acid, and pyrophosphoric acid. Explain what is meant by the term *phosphoric anhydride*. Which of the three acids is the most hydrated?

11. Write equations showing the neutralization of phosphoric acid in stages by the alkali potassium hydroxide. Label all the salts formed with their proper names.

12. Four phosphate fertilizers are described in Sec. 22-7. In the three-number system of labelling fertilizers ("7-7-7"), the middle number gives the percentage of phosphorus pentoxide in the material. Work out for the four named fertilizers the respective "phosphorus numbers" for labelling. For two of the fertilizers named, which contain nitrogen, work out the nitrogen numbers as well. (See Question 21, Chapter 7.)

13. What conclusion may be drawn from the information that the density of the vapour of phosphorus is 2.81 g/L at 300°C and 101.3 kPa?

14. What are the two common valences exhibited by phosphorus? What factors may encourage the formation of binary compounds in which the lower valence of phosphorus occurs? What factors lead to the higher valence?

15. Identify by formula or composition the following useful phosphorus compounds, and indicate why they are useful: calcium dihydrogen phosphate, trisodium phosphate, tetraphosphorus trisulphide, superphosphate of lime, ferrophosphorus.

16. Assuming that phosphate rock is pure $Ca_3(PO_4)_2$—which it probably isn't—and that the reaction in the electric furnace occurs completely as written in Sec. 22-2—which it probably doesn't—calculate the maximum mass of phosphorus that can be extracted from one tonne of phosphate rock.

17. Explain the significance of the term *eutrophication*, and indicate why phosphates have been identified as a contributor to eutrophication in the Great Lakes.

18. Name, and give symbols for, five elements including phosphorus which make up a chemical family.

19. Describe the progression from non-metallic character to metallic character within the Group of elements N, P, As, Sb, Bi. In spite of this variation in properties, give evidence why they are treated as a related family of elements. Discuss why this trend toward metallic character occurs in moving through this Group from low to high atomic number.

20. Nitrogen occurs under ordinary conditions as diatomic molecules which are comparatively reluctant to enter into chemical reactions. Phosphorus, in one allotropic modification, occurs as tetra-atomic molecules which are so active that this form of the element is kept under water. Can you account for this difference?

*21. The gas phosphine can be decomposed by heat to the elements phosphorus and hydrogen. Each volume of phosphine produces ¼ volume of phosphorus vapour and 1½ volumes of hydrogen (all volumes at the same temperature and pressure). From the fact that the volume of hydrogen is six times the volume of phosphorus would you deduce that the formula of phosphine is PH_6? Discuss.

Sulphur – Another Essential Element

23

1. Oxygen and sulphur are two of the most important non-metals. Together with selenium, tellurium, and polonium, they constitute a family of elements, sometimes called the *oxygen family*. Elsewhere we have discussed oxygen and many of its compounds; this chapter is devoted mainly to sulphur and its important compounds.

Sulphur has been known and used for thousands of years. The Roman naturalist Pliny the Elder (AD 23-79) described the deposits of sulphur in Sicily, and the bleaching of cloth with the vapour of burning sulphur. And, in the Old Testament, ancient even in Pliny's time, there are references to sulphur ("brimstone"). Much more recently—about 800 years ago—it was found that a mixture of sulphur, charcoal, and potassium nitrate ("saltpeter") was explosive when ignited. This discovery of gunpowder revolutionized warfare.

But sulphur, like phosphorus, has another side to its nature. Sulphur is a constituent of many of the proteins—substances that function in body processes that are essential to life. Sulphur compounds, particularly sulphuric acid, are essential to modern industrial life, too.

This is an unusually perfect natural crystal of pyrite, FeS_2, a mineral nicknamed "fool's gold" because its colour and lustre, being very like those of gold, have fooled many an amateur prospector.

In pyrite, the iron atoms and pairs of sulphur atoms, S_2, are regularly spaced in a three-dimensional array. The structure is held together by bonds that are predominantly covalent.

TABLE 23-1

SOME SULPHUR-BEARING MINERALS	
MINERAL	MAIN CONSTITUENT
Pyrite	FeS_2
Sphalerite	ZnS
Galena	PbS
Cinnabar	HgS
Chalcopyrite	$CuFeS_2$

This beautifully formed natural crystal of rhombic sulphur (2.5 cm wide) was found in northern Italy, near Bologna.

Monoclinic sulphur, which does not occur in nature, crystallizes in the form of long needles.

2. OCCURRENCE AND RECOVERY. Sulphur occurs in nature as the element itself, the most important deposits being those mined in Texas. In combined form, sulphur occurs in many minerals, some of which are listed in Table 23-1. Although most of these are mined for their metal content, sulphur in the form of sulphur dioxide (SO_2) is obtained in vast amounts as a by-product of the smelting operations.

Hundreds of thousands of tonnes of sulphur are recovered annually in western Canada during the "cleaning" of natural gas. Such gas is mainly methane (CH_4) but some deposits—of so-called "sour gas"—contain an appreciable amount of hydrogen sulphide (H_2S). The sulphur is obtained by first burning some of the hydrogen sulphide to sulphur dioxide

$$2H_2S + 3O_2 \rightarrow 2H_2O + 2SO_2 \tag{1}$$

and then allowing this to react with more hydrogen sulphide:

$$SO_2 + 2H_2S \rightarrow 2H_2O + 3S \tag{2}$$

3. PHYSICAL PROPERTIES. Sulphur exists in several allotropic forms (Sec. 22-3). The two most important are known as **rhombic sulphur** and **monoclinic sulphur**. Each of these is yellow and crystalline and each consists of molecules of S_8 (Fig. 15-2), but the molecules are *packed* differently in the crystals of the two forms. As a consequence, these allotropes have different densities and different melting points. Rhombic sulphur is the form that is stable at room temperature. The monoclinic variety is stable above 95.5°C; below this temperature, crystals of monoclinic sulphur gradually change to rhombic crystals.

When sulphur is heated above its melting point (120°C), it undergoes interesting and unusual changes. The liquid, which at first is yellow and mobile, becomes dark red-brown and very viscous. What is believed to happen is that the rings of S_8 molecules break open at some bond and then several such 8-membered chains link up to form longer chain molecules. These in turn become intertwined and cannot flow past each other easily. If this viscous liquid is rapidly cooled it forms a rubbery solid material known as **plastic sulphur**, consisting of a tangled mass of these chains of sulphur atoms. On prolonged standing, plastic sulphur gradually reverts to a yellow powder which consists of tiny crystals of rhombic sulphur. This is a consequence of the chains gradually reforming into rings of S_8 molecules which, in turn, line up in a regular way to become crystals.

Liquid sulphur boils at 445°C, yielding a red vapour in which there are S_2, S_4, and S_8 molecules.

Sulphur is insoluble in water, but the rhombic and monoclinic forms are soluble in carbon disulphide (CS_2). Sulphur is typical of non-metals in being a poor conductor of electricity and heat.

4. CHEMICAL PROPERTIES. Chemically, too, sulphur is a non-metal, and an active one. In many of its reactions it behaves like oxygen; this is because both elements have the same number of electrons in their outermost shell (Table 23-2).

TABLE 23-2

ELECTRON ARRANGEMENTS IN THE ATOMS
OF THE OXYGEN FAMILY

	SHELL					ATOMIC
	K	L	M	N	O	P	NUMBER (Z)
Oxygen	2	6					8
Sulphur	2	8	6				16
Selenium	2	8	18	6			34
Tellurium	2	8	18	18	6		52
Polonium	2	8	18	32	18	6	84

Like oxygen, sulphur will unite directly with most elements, for example:

$S + 2Na \rightarrow Na_2S$ (vigorously, even at room temperature)
         sodium
         sulphide

$S + Zn \rightarrow ZnS$ (with powdered metal, when warmed)
         zinc
         sulphide

$S + O_2 \rightarrow SO_2$ (on igniting the sulphur)
         sulphur
         dioxide

$2S + C \rightarrow CS_2$ (glowing carbon in sulphur vapour)
         carbon
         disulphide

$S + H_2 \rightarrow H_2S$ (hydrogen bubbled through molten sulphur)
         hydrogen
         sulphide

Notice the similarity with the formulas of the compounds that oxygen forms with these elements: Na_2O, ZnO, CO_2, H_2O.

5. USES. The most important use for sulphur is for making sulphur dioxide for conversion to sulphuric acid (Sec. 23-11). Sulphur is also used for making gunpowder (Sec. 23-1), vulcanizing rubber, destroying fungi on fruit trees and grape vines, and it may soon be an important component of a new paving material for highways.

HYDROGEN SULPHIDE AND SULPHUR DIOXIDE

6. Both **hydrogen sulphide**, H_2S, and **sulphur dioxide**, SO_2, are important but unpleasant gases. The former stinks and the latter has a sharp and choking odour. Both are poisonous.

This huge pile of sulphur was recovered from "sour gas" in southern Alberta. "Sour gas" is really sour: it is natural gas containing hydrogen sulphide, whose aqueous solution is weakly acid.

With suitable conditions of temperature and pressure, each of these colourless gases can be condensed to a liquid and to a solid, as indeed any gas can be.

Each of these gases dissolves in water to give an acidic solution, but sulphur dioxide is very much more soluble and its solution is a stronger acid:

$$SO_2 \; + \; H_2O \; \rightarrow \; \underset{\substack{\text{sulphurous} \\ \text{acid}}}{H_2SO_3}$$

Sulphur dioxide can react with oxygen to give sulphur trioxide, SO_3 (Sec. 23-11). Hydrogen sulphide burns in air or oxygen (Equation (1)), and reacts with sulphur dioxide to yield sulphur (Equation (2)).

When hydrogen sulphide is bubbled into an aqueous solution of a metal salt, a metal sulphide is in most cases precipitated. Zinc sulphide is white, manganese sulphide is pink, arsenic sulphide is yellow, antimony sulphide is orange-red, and lead and silver sulphides are black.

Silver sulphide, Ag_2S, is responsible for the tarnishing of household silver; see the marginal note with Sec. 9-7.

7. PREPARATIONS. In the laboratory, hydrogen sulphide is usually prepared by treating iron(II) sulphide (ferrous sulphide) with hydrochloric acid:

$$FeS + 2HCl \rightarrow FeCl_2 + H_2S\uparrow$$

Do the experiment in a good fume-hood!

Sulphur dioxide is conveniently made by reacting sodium sulphite with sulphuric acid:

$$\underset{\substack{\text{sodium}\\\text{sulphite}}}{Na_2SO_3} + \underset{\substack{\text{sulphuric}\\\text{acid}}}{H_2SO_4} \rightarrow \underset{\substack{\text{sodium}\\\text{sulphate}}}{Na_2SO_4} + H_2O + SO_2\uparrow$$

A suitable apparatus is shown in Fig. 23-1.

8. USES. Hydrogen sulphide is used in the recovery of some metals from their ores, by precipitating them as insoluble sulphides.

The major use for sulphur dioxide is for making sulphuric acid (Sec. 23-11), but large amounts are also consumed as a bleaching agent (for silk, paper, and straw), as a preservative (for dried prunes, apricots, etc.), and in making calcium hydrogen sulphite (for dissolving lignin from wood in one of the processes by which paper is made).

9. AN ENVIRONMENTAL PROBLEM. Sulphur dioxide emitted into the atmosphere from the smelting of metal sulphide ores and the burning of coal contributes to the increasing acidity of rainwater, streams, and lakes that has been significant in recent years. This has adverse effects on fish life, vegetation, metal structures, paint and other coatings, stone cathedrals, etc., and poses hazards to human health. Some of the sulphur dioxide from smelters is converted into sulphuric acid (Sec. 23-11), but this consumes only a small fraction of what smelters produce. As well, the burning of fossil fuels, particularly in large power plants, releases much more sulphur dioxide than smelters do. Moreover, sulphur dioxide is not the only acid-producing atmospheric contaminant: oxides of nitrogen, notably from the exhaust of motor cars, dissolve in rainwater to yield acidic solutions.

SULPHURIC ACID AND OTHER SULPHATES

10. Sulphuric acid has been known as a laboratory chemical for at least a thousand years. Its manufacture on a commercial scale began in England more than two hundred years ago and now, the world over, millions of tonnes of it are made every year. Other than water, sulphuric acid is the most important industrial chemical.

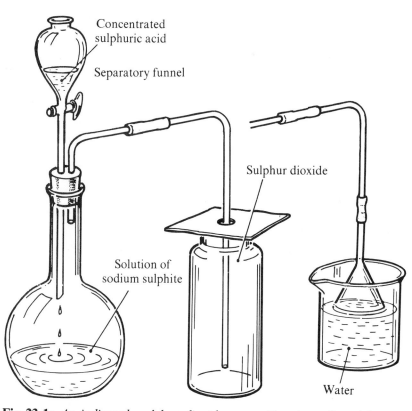

Fig. 23-1: *As indicated, sulphur dioxide may either be collected by upward displacement of air or dissolved directly in water. The latter procedure is less dangerous in the open laboratory, and if the gas is wanted it can be recovered by heating the solution. With a round bottom on the flask and concentrated sulphuric acid in the separatory funnel, this apparatus certainly needs the supports we haven't shown.*

11. PRODUCTION OF SULPHURIC ACID. Sulphuric acid, H_2SO_4, is made from sulphur dioxide by first converting this gas to sulphur trioxide

$$2SO_2 + O_2 \rightarrow 2SO_3 \qquad (3)$$

and then dissolving the gaseous sulphur trioxide in water.

$$SO_3 + H_2O \rightarrow H_2SO_4$$

The reaction of Equation (3) is best accomplished at a temperature of about 450°C in the presence of a suitable catalyst (commonly made from finely divided vanadium pentoxide, V_2O_5). The catalyst speeds the reaction in part by bringing the gases into close contact at its surface, which is why the process is called the *contact process.*

12. PROPERTIES OF SULPHURIC ACID. Pure sulphuric acid, or hydrogen sulphate, is a colourless, oily, dense, corrosive liquid. It mixes with water in all proportions, and the mixing generates considerable heat.

Sulphuric acid is a strong acid, has a *high boiling point* (acid of 98.5%

Because sulphur trioxide is not easily absorbed in pure water, it is passed into 98-99% sulphuric acid where it reacts with the 1-2% of water in that acid. At the same time, water is run into the acid at a rate which maintains the concentration of the acid at 98-99%. Thus the product of the process is sulphuric acid of this concentration.

The mixing should always be done by adding, slowly and with stirring, the acid to the water; never the other way around, or else you may get spattered with a hot, corrosive acid. This experience can leave a lasting impression on you, an impression in the form of some nasty scars.

concentration boils at 317°C), is a good *oxidizing agent* (when hot and concentrated; see Sec. 30-13), and is a drying and *dehydrating agent* (when concentrated). These properties, alone or in combination, together with its *low cost,* account for the great variety of uses to which sulphuric acid is put.

13. **USES OF SULPHURIC ACID.** Although sulphuric acid only rarely remains as such in a finished product, it is indispensable in a great many industries. It is consumed in tremendous quantities in making the fertilizers ammonium sulphate (Fig. 7-2) and superphosphate of lime (Sec. 22-7). It is used in recovering uranium and other metals from their ores, for removing the oxide scale that forms on hot steel when it is being shaped into sheets, and for making synthetic detergents. It is used (with nitric acid) to make TNT, dynamite, and other explosives. It is used in the petroleum industry, the pulp and paper industry, the leather industry. And so on and on—the making of hundreds of products requires this "king of chemicals."

14. **SULPHATES.** These are salts of sulphuric acid: they all contain the sulphate ion, SO_4^{2-}. They may be made by the action of sulphuric acid on metals, on metal hydroxides, on metal oxides, and on metal carbonates. Some important sulphates are listed in Table 23-3.

In collaboration with his friend J.-L. Gay-Lussac, L.-J. Thenard (1777-1857) first isolated the element boron and proved that sulphur is an element. Perhaps you can see the sulphur crystals in the background of this stamp.

Brunettes who have been oxidized to blondes by means of hydrogen peroxide owe a debt to Thenard, who discovered this bleaching agent.

TABLE 23-3

SOME IMPORTANT SULPHATES

FORMULA	NAME	REFERENCE
$(NH_4)_2SO_4$	Ammonium sulphate	Fig. 7-2
$(CaSO_4)_2 \cdot H_2O$	Calcium sulphate hemihydrate (plaster of Paris)	Sec. 29-11
$CaSO_4 \cdot 2H_2O$	Calcium sulphate dihydrate (gypsum)	Sec. 29-11
$CuSO_4 \cdot 5H_2O$	Copper(II) sulphate pentahydrate (bluestone)	Sec. 24-12
$MgSO_4 \cdot 7H_2O$	Magnesium sulphate heptahydrate (Epsom salts)	Table 29-6
$Na_2SO_4 \cdot 10H_2O$	Sodium sulphate decahydrate (Glauber's salt)	Table 24-3

15. Sulphur is clearly an element of great significance. One of the earliest known non-metals, it is still one of the most important. It is a constituent of a great many ores, of one of the most important industrial chemicals, and of many other valuable and versatile compounds. And it will be indispensable for as long as anyone is around to say what is indispensable, because it is an essential constituent of the proteins, the compounds that are the very basis of life.

The essential role of sulphur in living matter is often not appreciated. The fact that sulphur *is* present in plants and animals becomes more evident when rot or decomposition sets in. Then structurally complex substances (like proteins) break down into simpler ones, including some substances that can be detected by smell. For instance, rotting eggs, cabbage, or onions give off bad odours due to sulphur compounds such as hydrogen sulphide.

SELENIUM, TELLURIUM, AND POLONIUM

Polonium was discovered by Marie Curie in 1898, who named it after the country of her birth.

8
O
16
S
34
Se
52
Te
84
Po

16. Oxygen and sulphur are much more important than the other three members of their family: selenium, tellurium, and rare radioactive polonium.

Selenium and tellurium resemble sulphur, but they are less non-metallic. (Acquiring and holding additional electrons—which is what makes an element a non-metal (Sec. 13-5)—is more difficult for the larger atoms of selenium and tellurium, because the acquired electrons are farther from the attractive force of the positive charge of the nucleus.)

Some gradations among physical properties of these elements are illustrated by the data of Table 23-4. Gradations exist in the properties of their compounds, too. An interesting one is in the odour of their hydrogen compounds: hydrogen oxide (water) is odourless; hydrogen sulphide's odour is offensive (that of rotting eggs); hydrogen selenide's is outrageous; and hydrogen telluride's is indescribably foul!

TABLE 23-4

SOME PROPERTIES OF ELEMENTS OF THE OXYGEN FAMILY

	OXYGEN	SULPHUR	SELENIUM	TELLURIUM
Atomic number (Z)	8	16	34	52
Atomic mass	16.00	32.07	78.96	127.61
Density of solid (g/cm³)	1.27	2.07*	4.80	6.24
Melting point (°C)	–219	113*	217	450
Boiling point (°C)	–183	445	685	1390

*Rhombic variety

Selenium is used in making the pigment that gives the bright ruby-red colour to automobile tail lights and railway and other signal lights.

QUESTIONS

1. Sulphur occurs in two allotropic modifications in the solid state. What are the names given to these forms, and how do the two forms of sulphur differ structurally? How does this structural difference compare to the structural differences previously noted for the allotropes of carbon and of phosphorus?

2. Draw a sketch of a sulphur molecule. What is the covalence of sulphur in this structure?

3. The mass of 1.00 L of sulphur vapour at 450°C and 66.7 kPa is 2.42 g. Calculate the molar mass of sulphur under these conditions, and draw conclusions.

4. Plastic sulphur is an example of a non-crystalline solid (Sec. 15-16). Explain what that means.

5. List some important sulphur-bearing minerals. (This could be a library project.)

6. Summarize a number of important chemical reactions of sulphur with other elements.

7. Although no reaction with chlorine is described in the text, sulphur will readily form a compound S_2Cl_2 when heated and chlorinated. Write an equation for this reaction. Write a plausible Lewis diagram for this molecule.

8. Describe three ways in which sulphur dioxide may be formed. Contrast the reaction of sulphur dioxide with water (H_2O) and with hydrogen sulphide (H_2S).

9. Outline the chemical reactions involved in the production of sulphuric acid. Why is the industrial process for this manufacture known as the "contact process"?

10. Sulphuric acid for many years has been the manufactured chemical produced in the greatest amount. Account for some of the demand for this substance. (This question could be turned into a major project on the chemical industry.)

11. How is it that increasing amounts of sulphur dioxide are finding their way into the atmospheric environment, and why is this causing problems? What are some of these problems?

12. Outline how you might go about producing and collecting two or three bottles of hydrogen sulphide in the laboratory. Why would you be required to do this in a fume cupboard? How would you collect the gas?

13. Sometimes the presence of hydrogen sulphide is detected by an indicator paper (as if your nose weren't a good enough detector!). This paper is impregnated with lead nitrate solution and is used moist. What would you expect to see if this indicator paper were exposed to hydrogen sulphide? (It actually is more sensitive than the average nose.) Explain the action of the lead nitrate for this purpose.

14. Draw Lewis diagrams for sulphur dioxide, sulphur trioxide, and the sulphate ion. In which of these cases do you encounter the problem of more than one possible representation?

15. What is meant by the term "sour gas"? Why is sour gas treated for the removal of an unwanted substance? How is this done, and what useful by-product is thereby obtained?

16. Sulphur dioxide and sulphur trioxide are acid *anhydrides*. Explain what that means.

17. Write balanced chemical equations for the following reactions:

(a) the roasting of pyrite

(b) the addition of sulphuric acid to iron(II) sulphide

(c) the gradual addition of 2 mol of ammonia to 1 mol of hydrogen sulphate (in dilute solution)

(d) the addition of hydrogen sulphide gas to a solution of arsenic trichloride

(e) the addition of sulphuric acid to potassium sulphite

18. A substance has the following composition: sulphur 27.0%, oxygen, 13.4%, and chlorine, 59.6%. At 100°C and 98.6 kPa pressure, 124 cm³ of the vapour of the substance has a mass of 0.448 g. Find the molecular formula of the substance. You might continue the problem by trying to work out the structure of the molecule, and drawing a Lewis diagram for it.

19. Carbon disulphide has a boiling point of 46.2°C, and a density (at 0°C) of 1.29 g/mL. Calculate the volume occupied by 10.0 g of carbon disulphide at 101.3 kPa pressure and (a) 0°C, (b) 100°C.

20. In the compounds mentioned in this chapter what valence does sulphur exhibit?

21. Name, and give symbols for, five elements including oxygen and sulphur, which together make up a family in the Periodic Table. Write the electron configuration of the valence shell in the atoms of each of these elements.

22. Table 23-4 discloses certain trends in the physical properties of the elements that make up the oxygen family. Can you suggest why the densities of the solids increase as they do with increasing atomic number? Why do the diameters of the atoms (Fig. 13-5) increase with increasing atomic number?

23. Although oxygen and sulphur show no metallic properties whatever, tellurium shows limited electrical conductance, and polonium shows electrical conductance resembling a metal. Account for this.

24 Water – an Odd Liquid

1. Water is really a very odd substance.

It is the only chemical species that occurs naturally on the earth in all three states: solid, liquid, and gaseous. It is close to being the universal solvent; almost everything dissolves in water, at least to some extent. It expands on freezing, something that very few liquids do. It has an unusually high specific heat capacity and latent heat of vaporization. Even the very liquidity of water is odd: if ammonia (NH_3) and hydrogen fluoride (HF)—which you recognize as hydrides of the elements flanking oxygen in the Periodic Table—are compared with water (H_2O), the first two are gaseous over all or most of the range of temperature for which water is a liquid.

These are some of the properties that make water a truly unusual chemical. In this chapter we shall indicate some of the consequences of this and offer explanations for some of the oddities, and then have something to say about the importance of caring for our natural supplies of this vital compound.

2. SOME PHYSICAL PROPERTIES OF WATER. Water behaves in the same sort of way that other liquids do: it flows, it takes the shape of its container, it solidifies on cooling, it evaporates on heating, and its vapour pressure increases with increasing temperature (Fig. 19-5).

Nevertheless, water is unique; it has its own specific properties by which we can identify it. It is clear, as all pure liquids are, and it is practically colourless, although if you look through a considerable depth of pure water it is blue. Water has no taste or odour of its own, although dissolved impurities may make it anything but tasteless and odourless. Its *freezing point* is 0.00°C, its *boiling point* 100.00°C at a pressure of 101.3 kPa. Its *density* is 1.0 g/cm³. If its density is measured more precisely than this, it is found to vary slightly with temperature, being a maximum at 3.98°C (Table 24-1). Water's specific heat capacity (Sec. 20-4) is 4.184 J/(g·°C), and its heat of vaporization (Sec. 17-9) is 2280 J/g. Both these "heats" are larger than for any other liquid.

Many people confuse "clear" and "colourless." A liquid can be clear, that is, transparent, and yet be coloured, but it cannot be colourless unless it is also clear.

TABLE 24-1

DENSITY OF WATER AT VARIOUS TEMPERATURES

TEMPERATURE (°C)	DENSITY (g/cm³)	TEMPERATURE (°C)	DENSITY (g/cm³)
0.00	0.999 87	30.00	0.995 68
3.98	1.000 00	50.00	0.988 07
10.00	0.999 73	70.00	0.977 79
20.00	0.998 23	100.00	0.958 38

3. It is no accident that some of the numbers we have cited have been convenient ones like 0, 1, and 100. For water these numbers are simple and exact because the units were *defined* to make them so. For example, on the *Celsius scale of temperature,* 0 is defined as the freezing point of pure water and 100 as the boiling point of pure water (at standard atmospheric pressure).

4. SOME CONSEQUENCES OF WATER'S ODD PROPERTIES. When water is cooled, its density first increases and then, below 3.98°C, decreases (Table 24-1 and Fig. 24-1). When it freezes to ice its density decreases still further (to 0.917 g/cm³ at 0.00°C). It is this **unusual variation in density** that makes aquatic life possible in cold waters. When the temperature of the air falls below the freezing point, the water at the surface of lakes, ponds and rivers cools first, and, then being denser than the water below it, sinks. Warmer water rising to the top is cooled and sinks in turn, and so on until all the water is at the temperature of its maximum density. When the surface water is cooled below this temperature, it stays on top (being less dense now) and eventually freezes there. The ice, being less dense than water, stays on the surface: hence the lake "freezes over." Since both ice and water are poor conductors of heat, the water below the ice thereafter loses its heat very slowly and the ice layer thickens very slowly. If the cold water and ice were denser than the warmer water, lakes and rivers would quickly freeze from the bottom up—which would make things very hard for the animals and plants that live in them.

The fact that water has a higher density than ice has other important consequences: icebergs float and so become a menace to shipping; in winter, water pipes burst, engine blocks crack, rocks "weather" and the soil is opened up. This **expansion on freezing** is most unusual behaviour. Almost all other substances shrink on freezing.

The **unusually large specific heat capacity** of water (Table 24-2) has profound effects on the climate. Bodies of water heat up and cool down more slowly than land. Hence, on the Prairies the temperature variation between winter and summer—even between night and day—is much greater than on the seacoasts of British Columbia or Nova Scotia. The Niagara Peninsula owes its fame as a fruit belt not primarily to its latitude, but to the protection against temperature extremes given by the two Great Lakes that bound it. And because of water's large specific heat capacity, the Labrador Current carries the northern chill to the coasts of Newfoundland and Nova Scotia. The large specific heat ca-

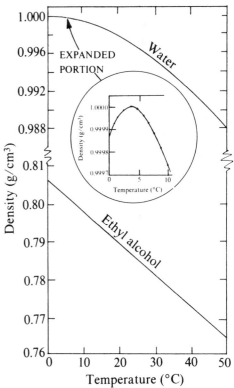

Fig. 24-1: *The variation of density with temperature for water (an unusual liquid) and for ethyl alcohol (a more normal liquid).*

pacity of water also means that the heating of water consumes more energy than the heating of the same mass of another liquid. If the specific heat capacity of water were less, all our gas and electricity bills for heating water would be lower.

TABLE 24-2

A COMPARISON OF PROPERTIES OF WATER
AND OF OTHER MORE TYPICAL LIQUIDS

SUBSTANCE	SPECIFIC HEAT CAPACITY (20°C) (J/(g·K))	LATENT HEAT OF FUSION (J/g)	LATENT HEAT OF VAPORIZATION (J/g)
Water	4.184	333	2280
Acetone	2.2	98	551
Ethyl alcohol	2.5	109	880
Benzene	1.7	127	437
Carbon tetrachloride	0.86	21	215
Mercury	0.14	11	295
Bromine	0.47	67	191
Hydrogen sulphate	1.4	100	510

The cost of producing steam is made still greater by water's **unusually large heat of vaporization** (Table 24-2). It takes more than five times as much heat to evaporate a gram of water as to heat it all the way from 0°C to 100°C. This evaporating can occur long before the temperature reaches 100°C. Hence the evaporation of water serves to minimize changes of temperature. The evaporation of perspiration on the skin is one of the body's means of temperature control. The rate of evaporation is increased (1) by an increase in temperature (the hotter the day, the better the body's cooling mechanism works); (2) by an increase in the surface of water exposed to the air; and (3) by the removal of the moist air over the surface, for example, by natural or artificial air currents. Remember "Smokey"?

5. SOME EXPLANATION OF WATER'S ODD PROPERTIES. The abnormal properties of water which we have been describing can be explained in large part by structural considerations. The water molecule is bent, like a broad letter V (Sec. 14-16). Oxygen is strongly electronegative, more so than hydrogen, and so its atoms pull the electrons that make up the O—H bonds toward themselves at the expense of the hydrogen atoms. The water molecule thereby develops a slight positive and negative polarity (Fig. 24-2 (a)). Consequently some head-to-tail intermolecular attraction develops (much as would happen with a collection of tiny magnets). In water and a few other compounds this attraction appears to be greater than can be explained by electrical polarity alone. The additional force of attraction is believed to involve a special sort of chemical bond, called a **hydrogen bond.** This comes into play when a hydrogen atom takes up a position between two strongly electronegative atoms (Fig. 24-2 (b)).

When water freezes, its molecules become arranged in a three-dimensional geometric pattern illustrated in Fig. 24-3. You should notice that the oxygen atoms are arranged similarly to the carbon atoms in diamond (Fig. 15-7), and

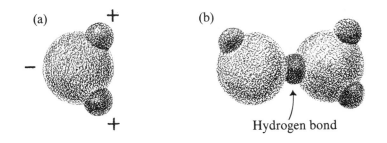

Fig. 24-2: *A slight displacement of electrons in the water molecule leads to the charge distribution shown in (a), and the molecule is said to be "polar." It should be understood that the + and − signs do not convey a whole electronic unit of charge.*

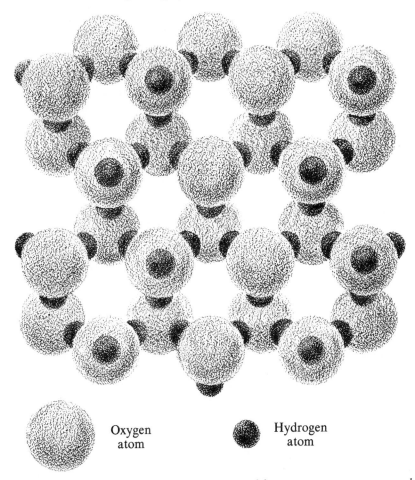

Fig. 24-3: *In ice, hydrogen atoms are located between oxygen atoms, and by forming hydrogen bonds with the latter bind the whole structure together into a vast network of atoms. Throughout the network there are four hydrogen atoms arranged tetrahedrally about each oxygen atom, and two oxygen atoms on either side of each hydrogen atom.*

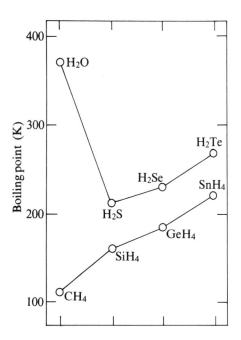

Fig. 24-4: *Although oxygen, sulphur, selenium, and tellurium are members of the same family in the Periodic Table, the boiling point of water (H_2O) is "out of line" with those of the other hydrides (H_2S, H_2Se, and H_2Te). This is one evidence of the associated character of water. For comparison with substances that reveal no special association between molecules, the boiling points of four hydrides of another family of elements are shown.*

that the hydrogen atoms lie between the oxygen atoms. This arrangement affords an opportunity for hydrogen bonds to form between adjacent molecules. Because of these bonds the ice structure acquires a network character. If you were to make a scale model of this structure you would find it rather "open"; that is, there is a good deal of space within the structure not filled by atoms. Somewhat closer packing of the molecules can be achieved if they are no longer required to occupy the fixed positions of the network shown in Fig. 24-3, but are free to mingle in a random way. What this means is that more water molecules can be accommodated in a given volume by the disordered packing typical of a liquid than can be arranged in the same volume by the ordered pattern characteristic of ice. This, then, is why expansion occurs when water freezes.

You may find it easier to think of the ice during melting. As the ice is heated, some of the heat energy breaks hydrogen bonds in the three-dimensional crystalline structure, leaving holes large enough to accommodate broken-off water molecules. These get into the holes, and in so doing increase the number of molecules per unit volume. Putting it another way, the total number of molecules takes up less space; the warmed ice, turning to water, contracts—that is, its density increases. This more efficient packing continues even after all the ice has melted, at least up to a temperature of 3.98°C. This is because bunches or clusters of water molecules linked by hydrogen bonds persist even above the melting point. Just as with the solid, these clusters do not pack as compactly as single molecules. The shrinkage between 0°C and 3.98°C must be interpreted as evidence of further uncoupling of these clusters. Offsetting this shrinkage, and taking precedence above 3.98°C, is the normal expansion that occurs with increase in temperature of most materials. This simply results from the greater movement of the molecules in accordance with the kinetic-molecular theory (Chapter 19).

The melting point and boiling point of water are much higher than might be expected by comparison with structurally related compounds (Fig. 24-4). This is further evidence of the existence of extensive association of the molecules through hydrogen bonding, and suggests that association persists even up to the boiling point.

By comparison with other substances water has large latent heats of fusion and vaporization (Table 24-2). In Sec. 17-7 and 17-9 we indicated that the magnitudes of these quantities depended on the *number of molecules* requiring separation from fixed positions or from each other, and on the *forces of attraction* between molecules. Water has the lowest molar mass of any substance that is a liquid at ordinary temperatures. Therefore it will have the largest number of molecules per gram of any such substance. With so many molecules per gram to separate, it is not surprising that water has high values for its latent heats. Moreover, since melting and evaporation of water will also require the breaking of hydrogen bonds between molecules, this factor too will drive up the values of the latent heats compared to substances in which such bonding is absent or less pronounced.

The specific heat capacity of water is also unusually large (Table 24-2). This quantity signifies the amount of heat energy that must be added to increase the temperature of one gram of substance by one Celsius degree. Increasing the temperature means increasing the motion of the molecules (translation, rotation, and vibration). When allowance is made for the large number of molecules in each gram of water, and for the fact that the motion of the molecules is opposed by strong intermolecular forces, the large value for the specific heat capacity of water is not surprising.

WATER FOR EVERYONE

6. Water means different things to different people. Barbers, bartenders, and bathing beauties; cooks, canoeists, and clergymen; farmers, fishermen, and firefighters; sailors, skaters, and swimmers; waiters, water-skiers, and window-washers—all make use of water. But each is interested in a different property of water; each uses water for a different purpose.

Each kind of scientist is interested in water, too, and each has his or her special point of view. The meteorologist sees water as the basis of clouds and rain and snow; the metallurgist sees water as a corrosive liquid that attacks metals and alloys; the geologist sees water as an agent in the formation, modification, and disintegration of rocks; the biologist sees water as a home for plants and animals; the engineer sees water as something to be pumped, bridged, and dammed.

The chemist is just as interested in water, perhaps even more so: it is the commonest compound and the commonest liquid, a stable substance, an indispensable reagent in many chemical processes, the most nearly universal solvent, the medium in which an almost limitless number of chemical changes take place or can be made to take place.

7. THE IMPURITY OF WATER. Water, as it occurs in nature, is never pure in the sense of consisting of only dihydrogen oxide, H_2O. Sea water is a solution of hundreds of substances; every cubic metre of sea water contains more than 35 kg of dissolved salts. River and lake water is also a solution of many substances leached from rocks and soil, though it is a much more dilute solution than sea water. (Even so, the rivers every year carry trillions of kilograms of dissolved salts to the sea.) River water often has matter suspended in it and so is really a mixture (of solids and solution). Rain water contains dissolved gases (oxygen, nitrogen, carbon dioxide), and fine particles of dust. And rain water, as soon as it lands, starts to dissolve substances from the soil. Well water and spring water owe their taste to the dissolved substances they contain: pure water is tasteless.

8. THE PURIFICATION OF WATER. One of the consequences of water's excellent dissolving power is the difficulty of obtaining pure water. Usually we are content with water which, though by no means pure, has had the harmful or objectionable impurities removed. *Potable water,* that is, water fit to drink, need not be pure in the chemical sense but it must be free of dirt, of harmful bacteria, of dissolved compounds that would be harmful to the body or even objectionable in taste or smell. Water for washing should be relatively free of substances that render it "hard" (Sec. 29-15 and 29-16), but can contain high concentrations of other substances. For some industrial uses and for many laboratory purposes water of high purity is essential. This may be obtained by distillation (Sec. 17-12) and by a variation of the ion-exchange method for "softening" water (Sec. 29-16).

9. THE POLLUTION OF WATER. The pollution of rivers by the activities of man is not exactly new, as the note below makes clear, but in the last 25 years or so it has become much more widespread, and made more serious by many new and hazardous substances. Increased population, increased industrialization, increased use of fertilizers, herbicides, insecticides and other pesticides—all these have augmented pollution. Nowadays, too, we are more aware of the potential dangers of certain substances, and have increasingly sensitive methods for detecting and measuring amazingly small amounts of them. Only a few years ago we didn't know that as little as one part of mercury in 5 000 000 parts of your blood could be a serious danger to your health—and we couldn't have accurately measured it if we had known it.

Earlier, we alluded to the pollution of natural bodies of water by phosphates (Sec. 22-8 and 22-9) and by acids (Sec. 23-9). In what follows, we discuss contamination by mercury.

Among other things, mercury poisoning may lead to emotional disturbances, constriction of the visual field, impairment of hearing, speech, and co-ordination. Chronic cases lead to muscular atrophy, epileptic seizure, coma, and death. Mercury poisoning is commonly called *Minamata disease*, following a tragedy in Japan in the 1950s, when mercury-contaminated seafood from Minamata Bay took the lives of more than 100 people and left nearly 1000 more with varying degrees of incapacity.

Few can readily sense how small a proportion one part in two million is. It helps to note that it is equivalent to one cent in twenty thousand dollars.

10. MERCURY AND FISH. In 1969 commercial fishing in the South Saskatchewan River was banned because of the amount of mercury found in the fish. Since then, for the same reason, similar prohibitions have been applied to several rivers and lakes in Canada. *Why the bans?*

Mercury poisoning is an insidious affliction, because there is no single symptom or set of symptoms by which it can be identified with certainty. There is always some mercury in the air we breathe and the food we eat. This arises from natural processes, such as volcanic action and the weathering of rocks that contain trace amounts of mercury. No one yet knows how much mercury the human body can tolerate without damage. Experience in Japan indicates that a continued intake of only 0.3 mg per day may produce toxic symptoms and that a daily intake of 2 mg is lethal. In Canada, the distribution or sale of fish having more than 0.000 05% of mercury (1 part in 2 000 000) is forbidden. An alarming number of lakes and streams in Canada have one or more species of fish that harbour more, sometimes much more, than this. *Where did it come from?*

The pollution has arisen mainly from the prolonged discharge into waterways of metallic mercury from electrolytic cells (Sec. 26-13) for the production of chlorine, particularly at paper mills which use vast quantities of this halogen (Sec. 8-7). Because mercury in the metallic state does not dissolve significantly in water, there would be no problem if it settled permanently into the river and lake sediments. But it doesn't remain there. Bacteria con-

In 1357 King Edward III, after an outing on the River Thames, issued a Royal Order about the "dung and other filth . . . in divers places upon the banks of the river." Four hundred years later the novelist Smollett complained that the river was "composed of all the drugs, minerals and poisons used in mechanics and manufacture." But the condition of the Thames was greatly to worsen: the population explosion and industrial growth of the nineteenth and twentieth centuries were yet to come. The resultant increases in the discharge of human wastes and industrial effluents were more than the Thames at London and eastwards could bear. Pollutants in the water reacted with dissolved oxygen faster than fresh oxygen could be absorbed from the atmosphere. So, the fish

suffocated; the river died. Then, beginning in the 1960s, as a consequence of the construction of efficient sewage disposal plants and rigid control of effluents from industries, the Thames began to come to life again. By 1977 more than 90 species of fish were living where, for many years, no fish had existed. Waterfowl and sea birds that feed on aquatic life are returning in increasing number and variety. If Edward III could sail on the Thames today, he would not be assailed by the "fumes and other abominable stenches" which so offended him six hundred and more years ago.

For this fascinating story of what modern technology, money, and determination can do, see the little book, *The Living Thames*, by John Doxat (Hutchinson Benham, London, 1977).

vert it into soluble compounds, such as CH_3HgCl, which are absorbed by living organisms. Then the mercury compounds enter a "food-chain": for example, from the water to mosquito larvae which are eaten by minnows which are eaten by pike which are eaten by humans. In each organism the uptake and accumulation of mercury is much greater than its elimination. Accordingly, each member of a food-chain (and we cited a simple one) has more mercury per gram of tissue than the organism on which it fed. So it is that a gram of pike muscle may contain some thousands of times as much of this element as a gram of the water from which the fish was caught. *What can be done about this contamination?*

Obviously the first thing is to stop the discharge of mercury into the waterways. This has now largely been done, by efficient systems for retaining the mercury within the plants making chlorine by so-called mercury cells, and by expensive "change-overs" to methods of chlorine production that do not use mercury. But that, of course, does nothing about the mercury that has already polluted vast stretches of river and lake systems. Since the stopping of discharges, the mercury content of fish from Lake Erie and lower Lake St. Clair has steadily declined, but such self-cleansing is slow—in some waterways up to a hundred years might be needed. Other approaches, such as "burying" the mercury under more sediment or expensive dredging operations, are being studied. Apart from the huge cost of such measures, *what are the consequences of this mess?*

Foremost is the serious damage to the health, and the possible death of—we don't yet know how many—people. We do know that hundreds who depend on fishing have lost their livelihood. And we do know that a potent hazard remains in many areas. The problems are greatest among the native (Indian) population because of the importance of fish in their diet and their employment as guides and fishermen. As a recent report puts it: "mercury contamination . . . may represent irreversible crippling disease, death, and the destruction of the livelihood and the integrity of a people who are dependent on fishing, recreation and tourism for their very survival."

The Matagami Indian fisheries in northwestern Quebec, for example, employed 200 men before it was shut down because its catches were too contaminated to be sold.

11. THE DISTRIBUTION OF WATER. Water is distributed over the earth very unevenly. Most of it—97%—is in the oceans. A tiny proportion, 0.000 05%, is in the atmosphere. And most of the remaining 3% is locked up in the Arctic and Antarctic ice caps. In fact, less than 0.03% of the total water on the earth is fresh and available, and all too much of that is polluted. So, good water is less common and more precious than those who mistreat it know or care.

You are about 70% water (and a ripe tomato about 90%). You take into your body every day, through food and drink, about 2100 cm³ of water (and produce 300-400 cm³ more by chemical reactions in your digestive system). Unless you are gaining weight very rapidly, you rid yourself daily of 2400-2500 cm³ of water by exhaling moist breath, by evaporation from your skin, and by excretion.

Water occurs naturally in combined form, too, as *hydrates*. These are solid crystalline compounds that contain "water of constitution"—molecules of water which form a part of the structure of the compound. The water molecules in crystalline hydrates are usually all or mostly associated with the metal ions; for example, in magnesium sulphate

This Antarctic glacier must look overwhelming to that explorer. "Overwhelming" is a proper word to describe the vast amount of ice in the Antarctic because, if all of it were to melt, the oceans would rise by more than 100 m, inundating all the chief seaports of the world and great expanses of land. Incidentally, this picture was taken by moonlight during the polar night.

heptahydrate, $MgSO_4 \cdot 7H_2O$, six of every seven molecules of water are associated with the magnesium in the form of the ion $Mg(H_2O)_6^{2+}$.

Some important hydrates that occur naturally are listed in Table 24-3.

TABLE 24-3

SOME NATURALLY OCCURRING HYDRATES		
PROPER NAME	COMMON NAME	FORMULA
Calcium sulphate dihydrate	Gypsum	$CaSO_4 \cdot 2H_2O$
*Magnesium sulphate heptahydrate**	Epsom salts	$MgSO_4 \cdot 7H_2O$
*Sodium sulphate decahydrate**	Glauber's salt	$Na_2SO_4 \cdot 10H_2O$
*Sodium tetraborate decahydrate**	Borax	$Na_2B_4O_7 \cdot 10H_2O$

*Hepta and deca are Greek roots meaning seven and ten, respectively.

MORE ABOUT HYDRATES

12. Water will combine with certain salts to form hydrates. An example of this process is

$$CuSO_4 + 5H_2O \rightarrow CuSO_4 \cdot 5H_2O \qquad (1)$$
anhydrous   copper
copper   sulphate
sulphate   pentahydrate
(white)   (blue)

The water in most hydrates is loosely combined, and may be driven off as a vapour by heat:

$$CuSO_4 \cdot 5H_2O \xrightarrow{heat} CuSO_4 + 5H_2O\uparrow \qquad (2)$$

The process represented by Equation (2) is known as *dehydration*, and that represented by Equation (1) is known as *hydration*. **The water of hydration** (also called the *water of crystallization*) passes off as water vapour, leaving the anhydrous salt (Fig. 24-5). Dehydration is hastened by heating, but it will occur at room temperature if the content of water vapour in the air above the hydrate is low enough. (Like evaporation, it takes place more rapidly if the temperature is raised, if the area of surface exposed is increased, or if the air is constantly renewed.) When a hydrate loses its water it usually crumbles to a fine powder. The process is called **efflorescence**, and the hydrate is said to be an *efflorescent hydrate*. The dehydration need not be complete. Common washing soda (sodium carbonate decahydrate, $Na_2CO_3 \cdot 10H_2O$) effloresces to the monohydrate:

$$Na_2CO_3 \cdot 10H_2O \rightarrow Na_2CO_3 \cdot H_2O + 9H_2O$$

13. The *qualitative* detection of the presence of water in a substance such as copper sulphate pentahydrate, or "bluestone", can be done very simply, as illustrated in Fig. 24-5 and explained in its caption.

The means by which the content of water in a hydrate can be established quantitatively is illustrated by the following problem.

Problem 24-1. When the hydrate of barium chloride is heated sufficiently, it is converted to the anhydrous salt ($BaCl_2$). In an experiment, 1.500 g of this hydrate was appropriately heated, and then the residue was cooled, and found to have a mass of 1.279 g. What is (a) the percentage of water in this hydrate, and (b) the formula of this hydrate?

Solution: (a) The amount of water driven off on heating equals the difference in mass = (1.500−1.279) g = 0.221 g

Therefore, the percentage of water = $\dfrac{0.221\ g}{1.500\ g} \times 100 = 14.7$

(b) From 1.500 g of the hydrate, there were obtained 1.279 g of the anhydrous salt ($BaCl_2$) and 0.221 g of water.

From the atomic mass table (inside back cover), the molar mass of $BaCl_2$ (to one decimal place) is

$$137.3 + 2(35.5) = 208.3\ g/mol$$

Accordingly, 208.3 g of $BaCl_2$ corresponds to one mol of $BaCl_2$, and so 1.279 g of $BaCl_2$ is

$$\frac{1.279\ g}{208.3\ g/mol} = 0.006\ 14\ mol$$

"Anhydrous" means "without water." The change in colour from white to blue, which occurs when anhydrous copper sulphate combines with water, is sometimes used to detect the presence of water.

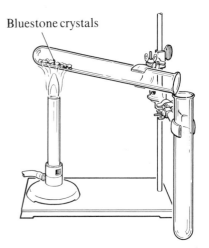
Bluestone crystals

Fig. 24-5: *To detect water in a hydrate, the bluestone or other hydrate is heated gently at first, and then more strongly until no further changes in the solid residue are observed. The flame is repeatedly swept toward the mouth of the slanting tube until it is dry. In the vertical test tube, which should initially have been dry, there will accumulate some droplets of a clear and colourless liquid. This can be identified as water by its freezing point, density, or other characteristic property.*

The molar mass of H_2O is $2(1.0) + 16.0 = 18.0$ g/mol

So, 0.221 g of H_2O is $\dfrac{0.221 \text{ g}}{18.0 \text{ g/mol}} = 0.0123$ mol

Thus, in the hydrate, 0.0123 mol of water is associated with

$0.006\ 14$ mol of barium chloride, or $\dfrac{0.0123}{0.006\ 41} = 2.00$ mol of water

are associated with 1.00 mol of barium chloride.

Accordingly, the formula of the hydrate is $BaCl_2 \cdot 2H_2O$.

14. Sodium carbonate decahydrate gives off water *to* air (Sec. 24-12), but some salts and other substances absorb water *from* air (without necessarily forming a hydrate). Such substances are said to be **hygroscopic**. A hygroscopic substance may be liquid (such as concentrated sulphuric acid, H_2SO_4, or glycerol, $C_3H_5(OH_3)$ or a solid (such as sodium hydroxide, $NaOH$, or anhydrous calcium chloride, $CaCl_2$). When a hygroscopic substance is a solid that picks up water so avidly that it dissolves in the water, the substance is said to be **deliquescent**. Sodium hydroxide and anhydrous calcium chloride are both hygroscopic and deliquescent.

15. We now leave the topic water, as such, but we must emphasize that what we have said so far gives a most inadequate idea of the importance of water in chemistry. Our next chapter is devoted to solutions, and solutions in water—aqueous solutions as they are commonly called—are the most important of all solutions. Later we shall discuss water as an ionizing solvent (in Chapter 26), ionic reactions in aqueous solution (in Chapter 27), the "softening" of "hard" water (in Chapter 29), and many reactions in which water has an important role. In fact, as you read on, you may begin to feel as did the Ancient Mariner: "water, water, everywhere." And it is, almost.

QUESTIONS

1. Make clear in your own words the meaning of the following terms: (a) specific heat capacity, (b) heat of fusion, (c) heat of vaporization.

2. (a) Given a clear colourless liquid, name at least three physical properties that you could measure to see if it was pure water.

(b) If the measured properties do not coincide with those of pure water, how could you find out if water were present in the liquid?

3. List three respects in which water is a typical liquid and three respects in which it is an abnormal one.

4. Why is the melting point of a solid or the boiling point of a liquid a useful temperature for defining (or checking) thermometer scales? Why is it important that the solid or liquid used for this purpose be pure?

5. Two properties of water—the maximum density at about 4°C and the expansion on freezing—are both of great importance in maintaining aquatic forms of life. Explain.

6. Describe how a covalent bond may possess an electrical polarity. Which of the following bonds would you expect to be polar: H—H, H—Cl, Cl—Cl, Cl—F?

7. Assuming that the hydrogen atom differs in electronegativity from each other atom in the following compounds, decide which molecules would be polar, and which would not: HCl, H_2S, PH_3, CH_4. Indicate with a simple diagram the direction along which the polarity would develop.

8. Explain how the water molecule possesses an electrical polarity. What shape would the water molecule have to be so that it would be non-polar?

9. Having in mind the polarity of the water molecule, predict what might happen when this molecule comes into close proximity to a positive ion such as Na^+; to a negative ion such as F^-.

10. Describe how two or more water molecules may become "associated" by hydrogen bonding. What are some of the consequences of this association?

11. Account for the fact that the density of ice is less than that of water.

12. Explain the terms *pure water* and *potable water*. Outline briefly how water may be rendered "pure" (a) for drinking, (b) for use in chemical research.

13. Account for (a) the widespread use of water, (b) the impurities in natural water, (c) the economic importance of water, (d) the pollution of water.

14. On what evidence are hydrates classified as true chemical compounds? In what ways does a hydrate differ from (a) a solution, (b) a hydroxide?

15. A crystalline form of barium hydroxide is represented by the formula $Ba(OH)_2 \cdot 8H_2O$ rather than $BaO_{10}H_{18}$. Why?

16. Write the formula for each of the following: gypsum, borax, washing soda, bluestone, Epsom salts, Glauber's salt.

17. Criticize the following "logic": Hydrates are crystalline; common salt forms cubic crystals; therefore common salt is a hydrate. How could you demonstrate that a crystalline substance *was* a hydrate?

18. Explain the meaning of, and any relationships among, the following terms:

(a) hydrate   (e) anhydrous salt
(b) hydration   (f) efflorescence
(c) dehydration   (g) deliquescence
(d) water of hydration   (h) hygroscopic

19. Magnesium sulphite is ordinarily a hydrated salt, but when heated to 200°C it loses its water of crystallization. In an actual experiment to determine the formula of the hydrate the following data were recorded:

Mass of crucible empty	12.5130 g
Mass of crucible + salt hydrate	13.5751 g
Mass of crucible + anhydrous salt	13.0348 g

Calculate the formula of this hydrate.

20. Exactly one gram of cobalt chloride hydrate, $CoCl_2 \cdot xH_2O$, was heated to drive off water. The mass of the residue was 0.547 g. Find the value of x in the formula.

21. The terms *deliquescent* and *hygroscopic* are sometimes confused. Which term is more appropriate to each of the following applications?

(a) Calcium chloride is spread on gravel roads to "lay" the dust; it does this by absorbing enough moisture to become damp.

(b) A liquid compound, ethylene glycol (also used as antifreeze), is added to tobacco to keep it moist. It does so by absorbing moisture from the air.

(c) Gases, to be dried for experimental purposes, are often bubbled through concentrated sulphuric acid which absorbs any moisture from the gas bubbles.

(d) Anhydrous calcium sulphate is used in tubes to absorb water vapour from a stream of gas. It does so by forming the hydrate $CaSO_4 \cdot 2H_2O$.

*22. In Sec. 17-9 we explained that latent heat of vaporization could be related to the energy required to overcome the forces of attraction between molecules in the liquid state. The molar heat of vaporization expresses these intermolecular attractive forces on the basis of a constant number of molecules. (Why?) According to Trouton's rule the molar heat of vaporization is approximately proportional to the boiling point (in kelvins). Thus, roughly, the higher the boiling point, the greater the attraction between molecules. Show the validity of Trouton's rule by working out the molar heats of vaporization for the compounds below (see Table 24-2) and dividing by the boiling points (in kelvins). The quotient is called Trouton's constant.

SUBSTANCE	BOILING POINT	MOLAR MASS
	(K)	(g/mol)
Water	373	18
Acetone	329	58
Ethyl alcohol	352	46
Benzene	353	78
Carbon tetrachloride	350	154
Mercury	630	201
Bromine	334	160

For the liquids other than water and alcohol, what is the average value of Trouton's constant? Comment on the higher-than-average values of Trouton's "constant" for water and alcohol.

*23. Since boiling points (in kelvins) are approximately proportional to intermolecular attractive forces (Trouton's rule—Question 22), answer the following questions about Fig. 24-4. Why for the tetrahydrides do the boiling points increase more or less linearly according to quantum number of the valence shell? Why does the boiling point of water lie so far from the corresponding progression for the dihydrides? (See also Question 8, Chapter 18.)

24. Compare the energy required to vaporize a mole of liquid water (Table 24-2) and to decompose a mole of water by electrolysis (Chapter 16, Problem 6). Account for the difference.

25. There is another compound of hydrogen and oxygen besides water. This one contains 94.1% oxygen by mass. Deduce its simplest formula. This compound cannot be vaporized without decomposition, so its molar mass cannot be deduced from vapour density. Can a Lewis diagram be drawn for a molecule with the simplest formula? Can such a diagram be drawn if the simplest formula is doubled? (The compound is hydrogen peroxide.)

25 Solutions and Solubility

1. Early in this book (Sec. 1-8) we introduced the idea that some substances could *dissolve* in other substances to form *solutions* and, by the same token, that some substances could not. Dissolving or not dissolving is one property by which a pure substance can be identified. A great many important chemical changes, such as those related to life and growth of plants and animals, occur among substances in the dissolved state. Because of the importance of solutions in chemical processes we shall devote this and the three succeeding chapters to an account of solutions and to chemical reactions that occur in solutions.

Before reading on, you should review and be sure you understand clearly what is meant by the terms *homogeneous, heterogeneous* (Sec. 1-9), and *phase* (Sec. 2-6).

2. THE NATURE OF A SOLUTION. There are several characteristics of solutions which enable an investigator to recognize that a particular material *is* a solution, *not* a pure substance, and *not* a mechanical mixture. A critical characteristic is that a solution is *homogeneous*; every portion, however small, taken for examination is exactly like every other portion. A solution can have only one phase, so any operation which demonstrates that a material possesses two or more phases is sufficient to disqualify that material as a solution. Such operations might include filtration, centrifuging, application of magnets, scattering of light, and so on.

A solution of salt in water is clear and colourless, and readily can be shown to consist of a single phase. A solution of potassium permanganate in water (sometimes used as a disinfectant footbath at swimming pools) is very dark purple, and one often cannot see through even thin layers of it; nevertheless, it is homogeneous. A specimen of 12-carat gold is a solution of that metal with another metal such as copper or silver; it is certainly not clear, but microscopic and other examination shows that it is homogeneous.

A solution is *permanent* in the sense that nothing settles out of it (except, perhaps, for "supersaturated" solutions, which we discuss later). The substances that make up a solution, known as constituents, do not of their own accord separate from one another. But the constituents of a solution usually *can* be separated by processes such as distillation or crystallization. The substances so separated are usually identical to those put into the original solution, so that the process of dissolving does not seem to cause any permanent changes in the constituents. The fact that the constituents can be separated in relatively simple ways, and thereby recovered unchanged, is one thing that distinguishes a solution from a pure substance.

Another difference between solutions and pure substances can be expressed briefly by saying that solutions are capable of *variable composition*, whereas substances have definite composition.

Substances that can form one solution can form a whole series of solutions, each differing slightly but significantly from its neighbours in the series, both in composition and in properties. That is what is meant when it is said that solutions have variable composition. For example, copper(II) sulphate ($CuSO_4$) will form a solution in water containing 10.0% (by mass) of this substance, with the remainder water. It will also form a solution that is 10.1% copper sulphate, another that is 10.2%, and so on. Each member of this series of solutions will be slightly bluer in colour, and slightly denser, than the previous member. In contrast, there is one compound containing copper sulphate and water; in it there is exactly 63.9% copper sulphate. This is the hydrate $CuSO_4 \cdot 5H_2O$ (Sec. 24-12). If you try to prepare a material with a composition slightly different from this, what you will get is a mechanical mixture; you cannot tamper with the composition of a pure substance.

Solutions and pure substances differ in yet another way which we discussed in Sec. 1-7. Pure substances *change state* (melt or boil, freeze or condense) *entirely at one temperature*, but solutions generally do so over a range of temperatures. This occurs with solutions because their freezing or boiling points depend on their composition. To take a specific example, as a salt solution gradually freezes, the solid phase that forms is ice; its formation leaves less water in the solution, but the same amount of salt. On this account the solution becomes more concentrated in salt as it freezes, and therefore its freezing temperature changes.

The foregoing description of solutions and of how they can be distinguished from pure substances and mechanical mixtures provides a sort of "operational" account of the nature of a solution. Another way to describe solutions is in terms of the structural units of matter, and since we cannot see these we have to make inferences about them from what we can observe. As a simple description, what we think happens when one substance dissolves in another is that the molecules or ions of the former become individually and uniformly dispersed throughout the solution. That is how a solution is homogeneous, and how only one phase can be recognized in it. Such a description of a solution is "conceptual" —based on models which help us to understand what we observe. This second description of solutions is obviously an over-simplification as we shall see later (Sec. 25-18 and 26-7).

"To most people solutions mean finding the answer, but to chemists solutions are things that are all mixed up." (Nine-year-old child)

3. TYPES OF SOLUTIONS. Because water is so abundant and can dissolve so many other substances, aqueous solutions are by far the most common solutions. They are so familiar, indeed, that one is apt to forget that not all solutions are liquid and not all liquid solutions are aqueous. In your family car, the metal of the carburettor is a solid solution, and the air and the gasoline that enter it to be mixed are a gaseous solution and a non-aqueous liquid solution, respectively.

Although solutions can have many constituents (there are scores of substances dissolved in sea water and in blood plasma, for example) those containing two constituents, *binary solutions* as they are called, illustrate well enough the essential features of solutions. The two constituents are, for convenience, called the **solute** and **solvent**, the solvent being the constituent in which the solute is dissolved. Usually the solvent is the constituent present in the greater amount. For example, brine is a solution, water being the solvent and salt the solute.

Solutions are often classified on the basis of whether they are gaseous, liquid, or solid, and further, on the basis of whether the undissolved solute is gaseous, liquid, or solid. Oxygen dissolves in water to form a liquid solution; the dissolved oxygen, therefore, has assumed the liquid state. Similarly, water dissolves in air, becoming water vapour (a gas) in the process. In Table 25-1 are assembled examples of the nine possible types of solution according to this classification.

If, however, a solid substance and a liquid substance form a liquid solution, the liquid substance is usually called the solvent even if it is not present in the larger proportion. In a syrup consisting of sugar and water in the mass ratio 3:2 the water is still called the solvent.

TABLE 25-1

TYPES OF SOLUTION

SOLUTION	EXAMPLE
Gas in Gas	Air
Liquid in Gas	Bromine in air
Solid in Gas	Iodine in air
Gas in Liquid	Any carbonated beverage
Liquid in Liquid	Alcohol in water
Solid in Liquid	Sugar in water
Gas in Solid	Hydrogen in palladium
Liquid in Solid	Amalgams (alloys of mercury)
Solid in Solid	Coin metal (a copper-nickel alloy)

Solutions may, of course, have more than two constituents. Gasoline is a liquid solution of several liquids in one another; air is a gaseous solution of several gases in one another; stainless steel is a solid solution of several metals in one another.

THE COMPOSITION OF SOLUTIONS

4. Often we are more interested in the solute than in the solvent. Many reactions that occur between solutions are really reactions between the solutes, and the solvent appears to be merely a medium for the reaction.

Since we are often interested in the masses or amounts of substances participating in reactions, when these reactions occur in solutions we need to have ways of stating how much solute is in a certain amount of solvent or solution. Because there are different ways of preparing and using solutions, there are a variety of ways of expressing their composition or concentration. We shall describe a number of these expressions, and explain how a concentration expressed in one set of units can be transposed into a different set of units if so required.

First we should explain that the terms **concentrated** and **dilute** are commonly used to convey in an approximate way that there is relatively much or little solute in a solution. Maple syrup is a concentrated solution of sugars (with some natural flavourings) in water; well water (even though we may call it "hard"; Sec. 29-14) is a very dilute solution of certain mineral salts.

The quantitative composition, or *concentration*, of a solution can be expressed in either of the following ways:

$$\frac{\text{the quantity of solute}}{\text{the quantity of solvent}}$$

or
$$\frac{\text{the quantity of solute}}{\text{the quantity of solution}}$$

These quantities may be given as *masses, volumes,* or *amounts of substance (numbers of moles)*. A variety of combinations of units are used in describing the concentration of solutions, and we shall single out and explain some of the more common ways of doing so.

5. PER CENT BY MASS. In this way of expressing the concentration of a solution we state:

$$\frac{\text{the mass of solute}}{\text{the mass of solution}} \times 100\%$$

Thus, a 15% (by mass) solution of salt in water contains 15 g of salt for every 85 g of water, for a total mass of 100 g.

Problem 25-1. A sample of an aqueous solution of sodium chloride with a mass of 12.24 g was carefully evaporated to dryness. The dry residue had a mass of 0.98 g. What was the percentage by mass of sodium chloride in the solution?

Solution: 12.24 g of solution contained 0.98 g of salt

$$\therefore \quad 100 \text{ g of solution would contain } 0.98 \text{ g} \times \frac{100.0 \text{ g}}{12.24 \text{ g}} = 8.0 \text{ g of salt}$$

Accordingly, the percentage by mass of sodium chloride was 8.0%

6. MASS OF SOLUTE PER 100 g OF SOLVENT. This representation of the concentration of a solution takes the form:

$$\frac{\text{the mass of solute}}{\text{the mass of solvent}} \times 100 \text{ g}$$

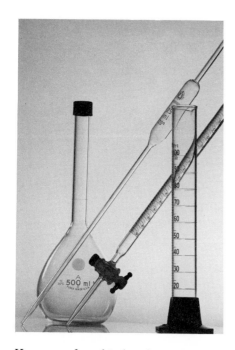

Here are four kinds of apparatus for measuring volumes of solvents or solutions: a volumetric flask and a graduated cylinder (or "graduate") and, diagonally, a pipet and a buret.

This is not the same as the percentage by mass, for the total mass of solution is always greater than the mass of solvent. If it is desired to compare solutions of different solutes, or to show how the solubility (Sec. 25-12) of a single solute varies with temperature, this representation of the concentration of different solutions enables comparisons to be made easily. It is a simple matter to change from this expression of concentration to percentage by mass, or vice versa.

Problem 25-2. Express in the units grams of solute per 100 g of solvent the concentration of a 15.0% solution.

Solution: 15.0 g of solute are contained in 100.0 g of solution

Thus 15.0 g of solute are dissolved in 85.0 g of solvent

The quantity of solute that would dissolve in 100.0 g of solvent

would be $15.0 \text{ g} \times \dfrac{100.0 \text{ g}}{85.0 \text{ g}} = 17.6 \text{ g}$

Therefore, the concentration of the solution is 17.6 g of solute per 100 g of solvent

7. MASS OF SOLUTE PER STATED VOLUME OF SOLUTION. In preparing solutions for laboratory use, it is convenient to weigh out a sample of solute, transfer it to a volumetric flask (illustrated in the adjacent photograph), and add enough solvent to bring the volume of solution up to the stated capacity of the flask. Measured volumes taken from this solution will then contain a known mass of solute.

In this case the concentration of the solution is given by:

$$\frac{\text{the mass of solute}}{\text{the volume of solution}}$$

In this way we may speak of a solution as containing, say, 0.200 g of solute per 1.0 mL of solution, 20.0 g of solute per 100 mL, or alternatively 200 g/L. Notice that it is the volume of solution, not the volume of solvent, that appears in this expression.

Problem 25-3. A solution is prepared by dissolving 1.50 g of potassium nitrate in a little water, and then diluting this solution to a measured volume of 200 mL. What is the concentration of the solution in grams per litre of solution?

Solution: 200 mL of solution contains 1.50 g of potassium nitrate

∴ 1000 mL of solution would contain $1.50 \text{ g} \times \dfrac{1000 \text{ mL}}{200 \text{ mL}} = 7.50 \text{ g}$

Accordingly, the concentration of the potassium nitrate solution is 7.50 g/L

8. NUMBER OF MOLES OF SOLUTE PER STATED VOLUME OF SOLUTION. Chemists find it convenient to express amounts of substances in moles

(Sec. 10-23). Consequently, a very important way to indicate the concentration of a solution is the following:

$$\frac{\text{the amount of solute (moles)}}{\text{the volume of solution}}$$

For most purposes, chemists give the volume of solution in this expression in litres, so that the concentration has units of moles per litre (symbol mol/L). In SI the preference is for volumes to be given in cubic metres (m^3), so that concentrations may also be expressed as a number of moles per cubic metre (mol/m^3).

To illustrate this way of expressing concentration we refer to the solution described in Problem 25-3. We saw that this contained 7.50 g of potassium nitrate (KNO_3) per litre of solution. The molar mass of potassium nitrate is ($39.1 + 14.0 + 3 \times 16.0$) g/mol = 101.1 g/mol. Therefore 7.50 g of potassium nitrate

$$= \frac{7.50 \text{ g}}{101.1 \text{ g/mol}} = 0.074 \text{ mol}$$

The solution thus has a concentration = 0.074 mol/L of potassium nitrate.

Problem 25-4. The concentration of a sample of hydrochloric acid is 0.730 g of hydrogen chloride/100 mL of solution. Express the concentration of the acid as moles per litre.

Solution: The molar mass of hydrogen chloride is (1.0 + 35.5) g/mol = 36.5 g/mol

In 100 mL of the acid there is 0.730 g of hydrogen chloride

$$0.730 \text{ g of hydrogen chloride} = \frac{0.730 \text{ g}}{36.5 \text{ g/mol}} = 0.0200 \text{ mol}$$

In 100 mL of the acid there is 0.0200 mol of hydrogen chloride

$$\therefore \text{ in 1000 mL} (= 1.000 \text{ L}) \text{ there is } 0.0200 \text{ g} \times \frac{1000 \text{ mL}}{100 \text{ mL}} = 0.200 \text{ mol}$$

Therefore, the concentration of the hydrochloric acid = 0.200 mol/L

Problem 25-5. You are provided with a solution of sodium hydroxide labelled 0.120 mol/L. How many moles of sodium hydroxide are there in a 25.0-mL portion of this solution?

Solution: One litre (1000 mL) of the solution contains 0.120 mol of sodium hydroxide

$\therefore$ 25.0 mL of the solution contains

$$0.120 \text{ mol} \times \frac{25.0 \text{ mL}}{1000 \text{ mL}} = 0.003 \text{ 00 mol of sodium hydroxide}$$

This amount, 0.003 00 mol = 3.00 mmol (millimoles)

9. CONVERSION FROM ONE SET OF CONCENTRATION UNITS TO ANOTHER. We often encounter the problem in laboratory work where we need to know the concentration of a solution in one set of units, but the available information gives the concentration in different units. It is necessary, therefore, to be able to convert from one unit to another. We have already given some simple examples of this. With the aid of these you should be able to convert a concentration in percentage by mass to one giving (mass of solute)/(mass of solvent), and also from concentration in (mass of solute)/(volume of solution) to (amount of solute)/(volume of solution).

The task is a little more difficult if one unit of concentration has "mass of solution" and the other has "volume of solution" in the denominator. An extra step is then required: to convert a mass of solution to the corresponding volume. For this, the density of the solution is required. The procedure can best be illustrated by an example.

Remember, amount of a substance means a number of moles.

Problem 25-6. According to the label on a bottle of concentrated sulphuric acid (H_2SO_4) the concentration of acid is 96% (by mass) and the density is 1.84 g/mL. What is the concentration in moles per litre?

Solution: First, we find the mass of one litre of the acid.

1000 mL of acid has a mass of 1000 mL $\times$ 1.84 g/mL = 1840 g

Then, find the mass of hydrogen sulphate in the acid

100 g of the acid contains 96 g of hydrogen sulphate

$\therefore$ 1840 g contains 96.0 g $\times$ $\dfrac{1840\ g}{100\ g}$ = 1766 g of hydrogen sulphate

Finally, find the number of moles of hydrogen sulphate in the litre of acid

The molar mass of H_2SO_4 is (2 $\times$ 1.0 + 32.1 + 4 $\times$ 16.0) g/mol
$$= 98.1\ g/mol$$

$\therefore$ the amount of hydrogen sulphate is $\dfrac{1766\ g}{98.1\ g/mol}$ = 18.0 mol

Accordingly, the concentration of the sulphuric acid = 18.0 mol/L

Problem 25-7. A solution of hydrochloric acid contains 7.0 mol/L of hydrogen chloride and has a density of 1.11 g/mL. Calculate its concentration as percentage by mass.

Solution: First, find the mass of solute in one litre of the acid.

The amount of solute per litre of solution = 7.0 mol

The molar mass of HCl = (1.0 + 35.5) g/mol = 36.5 g/mol

$\therefore$ the mass of solute per litre of solution = 7.0 mol $\times$ 36.5 g/mol
$$= 256\ g$$

Now, find the mass of one litre of solution.

1000 mL of acid has a mass of 1000 mL × 1.11 g/mL = 1110 g

Now express the concentration as $\dfrac{\text{mass of solute}}{\text{mass of solution}} \times 100\%$

This will be $\dfrac{256 \text{ g}}{1110 \text{ g}} \times 100\% = 23.1\%$

Therefore, the concentration of the solution = 23.1% of hydrogen chloride by mass

10. PREPARATION OF SOLUTIONS OF DESIRED CONCENTRATION. Solutions of a required concentration are prepared, if possible, by dissolving the correct mass of solute in a known mass of solvent, or in sufficient solvent to yield a known volume of solution. The volume of a solution, however, is usually a little different from the sum of the volumes of the solute and solvent, so that one cannot readily predict how much solvent to measure out in order to have a desired volume of solution. Accordingly, what must be done is to dissolve a known mass of the solute in a portion of the solvent and then add solvent until the desired volume is attained.

Problem 25-8. Compare the volume of 1.000 kg of a 10.0% (by mass) solution of sodium chloride with the sum of the volumes of the 100 g of sodium chloride (density = 2.17 g/mL) and 900 g of water (density = 0.997 g/mL) used in its preparation. The density of the 10.0% salt solution is 1.0726 g/mL.

Solution: Volume of 100 g of salt = $\dfrac{100 \text{ g}}{2.17 \text{ g/mL}}$ = 46 mL

Volume of 900 g of water = $\dfrac{900 \text{ g}}{0.997 \text{ g/mL}}$ = 903 mL

Sum of these volumes = 949 mL

Volume of 1000 g of solution = $\dfrac{1000 \text{ g}}{1.0726 \text{ g/mL}}$ = 932 mL

There is a shrinkage of 17 mL in the formation of the solution. Such shrinkages are quite common.

Some substances cannot be obtained in a pure enough condition to be weighed out "formula pure". A common source of contamination is moisture absorbed from the air (Sec. 24-14). Solutions of such substances can be prepared having approximately the desired concentration, and then the exact concentration can be found in some other way.

Solutions of desired concentration are often prepared by dilution of a measured quantity of a more concentrated solution whose concentration is known.

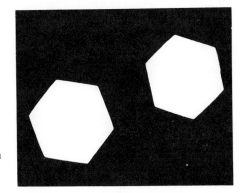

These perfect hexagons are faces of tiny crystals of $3PbCO_3 \cdot 2Pb(OH)_2$, a substance related to the paint pigment known as white lead ($2PbCO_3 \cdot Pb(OH)_2$). They were formed as a precipitate by passing carbon dioxide into a basic solution of lead(II) acetate, under very carefully controlled conditions.

The crystals are only 1.8×10^{-3} cm wide (from which you can calculate, if you measure their picture, that the magnification here is about 1300). They are so thin that more than 250 of them would be needed to make a pile as high as the width of one of them.

Is it desirable that the particles of a paint pigment be thin "platelets" such as these?

Problem 25-9. What volume of the concentrated sulphuric acid described in Problem 25-6 should be taken to prepare 2.00 L of a sulphuric acid solution containing 1.00 mol/L of hydrogen sulphate?

Solution: The amount of hydrogen sulphate required for 2.00 L of solution containing 1.00 mol/L of this substance = 2.00 L × 1.00 mol/L

$$= 2.00 \text{ mol}$$

The concentrated sulphuric acid had a concentration of 18.0 mol/L (Problem 25-6)

Let V L be the volume of this acid which contains the required amount (2.00 mol) of hydrogen sulphate.

Then $\dfrac{200 \text{ mol}}{V \text{ L}}$ is the same concentration as 18.0 mol/L

Therefore, the volume V L $= \dfrac{2.00 \text{ mol}}{18.0 \text{ mol/L}}$ = 0.111 L = 111 mL

To prepare two litres of 1.00 mol/L of sulphuric acid, 111 mL of concentrated acid would be added **carefully** to about a litre of water. After this solution had cooled to room temperature it would be diluted with water (and well mixed) until the final volume was 2.00 L.

SOLUBILITY

11. SATURATED SOLUTIONS. Solvents differ very much in their ability to dissolve a solute: water readily dissolves more than its own mass of sugar, whereas alcohol dissolves very little sugar. Similarly, solutes differ very much in their ability to dissolve in a solvent: magnesium sulphate dissolves abundantly in water, but barium sulphate dissolves hardly at all. Some substances dissolve in each other in all proportions: examples are ethyl alcohol and water, and gasoline and kerosene. Such substances are said to be *completely miscible*. There are cases, such as oil and water, where substances are practically *immiscible*. There are a great many instances of one substance dissolving in another, but only to a limited extent, and we describe these by saying that the substances are *partially miscible*.

The limit of miscibility gives rise to the idea of a *saturated* solution. When common salt, for instance, is stirred with water at 20°C, it dissolves rapidly at first, then more and more slowly. Eventually, dissolution seems to stop. The concentration of the solution increases while the salt is dissolving, but eventually reaches a constant value. No matter how long or how vigorously the mixture of salt and solution is stirred, the amount of salt remaining and the concentration of the solution remain unchanged provided the temperature remains at 20°C. The solution is said, then, to be saturated at that temperature. If the mixture is warmed to 30°C and maintained at that temperature, more salt will dissolve and the solution will become more concentrated. But again a point is reached at which no more salt goes into solution. The

One of the dreams of the alchemists, some hundreds of years ago, was to find the "universal solvent"—a liquid that would dissolve any and every other substance. If they had found it, what would they have kept it in? (Incidentally, there *is* a satisfactory answer to that.)

For two substances to be completely miscible they must both be in the same physical state (solid, liquid, or gaseous). Why? By no means all pairs of solids or liquids *are* completely miscible.

extent to which one substance will dissolve in another substance depends on the temperature.

In the example of salt and water, the amount of salt dissolving depends on the amount of water used. Ten times as much salt will dissolve to form a saturated solution in a litre of water as will dissolve in 100 mL of water. So the concentration of the saturated solution has a fixed value at a specified temperature. We call this particular concentration the **solubility.**

12. **SOLUBILITY.** The solubility of one substance in another is expressed by stating the *concentration of the saturated solution.* Since this concentration varies considerably with temperature for many substances (Sec. 25-15), the temperature at which a stated solubility applies should be indicated. If a solute is a gas, the pressure must also be stated, as the pressure of a gas has a tremendous effect on its solubility in a given solvent.

The solubility of a substance in a particular solvent is a quantitative and characteristic property of the substance, like its melting point, boiling point, or density, and can be used to identify the substance or to serve as a check on its purity (Sec. 1-5).

The solubility may be expressed in any of the concentration units given in Sec. 25-5 to 25-8.

13. For a specified temperature (and pressure, if we happen to be dealing with gases) there is one—and only one—solubility of a particular substance in another. But we could prepare as many different solutions as we wished having concentrations lower than that of the saturated solution. These are known as **unsaturated solutions.** The concentration of an unsaturated solution could lie anywhere from essentially zero up to just below that of the saturated solution.

There can even be solutions whose concentrations are greater than that of the saturated solution at the same temperature and pressure. This may seem to be a contradiction of our description of a saturated solution, but actually it isn't. A solution that is saturated at a given temperature is one in which no more solute can be dissolved *at that temperature.* However, if a saturated solution is heated (or, for a few substances, cooled), more solute will usually dissolve. Then, if this more concentrated solution is carefully cooled (or, for those few substances, warmed) back to the original temperature, the excess solute *may* stay in solution. If so, the solution will be more concentrated than the solution saturated at that temperature. Such a solution is, quite appropriately, said to be a **supersaturated solution.** But it doesn't take much to bring the excess solute out of solution. Jarring the solution may be enough; stirring it probably will be enough; adding a tiny crystal of the solute certainly will be enough.

The phenomenon of supersaturation can be illustrated very well with sodium thiosulphate pentahydrate ($Na_2S_2O_3 \cdot 5H_2O$)—the photographer's "hypo"—and water. If hypo is dissolved in water at 50°C until the solution is saturated, the solution will contain much more of the salt than it would if saturated at 20°C.

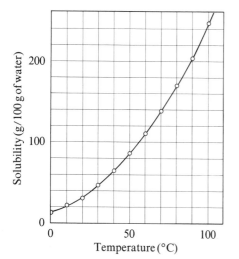

Fig. 25-1: *Solubility of potassium nitrate in water*

If, however, this solution is filtered free of any crystals of the solute, and cooled carefully to 20°C, without disturbing it in any way and without letting any dust into it, no crystallization will occur. It will now be a supersaturated solution. If a crystal of bluestone is dropped into it gently, nothing happens. But if a crystal of hypo—even a very tiny one—is added, crystallization occurs in dramatic fashion and continues at a steadily diminishing rate until the excess solute has all come out of solution and the concentration has become that of the saturated solution. (The process of starting crystallization by adding a crystal is known as "seeding" the solution; the added crystal is called a "seed" crystal.)

14. TEST FOR SATURATION. Whether a solution is unsaturated, supersaturated, or saturated can be discovered by a very simple test. A small crystal of the solute is stirred with the solution. If the crystal becomes smaller, the solution was unsaturated. If it becomes larger, the solution was supersaturated. If it stays the same size, the solution is saturated (or very near to it).

15. SOLUBILITY CURVES. The solubility of a particular solute in a particular solvent has a different value at each different temperature. With few exceptions, the solubility of a solid in a liquid increases with temperature. This is evident from the data in Table 25-2: solubilities of potassium nitrate in water at temperatures ranging from 0°C to 100°C. The way the solubility increases with temperature is demonstrated by plotting solubility versus temperature, as in Fig. 25-1. The result is called a *solubility curve.* From it one can read the plotted values. What's more, one can "read" the solubility at any intermediate temperature. (For example, the solubility at 75°C is about 153 g/100 g.) The assumption made in drawing the curve, and in reading values from it, is that the solubility changes continuously with temperature—that is, that the

TABLE 25-2

SOLUBILITY OF POTASSIUM NITRATE IN WATER	
SOLUBILITY (g/100 g of water)	TEMP (°C)
246	100
202	90
169	80
138	70
110	60
85.5	50
63.9	40
45.8	30
31.6	20
20.9	10
13.3	0

curve is a smooth one, without kinks in it. (This is usually but not always true. It is wise not to draw a curve unless the points are fairly close together.)

16. PRECIPITATION FROM SOLUTION. From solubility curves one can calculate the proportion of a dissolved pure substance that can be recovered by crystallization under various conditions. An example will show how this is done.

Problem 25-10: The solubility of a certain salt at 70°C is 60 g/100 g of water and at 20°C is 40 g/100 g of water. (a) How much of the salt that will dissolve in 200 g of water at 70°C will crystallize out when the solution saturated at 70°C is cooled, with seeding, to 20°C? (b) What fraction of the salt is thus recrystallized?

Solution: (a) At 70°C, 200 g of water will dissolve (to form a saturated solution)

$$\frac{200 \text{ g}}{100 \text{ g}} \times 60 \text{ g of salt} = 120 \text{ g of salt}$$

At 20°C, 200 g of water—the mass of water doesn't change—

will dissolve $\frac{200 \text{ g}}{100 \text{ g}} \times 40 \text{ g of salt} = 80 \text{ g of salt}$

Therefore, the mass of salt that will crystallize out is
(120 – 80) g = 40 g

(b) Of the 120 g of salt that dissolved at 70°C, 40 g crystallize at 20°C

Therefore, the fraction of the salt that crystallizes is $\frac{40 \text{ g}}{120 \text{ g}} = \frac{1}{3}$

Satisfy yourself that this same fraction would crystallize no matter what mass of water were used in preparing the original, saturated solution.

17. RATE OF DISSOLUTION. Just as solutes differ in their solubility in the same solvent, so they differ in the rate at which they dissolve in the same solvent. It usually takes much longer to dissolve one gram of sodium chloride in 100 g of water than it does to dissolve one gram of sugar in that mass of water under comparable conditions.

It does not follow, though, that the solute that dissolves faster is the more soluble. A greater rate of dissolution does *not* necessarily indicate greater solubility.

It is important not to confuse solubility with rate of dissolution (the mass of solute that dissolves in a certain mass of solvent in unit time). The solubility of a solute in a solvent has a definite value at a given temperature and pressure. In contrast to this, the rate at which a solute dissolves is very much affected by the conditions of the experiment.

For example, the mass of bluestone that will dissolve in 100 g of water at 20°C in one minute depends on whether the bluestone is in one piece or in many, and whether or not the bluestone is stirred with the water. The bluestone dissolves much faster when finely divided and much faster when the mix-

The early training of P. J. W. Debye (1884-1966) was in the Netherlands, in electrical engineering, but his professorships were in physics and chemistry in Switzerland, the Netherlands, Germany, and the United States. His outstanding research work, including major contributions to the idea of electrical polarity within molecules, led to many honours, the greatest being the Nobel Prize in Chemistry (1936).

It may be added that Debye was an excellent lecturer, an ardent fisherman, and a devotee of murder mystery stories.

ture is agitated by stirring or shaking. Moreover, as dissolving goes on, the rate of dissolution decreases, finally becoming zero when the solution is saturated.

The rate of dissolution, like the solubility, is affected by changing the temperature. But whereas the solubility is *usually* increased by increasing the temperature, the rate of dissolution *always* is. So we can always hasten dissolving by heating the solvent.

Summarizing, a given solute will dissolve faster in a given solvent

(1) if the solute is more finely divided, presenting more surface to the solvent (Fig. 25-2);

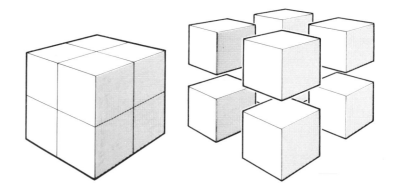

Fig. 25-2: *When an object is broken into smaller pieces more surface is created. The finer the subdividing the greater is the surface, and the greater the surface the more rapidly will the substance dissolve in a solvent or react with a liquid. Here, dividing one cube into eight cubes has not changed the volume or mass but it has doubled the surface area. (Prove this.)*

(2) if the temperature of the solvent is raised;

(3) if the mixture is stirred (for this continually brings the undissolved solute in contact with fresh solvent).

18. CAN DISSOLVING BE EXPLAINED? It would be helpful to conclude this chapter with a description of the factors governing the dissolving of one substance in another. Unfortunately, the theory of solutions is still far from complete, and we can do no better than to give a sketchy account of some broad principles.

There is an old—and useful—saying that "like dissolves like." Substances with similar structural features generally show considerable miscibility. Hydrocarbons dissolve readily and often without limit in other hydrocarbons. Metals that crystallize with the same kind of packing (Fig. 15-10) and that have about the same atomic diameters show extensive, if not complete, miscibility. Because of the wide-open structure typical of gases, they are all miscible in all proportions.

Water—the commonest of all solvents—is an associated liquid, by which we mean that there is a good deal of linking from one molecule to the next. This linking has been explained (Sec. 24-5) as a consequence of electrical "polarity" within each molecule, and due to "hydrogen bonding" between molecules. For a molecule or other particle of a solute to find a place within a collection of water molecules, the solute molecule is obliged to create a place for itself by pushing water molecules apart. That will perhaps mean breaking some hydrogen bonds so that holes in the water structure are created. Molecules like hydrogen (H_2), nitrogen (N_2), oxygen (O_2), or methane (CH_4) are not electrically polar, and have no means of attaching themselves to a water molecule or of otherwise opening up the water structure. Accordingly, these substances show little solubility in water. By contrast, electrically polar molecules like ammonia (NH_3), hydrogen fluoride (HF), or hydrogen sulphide (H_2S) can share in the electrical attractions which are characteristic of water. These substances are moderately to very soluble in water.

Network solids generally do not dissolve to any extent in solvents. Because of the many bonds that link the atoms in a network, it requires a great deal of energy to separate individual atoms from the aggregate. This creates an opposition to the formation of solutions. Of ionic solids, some are soluble in water, but others are only slightly soluble. As we shall show in Chapter 26, the particles in solutions of ionic substances are still ions, though modified by the solvent. But for these ions to break away from the other ions that make up the ionic lattice of the solid, and to pass into solution as individual ions, requires that a lot of work be done to overcome the lattice energy (Sec. 14-7). This energy can come only from strong interactions between individual ions and molecules of a solvent. Such interactions are only possible in solvents that have molecules which are quite polar electrically, such as water, liquid ammonia, liquid hydrogen fluoride, and a few others. Thus, ionic compounds, when they dissolve, do so only in polar solvents. But even a polar solvent may not be able to entice the partners of a stable ionic lattice to break up. Water can dissolve solid Na^+F^-, but cannot overcome the much greater force of attraction between the ions in the isoelectronic compound $Mg^{2+}O^{2-}$.

These remarks may help you to appreciate that dissolving occurs or does not occur as a result of attractions among the particles within a solute, among those within a solvent, and between the particles of solute and solvent. The process of dissolution is not capable of a quick simple description.

For one gram of solid sodium chloride to be dispersed into its individual ions requires that 1.03×10^{22} positive ions be separated from an equal number of negative ions, with an input of 13.2 kJ of energy. This is as much energy as is needed to keep a sixty-watt light bulb burning for three minutes and forty seconds.

"Isoelectronic" is a term defined in Sec. 13-6.

QUESTIONS

1. Explain in your own words the meaning of:

(a) solution   (f) miscibility
(b) binary solution   (g) solubility
(c) aqueous solution   (h) concentration of a solution
(d) saturated solution   (i) solubility curve
(e) supersaturated solution   (j) precipitation

*2. In this chapter we gave what were called "operational" and "conceptual" descriptions of solutions. Explain the distinction between these. To demonstrate that you understand the distinction, write out operational and conceptual descriptions of the term *chemical element*.

3. Give two examples of each of (a) a gaseous solution, (b) a liquid solution, (c) a solid solution.

4. Give one example (other than that in the textbook) of each of the nine types of solution listed in Table 25-1.

5. Solutions are sometimes said to have "variable composition." Explain clearly what this statement means. Does a 10% salt solution have variable composition?

6. What is meant by the terms *solvent* and *solute*? Suggest solutions in which it is difficult to decide which constituent is solvent and which is solute.

7. List the factors that affect the rate of dissolving of a solute in a solvent, and indicate the effect of each.

8. List four factors that affect solubility. Do all the factors that affect rate of dissolving also affect solubility?

9. In Sec. 25-14 a test for saturation is described. Explain the basis of this test. Why is it important that a very *small* crystal of solute be added?

10. Gases are always completely miscible; some liquids may be completely miscible, and so may some solids. There is always a limit of dissolving when two constituents of a solution are initially in different states (for example, solid and liquid). Account for this.

11. Give at least one example of (a) a solution that is saturated, yet dilute; (b) a solution that is concentrated, yet unsaturated.

12. Can you suggest reasonable explanations for the following observations?

(a) A freshly poured glass of "Coke" contains visible gas bubbles.

(b) Warm "Coke" fizzes more than cold.

(c) "Coke" left in an opened bottle goes "flat."

13. You have two bottles, one containing clear sea water, the other turbid river water. Describe these from the point of view of homogeneity and permanence.

14. A solution contains 25 g of solute and 100 g of water. State the composition as percentage by mass. What is the mass of solute in 20 g of the solution?

15. A solution is prepared from 100 g of sugar and 150 g of water. Express its composition as (a) percentage by mass, (b) mass of sugar per 100 g of water.

16. A solution is prepared by dissolving 10.0 g of anhydrous sodium carbonate in 100 g of water. Express the composition of the solution as (a) percentage by mass, (b) amount of solute (in moles) per kilogram of solvent.

* 17. Ethylene glycol, $C_2H_4(OH)_2$, is widely used as an antifreeze in automobile cooling systems. For protection to –29°C it is recomended to use a solution that is 44% glycol by volume. What information is required, and how would it be used, to calculate the percentage of glycol by mass in such a solution?

18. You have 500 g of an aqueous solution containing 10.0% by mass of barium chloride. What mass of water must be added to this to make a 5.0% solution? What mass of barium chloride must be added to convert the original solution to a 20.0% solution?

19. If you mix 60 g of a 15% (by mass) solution of salt in water with 40 g of a 10% solution of the same substance, what will be the percentage composition of the resulting solution?

20. The density of 20% sulphuric acid is 1.14 g/mL. What mass of hydrogen sulphate is in 1.00 L of this solution?

21. What is the mass of hydrogen chloride in 250 cm^3 of a 20.0% solution of hydrochloric acid whose density is 1.10 g/cm^3?

22. What amount (in moles) of hydrogen nitrate is present in 1.00 L of a 20.0% solution of nitric acid the density of which is 1.12 g/mL?

23. The density of a 21.8% solution of ammonia in water is 0.920 g/mL. Calculate the amount of ammonia (in moles) per litre of solution.

24. The density of a 14.0% solution of sodium carbonate (anhydrous) in water is 1.15 g/cm^3. What mass of sodium carbonate would be obtained by evaporation of 200 cm^3 of this solution? What would be the amount of sodium carbonate, in moles?

25. A solution was prepared by dissolving 70.0 g of silver nitrate in water in a one-litre volumetric flask, and making the volume up to the mark on the neck of the flask. What was the concentration of the solution in moles per litre? (This means the amount of solute in moles per litre of solution.)

26. What mass of solute is present in 25.0 mL of a solution of potassium chloride whose concentration is 2.00 mol/L?

27. "Concentrated" hydrochloric acid in the laboratory usually has a concentration of 12 mol/L and a density of 1.19 g/mL. Express the composition of the acid as percentage of hydrogen chloride by mass.

28. Calculate the concentration (in moles per litre) of "concentrated" nitric acid from the information that its composition is 70% hydrogen nitrate and its density is 1.42 g/mL.

29. What mass of pure solute should be taken to prepare the stated quantities of solutions of given concentration?

(a) 50 g of a 12% solution of mercury(II) chloride

(b) 200 g of a solution of potassium nitrate whose concentration is 0.50 mol solute/kg solvent

(c) 250 mL of a solution of iron(III) chloride whose concentration is 3.00 mol/L

(d) 1000 g of a solution of copper(II) sulphate containing 12 g solute/100 g solvent.

30. A solution contains 1.0 mol/L of borax (see Table 24-3). What mass of (a) sodium tetraborate decahydrate, (b) anhydrous sodium tetraborate, would be obtained by the appropriate evaporation of 200 mL of the borax solution?

31. What volume of "glacial" acetic acid (98%, 17.2 mol/L) should be taken and diluted with water in order to make 1.00 L of 0.100 mol/L acetic acid?

32. Concentrated phosphoric acid (ortho) is supplied in 85% solution, having a density of 1.44 g/L. What volume of this acid should be measured out and diluted with sufficient water to make 10.0 L of 0.100 mol/L phosphoric acid?

* 33. Why is it that we must use the phrase "sufficient water" in Question 32, rather than specify the volume of water to be added?

34. What volume of concentrated aqueous ammonia, which has a concentration of 14 mol/L when fresh, should be measured out and diluted with sufficient water to make 5.0 L of 0.10 mol/L solution?

35. Since the exact concentrations of many purchased acids in solution are not known, they, or more dilute solutions prepared from them, must be "standardized." That is, their concentration must be found from a stoichiometric relationship (Sec. 16-5). A 25.0-mL sample of dilute sulphuric acid was treated with an excess of barium chloride in solution. A precipitate of barium sulphate formed, was removed by filtration, thoroughly dried, and weighed. Its mass was 0.584 g. Find the concentration of the dilute sulphuric acid in moles per litre. Give the equation for the chemical reaction. Why was an excess of barium chloride added?

36. To a 50.0-mL sample of dilute hydrochloric acid was added an excess of silver nitrate solution. This resulted in a precipitate of silver chloride which, after separation by filtration and drying, was found to have a mass of 1.147 g. Calculate the amount of hydrogen chloride (in moles) per litre of the dilute hydrochloric acid. Give the equation for the chemical reaction. Why was an excess of silver nitrate added?

37. The solubility of calcium sulphate is 0.208 g of anhydrous salt/100 g of water at 25°C. Express the solubility in moles per litre. (Assume the density of the solution = 1 g/mL.)

38. The solubility of copper(II) sulphate pentahydrate at 20°C is 32.4 g/100 g of water. Express this as percentage. Also state the solubility as the number of grams of anhydrous copper sulphate/100 g of water at 20°C.

39. The solubility of potassium chlorate in water varies with temperature as follows:

TEMPERATURE (°C)	SOLUBILITY (g/100 g water)
10	5.0
20	7.1
30	10.1
40	14.5
50	19.7
60	26.0

(a) Carefully plot these solubility data on graph paper, labelling all axes, and giving the plot a suitable title.

(b) From your curve, read the solubility at 18°C, 33°C, and 52°C.

(c) At what temperature is the solubility of potassium chlorate (i) 12 g/100 g of water, (ii) 23 g/100 g of water, (iii) 15 g/100 g of water?

(d) State the degree of saturation (saturated, unsaturated, supersaturated) of the solutions of composition (i) 8 g/100 g of water at 25°C, (ii) 20 g/100 g of water at 30°C, (iii) 10 g/100 g of water at 45°C.

(e) What mass of potassium chlorate would crystallize from a solution made by dissolving 15 g of this salt in 100 g of water at an elevated temperature, and cooling it to 30°C, when the solution is shaken and seeded at this temperature?

(f) What mass of potassium chlorate would precipitate from a solution made by dissolving 10 g of this salt in 100 g of water at 50°C, when the solution is cooled to 15°C, with seeding at the appropriate time?

(g) What mass of potassium chlorate would be required to saturate at 45°C a solution consisting of 10 g of this salt and 100 g of water?

40. The solubility of ammonium chloride is given below for various temperatures:

(a) Carefully plot these solubility data on graph paper, labelling the axes, and giving the plot a suitable title.

TEMPERATURE (°C)	SOLUBILITY (g/100 g water)
10	33.3
20	37.2
30	41.4
40	45.8
50	50.4
60	55.2
70	60.2
80	65.6
90	71.3

(b) Calculate the mass of crystals that should be obtained by cooling 1 kg of a solution saturated at 60°C from this temperature to 20°C.

(c) Calculate the mass of crystals that should be obtained by evaporating 400 g of water from 1.00 kg of this solution saturated at 20°C.

(d) Estimate from your plot the solubility of ammonium chloride at 25°C and at 75°C.

(e) A solution containing 30% ammonium chloride by mass is prepared hot and then allowed to cool, with constant stirring. Predict at what temperature crystals of solute should begin to appear as the solution is cooled.

41. A solution of alum containing 30 g of alum per 100 g of water at 50°C is cooled to room temperature. With what confidence can you predict whether or not crystals of alum will form as a result of the cooling? How is the certainty of your prediction affected by the information that the solubility of alum at 14°C is 14 g/100 g of water? How could you ensure that crystals would form?

*42. Although ethane, C_2H_6, shows very little solubility in water, ethyl alcohol, C_2H_5OH, is miscible with water in all proportions. An ethyl alcohol molecule differs from an ethane molecule only because one covalently bonded hydrogen atom has been replaced by one hydroxide radical. Can you suggest an explanation for this difference in solubility?

*43. When 50 cm³ of water and 50 cm³ of ethyl alcohol (C_2H_5OH) are mixed, the volume of the resulting solution is 96 cm³. Give an explanation of this shrinkage in the solution. (It may be helpful to consider the shape of the alcohol molecule, a model of which is shown below.)

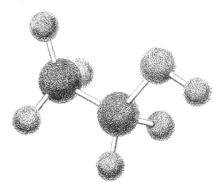

26 Electrolysis and Electrolytes

1. In our discussion of solutions so far, we have emphasized what they have in common. But some solutions differ markedly from others. One point of difference exhibited by some liquid solutions is the ability to conduct an electric current. Before we can discuss this, however, we should say something about electrical conduction in general.

2. CONDUCTION OF ELECTRICITY. Some substances have the ability to conduct electricity well. A familiar example is the metal copper, which is widely used to carry current to and from—and inside—electrical equipment: motors, generators, radios, television sets, and so on. Other substances are poor conductors, some so poor as to be practically non-conductors. Many such non-conductors, such as glass and ceramics, rubber, plastics, and mica, are used as insulators.

It is easy to test whether a particular material is a good conductor or not with the help of the simple apparatus shown in Fig. 26-1. The two poles *a* and *b*, which are metal rods with some kind of insulating handles, are touched at two points on the surface of a solid material (so that good contacts are made) as in B, or immersed in a liquid as in C. If the material is a good conductor, the deflection of the needle in the ammeter will be large; if it is a poor conductor, the needle will show little or no deflection. Some representative results for pure substances are given in Table 26-1.

From these and similar observations certain general conclusions may be drawn. Of the *elements*, metals are good conductors (Sec. 9-3) and non-metals as a rule are not. *Compounds* are poor conductors in the solid state, and may or may not be good conductors in the liquid state.

Liquid *solutions*, like liquid compounds, may or may not conduct electricity well. A solution of sodium chloride in water is a relatively good conductor; a solution of sugar in water is a poor one.

Carbon, in the form of graphite, is an exception. It is a good enough conductor to be used as poles in dry cells, arc lamps, and so forth.

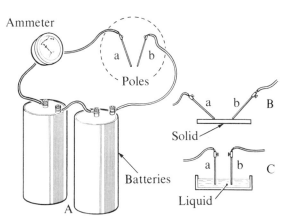

Ammeter

a b
Poles

a b B
Solid

a b C
Liquid

Batteries

A

TABLE 26-1

SOME GOOD AND POOR CONDUCTORS OF ELECTRICITY

SUBSTANCE	CONDUCTING ABILITY	
SOLIDS		
Elements		
Copper	good	
Silver	good	
Aluminium	good	
Sulphur		poor
Compounds		
Sodium chloride		poor
Potassium hydroxide		poor
Calcium oxide		poor
Water (solid)		poor
LIQUIDS		
Elements		
Mercury	good	
Bromine		poor
Compounds		
Sodium chloride (melted)	good	
Potassium hydroxide (melted)	good	
Water		poor
Methanol (methyl alcohol)		poor
Hydrogen chloride (liquid)		poor

3. TWO KINDS OF ELECTRICAL CONDUCTION. By testing a wide variety of substances for their ability to conduct an electric current, scientists have concluded that those which are reasonably good conductors may be divided into two groups. One group, which includes the metals, consists of substances which are not themselves affected by the passage of

The movement of electrons in solids can often be interpreted by consideration of their structure and bonding. Here Professor Rudi Haering, of the University of British Columbia, contemplates a model of molybdenum disulphide (MoS_2) which is being investigated as a new electrode material for batteries.

the current through them. A piece of copper wire, for instance, which has transmitted several amperes of current for several hours will exhibit no change in mass or properties as a result of the passage of charge through it. The other group of substances *are* affected by the passage of charge through them; at the poles—which are also called **electrodes**—where the current enters and leaves, chemical changes take place while any current is flowing. For example, when an electric current passes through melted sodium chloride, metallic sodium is formed at one electrode and gaseous chlorine at the other. Evidently a portion of the sodium chloride is decomposed by the electricity as it passes through the melt.

The difference between these two kinds of conductors can be explained as follows. In conductors such as metals, electric charge moves through the conducting material in the form of *electrons*. What we call a current is, in fact, a stream of electrons moving through the conductor from the negative pole to the positive pole. Only substances in which electrons are free to move from atom to atom are capable of this kind of electrical conduction. The method of bonding atoms together in crystals of metals, which we described in Sec. 15-18, provides for mobility of the bonding electrons; this is why metals make up the great majority of conductors of the first kind.

In the second kind of conductor, which is restricted to fluids, the charged particles that carry the current are *ions* rather than electrons. We have previously explained that many substances are made up of positive and negative ions arranged in some regular way and held together in the solid state by ionic bonding. At sufficiently high temperatures many such substances can be melted, and when this happens the ions become free to move about just as molecules do in liquids. If an electrical potential difference is then applied, through electrodes dipping into the melt, each ion will be attracted toward the electrode with charge opposite to its own. Thus, when a current flows through melted sodium chloride, what really flows is a stream of sodium ions moving toward the negative electrode, and a stream of chloride ions moving toward the positive electrode. Each of these streams of ions is equivalent to a flow of negative charge toward the positive electrode (Fig. 26-2).

4. ELECTROLYSIS. The chemical changes that accompany the flow of electrical current through this second kind of conductor occur at the electrodes. Here some of the ions are neutralized by a transfer of one or more electrons between the electrode and the ion to be neutralized. Specifically, in the case of melted sodium chloride, what happens is as follows. At the surface of the negative electrode (negative because there are extra electrons there) an electron passes from the electrode to a sodium ion, thereby neutralizing it and converting it to a sodium atom:

$$\underset{\substack{\text{from} \\ \text{electrode}}}{e^-} + Na^+ \longrightarrow Na$$

This is how sodium was discovered by Humphry Davy in 1807, except that he decomposed melted sodium hydroxide.

The electrode should be made of a substance that isn't itself chemically changed by the current. Platinum wires or graphite rods are suitable for most purposes.

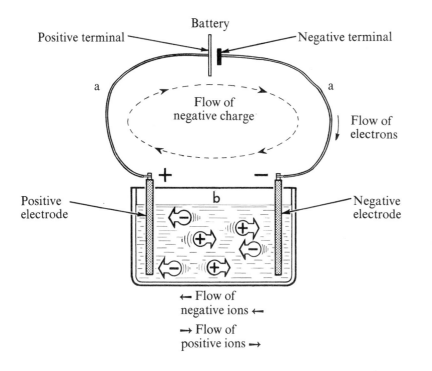

Fig. 26-2: *This circuit illustrates conductance by both electrons and ions. In the copper wire, a, the current is a flow of electrons. In the liquid, b, the current is a flow of negative ions toward the positive pole and of positive ions toward the negative pole. If, for example, the liquid is melted sodium chloride, the negative ions are chloride ions and the positive ions are sodium ions.*

At the positive electrode (where there is a shortage of electrons) there is a transfer of an electron to the electrode from each chloride ion that is neutralized to form an atom of chlorine:

$$Cl^- \rightarrow Cl + e^-_{\text{to electrode}}$$

The chlorine atoms then combine to form chlorine molecules:

$$Cl + Cl \rightarrow Cl_2$$

The combined over-all process arising from the passage of one electronic charge through the solution is

$$Na^+ + Cl^- \rightarrow Na + \tfrac{1}{2}Cl_2$$

The electric current, corresponding to many such units of charge passing through the solution, decomposes sodium chloride into its constituent elements. This type of decomposition caused by an electric current is called **electrolysis**.

In devices, such as dry cells or storage batteries, where chemical reactions produce a potential difference, the signs of the anode and cathode are reversed.

5. SOME DEFINITIONS. Before we discuss other cases of electrolysis, we shall define some terms used in electrochemistry. Electrochemistry is the branch of chemistry concerned with chemical reactions which may be *produced by* electrical energy or which may be the *source of* electrical energy.

In electrolysis the electrode at which electrons enter the solution is called the **cathode**; that by which electrons leave the solution is called the **anode**. In electrolysis the cathode is negative and the anode is positive. The positively charged ions, which move toward the cathode when a current flows, are called **cations**; the negatively charged ions are called **anions**. These definitions are illustrated in Fig. 26-3.

6. AQUEOUS SOLUTIONS AS CONDUCTORS. Pure water is a poor conductor of electricity. So is an aqueous solution of sugar or of alcohol. But an aqueous solution of hydrogen chloride, or of a salt such as copper(II) chloride, is a good conductor. We deduce from this conduction that these solutions contain charged particles that move and carry the current when a potential difference is applied. The charged particles in these conducting solutions are also ions. The way in which they are formed or released in solution will be explained in the following section.

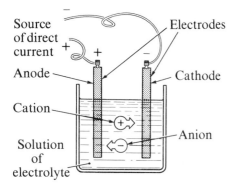

Fig. 26-3: *Diagram illustrating the meaning of various electrochemical terms*

When a current passes, electrolysis occurs at the electrodes. For instance, when a current flows through an aqueous solution of copper(II) chloride ($CuCl_2$), metallic copper plates out on the negative electrode, or cathode, and chlorine bubbles off at the positive electrode, or anode (Fig. 26-4). We can explain this by assuming that the solution contains ions from the solute, namely copper(II) ions and chloride ions. The copper(II) ions, Cu^{2+}, move to the negative electrode and there lose their charge, each by accepting two electrons to become a (neutral) copper atom:

$$2e^- + Cu^{2+} \rightarrow Cu$$

Similarly the chloride ions move to the positive electrode. There, in the same way as we described in the previous section, they give up their electrons, become atoms, and finally molecules of chlorine:

$$2Cl^- \rightarrow 2Cl + 2e^-$$
$$\downarrow$$
$$Cl_2$$

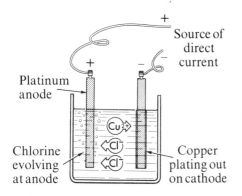

Fig. 26-4: *Schematic diagram of the electrolysis of a solution of copper(II) chloride*

The *net* process in this case is thus decomposition of the solute.

It should be stressed that the chemical changes occur *only at the electrodes*—not at all in the body of the liquid conductor. Also, the principle of electrical neutrality (Sec. 14-8) dictates that whenever an electron is transferred *to* a positive ion at one electrode another electron is simultaneously transferred *from* a negative ion at the other electrode.

Substances which provide ions in solution are called **electrolytes**; substances which do not are called **non-electrolytes**.

7. IONS IN SOLUTION. From what has been said earlier you should be familiar with the nature of ionic compounds, of which sodium chloride is a representative example. These substances are normally solids, with a structure based on the close packing of ions (Sec. 14-10). We mentioned in Sec. 26-3 that at high temperatures (800°C in the case of sodium chloride) this solid structure breaks down, and the ions become free to move about. As a consequence of this, melted ionic compounds are fairly good conductors of electricity. It is in part because of this electrical conductance that we believe these compounds to be made up of ions, rather than atoms or molecules.

Many ionic compounds will dissolve in water, and again sodium chloride is a convenient example. As we explained near the end of the previous chapter (Sec. 25-18) it is remarkable that this happens at all, since it evidently implies a complete breakdown of the crystal lattice of the solid. And the calculated lattice energy of 773 kJ/mol indicates that a lot of energy from somewhere is required to achieve this disintegration of the ionic crystal lattice.

8. Where does that much energy come from? If it came from the molecules of solvent and the ions themselves, their kinetic energy would be considerably reduced and that would be apparent as a large decrease in temperature. However, if you were to dissolve one mole of salt in a kilogram of water and observe any change in temperature with a thermometer, you would not find any significant variation in the thermometer reading. This proves that the energy required to break down the sodium chloride lattice did not come to any significant extent from the kinetic energies of the particles.

To account for this "missing" energy, and a number of other phenomena as well, scientists came to the conclusion that the dissolving of ionic compounds is accompanied by reactions of individual ions with molecules of the solvent. In aqueous solutions that means that each ion becomes linked to one or more water molecules. Such an attachment is possible because of the electrical polarity of the water molecule (Sec. 24-5); the negative part (oxygen) of a water molecule is attracted to a positive ion, and the positive part (hydrogen) is attracted to a negative ion. An ion, so wrapped up in its cluster of water molecules, is said to be *hydrated*. In general, to make this description applicable to any solvent, the term is *solvated*. A solvated ion is very different from the gaseous ions we described in Chapter 13. For one thing, it is very different in energy. Solvation of an ion is highly exothermic. (Conversely, the separation of an ion from its cluster of solvent molecules is highly endothermic—that is, requires that considerable work be done.)

9. The following scheme illustrates the processes involved in the dissolving of sodium chloride in water. With it we introduce a labelling system widely used in chemistry in which the state of a substance or ion—solid, liquid, gaseous, or hydrated—is designated (*s*), (*l*), (*g*) or (*aq*), respectively.

Heating raises the energy of the ions so that they can overcome the attraction of other ions of opposite sign in the solid state. The process of melting marks the ions' gaining freedom of motion—like prisoners breaking out of a cell block.

To convert one mole of solid sodium chloride into separated ions (Avogadro's number of each) requires that 773 kJ of work be performed, the energy coming from the surroundings or "somewhere." That is what the lattice energy means.

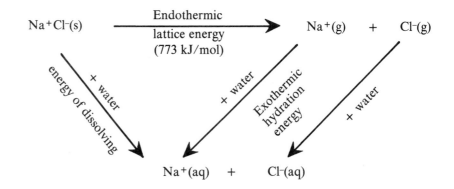

The energy of dissolving, in the case of sodium chloride, is quite small. That indicates that the lattice energy is just about balanced by the hydration energies of the two ions (Na^+ = 406 kJ/mol, Cl^- = 363 kJ/mol). There are substances (for example, sodium hydroxide) for which the hydration energy of the ions exceeds the lattice energy, and therefore for which the dissolving of the solid in water is exothermic. Likewise, there are substances such as ammonium nitrate for which the dissolving in water is endothermic, and from that evidence we conclude that the lattice energy exceeds the hydration energy. In the extreme cases, where the lattice energy greatly exceeds the hydration energy, it can be predicted that the substance will simply not dissolve at all.

Try adding together about 10 g each of sodium hydroxide and water in a test tube, and by holding the tube in your hand note any temperature change. In another test mix approximately 10 g each of ammonium nitrate and water, and in the same way note any temperature change.

10. Hydrogen chloride is very different from sodium chloride. Pure liquid hydrogen chloride (boiling point = –85°C) scarcely conducts electricity at all. The structure of hydrogen chloride accounts for this: it is a covalent compound, consisting of molecules, not ions. (All pure covalent compounds are very poor conductors of electricity.) But an aqueous solution of hydrogen chloride *does* conduct electricity very well, and aqueous solutions of *some* other covalent compounds also conduct electricity well. This is surprising because water itself is a very poor conductor.

The explanation is simple: when an aqueous solution of a covalent compound conducts electricity, it is because *the compound has reacted with water to form ions*. In an aqueous solution of hydrogen chloride, the ions responsible for conducting an electric current are $H^+(aq)$ and $Cl^-(aq)$ formed by the reaction of hydrogen chloride with water. It has become customary, though not necessarily correct, to write $H^+(aq)$ as $H^+ \cdot H_2O$ or H_3O^+, and to give to this ion the special name *hydronium ion*. So we may write for the formation of ions by hydrogen chloride dissolved in water:

The hydronium ion is also called the oxonium ion.

$$HCl \rightarrow H^+(aq) + Cl^-(aq) \qquad (1)$$

or $$HCl + H_2O \rightarrow H_3O^+ + Cl^- \qquad (2)$$

Both of these representations are in common use. Equation (1) is non-committal about the amounts of water associated with each ion, but reminds the reader that each ion *is* hydrated. Equation (2) emphasizes the important fact that water is required to *cause* the ionization of hydrogen chloride. However,

Equation (2) seems to convey a *particular* hydrate of the proton, whereas much evidence points to a formula more like $H^+\cdot 4H_2O$ or $H_9O_4{}^+$. Equation (2), as written, does not include a label to indicate that the chloride ion is also hydrated. We shall employ both styles of describing the hydrogen ion: $H^+(aq)$ and H_3O^+, with the name hydronium ion given to the latter. In the rest of this chapter we stress the (*aq*) label whenever we refer to ions in aqueous solution.

Ammonia, NH_3, is a covalent, molecular substance which, like hydrogen chloride, dissolves in water to form ions. It does so in this way:

$$NH_3 + H_2O \rightarrow NH_4{}^+(aq) + OH^-(aq) \qquad (3)$$

ammonia   ammonium   hydroxide
                                     ion   ion

As a result of the formation of hydroxide ions this solution is alkaline. (Hydroxide ions are also put into solution by soluble ionic hydroxides such as sodium hydroxide or calcium hydroxide.)

Reactions such as those represented by Equations (1) and (3) are called *ionization reactions*. An ionization reaction is simply a reaction in which ions are formed.

11. All ionic compounds, then, are electrolytes. Some covalent compounds are electrolytes, by virtue of a reaction with the solvent. Other covalent compounds are non-electrolytes. Some substances can be electrolytes in one solvent but non-electrolytes in another.

It is important to stress that with all electrolytes the ions, however they are formed, exist before there is any passage of electricity. It is not the passage of electricity that generates the ions. However, the conductance of an electrical current by a solution or a melt is proof that ions are present, and is therefore a means of detecting the presence of ions. The passage of an electric current also causes reactions to occur at each of the electrodes; thus electrolysis is a *consequence* of the conductance of electric current through a liquid containing an electrolyte.

12. ELECTROLYSIS OF HYDROCHLORIC ACID. A reaction analogous to that which occurs in the electrolysis of copper(II) chloride (Sec. 26-6) takes place when current flows through a solution of hydrochloric acid. The only difference is that hydrogen gas is evolved at the cathode.

Cathode	Anode
$e^- + H^+(aq) \rightarrow H$	$Cl^- \rightarrow Cl + e^-$
followed by:	followed by:
$H + H \rightarrow H_2(g)$	$Cl + Cl \rightarrow Cl_2(g)$

The over-all or net reaction can be represented by:

$$2H^+(aq) + 2Cl^- \rightarrow H_2(g) + Cl_2(g)$$

13. ELECTROLYSIS OF COPPER(II) SULPHATE SOLUTION. When current passes through an aqueous solution of copper(II) sulphate (Fig. 26-5), copper metal is formed at the cathode, as you might expect:

$$2e^- + Cu^{2+}(aq) \rightarrow Cu(s) \qquad (4)$$

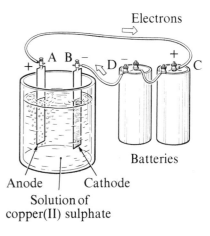

Fig. 26-5: *Electrolysis of an aqueous solution of copper(II) sulphate. In the batteries chemical reactions take place which deliver a surplus of electrons at the negative terminal D and create a deficiency of electrons at the positive terminal C. This creates an electrical potential difference which can pump electrons around the circuit as shown. Within the electrolytic cell electrons are consumed by a chemical process at the cathode B, and an equal number are simultaneously released by another chemical process at the anode A.*

At the anode a gas is formed, which can easily be shown to be oxygen. This is unexpected; you would probably have thought that some product related to the sulphate ion might appear. Why do we get oxygen instead? And where does the oxygen come from?

It might help in answering the second of these questions if we also mention that the solution close to the anode gets acidic as oxygen is evolved. The acidity can be linked to hydrogen ions in solution. This information prompts us to look to the water as the source of oxygen. Up to now we have spoken of water as though it consisted only of molecules of hydrogen oxide, H_2O. If it did, then water would show no electrical conductance at all, since molecules (being neutral) do not carry any electrical current. Ordinary water may carry a very small current because of traces of impurities in it, but it has been found that, no matter what pains were taken to rid water of these impurities, there always remains a very small residual electrical conductance. This is attributed to the presence of ions—specifically hydrogen (hydronium) ions and hydroxide ions —that arise from the "self-ionization" of water. For this, one molecule of water donates a hydrogen ion (proton) to another, thus:

$$H_2O + H_2O \xrightarrow{\quad H^+ \quad} H_3O^+ + OH^-(aq) \qquad (5)$$
$$\text{(or } H^+(aq))$$

A remarkably small fraction of water molecules undergo this self-ionization: in pure water, about two in every 555 million molecules! This small proportion of ions is what gives to water the little electrical conductance it has.

Now, let us return to the electrolysis of aqueous copper(II) sulphate. We can now say that this solution contains two kinds of negative ions (anions): sulphate ions, $SO_4^{2-}(aq)$, from the dissolved salt, and hydroxide ions, $OH^-(aq)$, from the water itself. As the current flows through the solution, both these ions are attracted to the anode. But it turns out (and this is something we shall return to in Chapter 28) that one of these ions can more easily part with an electron to the anode than the other. Although there will be many more sulphate ions than hydroxide ions around the anode, the sulphate ions are more reluctant to give up their electrons than the hydroxide ions. Consequently, the reaction at the anode is

$$4OH^-(aq) \rightarrow O_2(g) + 2H_2O(l) + 4e^- \qquad (6)$$

As hydroxide ions are neutralized in this way to form oxygen and water, hydrogen ions remaining in the water accumulate near the anode, causing that part of the copper sulphate solution to become more acidic.

The total chemical change brought about by the electric current is the sum of the reactions occurring at each electrode.

Cathode: $\qquad 2e^- + Cu^{2+}(aq) \rightarrow Cu(s)$

Anode: $\qquad 4OH^-(aq) \rightarrow O_2(g) + 2H_2O(l) + 4e^-$

However, before adding these equations together, we shall double all the coefficients in the first one so that, after addition, electrons are eliminated.

Cathode: $\qquad 4e^- + 2Cu^{2+}(aq) \rightarrow 2Cu(s)$

Anode: $\qquad \underline{4OH^-(aq) \rightarrow O_2(g) + 2H_2O(l) + 4e^-}$

Over-all: $\quad 2Cu^{2+}(aq) + 4OH^-(aq) \rightarrow O_2(g) + 2Cu(s) + 2H_2O(l)$

In the over-all or net reaction, $SO_4^{2-}(aq)$ does not appear as a reactant or product. Furthermore, neither do electrons appear on either side of the over-all equation, in recognition of the fact that a flow of current through the solution means that as many electrons leave at the anode as arrive at the cathode.

14. ELECTROLYSIS OF SODIUM CHLORIDE SOLUTION. The electrolysis of an aqueous solution of sodium chloride also illustrates that *a reaction at an electrode does not necessarily involve an ion from the dissolved electrolyte*. An aqueous sodium chloride solution contains four kinds of ions: $Na^+(aq)$ and $Cl^-(aq)$ from the salt, and $H^+(aq)$ and $OH^-(aq)$ from the water itself. Of the two anions, $Cl^-(aq)$ and $OH^-(aq)$, the one that gives up its electron more easily is $Cl^-(aq)$, and so the reaction at the anode is, as before:

$$2Cl^-(aq) \rightarrow Cl_2(g) + 2e^-$$

Of the two cations, $Na^+(aq)$ and $H^+(aq)$, the one that can acquire an electron more easily is the hydrogen ion. Therefore the reaction at the cathode is

$$2e^- + 2H^+(aq) \rightarrow H_2(g) \qquad (7)$$

The over-all cell reaction is therefore the sum of the anode process, the cathode process, and the self-ionization of water; this may therefore be represented as:

$$2Cl^-(aq) + 2H_2O \rightarrow Cl_2(g) + H_2(g) + 2OH^-(aq)$$

The products of the electrolysis of an aqueous solution of sodium chloride are, then, chlorine (at the anode) and hydrogen (at the cathode). By contrast, the products of the electrolysis of *melted* sodium chloride (Sec. 26-4) are chlorine (at the anode) and sodium (at the cathode). In melted sodium chloride there are no cations other than Na^+, so it is to these that the electrons must be transferred.

15. ELECTROLYSIS OF WATER. Because even the purest water contains some ions (Sec. 26-13) it can be electrolysed. The electrode reactions are

Cathode	Anode
$4e^- + 4H^+(aq) \rightarrow 4H$	$4OH^-(aq) \rightarrow 2O + 2H_2O + 4e^-$
followed by:	followed by:
$4H \rightarrow 2H_2(g)$	$2O \rightarrow O_2(g)$

So, the over-all or net reaction for the electrolysis can be represented by

$$4H^+(aq) + 4OH^-(aq) \rightarrow 2H_2(g) + O_2(g) + 2H_2O$$

or, since the hydrogen and hydroxide ions come from water molecules (Equation (5)), by

$$2H_2O \rightarrow 2H_2(g) + O_2(g)$$

In his early youth Michael Faraday (1791-1867) was a bookbinder's apprentice; in his manhood he was one of England's greatest scientists. Chemists honour him particularly for his pioneering and quantitative investigations of chemical changes induced by electricity, and for his studies on the liquefaction of gases. Physicists honour him for his researches in electricity and magnetism, which led to the modern electrical industry.

If the evolved hydrogen and oxygen are measured at the same temperature and pressure, the volume of the hydrogen is twice that of the oxygen. Remember Avogadro's Principle.

The electrolysis of pure water is very slow because of the relatively few ions present in it. The electrolysis is greatly speeded up by the addition of ions such as Na^+, K^+, NO_3^-, or SO_4^{2-}; this is achieved by having a moderate concentration of a salt, such as potassium nitrate or sodium sulphate, in the water to be electrolysed. These added ions do not undergo reaction at the electrodes because, as we have explained, it is easier to discharge the hydrogen and hydroxide ions of the water. A similar increase in the rate of electrolysis is achieved by adding $H^+(aq)$, from sulphuric acid, for instance, or $OH^-(aq)$, from an alkali such as sodium hydroxide.

16. APPLICATIONS OF ELECTROLYSIS. The chemical changes that are brought about by the passage of an electric current through conducting solutions or melts are often of considerable practical importance. This can be illustrated, for example, by two cases we have described.

The electrolysis of melted sodium chloride is the way in which sodium metal is produced commercially. The other product of this electrolysis is chlorine, a chemical of which there are scores of industrial applications. Other metals are prepared by electrolysis also, including magnesium and calcium (Sec. 29-6), and aluminium.

The electrolysis of a solution of a copper salt is the basis of several processes in which copper, in solution as copper(II) ions, is plated out on a negative electrode. Among these are the *electroplating* of objects with copper, and the *electrolytic refining* of copper.

17. THE ENERGETICS OF ELECTROLYSIS. We have explained various electrolyses in terms of electron transfer processes which take place at the anode and cathode. These processes are often called *electrode reactions*. The over-all or net reaction occurring is then the sum of the electrode reactions, subject to the proviso that in adding the electrode reactions coefficients are inserted so as to eliminate electrons from the net reaction. This is equivalent to saying that in a given time as many electrons must leave the solution (at the anode) as enter it (at the cathode).

A typical electrode reaction such as

$$e^- + Ag^+(aq) \rightarrow Ag(s)$$

may be "read" at the atomic level or at the molar level. At the atomic level e^- stands for one electron; at the molar level e^- stands for Avogadro's number of electrons. Since the charge on one electron is known (1.602×10^{-19} C), the charge corresponding to e^- at the molar level is

$$1.602 \times 10^{-19} \text{ C} \times 6.02 \times 10^{23} \text{ mol}^{-1}$$

$$= 9.65 \times 10^4 \text{ C/mol}$$

This quantity is given a special name, the Faraday constant (symbol F). The amount of charge denoted by the Faraday constant is actually *one mole*. It will deposit one mole of silver according to the above electrode reaction. For an electrode reaction such as

$$2e^- + Cu^{2+}(aq) \rightarrow Cu(s)$$

One coulomb is the amount of charge passing a point in a conductor when a current of one ampere flows for one second.

Charge (coulombs) = Current (amperes) × Time (seconds)

A current of one ampere would have to flow into an electrolysis cell for 26.8 h in order to deliver a mole of charge.

Ohm's Law states that for a fixed applied potential difference the current flowing through a conductor is proportional to the conductance. In the electrolysis of pure water, for which the conductance is very small, the current flowing is very small, and it therefore requires a very long time to deliver a mole of charge through an electrode. With the addition of a salt whose ions do not participate in the electrode reactions, the conductance, and hence the current, is greatly increased and the time required to produce a certain amount of hydrogen or oxygen is much decreased.

Electrical energy is given by the product of the applied potential difference and the quantity of charge moved. Thus

$$
\begin{aligned}
\text{Energy} \\
\text{(joules)} \quad &= \text{Potential Difference (volts)} \quad \times \quad \text{Charge (coulombs)} \\
&= \text{Potential Difference (volts)} \quad \times \quad \text{Current (amperes)} \\
&\phantom{= \text{Potential Difference (volts)} \quad} \times \quad \text{Time (seconds)}
\end{aligned}
$$

it follows that one mole of negative charge will deposit only half a mole of copper metal.

In electrochemistry electrical energy is made to carry out a chemical change (as in electrolysis) or vice versa (as in a battery). The voltage (potential difference) required for a particular electrolysis depends on the energy required to make the chemical change occur. In Sec. 26-14 we stated that the reaction

$$Cl^-(aq) + H_2O \longrightarrow \tfrac{1}{2}H_2(g) + \tfrac{1}{2}Cl_2(g) + OH^-(aq)$$

would occur, during the electrolysis of a sodium chloride solution, more easily than the reaction

$$Na^+(aq) + Cl^-(aq) \longrightarrow Na(s) + \tfrac{1}{2}Cl_2(g)$$

The fact is that the former reaction requires less energy than the latter. Each requires the passage of one mole of charge, and accordingly the first of these two reactions will take place at a lower potential difference between the electrodes. We shall have a little more to add to these ideas in Chapter 28.

18. OXIDATION AND REDUCTION IN ELECTROLYSIS. Cations, on acquiring or accepting electrons at the cathode, have their positive ionic valence decreased, for example:

$$2e^- + Cu^{2+} \longrightarrow Cu \text{ (with a valence of zero)}$$

Such a process, in which electrons are added to or accepted by a substance, is called a *reduction*: copper(II) ions, Cu^{2+}, are said to be reduced to atoms of copper metal, Cu.

Anions, on giving up or donating electrons to the anode, lose their negative ionic valence, for example:

$$2Cl^- \longrightarrow Cl_2 \text{ (with a valence of zero)} + 2e^-$$

Such a process, in which electrons are taken from or donated by a substance, is called an *oxidation*: chloride ions, Cl^-, are said to be oxidized to chlorine, Cl_2.

Thus an *electrolysis involves both reduction and oxidation: reduction at the cathode and oxidation at the anode.* Electron-transfer processes between ions and electrodes are the very essence of electrolysis: electron-transfer from the cathode to cations, and electron-transfer from anions to the anode. *Reduction involves the acceptance of electrons; oxidation involves the donation of electrons.*

19. A SUMMARY OF ELECTROLYSIS. The following general statements apply to all electrolyses.

(a) Every electrolysis involves two distinct processes: *electrolytic conduction* of the current through the solution, and the *electrolysis* proper at the electrodes. The first is the directed movement of ions: anions towards the anode and cations towards the cathode. The second is the chemical changes occurring when, and after, ions lose their electrical charges at the electrodes.

(b) The ions that conduct the current may or may not be the ions that are involved in the chemical changes at the electrodes. They *are* the same in the electrolysis of an aqueous solution of copper(II) chloride; they are *not* the same in the electrolysis of an aqueous solution of sodium sulphate.

(c) The chemical changes (electrolysis proper) occur *only* at the electrodes, not in the body of the solution.

(d) The *nature* of the action at one electrode is independent of the nature of the action at the other. For example, in the electrolysis of aqueous solutions of hydrogen chloride, copper(II) chloride, zinc chloride, and nickel(II) chloride, the action at the anode is, in every case, the formation of chlorine from chloride ions. It doesn't matter at all that at the cathode what is being formed is hydrogen in one case, copper in another, zinc in a third, and nickel in a fourth.

(e) The electrode reaction at the cathode always involves the *gaining of electrons by cations*; the cations are *reduced*. The electrode reaction at the anode always involves the *loss of electrons by anions*; the anions are *oxidized*.

(f) The extent of the reduction at the cathode is exactly equal to the extent of the oxidation at the anode, as measured by electron-transfer. That is, during an electrolysis, the *number of electrons gained by cations from the cathode is exactly equal to the number of electrons lost by anions to the anode*.

QUESTIONS

1. In your own words explain the meaning of:

(a) conductor   (f) electrode

(b) insulator   (g) anode

(c) electrolyte   (h) cathode

(d) non-electrolyte   (i) electron transfer

(e) electrolysis   (j) electrode process

2. Define in your own words:

(a) cation   (d) hydronium ion

(b) anion   (e) oxidation

(c) hydrated ion   (f) reduction

3. Describe what happens when an electric current passes through (a) a silver wire, (b) melted potassium chloride.

4. Electrical conductance through bodies can be classified as *electronic* or *electrolytic*. Explain the difference.

5. With the aid of a diagram, explain how you would determine which of two liquids is the better conductor of electricity.

*6. If you were attempting an accurate measurement of the conductance of a solution of an electrolyte, how would the flow of current through the liquid be affected by:

(a) the concentration of the electrolyte in solution?

(b) the distance between the electrodes?

(c) the depth to which the electrodes are immersed in the solution?

7. Account for the fact that hydrochloric acid is a good conductor of electricity, whereas a solution of hydrogen chloride in carbon tetrachloride is a non-conductor.

8. A current of electricity passes through an aqueous solution of copper(II) chloride.

(a) What is observed at the electrodes?

(b) Name the products formed at the electrodes.

(c) Explain clearly, in terms of electron transfer, the formation of the products named in (b).

(d) Write the over-all equation for the electrolysis.

9. Account for the existence of both positive and negative ions in molten sodium chloride.

10. How does the electrolysis of sodium chloride when melted tend to affirm the structure of the crystals of this compound which was described in Chapter 14?

11. Why does the electrolysis of a solution of sodium chloride result in the production of a different product at the cathode than in the electrolysis of molten sodium chloride?

12. In the electrolysis of molten chlorides of the metals, compare the masses and the amounts (in moles) of (a) sodium, (b) magnesium, (c) aluminium, which would be produced by the passage of one mole of charge through the melt.

13. Both copper chloride and copper sulphate solutions produce copper metal at the cathode in electrolysis. In the former solution chlorine is formed at the anode. Why is no sulphur-containing substance formed at the anode in the latter solution?

14. Write suitable equations to describe the following electrode processes:

(a) the formation of iodine from aqueous potassium iodide solution

(b) the deposition of silver from aqueous silver acetate solution

(c) the formation of oxygen gas from aqueous ammonium nitrate solution

(d) the formation of aluminium from molten aluminium oxide

15. Write electron-transfer reactions for the following processes, and state in each case whether the process described is an oxidation or a reduction:

(a) the conversion of iron(II) to iron(III)

(b) the deposition of metallic nickel from an aqueous nickel salt ($Ni^{2+}(aq)$)

(c) the formation of bromide ion from bromine

(d) the dissolving of zinc to form a zinc salt

(e) the conversion of silver bromide to silver metal and bromide ion (as in the emulsion on a photographic film).

16. What is meant by the "self-ionization" of water? From the information given in Sec. 26-13, calculate the number of hydronium ions and the number of hydroxide ions present in one mole of water. For many purposes the concentration of these ions is more important than their number. How many moles of water are in one litre of water? How many moles of hydronium ion and of hydroxide ion are present in one litre of water? (One of each kind of ion is produced from two molecules of water according to Equation (5).)

17. The properties of aqueous solutions of electrolytes suggest that they contain hydrated ions. These differ significantly from the ions whose formation was described in Chapter 13. Explain the difference.

*18. The following calculation may impress on you the energy balances involved in the dissolving of electrolytes. Imagine 1.0 mol of sodium chloride being dissolved by 1.0 kg of water at 25°C. The energy required to dismantle the sodium chloride lattice is 773 kJ/mol. If this energy were only available from the kinetic energy of the water molecules there would be a decrease in the temperature of the water. Show that the loss of 773 kJ from the water in this case would lower the temperature and cause all the water to freeze. Calculate the final temperature, given the following information: specific heat capacity of water = 4.2 J/g·K; of ice = 2.1 J/g·K; latent heat of fusion of ice = 333 J/g. Why does the temperature not fall to such an extent when electrolytes dissolve in water?

19. List several practical applications of electrolysis.

20. It is helpful to devise "memory crutches" to relate ideas to be memorized. Thus you might remember **cage** for "**ca**thode—**g**ain **e**lectrons" and **ale** for "**a**node—**l**ose **e**lectrons." Try having a competition in your class for the memory device judged most helpful for remembering this relationship.

21. Throughout the discussion of electrolysis in this chapter it has been implied that the cells were being supplied with direct current electricity. Predict what would happen if an electrolysis cell containing dilute sulphuric acid were connected to a source of 60 Hz alternating current.

22. Calculate the volume of chlorine gas, measured at STP, which will be produced during the complete electrolysis of 11.7 g of molten sodium chloride.

23. What volume of hydrogen gas, measured at 25°C and 97.3 kPa pressure, will be generated at a cathode by the transfer of 1930 C?

24. How long would a steady current of 1.00 A have to be maintained through an electrolysis cell in order to produce 50.0 cm³ of oxygen gas at an anode? The gas is measured at 27°C and 101.3 kPa.

25. What will be the minimum current-carrying capacity for a plant designed to produce ten tonnes of aluminium per hour by the electrolysis of molten Al_2O_3?

*26. It is required to electroplate a medal, which has a diameter of 3.0 cm and a thickness of 0.20 cm, with a layer of gold 0.002 cm thick. Calculate the mass of gold required. (Density of gold = 19.3 g/cm³.) The electrode process is $e^- + AuCN = Au(s) + CN^-$. Find how long it will take to plate the medal with a current of 0.200 A (assuming 100% yield).

Ions in Solution

1. We have seen that solutions of electrolytes undergo electrolysis when a current of electricity is passed through them, and that electrolysis involves reactions of ions at electrodes. In this chapter we shall discuss some other properties and reactions of electrolytes in solution, and shall see that it is the ions in these solutions that are responsible for their properties and reactions.

2. COMMON PROPERTIES OF ELECTROLYTE SOLUTIONS. Aqueous solutions of soluble copper(II) salts ($CuCl_2$, $CuBr_2$, $Cu(NO_3)_2$, $CuSO_4$, etc.) are blue. The salts themselves are not all blue; the water isn't blue. Therefore the blue colour must be due to something common to all the solutions; the common feature is independent hydrated copper(II) ions, $Cu^{2+}(aq)$. Similarly, aqueous solutions of nickel salts are green because they all contain a common cation, $Ni^{2+}(aq)$. Solutions of permanganates ($KMnO_4$, $NaMnO_4$, $HMnO_4$, etc.) are purple in colour, because they all contain permanganate ion, $MnO_4^-(aq)$.

Just as a solution of copper(II) chloride has some properties in common with solutions of all other copper(II) salts, so it has some properties in common with solutions of all other chlorides. Any soluble chloride (for example, $CuCl_2$, $NaCl$, $CaCl_2$, $AlCl_3$, HCl) will react with any soluble silver salt (for example, $AgNO_3$, $AgC_2H_3O_2$) to form white, insoluble silver chloride. This is because the solutions of the chlorides all contain chloride ion, $Cl^-(aq)$. The same insoluble substance is formed in every case because the same reaction is occurring, namely:

$$Ag^+(aq) + Cl^-(aq) \rightarrow AgCl(s)$$

Incidentally, we draw your attention to the manner in which the above equation is written. What it states is that silver ions in solution react with chloride ions in solution to form solid, insoluble silver chloride. The process described by the equation is carried out by mixing two solutions, one of a soluble silver salt (*any* soluble silver salt), and the other of a soluble ionized chloride (*any* substance that puts chloride ion into the solution). The other ion of the silver salt and the other ion of the chloride really have no effect on the outcome of the reaction, so we don't bother to show them. Equations like this are called **ionic equations**, and many of the equations in this chapter will be written in this way. Even in the previous chapter we presented a few equations in this form, without explanation.

There are a great many *acids*, but their aqueous solutions all share a common set of properties: sour taste, and ability to turn litmus dye red, to react with carbonates to liberate carbon dioxide, and to neutralize bases (Sec. 21-4). These are properties due to a common constituent of all these solutions, namely the hydrogen (or hydronium) ion ($H^+(aq)$ or H_3O^+). Similarly, solutions of *bases* have a common set of properties, which are those of the hydroxide ion ($OH^-(aq)$). (See Sec. 21-4.)

3. ACIDS AND BASES. All acids when dissolved in water yield hydrogen (or hydronium) ions. Since these ions in most cases are believed to be formed as a result of a reaction between water and the acid substance, we shall stress this by showing the formation of the hydronium ion (Sec. 26-10). Examples of acid substances forming ions include:

$$HCl + H_2O \rightarrow H_3O^+ + Cl^-$$
hydrogen chloride   hydrochloric acid

$$HNO_3 + H_2O \rightarrow H_3O^+ + NO_3^-$$
hydrogen nitrate   nitric acid

$$HC_2H_3O_2 + H_2O \rightarrow H_3O^+ + C_2H_3O_2^-$$
hydrogen acetate   acetic acid

Hydrogen chloride (HCl) and hydrogen nitrate (HNO_3) react almost completely with water as shown in these equations. Thus hydrochloric acid is essentially a solution of only hydronium (hydrogen) ions and chloride ions, and nitric acid consists almost entirely of hydronium ions and nitrate ions. On the other hand, hydrogen acetate ($HC_2H_3O_2$) reacts with water to only a modest extent; most of the solute remains in the form of molecules of hydrogen acetate. Acetic acid, therefore, is a solution of some hydronium ions, some acetate ions, and many hydrogen acetate molecules. The extent to which an acid substance forms ions by reaction with water will be discussed further in the next section.

All soluble bases (or alkalis) when dissolved in water put hydroxide ions into the solution. Some of these bases, like $NaOH$ or $Ca(OH)_2$, contain hydroxide ions in the solid state (they are ionic compounds); all that dissolving does is to set free these hydroxide ions from the crystal lattice. In aqueous solution, as we have already explained, the hydroxide ion attracts and becomes attached to some molecules of water.

Other bases do not contain hydroxide ions, but produce them by reaction with water. The oxide ion, if set free in water, immediately reacts to form hydroxide ions:

$$O^{2-} + H_2O \rightarrow 2OH^-$$

Ammonia, as we explained in Sec. 26-10, reacts with water to form ammonium ions and hydroxide ions:

$$NH_3 + H_2O \rightarrow NH_4^+ + OH^-$$

This reaction, like that of hydrogen acetate mentioned above, only occurs to a limited extent, so that aqueous ammonia (sometimes called ammonium hydroxide) contains some ions, and many molecules of unreacted ammonia. You can prove that an aqueous ammonia solution does contain free ammonia by **carefully** smelling the gas above the solution.

4. STRONG AND WEAK ELECTROLYTES. Hydrogen acetate and ammonia are two examples of electrolytes which are only *partially ionized* when dissolved in water. There are various ways of measuring the extent of ionization in such solutions; one, which might occur to you after reading the previous chapter, is a quantitative study of the conductance of electrolyte solutions. If you measure the conductance of (a) a solution containing 1.0 mol/L of hydrochloric acid, and (b) a solution containing 1.0 mol/L of acetic acid, you will find the former conducts a current about a hundredfold greater than the latter.

If you make these measurements you must be sure the electrodes are at a fixed distance apart and covered to the same depth in both trials.

Hydrogen chloride, dissolved in water, is said to be a **strong electrolyte**; hydrogen acetate or ammonia, in water, are said to be **weak electrolytes**. The words *strong* and *weak* in this connection have to do with the extent of ionization, and should not be confused with a description of the concentration of a solution, for which the words *concentrated* and *dilute* are appropriate.

Of the acids, bases, and salts that we have discussed so far, it may be helpful to indicate whether they are strong or weak. Like "fast" and "slow," strong and weak are relative terms, and some electrolytes are much weaker than others. "Strong" here means that the electrolyte is essentially completely ionized; "weak" means that a small percentage is ionized. Table 27-1 lists examples of these categories.

TABLE 27-1

STRENGTH OF ELECTROLYTES

	STRONG	WEAK
Acids	hydrochloric acid nitric acid sulphuric acid	acetic acid carbonic acid phosphoric acid
Bases	sodium (or potassium) hydroxide calcium hydroxide	ammonia
Salts	most salts	lead acetate some mercury(II) salts

The ant has made himself illustrious
Through constant industry industrious.
So what?
Would you be calm and placid
If you were full of formic acid?
(From *Verses From 1929 On* by Ogden Nash,
by permission of Little, Brown and Company.
Copyright 1935 by The Curtis Publishing Company.)

5. SOME NATURALLY OCCURRING ACIDS. There are many acids in nature. *Citric acid* occurs in lemons, oranges, and grapefruit—the citrus fruits. *Oxalic acid* occurs in rhubarb, *lactic acid* in sour milk, *acetic acid* in vinegar, *tartaric acid* in grapes. The characteristic "tang" of ginger ale and soda water is due to *carbonic acid*; the smell of rancid butter is due to *butyric acid*; the sting of ants and nettles is due to *formic acid*. These are all weak acids.

6. SOME COMMON BASES. There are not many common bases, and most of these are known in the home. "Household ammonia" is a dilute aqueous solution of ammonia used as a cleaning agent. Sodium hydroxide is familiar in the form of lye and is a constituent of such products as "Drano." Milk of magnesia is a suspension of magnesium hydroxide in water, and whitewash is a suspension of calcium hydroxide (Table 29-6).

7. NEUTRALIZATION. When a solution of an acid is gradually added to a solution of sodium hydroxide, the alkaline properties of the solution (Sec. 21-4) are gradually weakened and finally vanish. The base is said to be *neutralized* by the acid. To accomplish this neutralization it doesn't matter what acid is used. By the same token, to neutralize an acid it doesn't matter what base is used. This is because the essential reaction that characterizes neutralization is between hydronium ion and hydroxide ion to form water.

$$H_3O^+ + OH^- \rightarrow 2H_2O \tag{1}$$

(You see again how useful and how general an ionic reaction is.)

One of several pieces of evidence in support of the view that all neutralizations involve the same reaction: the reaction of one mole of NaOH with one mole of HNO_3 evolves exactly the same amount of heat, (56.9 kJ) as the reaction of one mole of KOH with one mole of HCl, or as the reaction of one-half mole of $Ca(OH)_2$ with one mole of HBr. If the reactions were different, one would expect the heat evolved to be different.

Neutralization may be performed in order to prepare a salt (Sec. 21-5), which can be recovered as a residue by evaporating the water. *Then,* the cation of the base and the anion of the acid *are* significant. The equation in this case ought to be written in greater detail. For example, the formation of sodium chloride from sodium hydroxide and hydrochloric acid is represented by the equation:

$$Na^+ + OH^- + H_3O^+ + Cl^- \rightarrow 2H_2O + Na^+ + Cl^- \xrightarrow{-2H_2O} Na^+Cl^-(s)$$

Similarly, with potassium hydroxide and nitric acid in solution:

$$K^+ + OH^- + H_3O^+ + NO_3^- \rightarrow 2H_2O + K^+ + NO_3^- \xrightarrow{-2H_2O} K^+NO_3^-(s)$$

8. POLYPROTIC ACIDS AND THEIR SALTS. The acids we have been considering, such as HCl, HNO_3 and $HC_2H_3O_2$, have in their molecules only one hydrogen that can react with water to give a hydronium ion. Such acids are called *monoprotic acids* because each molecule can furnish only *one proton* or hydrogen ion, H^+ (which reacts with a water molecule, to give a hydronium ion, H_3O^+). There are, however, acids that can furnish two or more more protons per molecule: these are the *polyprotic acids*.

Hydrogen sulphate, the aqueous solution of which is called *sulphuric acid*, is such an acid:

$$H_2SO_4 + 2H_2O \rightarrow 2H_3O^+ + SO_4^{2-} \tag{2}$$

Actually, the ionization of hydrogen sulphate doesn't occur in the way Equation (2) suggests but, rather in steps:

$$H_2SO_4 + H_2O \rightarrow H_3O^+ + HSO_4^- \tag{3}$$
$$HSO_4^- + H_2O \rightarrow H_3O^+ + SO_4^{2-} \tag{4}$$

If one mole of sodium hydroxide is added to a solution containing one mole of hydrogen sulphate, one mole of hydronium ions is neutralized (according to Equation (1)), and the ions left in solution are Na^+ and HSO_4^-—one mole of each. On evaporating the water, the salt $NaHSO_4$ crystallizes as a solid (ionic) compound.

If, on the other hand, *two* moles of sodium hydroxide are added to a solution containing one mole of hydrogen sulphate, the two moles of hydronium ions that are formed from one mole of hydrogen sulphate (by the reactions of Equations (3) and (4)) are both neutralized. The ions left in solution are Na^+ and SO_4^{2-}—two moles of the former and one mole of the latter. On evaporating the water, the salt Na_2SO_4 crystallizes as a solid (ionic) compound.

Hydrogen sulphate can thus be neutralized in step-wise fashion, partially or completely, with the formation of different salts. This is true of other polyprotic acids, too.

The nomenclature of salts that can be formed from some important polyprotic acids is illustrated in Table 27-2.

SOME FACTORS AFFECTING THE EXTENT OF CHEMICAL REACTIONS

9. If we mix together aqueous solutions of barium chloride and sodium nitrate, nothing seems to happen; the resulting solution is simply a solution of all four ions: Ba^{2+}, Cl^-, Na^+, and NO_3^-. An indistinguishable solution could be prepared by mixing together the appropriate concentrations of barium nitrate and sodium chloride. But if we mix aqueous solutions of barium chloride and sodium sulphate a reaction does take place, as we can tell by the formation of a white solid. The solid is barium sulphate and it is insoluble in water. Its formation from solution

It is true that hydrogen acetate, $HC_2H_3O_2$, has four hydrogen atoms per molecule, but only one of these can react with water. The ionizable hydrogen atom is bonded to an oxygen atom; the other three hydrogen atoms are bonded to a carbon atom:

Strictly speaking, probably no substance is completely insoluble in water (or any other liquid). But the solubility of barium sulphate in water is very small: it is only 4×10^{-5} mol/L, or less than 1 mg/100 g water, at 20°C. "Insoluble," then, really means "almost insoluble" or "of very low solubility."

TABLE 27-2

THE NAMING OF SALTS OF POLYPROTIC ACIDS

POLY-PROTIC ACID	SODIUM SALTS OF THE ACID	PREFERRED NAME	OTHER NAMES
H_2SO_4	$NaHSO_4$	sodium hydrogen sulphate	sodium acid sulphate; sodium bisulphate
	Na_2SO_4	sodium sulphate	
H_2SO_3	$NaHSO_3$	sodium hydrogen sulphite	sodium acid sulphite; sodium bisulphite
	Na_2SO_3	sodium sulphite	
H_2CO_3	$NaHCO_3$	sodium hydrogen carbonate	sodium acid carbonate; sodium bicarbonate
	Na_2CO_3	sodium carbonate	soda ash
H_3PO_4	NaH_2PO_4	sodium dihydrogen phosphate	primary sodium phosphate
	Na_2HPO_4	disodium hydrogen phosphate	secondary sodium phosphate
	Na_3PO_4	trisodium phosphate	tertiary sodium phosphate ("T.S.P.")

leaves dissolved sodium ions and chloride ions behind. So we can write an equation

$$Ba^{2+} + 2Cl^- + 2Na^+ + SO_4^{2-} \rightarrow BaSO_4(s) + 2Na^+ + 2Cl^-$$

or, more simply

$$Ba^{2+} + SO_4^{2-} \rightarrow BaSO_4(s) \qquad (5)$$

The reaction represented by Equation (5) proceeds until practically all of the barium ions or practically all of the sulphate ions have been removed from solution as a precipitate of $BaSO_4$.

It would be helpful to have some grounds for deciding when to expect a chemical reaction to occur and yield a new product, or when not to occur. In the following sections we shall point out some of the factors that affect the extent to which chemical reactions are expected to occur. It will have to be left to more advanced study of chemistry to learn how such predictions can be made more precisely and more quantitatively.

10. FORMATION OF A PRECIPITATE. An ionic reaction in solution will go essentially to completion if a product of the reaction is a very insoluble substance, for then ions are effectively removed from solution and the "reverse" reaction is prevented. Some examples are

$$Ag^+ + NO_3^- + Na^+ + Cl^- \rightarrow AgCl(s) + Na^+ + NO_3^-$$
$$\text{or}$$
$$Ag^+ + Cl^- \rightarrow AgCl(s) \quad \text{(See Sec. 27-2)}$$
$$Ba^{2+} + SO_4^{2-} \rightarrow BaSO_4(s) \quad \text{(See Sec. 27-9)}$$
$$Pb^{2+} + 2I^- \rightarrow PbI_2(s)$$
$$Cu^{2+} + S^{2-} \rightarrow CuS(s)$$

Many substances formed as a result of reactions in solution are precipitated as individual small crystals. Here, at a magnification of 40, you see crystals of ammonium hydrogen carbonate, NH_4HCO_3, an intermediate in the manufacture of baking soda, $NaHCO_3$, and washing soda, $Na_2CO_3 \cdot 10H_2O$.

11. So-called **solubility rules** are helpful in anticipating reactions that will result in the formation of a precipitate. The "rules" in Table 27-3 apply to compounds of the commoner cations (positive ions) including: Na^+ and K^+; Mg^{2+}, Ca^{2+}, Sr^{2+} and Ba^{2+}; Al^{3+}; Sn^{2+} and Pb^{2+}; Cr^{3+}; Mn^{2+}; Fe^{3+} (and Fe^{2+}), Co^{2+} and Ni^{2+}; Cu^{2+} and Ag^+; Zn^{2+}, Cd^{2+} and Hg^{2+} (and Hg_2^{2+}); and NH_4^+. "Soluble" means the solubility is greater than about 1 g/100 g of water; "insoluble" means the solubility is less than about 0.1 g/100 g of water and "slightly soluble" means the solubility is between these limits.

TABLE 27-3

SOLUBILITY RULES FOR SALTS AND HYDROXIDES
(IN WATER AT 20°C)

MAINLY "SOLUBLE"

1. **All nitrates** are soluble.
2. **All chlorates** are soluble.
3. **All acetates** are soluble.
4. **All chlorides, bromides,** and **iodides** are soluble except those of silver, mercury(I), and lead(II). Lead(II) chloride and lead(II) bromide are slightly soluble in cold water, soluble in hot.
5. **All sulphates** are soluble except those of calcium, barium, strontium, and lead(II). The sulphates of silver and mercury(I) are slightly soluble.
6. **All** salts of **sodium, potassium** (and the other alkali metal ions), and of **ammonium** ion are soluble (a very few unusual salts excepted).

MAINLY "INSOLUBLE"

7. **All hydroxides** are insoluble except those of the alkali metals, barium, and ammonium. The hydroxide of strontium is slightly soluble.
8. **All** normal **carbonates** and **phosphates** are insoluble except those of the alkali metals and ammonium ion. (Many hydrogen carbonates and hydrogen phosphates are soluble.)
9. **All sulphides** are insoluble except those of the alkali metals, the alkaline earth metals, and ammonium ion. (The sulphides of aluminium and chromium react with water to form insoluble hydroxides.)

These rules, though valuable, are only a rough guide. To cite some examples: potassium acetate is over two hundred times as soluble as silver acetate (253 g/100 g of water and 1.0 g/100 g of water, at 20°C), but both are classed as "soluble"; lead(II) iodide is almost three hundred thousand times as soluble as silver iodide (6.3×10^{-2} and 2.2×10^{-7} g/100 g, at 20°C) but both are classed as "insoluble."

12. FORMATION OF A GAS. If a gas is formed in a reaction and the gas is allowed to escape, the reaction will go essentially to completion as, for example, in the reaction of sodium carbonate with hydrochloric acid

$$2Na^+ + CO_3^{2-} + 2H_3O^+ + 2Cl^- \rightarrow 3H_2O + CO_2(g) + 2Na^+ + 2Cl^-$$

or, to focus attention on the essential reaction

$$CO_3^{2-} + 2H_3O^+ \rightarrow 3H_2O + CO_2(g)$$

Similarly, the reaction of a sulphide with an acid can be essentially complete because of the evolution of the gas hydrogen sulphide:

$$FeS + 2H_3O^+ \rightarrow Fe^{2+} + 2H_2O + H_2S(g)$$

Again, the completeness of the reaction of a metal with an acid is aided by the escape of hydrogen:

$$Zn + 2H_3O^+ \rightarrow Zn^{2+} + 2H_2O + H_2(g)$$

All these reactions are more commonly written in terms of hydrogen ion, for example:

$$Zn(s) + 2H^+(aq) \rightarrow Zn^{2+}(aq) + H_2(g)$$

When a gas is formed in solution, the "completeness" of the reaction is greater the lower the solubility of the gas. The solubility of any gas decreases with increased temperature. Hence, heating the solution will increase the degree of completeness of a reaction in which a gas is formed.

13. FORMATION OF AN UN-IONIZED (or very weakly ionized) PRODUCT. The best example is one we have already discussed (Sec. 27-7), namely neutralization—the reaction of an acid with a base in aqueous solution. For example,

$$K^+ + OH^- + H_3O^+ + NO_3^- \rightarrow 2H_2O + K^+ + NO_3^-$$

or, more briefly,

$$H_3O^+ + OH^- \rightarrow 2H_2O \qquad (6)$$

As we have pointed out earlier (Sec. 26-13), water is not completely un-ionized, and so the reaction of Equation (6) doesn't go quite to completion—but almost so. Equation (6) is more properly written

$$H_3O^+ + OH^- \rightleftharpoons 2H_2O \qquad (7)$$

14. pH. The fact that water ionizes to some degree, however small, means that all aqueous solutions contain both hydronium ions and hydroxide ions. A solution of sodium hydroxide contains some hydronium ions (though vastly more hydroxide ions); hydrochloric acid contains some hydroxide ions (though vastly more hydronium ions).

If, then, both basic and acidic solutions contain both hydroxide and hydronium ions, what distinguishes a basic solution from an acidic one? The answer is: the relative proportion of hydronium ions and hydroxide ions. A solution that has more hydronium ions than hydroxide ions is *acidic;* a solution that has more hydroxide ions than hydronium ions is *basic;* a solution that has equal numbers of hydroxide and hydronium ions is *neutral.*

For reasons we cannot go into here, it turns out that in any aqueous solution the *product* of the concentrations of hydronium ion and of hydroxide ion, both expressed in moles per litre, is 10^{-14}. Thus a solution in which the hydronium ion concentration is 10^{-4} mol/L, the hydroxide-ion concentration will be $10^{-14}/10^{-4} = 10^{-10}$ mol/L. Such a solution is acidic, since 10^{-4} is much greater than 10^{-10}.

Chemists find it convenient to express the hydronium-ion concentration of a solution by what is called the "pH" of the solution. This is defined by the relationship:

pH $= -\log_{10}$ (concentration of hydronium ions, in moles per litre)

Thus in a solution in which the concentration of hydronium ions is 10^{-4} mol/L,

$$pH = -\log_{10}(10^{-4}) = -(-4) = 4.$$

Acidic, basic, and neutral solutions can be defined as follows:

Acidic solutions are those in which the concentration of hydronium ions is greater than 10^{-7} mol/L, or the pH is less than 7.

Basic solutions are those in which the concentration of hydronium ions is less than 10^{-7} mol/L, or the pH is greater than 7.

Neutral solutions are those in which the concentration of hydronium ions is equal to 10^{-7} mol/L, or the pH is equal to 7.

The smaller the pH, the more acidic is the solution; the larger the pH, the more basic is the solution.

15. MEASUREMENT OF pH: INDICATORS. There are several ways of measuring the pH of an aqueous solution. One that is very simple, yet good enough for many purposes, involves the use of indicators. An **acid-base indicator** is a substance whose colour changes over a rather narrow pH range in such a way that at a pH below the lower limit of the range the indicator has one colour, and at a pH above the upper limit of the range it has another colour. The pH range for the colour change of some acid-base indicators is shown in Fig. 27-1. Let us illustrate how they can be used. For example, if a solution with a little bromthymol blue in it is yellow, the solution is acidic; more than that, its pH is *less than 6.0*. If we add a drop of methyl orange indicator to another sample of the same solution and it turns yellow, then we know its pH must be *greater than 4.4*. From the two tests together, we know that the pH of the solution lies between 4.4 and 6.0. Using other indicators, we could locate the pH within even narrower limits.

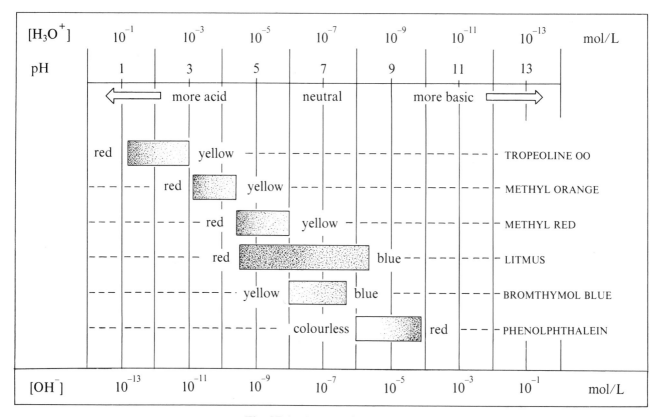

Fig. 27-1: *Some indicators and their colour ranges*

16. TENDENCY TOWARD OXIDATION OR REDUCTION. Under the general heading of factors that affect the extent to which chemical reactions proceed we should list the comparative ease with which elements are oxidized (Sec. 5-8), or the ease with which their compounds are reduced (Sec. 6-8). In Sec. 26-18 we mentioned briefly that these terms oxidation and reduction can be related to electron-transfer processes at electrodes, but the topic is of sufficient importance that it warrants our devoting the next chapter to it.

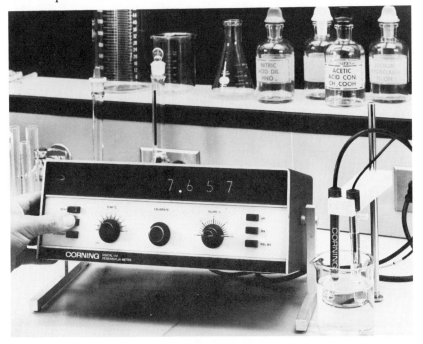

The acidity of an aqueous solution depends on the concentration of hydrogen ions or, more properly expressed, hydronium ions. The units usually used to express this concentration are moles per litre, and a related quantity is called the pH of the solution. Instruments for the determination of pH measure the electrical potential between two suitable electrodes dipping into the test solution. Here a chemist is using a pH meter to follow the course of a reaction occurring in the beaker at the lower right-hand corner of the picture.

QUESTIONS

1. Give a clear statement, in your own words, of the meaning of:

(a) neutralization

(b) stepwise neutralization

(c) monoprotic acid

(d) polyprotic acid

(e) ionic equation

(f) strong electrolyte

(g) weak electrolyte

(h) pH

(i) acid-base indicator

(j) range of an indicator

2. The properties of ions in solution are additive. Explain this statement, using aqueous copper(II) chloride as an example.

3. (a) List from memory the properties common to all aqueous acid solutions.

(b) Why have these solutions these properties in common?

4. In tabular form compare the properties of hydronium ion and hydroxide ion.

5. (a) What two ions are involved in every neutralization reaction?

(b) Write the ionic equation common to every neutralization reaction.

6. Describe two experiments by which you could compare two acids that differ in strength, and thereby determine which was the stronger.

7. How is it that every aqueous solution, irrespective of solute, contains hydronium ions and hydroxide ions?

8. Explain clearly, with at least one example of each, how you could have:

(a) a dilute solution of a strong acid

(b) a concentrated solution of a weak acid

9. What are the acids that occur naturally in: rhubarb, grapes, sour milk, rancid butter, ants?

10. Write equations representing the complete neutralization of:

(a) hydrochloric acid by barium hydroxide

(b) aqueous ammonia by acetic acid

(c) iron(III) hydroxide by nitric acid.

11. Write equations for the neutralization reactions that result in production of the following salts: (a) lithium carbonate, (b) copper(II) perchlorate, (c) calcium hypochlorite, (d) aluminium sulphate.

12. Write equations representing the stepwise neutralization of:

(a) sulphurous acid by calcium hydroxide

(b) phosphoric acid by potassium hydroxide

(c) magnesium hydroxide by hydrochloric acid

13. Arrange in order of decreasing hydrogen-ion concentration: water, solutions containing 1.0 mol/L of HCl, NH_3, $HC_2H_3O_2$, NaOH, H_2SO_4, $Ba(OH)_2$.

14. Solutions A, B, C, D, and E have pH values 3, 8, 7, 12, and 1, respectively. Which is the most basic solution? Which is the most acidic? Which one has the second highest hydrogen-ion concentration?

15. A solution gives a blue colour with the indicator bromthymol blue, but no colour with phenolphthalein. What must be its approximate pH?

16. A solution gives a yellow colour with the indicator bromthymol blue, and also a yellow colour with methyl red. What must be its approximate pH?

17. Discuss four factors that affect the extent to which chemical reactions proceed. Give one example of each.

18. Decide whether each of the following possible reactions will proceed to form new products; where a reaction is believed to occur, write an *ionic equation*, showing only the reacting ions.

(a) lithium chloride + barium hydroxide

(b) silver acetate + ammonium chloride

(c) sodium sulphide + zinc nitrate

(d) copper(II) nitrate + iron(III) sulphate

(e) potassium sulphate + strontium perchlorate

19. Into three beakers containing dilute sulphuric acid are put, respectively, powdered zinc, zinc sulphide, and zinc chloride. Reactions are observed in the first two cases, with evolution of gases, but no significant reaction is seen in the third. Give equations for the reactions that did occur, and identify the gaseous products. Account for the absence of evidence of reaction in the third case.

20. Most metallic oxides, except those of the alkali metals, and calcium and barium, are insoluble in water. They will dissolve in many acids, however, with formation of a salt in the same fashion as the hydroxide. Write an equation for the dissolving of magnesium oxide in nitric acid, and suggest an explanation for the reaction occurring.

21. Write an equation for the reaction that occurs when ammonia is dissolved in water. Write an equation for the reaction that occurs when hydrogen chloride is dissolved in water. Write an equation for the reaction that occurs when these two aqueous solutions are mixed.

22. Note in Table 27-3 that most salts containing the ion PO_4^{3-} are insoluble. Can you suggest a reason for this? (Hint: You should re-read Sec. 26-7 to 26-9, and consider which are the soluble phosphates.) Is your theory consistent with the fact that a good many salts of the ion $H_2PO_4^-$ are soluble?

23. Calculate the mass of potassium hydroxide required to neutralize 100 cm^3 of a 20% hydrochloric acid solution whose density is 1.10 g/cm^3.

24. How much anhydrous sodium carbonate would be required to react completely with 25.0 mL of a solution of nitric acid containing 2.00 mol/L?

25. What volume of 20% nitric acid (density 1.12 g/cm^3) would be required just to neutralize 100 g of quicklime, CaO?

26. Calculate the mass and the amount (in moles) of the following acids which would exactly neutralize 40.0 g of sodium hydroxide: hydrochloric acid (as hydrogen chloride), nitric acid (as hydrogen nitrate), sulphuric acid (as hydrogen sulphate), phosphoric acid (as hydrogen phosphate).

27. Excess hydrochloric acid is added to 200 mL of a potassium hydroxide solution whose concentration is 0.250 mol/L, and the resulting solution is evaporated to dryness. What mass of salt would remain? Could the experiment have been done in the reverse way, by adding excess potassium hydroxide to a known amount of hydrochloric acid, and a similar calculation made? Explain.

28. To "standardize" an acid solution of unknown concentration, the volume of it which will exactly neutralize a known mass of a pure basic substance is measured from a buret (Chapter 25). In such a determination 47.2 mL of nitric acid just neutralized 0.500 g of anhydrous sodium carbonate. Calculate the concentration of the acid in moles per litre.

29. Explain why a mixture of sodium nitrate and sulphuric acid yields nitric acid when heated.

∗30. Write the formulas of the various molecules or ions present (other than water), and state the approximate concentrations of each (in moles per litre) when the following are put into aqueous solution with a final volume of 1.0 L: (a) 0.02 mol $MgCl_2$, (b) 0.02 mol $MgCl_2$ + 0.03 mol KCl, (c) 0.02 mol $MgCl_2$ + 0.05 mol Na_2CO_3, (d) 0.02 mol $MgCl_2$ + 0.02 mol KOH, (e) 0.02 mol KOH + 0.05 mol HNO_3, (f) 0.1 mol $HC_2H_3O_2$, (g) 0.05 mol KOH + 0.1 mol $HC_2H_3O_2$, (h) 0.05 mol KOH + 0.05 mol H_3PO_4, (i) 0.02 mol Mg + 0.1 mol $HClO_4$.

28 Oxidation and Reduction

1. We have already mentioned oxidation and reduction a few times in this book, especially in Sec. 5-8, 6-8, 9-10, and 26-18. The term oxidation has been presented, much as it has evolved, with gradually altered meaning. In the beginning, it meant combination with oxygen, but as the nature of chemical combination came to be better understood, the original definition of oxidation was considered to be too restrictive. Reduction, which originally appeared to be just the reverse of oxidation has now come to be viewed as a complementary process: nothing can ever be oxidized without something else being reduced at the same time. In this chapter we hope to make this clearer.

2. OXIDATION. If a sample of the element magnesium, as an example, combines with oxygen, a new substance is formed in which we recognize that the original magnesium atoms have changed. They are now magnesium ions (Mg^{2+}) which occur along with oxide ions in the compound magnesium oxide (Sec. 14-9). That compound could then be transformed chemically into some other magnesium compound; for instance, it could be dissolved in hydrochloric acid to form magnesium chloride (dissolved) and from that it is an easy matter to produce magnesium chloride as a solid. In either solid magnesium chloride or its solution, the magnesium continues to be present as ions. We could also have made magnesium chloride some other way, perhaps by the direct reaction of magnesium with chlorine gas, perhaps by dissolving magnesium metal in hydrochloric acid and then removing water by evaporation.

We say that the element magnesium is oxidized when it forms magnesium oxide, and we recognize that the oxidized element is in the form of positive ions. But the same ions, Mg^{2+}, are present in magnesium chloride. The reaction of the element magnesium with chlorine converts the magnesium atoms into the same ions as did the reaction with oxygen. It was an evolutionary step to broaden the use of the term oxidation to in-

In a physics textbook this picture could serve as a dramatic illustration of Newton's Third Law of Motion, but we include it to show the importance of chemistry in space travel. A very vigorous oxidation-reduction reaction causes the rapid expulsion of gas that provides the thrust for a spacecraft's journey. (Incidentally, this is a photograph of the flight that carried the first humans to the surface of the moon, in 1969. At the stage pictured here, the burning of hydrogen in oxygen is propelling the craft.)

clude all reactions in which atoms of the element are converted to positive ions, such as the reaction of the element magnesium with chlorine.

The essential process for the oxidation of magnesium is given by the equation:

$$Mg \rightarrow Mg^{2+} + 2e^-$$

What applies to the oxidation of magnesium is just as valid for other metals, for instance:

$$Na \rightarrow Na^+ + e^-$$

$$Al \rightarrow Al^{3+} + 3e^-$$

That broadened description of oxidation could be made more general yet by including such cases as

(a) an ion already positively charged acquiring an even greater positive charge by the loss of one or more electrons, for example,

$$Fe^{2+} \rightarrow Fe^{3+} + e^-$$

(b) a negatively charged ion becoming neutral or even positive by the loss of one or more electrons, for example,

$$Cl^- \rightarrow Cl + e^-$$

or better:

$$2Cl^- \rightarrow Cl_2 + 2e^-$$

In general an *oxidation is a process in which the charge on an atom or an ion becomes more positive, as a result of the loss of one or more electrons.* Although this definition is consistent with the examples given, it is incomplete because it fails to provide for many cases in which ions are not formed. We shall return to this point in Sec. 28-5.

We referred above to atoms or ions "losing" electrons, but that statement is not to be taken as meaning that electrons get lost. Far from it! Because, for an oxidation to take place, there has also to be a receiver of electrons, and that is where reduction comes into the picture.

3. REDUCTION. If reduction is considered to be the opposite of oxidation, we should be able to relate it to the description of oxidation given above. It ought to be, according to what was said of oxidation, *a process in which the charge on an atom or an ion becomes more negative (or less positive) as a result of the gain of one or more electrons.* That is a good description as far as it goes but it, too, fails to account for reductions that do not involve ions.

You may find it useful to remember the expression **GERLEO**, which stands for Gain of Electrons is Reduction; Loss of Electrons is Oxidation.

We can illustrate this definition of reduction with some examples. When a metal ion is converted to the element, as in electrolysis, that is reduction, for instance:

$$e^- + Na^+ \rightarrow Na$$

$$2e^- + Cu^{2+} \rightarrow Cu$$

Likewise, the reduction of hydrogen (hydronium) ion involves a gain of electrons:

$$e^- + H_3O^+ \rightarrow H + H_2O$$

followed by:

$$2H \rightarrow H_2$$

or alternatively:

$$2e^- + 2H_3O^+ \rightarrow H_2 + 2H_2O$$

When the element oxygen combines with a metal, oxide ions are formed, so this too is a case of reduction:

$$O_2 \rightarrow 2O$$

$$2e^- + O \rightarrow O^{2-}$$

Similarly, when chlorine or other halogen element reacts with a metal to form an ionic chloride (or halide), reduction occurs:

$$Cl_2 \rightarrow 2Cl$$

$$e^- + Cl \rightarrow Cl^-$$

A metal ion may be reduced from one ionic valence to a lower value, as in the case of copper(II) forming copper(I):

$$e^- + Cu^{2+} \rightarrow Cu^+$$

4. OXIDATION-REDUCTION. Oxidation has been presented as a process in which electrons are given out; reduction, in contrast, is a process in which electrons are consumed. Experience teaches us that neither oxidation nor reduction takes place in isolation. If they did, this would contravene the principle of electrical neutrality. The closest we can come to observing an oxidation separated from a reduction, or vice versa, is at the electrodes during electrolysis. We pointed out in Sec. 26-18 that the process occurring at an anode is an oxidation, and that occurring at the cathode is a reduction. But we cannot carry out an electrolysis without *both* an anode and a cathode, and so during electrolysis oxidation and reduction do occur simultaneously.

However, we must make it clear that electrodes and an electric current are in no way essential to the occurrence of oxidation and reduction. What occurs in an electrolytic cell is that electrons generated by an oxidation process are transferred *to* an electrode (anode), and simultaneously electrons required for a reduction process are transferred *from* an electrode (cathode). But there are also hundreds of reactions in which a substance is oxidized and the electrons so liberated are transferred direct to another substance which is simultaneously being reduced. In these cases too, oxidation and reduction go hand in hand; you cannot have one without the other. Thus, it is perhaps better to describe reactions in which these processes of electron transfer occur as **oxidation-reduction reactions**. Another "made-up" name for these is **redox reactions**.

We shall illustrate the complementary nature of oxidation and reduction by considering two reactions introduced early in this book. The first is the combination of magnesium and oxygen:

$$2Mg + O_2 \rightarrow 2MgO$$

As we said earlier magnesium oxide is an ionic compound. The formation of magnesium oxide may be represented as an electron-transfer process as follows:

$$\overset{\overset{\displaystyle 2 \times 2e^-}{\frown}}{2Mg + O_2 \rightarrow 2Mg^{2+}O^{2-}}$$

Magnesium atoms are oxidized to magnesium ions, and oxygen atoms are reduced to oxide ions. Oxygen brought about the oxidation of magnesium and is therefore called the *oxidizing agent*. Similarly, magnesium caused the reduction of oxygen and is therefore called the *reducing agent*. Magnesium is said to be a donor (giver) of electrons, and oxygen an acceptor of electrons.

In Sec. 6-3 the reaction of zinc metal with hydrochloric acid was represented by the equation:

$$Zn + 2HCl \rightarrow ZnCl_2 + H_2$$

By now we know that hydrochloric acid consists mainly of $H^+(aq)$ and $Cl^-(aq)$ and that zinc chloride is an ionic salt. We could therefore write this equation more descriptively as:

$$Zn(s) + 2H^+(aq) + 2Cl^-(aq) \rightarrow Zn^{2+}(aq) + 2Cl^-(aq) + H_2(g)$$

We can write it more briefly by omitting the chloride ions:

$$Zn(s) + 2H^+(aq) \rightarrow Zn^{2+}(aq) + H_2(g)$$

Ions, such as chloride in this equation, which take no part in the essential reaction are sometimes termed "spectator ions." Although they must be present in solution for electrical neutrality, they can be omitted from the equation.

By the time we get the original equation trimmed down to this, it is clear what really happens. Each zinc atom loses two electrons to two hydrogen ions, the zinc atom thereby becoming a zinc ion, and the hydrogen ions becoming (via atoms) a molecule of gaseous hydrogen. Zinc is oxidized by hydrogen ions; hydrogen ions are reduced by zinc. Zinc in this reaction is the reducing agent; hydrogen ions are the oxidizing agent.

5. OXIDATION STATE. The description we have given for oxidation and reduction has been in terms of atoms changing to ions, or vice versa, or of ions changing in the number of unit charges they carry. This is easy to grasp and can be applied to many processes in which there is no doubt that ions take part. But there are many covalent compounds as well, and for these a description of oxidation and reduction in terms of ions is not appropriate.

Consider the two elements carbon and silicon, and their oxidation, respectively, to the gaseous molecular compound CO_2 and the network solid SiO_2. The structures of these were described in Sec. 15-5 and 15-14. In neither of these compounds is it suitable or correct to refer to the carbon or silicon as ionic. In both compounds electrons are shared between carbon or silicon atoms, on the one hand, and oxygen atoms on the other. There may be grounds for believing that this sharing of electrons is not on a 50:50 basis, and that on average the electrons spend a bit more time near the oxygen atoms than near the carbon or silicon atoms: the bonds are "polar" (Sec. 14-21). However, there are no grounds for believing that a complete transfer of electrons to the oxygen atoms has occurred in the manner assumed for magnesium oxide.

We should be able to speak of carbon or silicon as oxidized in these compounds, but our description of oxidation in terms of electron transfer isn't appropriate. Nor is it appropriate in general for elements in covalent compounds. To get around this difficulty chemists have invented a sort of "electron-bookkeeping" by which they determine what is called the **oxidation state** or **oxidation number** of an element in a compound. These terms are used interchangeably.

We shall give you a set of rules for assigning an oxidation number to an element, and then we shall tell you what we think that number means, and how it may be used.

6. ASSIGNMENT OF OXIDATION NUMBER. The following rules enable the oxidation number, or oxidation state, of an element to be determined.

(a) The oxidation number of an uncombined element is zero.

(b) For an element known to be in ionic form, the oxidation number is the charge on the ion (including sign).

(c) Hydrogen in compounds is almost always assigned the oxidation number +1. (An exception is in hydrides of electropositive metals, such as CaH_2, where hydrogen is known to be the anion, H^-.)

(d) Oxygen in compounds is almost always assigned the oxidation number –2. (Two exceptions: in oxygen fluoride, OF_2, it is +2; and in peroxides, like H_2O_2, it is –1.)

(e) Fluorine in compounds is invariably assigned the oxidation number –1. Chlorine, in compounds other than with fluorine or oxygen, is assigned the oxidation number –1. In the compounds excepted, chlorine's oxidation number is found by rule (f).

(f) Other oxidation numbers are worked out by algebraic addition such that the sum of the oxidation numbers for each element in the formula of a compound totals zero.

These rules are illustrated in the following examples.

(a) Oxidation state zero: Ne, O_2, S_8, Fe

(b) In K_2S, oxidation state of potassium = +1; of sulphur = –2

(c) In HBr, HCN, and NH_3, oxidation state of hydrogen = +1

(d) In CO_2, NO, and Al_2O_3, oxidation of oxygen = –2

(e) In HF, OF_2, and CF_4, oxidation state of fluorine = –1

   In HCl, PCl_3, and CCl_4, oxidation state of chlorine = –1

(f) In CO_2 and CCl_4, oxidation state of carbon = +4

   In NH_3, oxidation state of nitrogen = –3

   In H_2SO_4, oxidation states are: H = +1; S = +6; O = –2

      Thus $2 \times (+1) + (+6) + 4 \times (-2) = 0$

   In $KClO_3$, oxidation states are: K = +1; Cl = +5; O = –2

      $(+1) + (+5) + 3 \times (-2) = 0$

7. SIGNIFICANCE OF OXIDATION STATE. We said previously that assignment of an oxidation state to an element is a sort of bookkeeping device. By it we assign numbers—which are really charges—to the atoms of elements according to a set of rules. The rules are contrived to give negative oxidation states to the more electronegative elements, positive oxidation states to the more positive elements, and to let the remainder be worked out by difference. The resulting oxidation states, or charges, are those that *would apply if all the bonds in a substance were ionic.*

Since all bonds clearly are *not* ionic, it follows that the oxidation state is a somewhat fictitious number, and that it cannot be endowed with any physical significance. Thus, in sulphuric acid, as an example, you must not imagine that sulphur is really present as the S^{6+} ion, even though that is what the oxidation state seems to indicate. Nevertheless, oxidation states are useful as indicators of the extent to which an element has been oxidized.

Given that an oxidation state can be assigned to an element in a compound, we can easily perceive that the process we call oxidation is always accompanied by an increase in oxidation state of that element (to a more positive value). Likewise a reduction is always accompanied by a decrease in oxidation state (to a less positive, or more negative, value). In this way we can identify oxidations and reductions without having to specify loss or gain of electrons. This is essential for interpreting oxidation-reduction changes among elements in covalent compounds. It is difficult, for example, to interpret the oxidation of ammonia to nitric oxide in terms of electrons transferred:

$$4NH_3 + 5O_2 \rightarrow 4NO + 6H_2O$$

Another useful feature of oxidation states is that they provide a basis for classifying the compounds of a particular element. A ladder of known oxidation states can be constructed, and the formulas or names of compounds in which the element is in these oxidation states can be entered in the appropriate places. This is illustrated for some common compounds of nitrogen and sulphur.

		+6	SO_3, H_2SO_4, SF_6
+5	HNO_3	+5	
+4	NO_2	+4	SO_2, H_2SO_3, $SOCl_2$
+3	HNO_2, NCl_3	+3	
+2	NO	+2	$Na_2S_2O_3$ (sodium thiosulphate)
+1	N_2O	+1	
0	N_2	0	S_8
–1		–1	
–2	N_2H_4 (hydrazine)	–2	H_2S, CS_2
–3	NH_3, NH_4Cl		

8. OXIDATION STATES AND VALENCE. Valence began, more than a hundred years ago, as a simple idea—the combining capacity of the atoms of a particular element compared with the combining capacity of some reference element such as hydrogen. Thus the valence of carbon in methane or in carbon tetrachloride is four, for example. Such a simple idea served chemists well until just after World War I when an electronic theory of valence, which we described in Chapter 14, was advanced to explain the attractions between atoms. This same theory was able to account for the numerical relationships among atoms in combination. Two kinds of valence—ionic valence and covalence—were identified. However, there were ideas carried over from the original conception of valence which neither of these valence types could convey. We shall try to make this statement clearer by two examples.

Sulphur forms an oxide, SO_3, in which sulphur appears to exhibit a valence of 6. When sulphur trioxide reacts with water the product is sulphuric acid, H_2SO_4. Ionization of sulphuric acid produces the sulphate ion, SO_4^{2-}, with an ionic valence of -2. From Lewis structures it is seen that in both sulphuric acid and sulphate ion the covalence of sulphur is 4. But how did sulphur come to lose its 6-valence when sulphur trioxide reacted with water? In another case, ammonia, NH_3, contains nitrogen with a valence of 3. When a solution of ammonia is treated with an acid, ammonia adds a proton and becomes the ammonium ion, NH_4^+, with an ionic valence of $+1$. A Lewis diagram shows that in this ion nitrogen has a covalence of 4. But chemists had an intuitive feeling that something of the 3-valence of nitrogen persisted even when ammonia was acidified.

In the two examples given, sulphur and nitrogen maintain the same *oxidation state*: in sulphur trioxide, sulphuric acid, and the sulphate ion, sulphur is in the oxidation state $+6$; in ammonia and the ammonium ion, nitrogen is in the oxidation state -3. Thus we can recognize, under the notion of valence, three distinct and separable ideas:

ionic valence

covalence

oxidation state

Ammonium sulphate is a good example of a substance in which all three of these ideas are illustrated.

In those names for substances (Sec. 21-4) where a Roman numeral is included to indicate valence of an element, as in phosphorus(V) oxide, for example, the Roman numeral actually is the oxidation number of the element described. For cations, the ionic valence and the oxidation state are the same, for example, in copper(II) chloride.

9. BALANCING REDOX EQUATIONS. When an equation is written to describe a redox reaction the customary rules with respect to balancing the equation apply, but there is an additional requirement governing the matching of the numbers of electrons transferred, or of balancing the changes in oxidation states. These requirements can best be understood by considering some examples.

Aluminium metal dissolves in strong acids with the displacement of hydrogen gas. To write a balanced equation for the reaction, consider first the individual processes of oxidation and reduction:

Oxidation $\qquad\qquad Al(s) \rightarrow Al^{3+}(aq) + 3e^-$

Reduction $\qquad 2e^- + 2H^+(aq) \rightarrow H_2(g)$

In the over-all process, as many electrons must be consumed in reduction as are produced in oxidation. Therefore to combine these two equations the first must be multiplied by 2 and the second by 3. Then, upon addition, electrons are eliminated. The resulting equation is

$$2Al(s) + 6H^+(aq) \rightarrow 2Al^{3+}(aq) + 3H_2(g)$$

Sulphuric Acid

$$\begin{pmatrix} \ddots\ddot{O}: \\ :\ddot{O}:S:\ddot{O}: \\ :\ddot{O}: \end{pmatrix}^{2-}$$

Sulphate Ion

$$\begin{pmatrix} H \\ H:\ddot{N}:H \\ H \end{pmatrix}^+$$

Ammonium Ion

In the oxidation of ammonia to nitric oxide, for which the unbalanced equation is

$$NH_3 + O_2 \rightarrow NO + H_2O$$

nitrogen is changed in oxidation state from -3 to $+2$ (this is oxidation), and oxygen is changed in oxidation state from 0 to -2 (this is reduction). *For a balanced equation it is required that the total positive change in oxidation state must be just matched by the total negative change.* The total change in oxidation state is given by the product of the number of atoms changed times the number of units by which the oxidation state of that element changes. In this case each nitrogen atom changes by 5 units in oxidation state, and each oxygen atom changes by 2 units in oxidation state. For the total changes in oxidation state to be of the same magnitude, two nitrogen atoms must be oxidized for every five oxygen atoms reduced. This gives coefficients to balance the equation, in part:

$$2NH_3 + 2\frac{1}{2}O_2 \rightarrow$$

To complete the balancing, it is evident that the coefficient for NO must be 2 and that for H_2O must be 3 (based on numbers of nitrogen and hydrogen atoms). Continuing the balancing:

$$2NH_3 + 2\frac{1}{2}O_2 \rightarrow 2NO + 3H_2O$$

Clearing fractions, we finish with:

$$4NH_3 + 5O_2 \rightarrow 4NO + 6H_2O$$

The principles illustrated in these two cases can be applied to any redox reaction.

COMPARATIVE EASE OF REDOX PROCESSES

10. DISPLACEMENT REACTIONS. As part of a scheme of classifying chemical reactions (Sec. 16-6) we mentioned displacements as a distinct type of reaction. It is evident that, while displacements are a recognizable category of chemical change, they are really only part of a still larger group that we designate oxidation-reduction reactions. We showed that a typical displacement—that of hydrogen from acids by zinc metal—can be interpreted as an electron-transfer process (Sec. 28-4). But not all redox reactions are displacements.

Many displacements consist of one metal causing a second metal to deposit from a solution of a salt of the latter. For instance, when a piece of zinc is dipped into a solution of copper(II) sulphate, a coating of metallic copper appears on the zinc. The same reaction occurs in a solution of *any* copper(II) salt; therefore the reaction must involve only zinc and copper(II) ions. Suitable tests show that the solution remaining after the metal is removed contains zinc ions. The essential reaction is represented, therefore, by:

$$Zn(s) + Cu^{2+}(aq) \rightarrow Zn^{2+}(aq) + Cu(s) \tag{1}$$

However, if a piece of copper is suspended in a solution of a zinc

All Queens are females, but not all females are Queens.

salt, nothing happens. Zinc evidently displaces copper from solutions of copper(II) salts; but the reverse process, that is Equation (1) read from right to left, does not occur.

This illustrates a feature of most displacement reactions, and that is that they are highly directional: they "work" one way, but usually not in the other. A second feature is that if several metals and solutions of their salts are investigated in a systematic way, it becomes apparent that there are priorities among the metals as to "what will displace what." For example, magnesium will displace zinc, zinc will displace lead, lead will displace copper, and copper will displace silver. Not unexpectedly, then, magnesium will displace any of the other metals; zinc will displace any of the others except magnesium; lead will displace silver as well as copper, but cannot displace zinc or magnesium; and so on. This suggests that these metals can be arranged in a sequence on the basis of diminishing ability to displace. It looks like this:

$$\text{magnesium} > \text{zinc} > \text{lead} > \text{copper} > \text{silver}$$

This sort of arrangement might remind you of an activity series introduced and discussed in Sec. 9-10. The criteria for arranging the elements in the order of activity shown in Table 9-1 were somewhat different, but the principle behind the two ordered lists of metals is essentially the same. In both cases the metals are ranked in the order of diminishing ease of oxidation.

In the next section, and in Table 28-1, we describe a more complete displacement series. In terms of the reactions under consideration at present, we note that *any metal will displace another metal lower in the series from a solution of its salt, or will be displaced from its own salts by any metal higher in the series.* This gives us something to add to our discussion of factors influencing the extent of chemical reactions —a discussion included in Sec. 27-9 to 27-16.

11. THE ELECTROCHEMICAL SERIES. A displacement sequence such as we have just described exists because there are differences in the ease with which oxidations or reductions occur. Throughout this book there have been examples to illustrate this. For instance, we mentioned the rapid and vigorous reaction of the alkali metals (sodium and potassium) with water; as part of this reaction these metals undergo oxidation. At the other end of the scale, silver and gold (especially gold) are difficult to oxidize; much of their value and usefulness derives from their resistance to chemical attack. Copper and zinc (with atomic numbers 29 and 30), which were mentioned in the last section, provide an interesting contrast in reactivity. Although zinc easily and rapidly displaces hydrogen from hydrochloric acid, copper will not yield so much as a tiny bubble of hydrogen when placed in the same acid. Since, in the two reactions:

$$Zn(s) + 2H^+(aq) \rightarrow Zn^{2+}(aq) + H_2(g)$$
$$Cu(s) + 2H^+(aq) \rightarrow Cu^{2+}(aq) + H_2(g)$$

the reduction process is the same, namely:

$$2e^- + 2H^+(aq) \rightarrow H_2(g)$$

the difference in the two reactions boils down to the oxidation processes:

$$Zn(s) \rightarrow Zn^{2+}(aq) + 2e^- \tag{2}$$

$$Cu(s) \rightarrow Cu^{2+}(aq) + 2e^- \tag{3}$$

The processes given by Equations (2) and (3) occur with dramatically different ease.

Metal ions can be arranged in the order of their ease of oxidation or reduction into what is called the **electrochemical series**. A partial electrochemical series is given in Table 28-1. This table shows the equation for the reduction process and a corresponding "electrode potential." The significance of electrode potentials is explained in Sec. 28-13.

TABLE 28-1

ELECTROCHEMICAL SERIES

REDUCTION PROCESS	ELECTRODE POTENTIAL (VOLTS, 25°C)
$e^- + K^+(aq) \rightarrow K(s)$	−2.92
$e^- + Na^+(aq) \rightarrow Na(s)$	−2.71
$2e^- + Mg^{2+}(aq) \rightarrow Mg(s)$	−2.37
$3e^- + Al^{3+}(aq) \rightarrow Al(s)$	−1.66
$2e^- + Zn^{2+}(aq) \rightarrow Zn(s)$	−0.76
$2e^- + Fe^{2+}(aq) \rightarrow Fe(s)$	−0.44
$2e^- + Pb^{2+}(aq) \rightarrow Pb(s)$	−0.13
$2e^- + 2H^+(aq) \rightarrow H_2(g)$	0
$2e^- + Cu^{2+}(aq) \rightarrow Cu(s)$	+0.34
$2e^- + Hg^{2+}(aq) \rightarrow Hg(l)$	+0.79
$e^- + Ag^+(aq) \rightarrow Ag(s)$	+0.80
$4e^- + O_2(g) + 4H^+(aq) \rightarrow 2H_2O(l)$	+1.23
$2e^- + Cl_2(g) \rightarrow 2Cl^-(aq)$	+1.36

The ease of reduction increases as the electrode potentials increase, that is, as one reads down in the table. Conversely, the ease of oxidation (the reverse of the process shown in Table 28-1) is greatest at the top and decreases as one descends in the list. This kind of information and other facts that were cited and illustrated in Chapter 9 are summarized in Fig. 28-1.

12. ELECTROCHEMICAL CELLS. Transistor radios, automobiles, and many small portable tools depend on cells, or batteries of cells, for energy to operate. The chemistry of most commercial cells is somewhat more complicated than the examples given in this chapter, but in all cases the cell depends on some oxi-

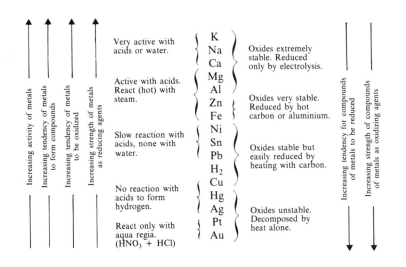

Fig. 28-1: *The activity series for some familiar metals (and hydrogen). Notice the amount of information about common chemical reactions that can be related to position in this series.*

Notice, too, that the observations of reactivity mentioned earlier place sodium above calcium. In the electrochemical series, measurements of cell voltages place calcium above sodium. This apparent anomaly is probably due to the relative speed with which these metal atoms shed valence electrons and become hydrated; calcium is slower at this than sodium.

dation-reduction reaction occurring in an electrolyte between two electrodes. The cell converts the energy of the chemical reaction into electrical energy. The cell operates to deliver a potential difference between the electrodes, and that potential difference arises because two electrode processes have a different tendency to take place.

An arrangement for an electrochemical cell that can be investigated in the laboratory is shown in Fig. 28-2. Two dissimilar metals are the electrodes and they dip into solutions of their own cations. The solutions of the different metal cations are linked by a conducting salt bridge. The voltmeter indicates a potential difference between the electrodes; the magnitude of this voltage depends upon the appropriate individual potentials such as those given in Table 28-1. The metal with the greater tendency to be reduced will form the positive pole of the cell; the other metal will be oxidized as current flows, will deliver electrons to the external circuit, and therefore is the negative electrode.

The cell reaction will be the sum of the oxidation and reduction processes taking place at the electrodes. The voltage delivered by the cell is related to the energy inherent in the cell reaction (Sec. 26-15). The current delivered by the cell will depend on the number of coulombs of charge transferred to the electrodes per second, and that in turn depends on the number of moles of substances oxidized and reduced per second.

13. ELECTRODE POTENTIALS. The significance of the potentials given in Table 28-1 requires a brief explanation. An **electrochemical cell**, such as we described in Sec. 28-12, will give rise to a potential difference (voltage) between

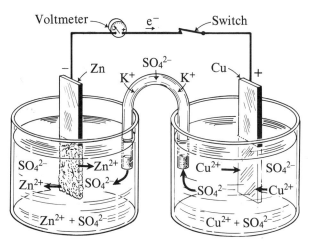

Fig. 28-2: *This represents a two-compartment electrochemical cell capable of generating an electric current when the switch is closed. In the left-hand compartment a zinc electrode dips into a solution of zinc sulphate; in the right-hand compartment the electrode is copper and the solution is copper(II) sulphate. The two compartments are joined by an inverted U-tube containing potassium sulphate solution; there are porous plugs in this tube to discourage liquid flowing from one compartment to the other. The cell is designed so as to isolate the individual electrode processes, yet still to make possible the flow of current through the solutions.*

the electrodes when these are connected by an external conductor. This potential difference may be represented as the difference in potentials of the two electrodes which form part of the cell. The voltage between the electrodes when practically no current is flowing will be given by the potential of the cathode (positive electrode) *minus* the potential of the anode. The values of these potentials shown in Table 28-1 all apply to the electrode in a 1.0 mol/L solution of the appropriate ions. When the concentration of the ions differs from 1.0 mol/L the electrode potentials change in a known way. There is actually no way of measuring a single electrode potential, so the values given are all relative to the value for hydrogen, which is defined as zero.

If the cell illustrated in Fig. 28-2 consists of a copper electrode dipping in 1.0 mol/L copper(II) sulphate (cathode) and a zinc electrode in 1.0 mol/L zinc sulphate (anode), the voltage expected between the electrodes (for very small current flow) is 0.34 V - (-0.76 V) = 1.10 V.

For an **electrolysis cell**, the voltage required to bring about the over-all chemical reaction which occurs at the two electrodes is slightly greater than the difference in potentials of the individual electrode processes. For instance, the electrolysis of copper(II) chloride will require a voltage slightly greater than 1.36 V - 0.34 V = 1.02 V. From the values given in Table 28-1 it is not difficult to understand why hydrogen ions are reduced at a cathode in preference to sodium ions during the electrolysis of sodium chloride solution (Sec. 26-14).

14. A WORD TO THE WISE. In chemistry when we discuss addition or removal of electrons to, or from, atoms there are actually two quite different processes that we may be describing. In one, gaseous atoms may be forming gaseous ions, in the manner described in Chapter 13,

$$Cu(g) \rightarrow Cu^+(g) + e^- \tag{4}$$

$$Cu^+(g) \rightarrow Cu^{2+}(g) + e^- \tag{5}$$

$$e^- + Cl(g) \rightarrow Cl^-(g) \tag{6}$$

and so on. The work required to accomplish reactions (4) and (5) is known as the first- and second-stage ionization energies, respectively (Sec. 13-2). The energy released in reaction (6) is called the electron affinity (Sec. 13-5). Values for all these quantities are known.

In this chapter we have been referring to the transfer of electrons between solid copper metal (to retain the same example for discussion) and aqueous copper(II) ions

$$Cu(s) \rightarrow Cu^{2+}(aq) + 2e^- \tag{7}$$

and the reduction of chlorine from gaseous molecules, via atoms, to aqueous chloride ions

$$2e^- + Cl_2(g) \rightarrow 2Cl^-(aq) \tag{8}$$

We cannot stress too much that although the processes *look* identical if written as

$$Cu \rightarrow Cu^{2+} + 2e^-$$

$$e^- + Cl \rightarrow Cl^-$$

they are vastly different, and the energies associated with gaseous ionization processes are different from those associated with processes such as (7) and (8). Comparisons of all these energies give some information from which hydration energies (Sec. 26-7) can be estimated.

QUESTIONS

1. Review the definitions of oxidation and reduction introduced in Chapter 26. How have these definitions been expanded in this chapter?

2. Give examples, other than those in Chapter 28, of oxidations in which: (a) a neutral atom becomes a positive ion, (b) a negative ion becomes a neutral atom, (c) a positive ion has its positive charge increased.

3. Give examples, other than those in Chapter 28, of reductions in which: (a) a positive ion becomes a neutral atom, (b) a neutral atom becomes a negative ion, (c) a positive ion becomes a positive ion of lesser charge.

4. Show that the two reduction processes in (a) and also the two oxidation processes in (b) are equivalent representations of the same process:

(a) $2e^- + 2H_2O \rightarrow 2OH^-(aq) + H_2(g)$
        $2e^- + 2H^+(aq) \rightarrow H_2(g)$

(b) $2H_2O \rightarrow O_2(g) + 4H^+(aq) + 4e^-$
        $4OH^- \rightarrow O_2(g) + 2H_2O + 4e^-$

5. Explain how oxidation and reduction processes always occur together. (It is interesting to make a comparison between debits and credits in finance.)

6. Assign oxidation numbers to the element whose symbol is italicized in the following formulas. In each case name the substance represented. HNO_3, $HClO$, CH_4, PF_5, K_2HPO_4, Ca_3N_2, NH_4NO_3, CS_2, $KMnO_4$, $NaIO_3$, $Ca(HSO_3)_2$.

7. Show that when methane is burned in air to carbon dioxide, carbon undergoes oxidation. What element is reduced at the same time?

8. Look up the equation for the reaction in which nitrogen dioxide and water form nitric acid. What element is oxidized in this reaction? What element is reduced? Show that when the equation is balanced the total positive change in oxidation state just matches the total negative change.

9. Write Lewis diagrams for the following: phosphate ion, hydrogen peroxide, sulphite ion. State the covalence and the oxidation states of phosphorus, oxygen, and sulphur in these structures. State the ionic valence of the two charged structures. (In assigning oxidation states to atoms in compound ions, the algebraic sum of the oxidation states equals the charge on the ion.)

10. Rewrite the following displacement reactions as the sum of two electron-transfer processes, and for each of the latter state which is an oxidation and which a reduction:

(a) $2Al + 3Cu^{2+} \rightarrow 2Al^{3+} + 3Cu$

(b) $Zn + Hg^{2+} \rightarrow Zn^{2+} + Hg$

(c) $Pb + 2H_3O^+ \rightarrow Pb^{2+} + H_2 + 2H_2O$

11. Explain how the electrochemical series can be used to predict whether or not a certain oxidation-reduction reaction will take place.

12. Predict what reaction, if any, will occur when (a) magnesium is dropped into a solution of lead nitrate, (b) sodium is dropped into a solution of magnesium nitrate, (c) lead is dropped into a solution of iron(II) nitrate, (d) lead is dropped into a solution of mercury(II) nitrate. Write equations for all reactions that occur.

13. Describe how you would go about ascertaining the position of tin in the electrochemical series (Table 28-1).

*14. Suppose that a previously weighed strip of nickel metal is suspended in 200 mL of a solution of copper(II) sulphate whose concentration is 0.100 mol/L, and allowed to remain there for some hours. The silvery nickel is seen to be coated with a red-brown deposit, and the solution, originally blue, turns green (the colour of $Ni^{2+}(aq)$). Would the metal strip now be heavier or lighter? By how much would its mass have changed?

15. Write the formulas of the various molecules or ions present (other than water), and state the approximate concentrations of each (in moles per litre) when the following are put into aqueous solution with a final volume of 1.0 L: (a) 0.02 mol Mg + 0.05 mol $Pb(NO_3)_2$, (b) 0.5 mol Zn + 0.5 mol $AgNO_3$, (c) 0.1 mol Fe + 0.5 mol HCl.

*16. Tin is used to protect iron from corrosion as in the familiar "tin" can; zinc is used to protect iron from corrosion as in galvanized pails or fencing. Are both of these facts consistent with the relative position of these three metals in the activity series? Can you suggest how zinc acts to protect iron from corrosion? How does tin act to protect iron from corrosion?

17. Suppose A, B, C, and D represent four metallic elements. Strips of B, C, and D are placed in a solution of a salt of A. B and C remain unchanged, but D becomes coated with a substance that closely resembles A. B and C are placed in a solution of dilute sulphuric acid. No reaction occurs with B, but metal C slowly reacts, liberating a gas which upon testing proves to be hydrogen.

(a) Arrange these elements in the order in which they would appear in the electrochemical series.

(b) Between which two elements would you place hydrogen?

(c) If only one of these metals occurs native in the uncombined state, which is it?

(d) If one of these metals can be extracted from its ores only by electrolysis, which is it?

18. From the relative position of hydrogen and copper in the electrochemical series, how can you account for the fact that copper will dissolve in nitric acid?

19. Exactly 10 g of magnesium is put into 100 mL of 2.00 mol/L sulphuric acid, and in due course all reaction comes to an end. Will the magnesium have all dissolved or not? If not, how much remains unreacted?

*20. There is a complication in the electrolysis of sodium chloride solution which we did not mention in Sec. 26-14. When the sodium chloride solution is relatively concentrated (1.0 mol/L or greater) chlorine is evolved at the anode. If the sodium chloride concentration is 0.1 mol/L or less the gas evolved at the anode is mainly oxygen. Can you offer an explanation of this?

21. In discussing electrolysis in Chapter 26 mention was made that electrodes should be of some unreactive substance such as platinum or graphite. This is particularly true of anodes. Why? What would happen if copper electrodes were used?

*22. The zinc-copper cell described in Sec. 28-13 was said to be capable of delivering a potential difference of 1.10 V. Apply the information in Sec. 26-17 to calculate the chemical energy, available for conversion to electrical energy, from the cell reaction:

$$Zn(s) + Cu^{2+}(aq) \rightarrow Zn^{2+}(aq) + Cu(s)$$

23. Analyze the following redox reactions selected from earlier chapters in this book, showing separately the oxidation process and the reduction process, and also stating the numbers of electrons transferred or the total changes in oxidation state:

(a) $3Cu + 8HNO_3 \rightarrow 3Cu(NO_3)_2 + 4H_2O + 2NO$

(b) $MnO_2 + 4HCl \rightarrow MnCl_2 + 2H_2O + Cl_2$

(c) $Cl_2 + H_2O \rightarrow HCl + HClO$

(d) $2KClO_3 \rightarrow 2KCl + 3O_2$

(e) $SO_2 + 2H_2S \rightarrow 2H_2O + 3S$

(f) $2Ca_3(PO_4)_2 + 6SiO_2 + 10C \rightarrow 6CaSiO_3 + 10CO + P_4$

*24. The cells in an automobile storage battery are filled with sulphuric acid, and one of the electrodes is made of lead. From its position in the electrochemical series, would you expect lead to displace hydrogen from sulphuric acid? This doesn't happen in batteries or in beakers. Can you suggest any reason why not? Is your reason consistent with the additional information that lead will displace hydrogen from a solution of chloric or perchloric acids?

The Alkaline Earth Family

1. In earlier chapters we have referred to magnesium and calcium and some of their reactions. Now, we intend to consider these elements more systematically and to associate them with the other members of their family. That family—the **alkaline earths**—comprises six related metals: *beryllium* (Be), *magnesium* (Mg), *calcium* (Ca), *strontium* (Sr), *barium* (Ba), and *radium* (Ra). These are all very active metals, though less active than potassium, sodium, and the other members of the alkali family of metals.

2. SIMILARITY IN PROPERTIES. Many years ago, the alkaline earth elements were grouped together as a family because their reactions are so similar. The similarity extends to their compounds (in all of which the alkaline earth element is bivalent). For example, the oxides are all white solids that have high melting points, the hydroxides are all basic compounds that have low solubility in water, and the carbonates are all decomposed by heat into the oxide and carbon dioxide.

TABLE 29-1

SOME PROPERTIES OF THE ALKALINE EARTH ELEMENTS

PROPERTY	ILLUSTRATIONS
Valence of 2+ in compounds	$BeCl_2$, MgO, $Ca(OH)_2$, $SrSO_4$, BaS, $Ra(NO_3)_2$
React directly with oxygen	$2Ca + O_2 \rightarrow 2CaO$
React directly with sulphur	$Sr + S \rightarrow SrS$
React directly with halogens	$Ba + Br_2 \rightarrow BaBr_2$
React with nitrogen on heating	$3Mg + N_2 \rightarrow Mg_3N_2$
*Displace hydrogen from water**	$Ca + 2H_2O \rightarrow Ca(OH)_2 + H_2$
	$Mg + H_2O \rightarrow MgO + H_2$
Displace hydrogen from acids	$Ca + 2H^+ \rightarrow Ca^{2+} + H_2$

*With beryllium and magnesium boiling water or steam is required, and the product is the oxide (BeO, MgO) rather than the hydroxide.

The similarities in the properties of these elements stem from similarities in their electron configurations. Their atoms each have two electrons in their outermost shell, in an s orbital, and the removal of these in each instance yields an ion with the electron configuration of an inert gas. Compare Table 29-2 with Table 29-3, and review Sec. 13-6.

TABLE 29-2

ELECTRON CONFIGURATIONS OF THE ALKALINE EARTH ELEMENTS	
Beryllium ($Z = 4$)	$1s^2\mathbf{2s^2}$
Magnesium ($Z = 12$)	$1s^22s^22p^6\mathbf{3s^2}$
Calcium ($Z = 20$)	$1s^22s^22p^63s^23p^6\mathbf{4s^2}$
Strontium ($Z = 38$)	$1s^22s^22p^63s^23p^63d^{10}4s^24p^6\mathbf{5s^2}$
Barium ($Z = 56$)	$1s^22s^22p^63s^23p^63d^{10}4s^24p^64d^{10}5s^25p^6\mathbf{6s^2}$
Radium ($Z = 88$)	$1s^22s^22p^63s^23p^63d^{10}4s^24p^64d^{10}4f^{14}5s^25p^65d^{10}6s^26p^6\mathbf{7s^2}$

TABLE 29-3

ELECTRON CONFIGURATIONS OF THE INERT GAS ELEMENTS	
Helium ($Z = 2$)	$1s^2$
Neon ($Z = 10$)	$1s^22s^22p^6$
Argon ($Z = 18$)	$1s^22s^22p^63s^23p^6$
Krypton ($Z = 36$)	$1s^22s^22p^63s^23p^63d^{10}4s^24p^6$
Xenon ($Z = 54$)	$1s^22s^22p^63s^23p^63d^{10}4s^24p^64d^{10}5s^25p^6$
Radon ($Z = 86$)	$1s^22s^22p^63s^23p^63d^{10}4s^24p^64d^{10}4f^{14}5s^25p^65d^{10}6s^26p^6$

3. The properties of the alkaline earth metals are similar, but they are not identical. Generally speaking, the properties of these elements and their compounds show gradations. For example, as the atomic number of the element increases, the degree of metallic character of the elements increases (Sec. 29-17), the solubility of their hydroxides in water increases

TABLE 29-4

SOME SOLUBILITIES (mol/L at 20°C)			
Z		SULPHATE	HYDROXIDE
4	Beryllium	3	2×10^{-6}
12	Magnesium	2	2×10^{-4}
20	Calcium	1×10^{-2}	2×10^{-2}
38	Strontium	7×10^{-4}	6×10^{-2}
56	Barium	1×10^{-5}	2×10^{-1}
88	Radium	6×10^{-6}	

and the solubility of their sulphates decreases (Table 29-4).

Such gradations are related to differences in the sizes of the atoms and to differences in the ease with which electrons can be removed from these atoms. We have more to say about this later (Sec. 29-17).

The most important members of the family are magnesium and calcium, and so most of this chapter is devoted to these two metals and their compounds.

4. OCCURRENCES. The alkaline earth metals are much too active to occur in nature uncombined. But they occur plentifully, particularly as solid carbonates and, as dissolved compounds, in sea water and in underground brines (which are residues of old seas).

Some of the important forms in which magnesium and calcium occur are given in Table 29-5. Another significant occurrence of calcium is in our bones, as calcium phosphate, $Ca_3(PO_4)_2$.

The scientific achievements of Pierre and Marie Curie (born Marya Sklodovska, in Poland) have led several countries to issue postage stamps in their honour. This French stamp is thought by at least one of this book's authors to be the most attractive, but Afghanistan, Bulgaria, Cuba, Germany, India, Monaco, Panama, Poland, Romania, Russia, Surinam, and Sweden are among the countries that have similarly honoured one or both of them.

TABLE 29-5

SOME OCCURRENCES OF MAGNESIUM AND CALCIUM			
NAME	MAIN CONSTITUENT	NAME	MAIN CONSTITUENT
Magnesite	$MgCO_3$	*Limestone*	$CaCO_3$
Dolomite	$CaCO_3 \cdot MgCO_3$	*Marble**	$CaCO_3$
Brucite	$Mg(OH)_2$	*Chalk**	$CaCO_3$
Carnallite	$KCl \cdot MgCl_2 \cdot 6H_2O$	*Anhydrite*	$CaSO_4$
Fluorite	CaF_2	*Gypsum*	$CaSO_4 \cdot 2H_2O$

*Marble consists of calcium carbonate with impurities scattered through it in a manner that often gives beautiful effects when the stone is polished. Sandstone consists of grains of sand embedded in calcium carbonate. Chalk and coral are forms of calcium carbonate that have been deposited by low forms of sea life. A pearl is largely calcium carbonate, too, made by an oyster in an effort to protect himself from some irritating bit of matter that has got into him.

5. BERYLLIUM occurs in the complex silicate mineral called *beryl*, of which the gems emerald and aquamarine are varieties. **Strontium** occurs chiefly as the sulphate, $SrSO_4$, in *celestite* and as the carbonate, $SrCO_3$, in *strontianite*. The most important mineral of **barium** is *barite* or *barytes*, consisting mainly of barium sulphate, $BaSO_4$.

Radium, the unique member of the family by virtue of its radioactivity, occurs in minute concentration in ores of uranium. It was radium's radioactivity that led to its discovery, by Marie and Pierre Curie, in 1898.

6. PRODUCTION. Calcium and magnesium metals are produced by the electrolysis of their molten chlorides. The method involves the reduction, at a cathode, of the calcium ions or magnesium ions:

$$2e^- + Ca^{2+} \text{ (or } Mg^{2+}) \rightarrow Ca \text{ (or } Mg)$$

Magnesium is also produced by the Pidgeon process in which magnesium oxide (obtained from dolomite) is reduced by means of silicon at high temperature:

$$2MgO + 2CaO + Si \rightarrow Ca_2SiO_4 + 2Mg(g)$$

An important source of magnesium is sea water. Magnesium is precipitated from sea water as the hydroxide; this is separated from the sea water by filtration and dissolved in hydrochloric acid, and magnesium chloride for the electrolytic process is obtained by evaporation.

This process was developed by Dr. L.M. Pidgeon when he was a chemist at the National Research Laboratories in Ottawa, Ontario.

7. SOME PROPERTIES OF MAGNESIUM AND CALCIUM. These are silver-white metals of low density; each has a density less than one-quarter that of iron.

Both magnesium and calcium are very active metals (see the activity series in Table 9-1). We have already described their reactions with oxygen (Sec. 9-7), with nitrogen (Sec. 7-5), with water (Sec. 6-3), and with acids (Sec. 9-9); you should review these.

Magnesium and calcium—and the other alkaline earth metals, too—react readily with sulphur and with the halogen elements. Typical equations for these reactions, all of which are exothermic, are given in Table 29-1.

8. The dazzling white light produced by burning magnesium in air or oxygen makes this metal useful in flashlight photography, signal flares, fireworks, and tracer bullets.

Magnesium is an excellent reducing agent and is used as such in the production of metallic zirconium, uranium, and titanium by reactions such as:

$$ZrCl_4 + 2Mg \rightarrow 2MgCl_2 + Zr$$

The readiness with which magnesium reacts with hot nitrogen and oxygen accounts for its use in removing these gases from molten metals before they are cast. Magnesium alloys go into the making of the wheels, engines, frames, and hundreds of other airplane parts. The lightness, strength, and durability of these alloys are advantageous in these applications, and in household appliances, motor car pistons, toys (including golf clubs), wheelbarrows, arctic sleighs, and so on.

Calcium compounds are more useful than magnesium compounds, but calcium itself is much less important than magnesium.

ALKALINE EARTH COMPOUNDS

9. Nearly all compounds of the alkaline earth metals are ionic solids. In Sec. 14-3 to 14-10 we described how compounds of this sort form from the atoms of the elements and what holds them together. The atoms of the alkaline earths, though not as easily ionized as those of the alkali metals, nevertheless form positive ions fairly readily. This accounts for the reactivity of the elements and the preference for ionic compounds.

Typical of these ionic compounds are the oxides of calcium and magnesium. These consist of a three-dimensional array of calcium or magnesium ions (Ca^{2+} or Mg^{2+}) and oxide ions (O^{2-}) held together by electrostatic attraction. The pattern in which these ions are assembled in the solid is exactly the same as in sodium chloride (shown in Fig. 14-1 and 14-2) except that magnesium or calcium ions occupy the positions shown there for sodium ions, and oxide ions occupy the positions shown for chloride ions. Because of the double charges borne by the ions, the forces binding the solid together are very strong; consequently these are stable compounds with high melting points.

Similarly, an alkaline earth sulphate, such as calcium sulphate, is an assemblage of calcium ions and sulphate ions, $Ca^{2+}SO_4^{2-}$, and a chloride like calcium chloride is best designated as $Ca^{2+}(Cl^-)_2$. It is for convenience and simplicity that we commonly write such formulas as $CaSO_4$ and $CaCl_2$.

10. MAGNESIUM AND CALCIUM OXIDES. As we have said earlier, these are formed when the metals burn in air (and so, of course, in oxygen), and magnesium oxide is a product of the reaction of magnesium with boiling water or steam.

The oxides are also formed when the carbonates or hydroxides are heated sufficiently, for example,

$$MgCO_3 \rightarrow MgO + CO_2(g)$$
$$Mg(OH)_2 \rightarrow MgO + H_2O(g) \tag{1}$$

Magnesium oxide, or *magnesia*, has a very high melting point (above 2500°C), which makes it useful for crucibles and furnace linings. Its abrasive properties and low solubility make it useful in toothpastes.

What little magnesium oxide does dissolve in water produces an alkaline or basic solution of magnesium hydroxide, in a reaction that is the reverse of that of Equation (1):

$$MgO + H_2O \rightarrow Mg(OH)_2$$

Magnesium hydroxide also has a low solubility in water (Table 29-4); a suspension of it in water is known as *milk of magnesia*.

Calcium oxide, or *lime* or *quicklime*, is much used for making other calcium compounds (as noted in Table 29-6) such as calcium hydroxide, or *hydrated lime* or *slaked lime*:

$$CaO + H_2O \rightarrow Ca(OH)_2$$

This dissolves in water, though sparingly, and the solution so obtained is known as *lime-water*. Calcium hydroxide is a fairly strong base, and often serves as a cheap source of hydroxide ions, as in the softening of water (Sec. 29-15).

11. CALCIUM SULPHATE This occurs in nature as the mineral *anhydrite*, which is mainly $CaSO_4$, and as *gypsum* which is mainly the dihydrate, $CaSO_4 \cdot 2H_2O$.

The hemihydrate, $(CaSO_4)_2 \cdot H_2O$, is a white powder known as *plaster of Paris*. It is made by heating gypsum to about 140°C:

$$2CaSO_4 \cdot 2H_2O \rightarrow (CaSO_4)_2 \cdot H_2O + 3H_2O(g)$$

When water is added to plaster of Paris, the water of crystallization that was lost in the heating is regained, and the wet powder sets in a few minutes to a solid mass of interlacing crystals of gypsum:

$$\underset{\text{plaster of Paris}}{(CaSO_4)_2 \cdot H_2O} + 3H_2O \rightarrow \underset{\text{gypsum}}{2CaSO_4 \cdot 2H_2O}$$

TABLE 29-6

SOME COMPOUNDS OF CALCIUM AND MAGNESIUM

NAME	FORMULA	USES
Calcium carbonate	$CaCO_3$	source of lime; as limestone, for building and in making iron and steel, glass, and cement
Calcium oxide (lime, quicklime)	CaO	making slaked lime, bleaching powder, calcium carbide, and other chemicals
Calcium hydroxide (slaked lime, hydrated lime)	$Ca(OH)_2$	making mortar, building plaster, whitewash, and bleaching powder; softening water (temporary hardness)
Calcium chloride-hypochlorite (bleaching powder)	$CaCl(OCl)$	bleaching and sterilizing agent in the household
Calcium chloride	$CaCl_2$	drying agent; laying of dust on roads; source of calcium metal
Calcium sulphate hemihydrate (plaster of Paris)	$(CaSO_4)_2 \cdot H_2O$	making statues, plaster casts, decorative ceilings, etc.
Calcium sulphate dihydrate (gypsum)	$CaSO_4 \cdot 2H_2O$	making wallboard, tile, etc., and plaster of Paris
Calcium dihydrogen phosphate mono-hydrate	$Ca(H_2PO_4)_2 \cdot H_2O$	in baking powder (Sec. 22-8)
Magnesium carbonate	$MgCO_3$	source of magnesium oxide
Magnesium oxide (magnesia)	MgO	crucibles; furnace linings; ingredient of toothpastes
Magnesium hydroxide (milk of magnesia)	$Mg(OH)_2$	in medicine, as an anti-acid and laxative
Magnesium chloride	$MgCl_2$	source of magnesium metal
Magnesium sulphate heptahydrate (Epsom salts)	$MgSO_4 \cdot 7H_2O$	in medicine as a purgative; in making leather

12. MAGNESIUM AND CALCIUM CARBONATES. The carbonates of all the alkaline earths have low solubility in water. They can be made by treating the oxides or hydroxides with carbon dioxide, for example,

$$CaO + CO_2 \rightarrow CaCO_3$$
$$Ca(OH)_2 + CO_2 \rightarrow CaCO_3 + H_2O \tag{2}$$

If much carbon dioxide is bubbled through a solution of calcium hydroxide, the white precipitate of calcium carbonate that forms (according to Equation (2)) will disappear because of its conversion to calcium hydrogen carbonate, which *is* soluble:

$$CaCO_3 + CO_2 + H_2O \rightarrow Ca(HCO_3)_2 \tag{3}$$

This is a test for carbon dioxide (Fig. 29-1).

When a solution of calcium hydrogen carbonate is heated, it yields a precipitate of calcium carbonate:

$$Ca(HCO_3)_2 \rightarrow CaCO_3(s) + H_2O + CO_2(g) \tag{4}$$

Equation (4) is the reverse of Equation (3). The reactions of Equations (3) and (4) account for the formation of stalactites and stalagmites in limestone caverns; see the caption of the accompanying photograph.

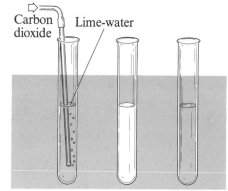

First clear   Then milky   Then clear

Fig. 29-1: *When carbon dioxide is bubbled through a filtered, clear solution of calcium hydroxide (lime-water), a fine white precipitate of calcium carbonate forms. If enough carbon dioxide is passed into the solution, the precipitate dissolves and the solution becomes clear again, being now a solution of calcium hydrogen carbonate.*

When water containing carbon dioxide percolates through limestone, it dissolves calcium carbonate, forming a solution of calcium hydrogen carbonate. When the solution drips through cracks in the roof of a limestone cave, as here, evaporation of water and carbon dioxide causes the calcium carbonate to reappear. The limestone "icicles" hanging from the roof are called stalactites; from the drippings of these, humps known as stalagmites build up from the floor. The two may meet and join to form a limestone pillar.

These structures grow very slowly. Some in this cave are more than 300 000 years old.

The carbonates of alkaline earth metals react readily with acids, liberating carbon dioxide. A typical equation is

$$CaCO_3 + 2H^+ \rightarrow Ca^{2+} + H_2O + CO_2(g)$$

On heating, the carbonates are converted into the corresponding oxide and carbon dioxide, for example,

$$MgCO_3 \rightarrow MgO + CO_2(g)$$

13. The most important use of magnesium carbonate is as a source of magnesium oxide, whose applications we have discussed (Sec. 29-10). Calcium carbonate in the form of limestone, sandstone, and marble is quarried in vast amounts for use as building stone: ease of cutting, resistance to weathering, and attractive appearance all contribute to this application. Limestone is the basis of the "slagging" process in a blast furnace for making iron: lime from the limestone reacts with silicaceous impurities in the iron ore to form a liquid glass that is readily separated from the molten iron. Limestone is used in making ordinary glass, portland cement and, particularly, lime, from which several other calcium compounds are made (Table 29-6).

HARDNESS OF WATER

14. Natural water is never pure. Rain water contains dust and dissolved gases, and starts to dissolve other substances as soon as it reaches the ground.

Water is said to be **hard** if it contains a significant concentration of salts whose ions will react with soap to produce a curdy precipitate before a lather is formed. Many ions do this, but the ones most prevalent in the soil through which water percolates are calcium ions and magnesium ions (and sometimes iron(II) ions). The production of a curdy precipitate ("ring-around-the-bathtub") is wasteful of soap, and is annoying. Furthermore, salts of calcium, magnesium, and iron precipitate in kettles, hot water pipes, and the boilers of steam-generating equipment to produce a hard "scale." This wastes heat, and may clog pipes sufficiently to lead to an explosion.

15. Water is said to have **temporary hardness** when the dissolved material consists mainly of calcium hydrogen carbonate, or magnesium hydrogen carbonate, or both. Boiling such water causes the "normal" carbonates of calcium and magnesium to precipitate (Equation (4)):

$$Ca(HCO_3)_2 \rightarrow CaCO_3(s) + H_2O + CO_2(g)$$
$$Mg(HCO_3)_2 \rightarrow MgCO_3(s) + H_2O + CO_2(g)$$

(If allowed to accumulate these precipitated carbonates form the objectionable "scale" already mentioned.) The carbonates can be filtered off, and the water is then said to be *softened*. The removal of temporary hardness by boiling is too expensive to be done on a large scale. A cheaper method involves adding an appropriate amount of slaked lime:

$$Ca(OH)_2 + Ca(HCO_3)_2 \rightarrow 2CaCO_3(s) + 2H_2O$$

16. If the calcium and magnesium salts are not the hydrogen carbonates, but (say) the chlorides or sulphates, then boiling will not remove the hardness. Such water is said to have **permanent hardness**. In spite of the name, however, it can be softened by appropriate treatment.

One method involves the precipitation of the offending calcium and magnesium ions. A common precipitating agent is *washing soda*, $Na_2CO_3 \cdot 10H_2O$. The following reactions occur with dissolved calcium compounds:

$$Ca^{2+} + 2Cl^- + 2Na^+ + CO_3^{2-} \rightarrow CaCO_3(s) + 2Na^+ + 2Cl^-$$

$$Ca^{2+} + SO_4^{2-} + 2Na^+ + CO_3^{2-} \rightarrow CaCO_3(s) + 2Na^+ + SO_4^{2-}$$

This has the effect of replacing the calcium and magnesium ions with sodium ions. These are usually not objectionable because they do not form precipitates with soap or form boiler scale.

A related method for softening water with so-called permanent hardness is called "ion-exchange." When the mineral *zeolite* or certain synthetic solid *ion-exchange resins* are put into water, they will release cations to the water in exchange for other cations from the water. An ion-exchange resin that originally contained sodium ions can "send" these into the water, at the same time "collecting" calcium ions from the water. An ion exchanger of course gets "used up," but it can be regenerated. See Fig. 29-2.

Ion exchanger

Fig. 29-2: *Here, in diagrammatic form, is pictured the exchange of ions between a solid ion exchanger and a solution. The process shown here is the second stage of a typical water-softening cycle. In the first stage, calcium ions in the water (which make the water "hard") are exchanged for sodium ions of the ion exchanger. This reaction is the exact reverse of that shown here. (The arrow would point the other way.) In the second stage, the ion exchanger, now clogged with calcium ions, is made ready for another water-softening stage by treating it with a concentrated solution of sodium chloride. The calcium ions of the ion exchanger are exchanged for sodium ions, as shown.*

GRADATIONS IN PROPERTIES

17. In Sec. 29-9 we pointed out that two electrons can fairly easily be removed from an atom of an alkaline earth metal. But we didn't make any distinction among the alkaline earths with respect to the ease with which the electrons can be removed. Experiments have shown that there is a regular trend in this: the amount of energy required to remove two electrons from an alkaline earth atom *decreases* steadily in the order: beryllium, magnesium, calcium, strontium, barium. This, then, is the order of *increasing* ease of removal of electrons from the outermost shell of the atoms of these elements. How may this be accounted for?

The clue is in the relative sizes of the atoms. These have been measured and they increase in the order: beryllium, magnesium, calcium, strontium, barium (Fig. 13-5). This is the same as the order of increasing ease of removal of electrons. And this correlation is understandable: the farther the outermost electrons are from the nucleus of an atom, the less they are attracted by the positive charge of the nucleus, and so the more easily they are removed.

We can express these facts and ideas in other ways. The ionization energies (Sec. 13-2) decrease in the order: beryllium, magnesium, calcium, strontium, barium. That is to say, the electropositive character (Sec. 13-5) of these elements increases with increasing atomic number or increasing atomic size. They are all metals, but barium is the most "metallic." Accordingly, these elements are all reducing agents (Sec. 28-4), barium being the most effective.

The electrode potentials (Sec. 28-13) given in Table 29-7 provide another illustration of the relative effectiveness of these metals as reducing agents.

For beryllium, magnesium and calcium, the decreasing trend is shown in Fig. 13-2 for the removal of one electron; the trend in ionization energies is the same when the energies for the removal of two electrons are measured.

| 4 |
| Be |
| 12 |
| Mg |
| 20 |
| Ca |
| 38 |
| Sr |
| 56 |
| Ba |
| 88 |
| Ra |

TABLE 29-7

ELECTRODE POTENTIALS OF ALKALINE EARTH ELEMENTS	
REDUCTION PROCESS	POTENTIAL (VOLTS, AT 25°C)
$Ba^{2+} \rightarrow Ba$	−2.91
$Sr^{2+} \rightarrow Sr$	−2.89
$Ca^{2+} \rightarrow Ca$	−2.87
$Mg^{2+} \rightarrow Mg$	−2.37
$Be^{2+} \rightarrow Be$	−1.85

Nicolas-Louis Vauquelin (1763-1829) was a peasant's son who became one of France's great chemists, and the discoverer of beryllium and chromium.

QUESTIONS

NOTE: *You may need to review sections of Chapter 9 in which some properties of calcium and magnesium were introduced.*

1. Give the name, the formula, and one use for each of four compounds of (a) calcium, (b) magnesium.

2. Write equations to represent the reactions of magnesium with (a) hydrochloric acid, (b) sulphuric acid.

3. (a) Distinguish between magnesia and milk of magnesia.

(b) Make a clear distinction between quicklime, slaked lime, and limewater.

4. Write the common name, chemical name, and formula for each of four naturally occurring compounds of calcium.

5. Write formulas for: calcium hydrogen carbonate, calcium sulphate hemihydrate, calcium chloride hexahydrate, calcium phosphate, magnesia, magnesium sulphate heptahydrate, gypsum, plaster of Paris.

6. What would be observed if a lump of calcium were dropped into a beaker of water? Write the equation for the reaction.

7. Magnesium is a reactive metal. Why, then, is it possible to use it in articles, such as wheelbarrows, which in use are exposed to atmospheric conditions?

8. Magnesium reacts slowly with cold water but rapidly with steam. Account for the difference in the rate of reaction. Is there any difference chemically between the two reactions? Write the equation or equations.

9. State how you could distinguish between: (a) calcium sulphate and magnesium sulphate, (b) slaked lime and quicklime, (c) calcium and magnesium, (d) Epsom salts and anhydrous magnesium sulphate.

10. Name and give the formula of a compound of calcium used: (a) as a bleaching agent, (b) in making plaster casts, (c) as a fertilizer, (d) in the manufacture of iron and steel, (e) to lay dust on the roads, (f) in making wallboard.

11. Name three common forms in which calcium carbonate occurs in nature.

12. Suggest an experimental demonstration to prove that there is a greater concentration of carbon dioxide in the breath than in ordinary air.

13. Account for the fact that magnesium wire or ribbon is much more easily ignited than a thick sheet or block of magnesium.

14. Write formulas for: beryllium sulphate tetrahydrate, radium bromide, strontium hydrogen carbonate, barium phosphate, strontium nitrate.

15. Describe how you might distinguish hard water from soft water.

16. Give the chemical reaction involved in the softening of permanently hard water by the use of sodium carbonate.

17. Explain the difference between temporary hardness and permanent hardness of water. How appropriate is the term temporary as applied to hardness of water?

18. In Waterloo, Ontario, the municipal water supply comes from artesian wells; in Hamilton, Ontario, the water supply is from Lake Ontario. The water in Waterloo is much harder than that in Hamilton. Account for this.

19. Small bottles of "scale remover" can be purchased, to be used for the removal of deposits of scale in electric kettles. These mostly contain hydrochloric acid plus a corrosion inhibitor (to protect the kettle). Explain the action of the acid in removing scale. If the scale had accumulated from water with permanent hardness, would the remover be effective? Explain.

*20. In laboratories handling hard water a common unit of concentration is "parts per million" (ppm). Show that 1 ppm is equivalent to 1 mg of solute/L of water. The hardness is determined by measuring, for instance, the calcium ion concentration and then reporting the hardness *as though* the solute were entirely $CaCO_3$. If a sample of well water contains 4×10^{-3} mol/L calcium ion, calculate the equivalent mass of $CaCO_3$, and report the hardness of the water as ppm $CaCO_3$.

21. Suppose water with a hardness of 100 ppm $CaCO_3$ and 84 ppm $MgCO_3$ were passed over a bed of ion exchanger loaded with sodium ion. What will be the sodium-ion content of the softened water expressed as ppm Na?

22. Describe how water is softened by ion-exchange materials. Why are softeners containing ion-exchange materials *regenerated* at intervals by passing a concentrated salt solution through them?

23. Explain why the alkaline earth elements have generally similar chemical properties.

24. Account for the progressive increase in diameter of the atoms of the alkaline earth elements as shown in Fig. 13-5. In Table 13-1, diameters of the ions of the three lightest members of this group are given. Why are the ionic diameters so much smaller than the corresponding atomic diameters?

25. Quicklime is produced in "kilns" by heating limestone to red-heat. Assuming available limestone to be 90% $CaCO_3$, what mass of quicklime can be made from each tonne of limestone heated?

*26. What mass of water is required to slake 1 kg of quicklime? The slaking reaction is exothermic, 65.3 kJ of heat being evolved for each mole of quicklime. How much heat is given out per kilogram? To get some feeling for the amount of heat this is, calculate what effect it would have on 1 kg of water (which might have been added in excess of the quantity needed for the slaking). The necessary data are in Table 24-2.

27. Calculate the mass of magnesium which, by reacting with hydrochloric acid, would produce 300 L of hydrogen measured at 20°C and 100 kPa.

28. If all the magnesium in 1 kg of magnesium carbonate were recovered as pure metal and formed into a cubical ingot, what would be the length of an edge of the cube? (See Table 3-1.)

29. An average concentration of magnesium in sea water is 1.27 parts per thousand. What mass of sea water would be required for the production of one kilogram of magnesium.

30. What mass of magnesium would be required to produce 1 kg of thorium by the reduction of thorium dioxide with magnesium?

*31. The following are the first- and second-stage ionization energies of the alkaline earth elements:

ELEMENT	FIRST STAGE (kJ/mol)	SECOND STAGE (kJ/mol)
Beryllium	899	1757
Magnesium	738	1450
Calcium	590	1145
Strontium	549	1064
Barium	503	965

Account for the decrease in each column from the top to bottom. Account for the second-stage energies being greater than the first. Calculate the ratio of the second-stage to the first-stage energies for each element. Compare this ratio with that of the charges on the ions formed at each stage.

*32. On graph paper plot the values of the first-stage ionization energies (Question 31) of the alkaline earth elements against their atomic diameters (Fig. 13-5). What correlation, if any, is suggested by the resulting plot?

33. Explain why the ionization energy of a metal atom is a factor in determining its chemical reactivity.

*34. How does the change in electrode potential (Table 29-7) relate to the change in ionization energy within the alkaline earth Group of elements.?

*35. Compare the alkaline earth metals with the alkali metals, and try to account for the differences noted, with particular reference to: (a) size of atoms, (b) reactivity of the elements, (c) solubility of salts, (d) degree of ionic character of salts of the metal.

More about
the Halogen Family

1. In Chapter 8 we introduced the halogen family of elements and discussed chlorine and some of its important compounds. In this chapter we intend to extend your knowledge of the halogens, and to amplify what has been said about the gradations in properties exhibited by these elements and their compounds.

The word "halogen" comes from Greek roots meaning "salt-producer."

You will find it helpful to refer often to Chapter 8, and so we are providing many "cross-references" to the relevant sections of that chapter (and to others, too).

2. We saw in the preceding chapter that the alkaline earth elements are characterized by the ease with which their atoms lose two electrons, to become positive ions such as Be^{2+}, Mg^{2+}, and Ca^{2+}. In sharp contrast, it is very difficult to remove even one electron from the atom of a halogen element. (In Fig. 13-2, compare the ionization energies of fluorine and chlorine with those of beryllium, magnesium, and calcium.)

What does occur readily, as we pointed out earlier (Sec. 13-5 and 13-6), is the *acquisition* of electrons by the atoms of the halogen elements. The atoms of each of these have seven electrons in their outermost shell (Table 30-1). By comparison with Table 29-3, you will see that in each instance this is one fewer electron than is possessed by the atom of an inert gas.

TABLE 30-1

ELECTRON CONFIGURATIONS OF THE HALOGEN ELEMENTS	
Fluorine ($Z = 9$)	$1s^2 2s^2 \mathbf{2p^5}$
Chlorine ($Z = 17$)	$1s^2 2s^2 2p^6 3s^2 \mathbf{3p^5}$
Bromine ($Z = 35$)	$1s^2 2s^2 2p^6 3s^2 3p^6 3d^{10} 4s^2 \mathbf{4p^5}$
Iodine ($Z = 53$)	$1s^2 2s^2 2p^6 3s^2 3p^6 3d^{10} 4s^2 4p^6 4d^{10} 5s^2 \mathbf{5p^5}$
Astatine ($Z = 85$)	$1s^2 2s^2 2p^6 3s^2 3p^6 3d^{10} 4s^2 4p^6 4d^{10} 4f^{14} 5s^2 5p^6 5d^{10} 6s^2 \mathbf{6p^5}$

Thus, by acquiring one electron, a halogen atom achieves the stable electron arrangement of an inert gas. So, halogen atoms readily become *negative* ions, singly charged: F^-, Cl^-, Br^-, I^-, At^-. These are collectively called the *halide* ions.

The halogen elements are, then, *electronegative*, in sharp contrast to the alkaline earth (and alkali) elements, which are *electropositive* (Sec. 13-5). Elements, such as the halogens, which are pronouncedly electronegative are *non-metals*; elements, such as the alkaline earth and alkali elements, which are markedly electropositive are *metals*.

3. Since the halogens readily acquire electrons, they are oxidizing agents (Sec. 28-4). Most of their importance stems from this, as you will notice while you read this chapter. Because the atoms (and the ions) of the halogens vary in size—increasing with increasing atomic number (Table 30-4)—you might expect gradations in properties among the halogens; you will notice this, too, as you read on.

4. OCCURRENCES. In discussing chlorine (Sec. 8-2), we pointed out that it is too reactive to occur uncombined. This is true of the other halogen elements too.

Fluorine, bromine, and iodine are found as ions in sea water and in underground brines and salt deposits that are the residues of ancient seas, though they occur in very much lower concentration than chloride ion (Table 30-2). Important minerals of fluorine are *fluorite* (mainly CaF_2) and *cryolite* (mainly Na_3AlF_6).

Sponges, coral, and some seaweeds have a remarkable ability to extract iodide ion from the sea, so much so that at one time most of the iodine for commerce was obtained from seaweeds. (It was in seaweeds that iodine was discovered, in 1811.)

TABLE 30-2

	AVERAGE CONCENTRATION OF HALIDE IONS IN SEA WATER	
ION	MILLIONS OF KILOGRAMS PER CUBIC KILOMETRE (or g/m^3)	PER CENT BY MASS
Fluoride ion	1.3	0.000 13
Chloride ion	19 400	1.90
Bromide ion	66	0.0065
Iodide ion	0.05	0.000 005

THE ELEMENTS THEMSELVES

5. COMMERCIAL PRODUCTION. The halogen elements other than iodine are produced by the oxidation of the corresponding halide ions.

Fluorine is made by the electrolysis of a molten fluoride, and chlorine by the electrolysis of a molten chloride (Sec. 26-4) or of an aqueous solution of a chloride (Sec. 26-13). The *oxidations* of course occur at the anode, for example,

$$2Cl^- \rightarrow Cl_2 + 2e^-$$

Much of the bromine produced on this continent comes from sea water, the bromide ion being oxidized by chlorine:

$$Cl_2 + 2Br^- \rightarrow 2Cl^- + Br_2(g)$$

Iodine is obtained by reducing sodium iodate ($NaIO_3$) from Chile with sodium hydrogen sulphite ($NaHSO_3$). The essential reaction is:

$$2IO_3^- + 5HSO_3^- \rightarrow 3HSO_4^- + 2SO_4^{2-} + H_2O + I_2(s)$$

6. LABORATORY PREPARATIONS. These, too, depend on the oxidation of the corresponding halide ions.

Chlorine may be prepared in the laboratory by the method we depicted earlier (Fig. 8-2). This involves the oxidation (by means of manganese dioxide) of chloride ion in acid solution, and the two equations in Sec.8-3 may now be simplified to:

$$MnO_2 + 2Cl^- + 4H^+ \rightarrow Mn^{2+} + 2H_2O + Cl_2(g)$$

Bromine is usually prepared in an analogous way, by heating a mixture of sodium bromide (or potassium bromide), manganese dioxide, and dilute sulphuric acid:

$$MnO_2 + 2Br^- + 4H^+ \rightarrow Mn^{2+} + 2H_2O + Br_2(g)$$

Bromine vapour is distilled from the mixture, and then immediately cooled (say, by placing the receiving container in ice water) to yield liquid bromine.

Iodine can be prepared similarly, by the oxidation of an iodide (Fig. 30-1).

7. PROPERTIES. In Chapter 8 we described physical properties of the halogens, and we need not repeat here what is in Sec. 8-12 and Table 8-1. In that chapter, too, we discussed chemical properties of chlorine (Sec. 8-5 and 8-6) and made comparisons with the properties of other halogen elements (Sec. 8-13).

What we stress here is that the halogens constitute the most reactive family of non-metals that exists. Halogen *atoms* are extremely reactive: when there is nothing else around for them to react with, they react with each other to give diatomic molecules (F_2, Cl_2, etc.), as we indicated earlier (Sec. 8-11). In the form of diatomic molecules, all the halogen elements react with phosphorus, hydrogen, most metals, and hundreds of other substances.

For example, the halogens react with many different carbon-containing compounds, to produce an impressive variety of important and useful products: the refrigerant and aerosol propellant "Freon" (CCl_2F_2), the solvents chloroform

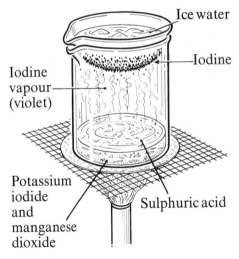

Fig. 30-1: *When a mixture of sodium iodide (or potassium iodide), manganese dioxide, and dilute sulphuric acid is heated, iodine is formed and passes off as a vapour. This condenses to solid crystals when it come in contact with a cold surface (here the under-surface of an evaporating dish containing ice water).*

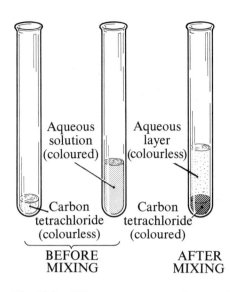

Aqueous solution (coloured)

Aqueous layer (colourless)

Carbon tetrachloride (colourless)

Carbon tetrachloride (coloured)

BEFORE MIXING

AFTER MIXING

Fig. 30-2: *When an aqueous solution of a halogen element is shaken with a little carbon tetrachloride, which is insoluble in water, the halogen concentrates in the carbon tetrachloride layer at the bottom, giving it a characteristic colour. No such effect is produced if the halogen is present only as the ion (chloride, bromide, or iodide). In this experiment, cyclohexane may be substituted for carbon tetrachloride. In this case, the displaced halogen accumulates in a cyclohexane layer above the aqueous solution.* **Take care: cyclohexane is flammable.**

($CHCl_3$) and carbon tetrachloride (CCl_4), the fumigating agent methyl bromide (CH_3Br), the antiseptic iodoform (CHI_3), dry-cleaning fluids (CH_2Cl_2; C_2Cl_4; $C_2Cl_3F_3$), plastics such as "Teflon," insecticides, weed-killers such as "2,4-D"—the list could go on and on.

Whatever the substance a halogen is reacting with, you can expect that fluorine will cause the most vigorous reaction, followed by chlorine, bromine, and iodine in that order of decreasing vigour. In most cases, the halogen will be serving as an oxidizing agent; in fact, the most important property of the halogen elements is their oxidizing ability.

8. All the halogens are very soluble in carbon disulphide, chloroform, and carbon tetrachloride. With carbon tetrachloride, chlorine forms a yellow solution, bromine an orange-red or brown solution, and iodine a violet or purple solution.

Chlorine or chlorine water will displace bromine from bromides, and iodine from iodides:

$$Cl_2 + 2NaBr \rightarrow 2NaCl + Br_2$$
$$Cl_2 + 2NaI \rightarrow 2NaCl + I_2$$

These reactions may be written more simply:

$$Cl_2 + 2Br^- \rightarrow 2Cl^- + Br_2$$
$$Cl_2 + 2I^- \rightarrow 2Cl^- + I_2$$

The displaced halogen (bromine or iodine) may readily be detected by adding carbon tetrachloride to the solution and shaking (shaking the test tube, that is). See Fig. 30-2. Similarly, bromine will displace iodine from iodides:

$$Br_2 + 2I^- \rightarrow 2Br^- + I_2$$

All these displacements are oxidation-reduction reactions. Chlorine can oxidize bromides and iodides, and bromine can oxidize iodides. Accordingly, chlorine is a stronger oxidizing agent than bromine, and bromine is a stronger oxidizing agent than iodine. And, it may be added, fluorine is stronger than any of the three.

METAL HALIDES

9. We have noted earlier the occurrences of sodium chloride and potassium chloride (Sec. 8-2) and uses of these and other important metal halides (Table 8-3).

The chlorides, bromides, and other halides of sodium and potassium (and other alkali metals) are white crystalline salts. All these alkali halides are ionic salts: each consists of alkali metal ions (K^+, Na^+, etc.) associated with halide ions (Cl^-, Br^-, etc.) in equal numbers. It is reasonable to expect these salts to be ionic, because they are formed by the reaction of strongly electropositive elements with strongly electronegative elements (Sec. 13-5).

10. All the alkali halides are soluble in water, though to varying degrees. Their crystals are held together by the attractive forces between the positively charged and negatively charged ions. When one of these salts is put into water, the water induces a separation, or disassociation, of the ions of the salt by effectively reducing the forces of attraction between the ions. Thus the geometrical arrangement of the ions that exists in the solid crystal is "broken down" and the ions, with associated sheaths of water molecules, become distributed throughout the water—that is, the crystal dissolves in the water.

HYDROGEN HALIDES

11. At ordinary temperatures, hydrogen fluoride, hydrogen chloride, hydrogen bromide, and hydrogen iodide are all colourless gases, with sharp and penetrating odours. All of them are very soluble in water (Table 8-2), yielding acidic solutions, by virtue of reaction with water, for example,

$$HCl + H_2O \rightarrow H_3O^+ + Cl^-$$

The aqueous solutions (hydrofluoric acid, hydrochloric acid, hydrobromic acid, and hydriodic acid), with the exception of hydrofluoric acid, are strong acids (Sec. 27-4). Hydrofluoric acid is exceptional, too, in its ability to attack silicaceous materials; this accounts for its use in etching glass (as in making "frosted" light bulbs), and cleaning stone, brick, and metal castings made in sand moulds.

The hydrogen halides can all be made by the direct union of the elements, for example,

$$H_2 + Cl_2 \rightarrow 2HCl$$

but this is not a convenient laboratory method. The reaction of hydrogen with fluorine or with chlorine can occur suddenly with explosive violence.

12. In the laboratory, **hydrogen chloride**, HCl, is readily prepared as illustrated in Fig. 8-3. The reaction can be represented by the equation:

$$Cl^- + H_2SO_4 \rightarrow HSO_4^- + HCl$$

A suitable method for preparing relatively pure **hydrogen bromide**, HBr, is the reaction of either phosphorus tribromide or phosphorus pentabromide with water:

$$PBr_3 + 3H_2O \rightarrow H_3PO_3 + 3HBr(g)$$
$$\text{phosphorous acid}$$

$$PBr_5 + 4H_2O \rightarrow H_3PO_4 + 5HBr(g)$$
$$\text{phosphoric acid}$$

This chunk of potash ore from deep under southern Saskatchewan consists of the minerals sylvite (mainly KCl) and carnallite (mainly KCl·MgCl₂·6H₂O), formed about 370 million years ago by the evaporation of a large inland sea.

The well-formed crystals you see here are sylvite; the carnallite, orange and less obviously crystalline, occurs in this specimen clinging to the faces of many of the sylvite crystals.

The attack of hydrofluoric acid on silicaceous materials, such as glass, is a consequence of reactions such as:

$$4HF + SiO_2 \rightarrow 2H_2O + SiF_4(g)$$
$$6HF + CaSiO_3 \rightarrow CaF_2 + 3H_2O + SiF_4(g)$$

The reaction of hydrogen with fluorine is highly exothermic. It is used in the hydrogen-fluorine torch, which has a flame hot enough to cut through cement and rock.

Hydrogen iodide, HI, can be made similarily, from phosphorus triiodide:

$$PI_3 + 3H_2O \rightarrow H_3PO_3 + 3HI(g)$$

13. Because hydrogen chloride is prepared by heating concentrated sulphuric acid with sodium chloride, you may be asking: why is hydrogen bromide not prepared by the action of concentrated sulphuric acid on sodium bromide, nor hydrogen iodide by the action of sulphuric acid on sodium iodide?

The answer has to do with the fact that concentrated sulphuric acid is an oxidizing agent. It is not strong enough to oxidize hydrogen chloride, but it is sufficiently strong to oxidize hydrogen bromide and, even more readily, hydrogen iodide.

If one attempts to make hydrogen bromide by the reaction of sodium bromide and sulphuric acid

$$Br^- + H_2SO_4 \rightarrow HSO_4^- + HBr(g)$$

some of the hydrogen bromide that is formed is oxidized by the sulphuric acid

$$2HBr + H_2SO_4 \rightarrow SO_2(g) + Br_2(g) + 2H_2O \qquad (1)$$

Accordingly, any hydrogen bromide that is collected is contaminated with sulphur dioxide and bromine.

With the hydrogen iodide that is initially formed by the action of sulphuric acid on sodium iodide, the oxidation occurs in this way:

$$8HI + H_2SO_4 \rightarrow H_2S(g) + 4I_2(g) + 4H_2O \qquad (2)$$

When sulphuric acid acts as an oxidizing agent, it itself must of course be reduced; in the reaction of Equation (2), sulphuric acid is reduced to hydrogen sulphide, which is a greater reduction than that in the reaction of Equation (1), where the reduction product is sulphur dioxide.

These facts can be summarized by saying that, as reducing agents, hydrogen iodide is stronger than hydrogen bromide, and hydrogen bromide is stronger than hydrogen chloride. In fact, it is true generally that the reducing power of the halide ions decreases in the order iodide, bromide, chloride, fluoride.

14. Hydrogen iodide is readily decomposed by light energy or heat energy into its elements:

$$2HI \rightarrow H_2 + I_2$$

Hydrogen bromide is less readily decomposed, hydrogen chloride still less so, and hydrogen fluoride is very stable. This order of stability is related to the heat evolved or absorbed (Table 30-3) when the hydrogen halides are formed from the elements. Can you see why this is so?

TABLE 30-3

HEAT EFFECTS IN THE FORMATION OF THE HYDROGEN HALIDES	
kJ/mol	
HF	269 (evolved)
HCl	92 (evolved)
HBr	36 (evolved)
HI	26 (absorbed)

GRADATIONS IN PROPERTIES

15. We have drawn attention to gradations among the halogens in physical properties (Table 8-1), such as gradations in the state of the elements at room temperature, in the colour of the elements in the gaseous and solid states, and in density, melting point, and boiling point. And we have seen gradations in chemical properties, as in the reactivity of these elements toward water and metals (Sec. 8-13) and in their oxidizing ability (Sec. 30-8).

Similarly, gradations exist in the properties of the hydrogen halides: for example, in their reducing power (Sec. 30-13), in their stability (Sec. 30-14), and in the heat effects that occur in their formation from the elements (Table 30-3).

16. Some of these gradations can be accounted for by the sizes of the atoms and ions of the halogen elements. Consider the gradation in the oxidizing ability or power of the elements: fluorine is the strongest oxidizing agent, and chlorine, bromine, and iodine are progressively weaker oxidizing agents. When an element acts as an oxidizing agent, its atoms acquire electrons (Sec. 28-4). We have seen that an atom of any halogen element tends to acquire an electron (to achieve the stable electron arrangement of an atom of an inert gas), but we might expect fluorine to have the greatest such tendency—and so be the strongest oxidizing agent—because its atoms are smallest (Table 30-4). The outermost shell, in which the acquired electron will be held, is in fluorine relatively close to the positive nuclear charge, and so we would expect an acquired electron to be attracted more to fluorine than to any other halogen. Put another way, we would expect that more energy would be released when an atom of fluorine acquires an electron than when an atom of chlorine does, and that the energy released when an atom of chlorine acquires an electron would be more than that when an atom of bromine does, and so on, through iodine and astatine. Still another way of saying it is that we would expect the electron affinity (Sec. 13-5) to decrease from fluorine through astatine.

Can you see that a similar kind of reasoning will account for the fact that the strengths of the halide ions as *reducing* agents *decrease* in the order iodide ion, bromide ion, chloride ion, fluoride ion?

17. SOME WORDS OF QUALIFICATION. The relative strengths of the halogen elements as oxidizing agents, and the relative strengths of their ions as reducing agents, are as we have stated them to be, but the explanation given in Sec. 30-16 is not the whole story.

When, for example, iodide ion in aqueous solution acts as a reducing agent, several processes occur: the iodide ions are dehydrated (lose their sheaths of water molecules), the dehydrated ions each give up an electron to yield atoms of

| 9 |
| F |
| 17 |
| Cl |
| 35 |
| Br |
| 53 |
| I |
| 85 |
| At |

TABLE 30-4

SIZES OF ATOMS AND
IONS OF HALOGEN ELEMENTS

	RADIUS IN PICOMETRES	
	OF THE ATOM	OF THE ION
Fluorine	64	133
Chlorine	99	181
Bromine	114	196
Iodine	133	220

TABLE 30-5

ELECTRODE POTENTIALS
OF HALOGEN ELEMENTS

REDUCTION PROCESS	POTENTIAL (VOLTS, AT 25°C)
$I_2 \rightarrow 2I^-$	0.62
$Br_2 \rightarrow 2Br^-$	1.08
$Cl_2 \rightarrow 2Cl^-$	1.36
$F_2 \rightarrow 2F^-$	2.87

iodine, the atoms combine in pairs to form molecules of iodine, and the molecules condense to solid iodine. Each of these four "steps" involves energy: in the first two, energy is absorbed; in the last two, energy is evolved (though relatively little, compared to the energy absorbed in the first two steps).

The second step (electron removal from the ion), although very important, is somewhat less important (in terms of the energy involved) than the dehydration step. Moreover, for reasons we can't go into here, to remove an electron from a chloride ion requires a bit *more* energy than to remove an electron from a fluoride ion, whereas we have implied otherwise, above. However, when the energies involved in all four "steps" are taken into account, the net amounts of energy required to convert aqueous halide ions to the elements are strictly in the order of the effectiveness of the ions as reducing agents (and of the elements as oxidizing agents). This is reflected in the electrode potentials (Sec. 28-13) given in Table 30-5.

QUESTIONS

NOTE: *You should also review Chapter 8 in preparation for answering these questions.*

1. What is the meaning of the term "halogen"? Name the members of the halogen family, and justify their inclusion in the same family. Why are these elements classed as non-metals?

2. What is the common feature of the electron configuration of the atoms in this family of elements?

3. Write equations for the reactions involved in the laboratory preparation of chlorine, bromine, and iodine.

4. What are the most important natural occurrences of each of the halogens?

5. Review the products of the electrolysis of an aqueous solution of sodium chloride. Can you suggest why the element fluorine cannot be prepared by electrolysis of an aqueous solution of sodium fluoride?

6. Write equations for the reactions of iron, lithium, and hydrogen with (a) chlorine, (b) bromine, and (c) iodine.

7. Compare the elements chlorine, bromine, and iodine, with respect to (a) relative solubility in water, (b) stability of their hydrogen compounds, (c) bleaching action.

8. Bromine is said to have properties midway between those of chlorine and iodine. Illustrate the truth of this statement.

9. Why do halogens not occur naturally in elemental form?

10. You are given three clear, colourless solutions: one of a chloride, one of a bromide, and one of an iodide. How could you prove which was which by chemical tests?

11. Cite experimental evidence to show that the order of increasing oxidizing power among the halogens is: iodine, bromine, chlorine, fluorine.

12. What would be observed (a) if an aqueous solution of chlorine were shaken with an equal volume of carbon tetrachloride in a test tube, and then the contents were allowed to stand? (b) if the mixture obtained in (a) were shaken in a test tube with 5 mL of an aqueous solution of sodium bromide? Explain these observations with the aid of equations.

13. What would be observed if an aqueous solution of bromine were shaken with an equal volume of carbon tetrachloride, and then the contents were allowed to stand? What would be observed if this mixture were now shaken with half its volume of an aqueous solution of potassium iodide? Account for your observations.

14. How is hydrogen chloride prepared in the laboratory? Why does a similar method of preparation not succeed for hydrogen bromide or hydrogen iodide?

15. Describe a suitable laboratory preparation of hydrogen bromide.

16. Aqueous solutions of hydrogen iodide (hydriodic acid) frequently turn brown on standing. Can you suggest an explanation for this? Can you suggest an experiment by which you could put your explanation to the test?

17. Cite experimental evidence to show that hydrogen iodide is a stronger reducing agent than hydrogen bromide, and this in turn is a stronger reducing agent than hydrogen chloride.

18. Why are the hydrogen halides collected in the laboratory by the upward displacement of air? What is the ratio of the density of each to that of the air at STP (1.293 g/L)?

19. Show by an equation the reaction by which hydrogen fluoride can etch silica.

20. Discuss, with examples, the gradation of physical and chemical properties within the family of the halogens.

21. Select from each of the following sets the atom, ion, or molecule represented by the formula which best fits the characteristic listed alongside:

(a) F, Cl, Br, I   Largest atom

(b) F, Cl, Br, I   Lowest ionization energy

(c) HF, HCl, HBr, HI   Weakest acid

(d) F⁻, Cl⁻, Br⁻, I⁻   Strongest reducing agent

(e) F, Cl, Br, I   Greatest electronegativity

(f) F_2, Cl_2, Br_2, I_2 Greatest density in solid

(g) HF, HCl, HBr, HI   Most likelihood of hydrogen bonding

22. The element astatine, the fifth member of the halogen family, has the atomic number 85 and the atomic mass 211. Predict what you can about its (a) physical state, (b) density, (c) colour, (d) reactions with hydrogen and with water, (e) hydride.

23. "The most important property of the halogen elements is their oxidizing ability." Discuss this statement.

24. Calculate the density of chlorine gas at a temperature of 30°C and a pressure of 106.7 kPa.

25. (a) Analysis of methyl chloride gives: chlorine 70.2%, hydrogen 6.0%, and carbon 23.8%. Calculate the simplest formula for the compound.

(b) The density of methyl chloride vapour at 25°C and 101.3 kPa is 2.05 g/L. Calculate an experimental molar mass.

(c) Give the true formula for methyl chloride, and compare the molar mass based on the formula with that derived from experiment.

26. What is the concentration (in moles per litre) of a solution of hydrochloric acid containing 7.3 g of hydrogen chloride in each 500 mL?

27. What is the amount of chlorine gas (in moles) produced by the electrolysis of 1.17 g of sodium chloride? What volume would be occupied by this amount of chlorine at STP?

28. Chlorine can be made in the laboratory from manganese dioxide and hydrochloric acid. What volume of concentrated hydrochloric acid (12 mol/L) would be required to react with 25 g of manganese dioxide?

29. Calculate the density of silicon tetrafluoride vapour at 77°C and 93.3 kPa pressure. What is the ratio of the density of this vapour to that of air at the same temperature and pressure?

*30. What is the concentration of hydrogen ions (in moles per litre) in a solution of hydrofluoric acid containing 2.0 g of hydrogen fluoride per litre if 8% of the molecules have reacted to form ions? In what way is the ionization of hydrogen fluoride different from that of the other hydrogen halides in aqueous solution?

*31. Fluorine is the most electronegative element known. Comparing it with its nearest neighbours in the Periodic Table, why is fluorine more electronegative than oxygen? Than chlorine?

32. Compare and account for what is observed when concentrated sulphuric acid is added to separate portions of sodium chloride, sodium bromide, and sodium iodide.

*33. On a single sheet of graph paper plot the melting points and the boiling points of the halogen elements (in kelvins) against the quantum number (n) of the valence shell of the respective halogen atoms. Comment on the relationships revealed.

*34. On a single sheet of graph paper plot atomic radii and ionic radii of the halogens (in picometres) against the quantum number (n) of the valence shell of the respective halogen atoms. Comment on the resulting plots.

*35. Use your results from Questions 33 and 34 to estimate atomic and ionic radii, melting point, and boiling point of astatine.

36. Reference was made in the text to chlorine dioxide, ClO_2. Write a plausible electron-dot structure for the molecule of this substance. Do you find any unusual feature of this molecule?

*37. Describe the formation of molecules of a hydrogen halide from molecules of hydrogen and of the corresponding halogen. If Q_1 is the heat evolved in the formation of 1 mol of H_2 from hydrogen atoms, and Q_2 is the heat evolved in the formation of X_2 (halogen) from its atoms, and Q_3 is the heat evolved in the formation of HX from its atoms, show how Q_1, Q_2, and Q_3 must be combined to give the heats of formation shown in Table 30-3.

*38. From the heat effects accompanying the formation of the hydrogen halides shown in Table 30-3, are you justified in assuming that the H—X bond is progressively weaker in passing along the series HF . . . HI? Explain.

*39. The density of iodine vapour measured at 800°C and 101.3 kPa, was found to be 2.611 g/L. Calculate the apparent molar mass of iodine under these conditions. Is this the answer you expected to get? If not, suggest an explanation for the discrepancy.

*40. The boiling point of hydrogen fluoride is 20°C. The density of the vapour was measured at two temperatures and at a pressure of 100 kPa. At 27°C the density was 2.00 g/L; at 80°C it was 0.682 g/L. Calculate the molar mass of hydrogen fluoride at each temperature. Can you account in any way for the results you get? (Refer to Sec. 24-5.)

*41. Plot on a single sheet of graph paper the melting and boiling points of the hydrogen halides (in kelvins) against the quantum number (n) of the valence shell of the constituent halogen atoms. Compare the plot with that obtained in Question 33. Comment on the position of HF on this plot. (Compare Fig. 24-4.)

42. With the aid of the electrochemical series (Table 28-1) and the data in Table 30-5, state whether (a) bromine is capable of oxidizing copper metal, (b) bromine is capable of oxidizing chloride ion, (c) copper(II) ion is capable of oxidizing chloride ion? Justify your answers.

*43. Bromine will oxidize iron(II) salts to iron(III), but iodine will not (unless in enormous excess). Decide approximately where in the electrochemical series you would place the electron-transfer process:

$$e^- + Fe^{3+} \rightarrow Fe^{2+}$$

31 The Community of Chemical Families

1. In Chapter 12 we introduced the Periodic Table and outlined the basis of its structure. There we pointed to chemical relationships among members of four families: the alkali metals, the alkaline earth metals, the halogen elements, and the inert gases. Since then we have had more to say about most of these elements—particularly the alkaline earth elements (Chapter 29) and the halogens (Chapters 8 and 30)—and we have referred to the nitrogen family (Sec. 22-10) and the oxygen family (Sec. 23-16). It has been stressed that the members of a particular family have similar chemical properties because the atoms of the elements in a family have the same number and arrangement of electrons in the outermost electron shell. In brief, similarities in chemical properties or behaviour stem from similarities in electron configuration.

In this chapter we shall expand the fragmentary Periodic Table depicted in Chapter 12 (Tables 12-2 and 12-3) to embrace the 105 chemical elements now known. In so doing, we hope to consolidate and increase your knowledge of the structure of the Table and your appreciation of its importance and usefulness.

2. Many different forms of Periodic Table have been devised, but the one most generally useful is that displayed in Table 31-1. Whatever the form, a Periodic Table is a tabular arrangement of the elements in the order of their atomic numbers such that elements with similar electron configurations are grouped together. Such a Table reveals the recurrence of similarities in properties that is the basis of the **Periodic Law**:

If the elements are arranged in the order of their atomic numbers, a recurring or periodic repetition of properties is obtained.

3. PERIODS AND GROUPS. The elements symbolized in the horizontal rows of Table 31-1 constitute what are called **Periods**. The first Period consists of only two elements; the second and third Periods each have

Perhaps we should remind you again that the atomic number, Z, is the number of protons in the nucleus of an atom (that is, the nuclear charge) or the number of electrons that surround the nucleus in a neutral (un-ionized) atom.

TABLE 31-1

A PERIODIC CLASSIFICATION OF THE ELEMENTS

The atomic number is given above the symbol of the element. The Groups are arranged vertically, and the Periods horizontally.

1	2											3	4	5	6	7	0
1 H																	2 He
3 Li	4 Be											5 B	6 C	7 N	8 O	9 F	10 Ne
11 Na	12 Mg											13 Al	14 Si	15 P	16 S	17 Cl	18 Ar
19 K	20 Ca	21 Sc	22 Ti	23 V	24 Cr	25 Mn	26 Fe	27 Co	28 Ni	29 Cu	30 Zn	31 Ga	32 Ge	33 As	34 Se	35 Br	36 Kr
37 Rb	38 Sr	39 Y	40 Zr	41 Nb	42 Mo	43 Tc	44 Ru	45 Rh	46 Pd	47 Ag	48 Cd	49 In	50 Sn	51 Sb	52 Te	53 I	54 Xe
55 Cs	56 Ba	57-71 see below*	72 Hf	73 Ta	74 W	75 Re	76 Os	77 Ir	78 Pt	79 Au	80 Hg	81 Tl	82 Pb	83 Bi	84 Po	85 At	86 Rn
87 Fr	88 Ra	89-103 see below†	104 Unq	105 Unp	106 Unh												

*LANTHANIDE SERIES	57 La	58 Ce	59 Pr	60 Nd	61 Pm	62 Sm	63 Eu	64 Gd	65 Tb	66 Dy	67 Ho	68 Er	69 Tm	70 Yb	71 Lu
†ACTINIDE SERIES	89 Ac	90 Th	91 Pa	92 U	93 Np	94 Pu	95 Am	96 Cm	97 Bk	98 Cf	99 Es	100 Fm	101 Md	102 No	103 Lr

eight elements; and the fourth and fifth Periods each have 18 elements. We shall account for these differences presently.

The elements symbolized in the columns constitute what are called **Groups**, and these correspond to the *families* of elements. The main Groups or families often are referred to by the numbers (0, 1, etc.) at the top of columns in Table 31-1. So, one speaks of "Group 7" or "the halogen family."

ATOMIC STRUCTURE AND THE PERIODIC TABLE

4. THE BUILDING-UP PRINCIPLE. We have previously accounted for resemblances among the elements having atomic numbers from 1 to 20 on the grounds that elements with similar properties had similar electron configurations in their outermost shells. The clue to physical and chemical similarity within families of elements lies in the arrangement of the electrons in their atoms. In this section we shall further examine the organization of the whole Periodic Table in terms of what we called the building-up principle (Sec. 12-4).

In the following discussion we shall assume that you are familiar with the terms *orbitals* and *shells*, that you know how these are labelled, and remember how many orbitals make up each shell, and therefore the maximum number of electrons that each shell can hold. This is discussed in Sec. 11-16, and is illustrated in Table 31-2 (which is a slightly modified version of Table 11-1). We also assume that you have reviewed the principal features of the building-up principle as outlined in Sec. 12-2 and 12-4 to 12-6. The order in which orbitals are populated by electrons depends on the relative energy of the orbitals, and may conveniently be remembered by the chart in Fig. 31-1. In the discussion of electron configurations which follows, the configuration given is that of lowest energy—that is, the configuration of each atom in the ground state (Sec. 11-17).

TABLE 31-2

ORBITALS, SHELLS, AND THEIR CAPACITIES FOR ELECTRONS

SHELL	VALUE OF n	ORBITALS	CAPACITY OF ORBITALS FOR ELECTRONS	CAPACITY OF SHELLS FOR ELECTRONS
K	1	1s	2	2
L	2	2s	2	8
		2p	6	
M	3	3s	2	18
		3p	6	
		3d	10	
N	4	4s	2	32
		4p	6	
		4d	10	
		4f	14	

5. STRUCTURE OF THE PERIODIC TABLE. First Period. The one electron that a hydrogen atom has is in the ls orbital. The two electrons of the helium atom ($Z = 2$) are in this same orbital, and two electrons are all that the first shell can accommodate (Table 31-2). The first Period in the Periodic Table consists of only these two elements, whose atoms have either one electron (hydrogen) or two (helium) in the first shell.

Second Period. This consists of eight elements, with $Z = 3$ to $Z = 10$. In the atoms of these there is a regular increase in the number of electrons in the second shell ($n = 2$). At neon (Ne, with $Z = 10$) this shell has its maximum of eight electrons. Accordingly, neon is like helium in having atoms with a filled or "closed" outer shell of electrons, and the inertness or lack of reactivity of helium and neon stems from this fact.

3 Li	4 Be	5 B	6 C	7 N	8 O	9 F	10 Ne
$2s$	$2s^2$	$2s^22p$	$2s^22p^2$	$2s^22p^3$	$2s^22p^4$	$2s^22p^5$	$2s^22p^6$

Electron Configuration (in addition to $1s^2$)

Third Period. This also consists of eight elements, with $Z = 11$ to $Z = 18$. The atoms of these elements all have a filled first shell (with electron configuration $1s^2$) and a filled second shell (with electron configuration $2s^22p^6$) and then 1,2,3, ... 8 electrons in the third shell ($n = 3$). Sodium (Na, with $Z = 11$) is like lithium (Li, with $Z = 3$) in having atoms with only one electron, in an s orbital, in their outermost shell. Magnesium (Mg, with $Z = 12$) is like beryllium (Be, with $Z = 4$) in having atoms with two electrons, also in an s orbital, in their outermost shell.

11 Na	12 Mg	13 Al	14 Si	15 P	16 S	17 Cl	18 Ar
$3s$	$3s^2$	$3s^23p$	$3s^23p^2$	$3s^23p^3$	$3s^23p^4$	$3s^23p^5$	$3s^23p^6$

Electron Configuration (in addition to $1s^22s^22p^6$)

Similar correspondences in electron configuration with the other elements of the second Period occur for the elements of $Z = 13$ to $Z = 18$, as you can see by comparing the configurations given under the "boxes" above. Argon (Ar, with $Z = 18$) is like neon in having eight electrons in the outermost shell of its atoms, six of the eight filling the p orbitals. However, the third shell is not filled at argon because this shell, having d orbitals, can accommodate up to 18 electrons (Table 31-2). Nonetheless, eight electrons in a shell is a very stable arrangement: argon is very inert, just as neon and helium are. These, together with three other elements, krypton (Kr), xenon (Xe), and radon (Rn) make up Group 0, the family of *inert gases*.

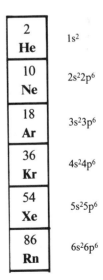

2 He	$1s^2$
10 Ne	$2s^22p^6$
18 Ar	$3s^23p^6$
36 Kr	$4s^24p^6$
54 Xe	$5s^25p^6$
86 Rn	$6s^26p^6$

Outer-shell Configuration

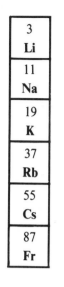

Outer-shell Configuration

Fourth Period. This begins with potassium (K, with $Z = 19$) in which electrons first appear in the fourth shell ($n = 4$). Potassium is like sodium and lithium of Group 1 (the *alkali metal* family) in having atoms with only one electron, in an s orbital, in their outermost shell. The other members of this family are rubidium (Rb), caesium (Cs), and francium (Fr); their electron configurations are similar.

Calcium (Ca, with $Z = 20$) is like magnesium and beryllium of Group 2 (the *alkaline earth* family) in having atoms with two electrons, in an s orbital, in their outermost shell. The other alkaline earth elements have atoms with similar electron configurations.

6. TRANSITION ELEMENTS. In the complete Periodic Table (Table 31-1) you will see that the Period which begins with potassium is longer than the preceding Periods. It is longer, in fact, by the inclusion of ten elements ($Z = 21$ to $Z = 30$) before gallium (Ga) which, because of its properties, belongs in the family with aluminium (Al). If electrons occupy orbitals in the order of their ascending energy, and if the energy levels shown for sodium (Fig. 12-3) apply to succeeding elements, it seems a reasonable deduction that the inclusion of this group of ten elements at this place in the Periodic Table corresponds to the occupancy of the five 3d orbitals. When these are filled (at zinc, with $Z = 30$), additional electrons begin to occupy the 4p orbitals, and the fourth shell resumes filling.

The elements from scandium to zinc constitute a series quite unlike any we have met before. They have no counterparts in electron configuration or chemical properties among the elements of lower atomic number. This is because, as shown, there are electrons in 3d orbitals as well as 4s orbitals, and both types of electrons contribute to the properties of the elements and their compounds. Incidentally, you will note that the electron configuration of copper constitutes one of the exceptions, about which we warned you in Sec. 12-7, to the simple order of filling orbitals suggested by Fig. 12-4 or 31-1.

21 Sc	22 Ti	23 V	24 Cr	25 Mn	26 Fe	27 Co	28 Ni	29 Cu	30 Zn
$3d4s^2$	$3d^24s^2$	$3d^34s^2$	$3d^54s$	$3d^54s^2$	$3d^64s^2$	$3d^74s^2$	$3d^84s^2$	$3d^{10}4s$	$3d^{10}4s^2$

Electron Configuration beyond the Argon "Core"

This series of ten elements is parelleled by two other series of elements whose atomic structure also features the filling of d orbitals. These are the series of elements having $Z = 39$ to $Z = 48$, and a series including lanthanum, with $Z = 57$, and the elements with $Z = 72$ to $Z = 80$. (See Table 31-1.) These three series make up what are called the *transition elements*. Because of the d electrons in their atoms these elements exhibit greater variability in oxidation state than is found among non-transition elements. It is also among compounds of transition elements that an appreciable number of coloured substances are to be found.

7. There are also *inner-transition* elements in the atoms of which f orbitals are being occupied by electrons. One series of such elements is known as the *lanthanides* because they follow lanthanum ($Z = 57$) in atomic number. Another such series is known as the *actinides*, and these follow actinium ($Z = 89$) in atomic number. Each of these latter series is made up of fourteen elements, and they can be related to the gradual filling of the seven f orbitals of the fourth and fifth shells respectively. They are shown printed separately in the lower part of Table 31-1, but it should be understood that they belong *within* the Periodic Table as indicated.

8. BLOCKS OF RELATED ELEMENTS. From what has been said in this chapter and elsewhere in this book you should have no trouble in grasping the notion that the elements in the Periodic Table can be divided into categories or "blocks" according to the type of electron last added in the hypothetical building-up process. Thus we can group together "s-block," "p-block," "d-block," and "f-block" elements as indicated in Fig. 31-2. This figure should be related to Table 31-1.

The s-block is made up of Groups 1 and 2. The p-block includes Groups 3 to 7 and Group 0. However, helium, though a member of Group 0, belongs in the s-block. The members of the s-block and p-block, taken together, comprise the **main-group elements**. The d-block is made up of the **transition elements**, and the f-block includes the series called **lanthanides** and **actinides**. Fig. 31-2 is a convenient way to relate these different kinds of elements.

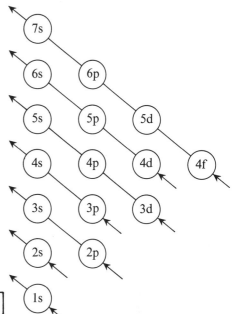

Fig. 31-1: *This is a "replay" of Fig. 12-5 showing the order in which atomic orbitals are filled in the imaginary building up of atoms. For an explanation of how to use the chart, refer to the original figure.*

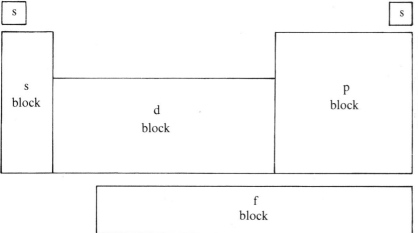

Fig. 31-2: *A "block" diagram for the Periodic Table*

GRADATIONS AND TRENDS

9. GRADATIONS IN FAMILY PROPERTIES. We have already given illustrations of gradations in the properties of the elements (and their compounds) of Group 2 (the alkaline earth family), of Group 5 (the nitrogen family), of Group 6 (the oxygen family), and of Group 7 (the halogen family). We have accounted for gradations in properties in a family of el-

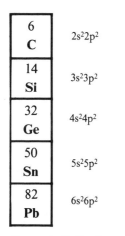

6 **C**	$2s^2 2p^2$
14 **Si**	$3s^2 3p^2$
32 **Ge**	$4s^2 4p^2$
50 **Sn**	$5s^2 5p^2$
82 **Pb**	$6s^2 6p^2$

Outer-shell Configuration

Although carbon in the form of graphite has fair electrical conductivity.

ements by the increasing size of the atoms, or increasing size of the ions, as the atomic number increases.

Similar considerations apply in the other families too. Consider the family of Group 4: carbon (C), silicon (Si), germanium (Ge), tin (Sn), and lead (Pb). The atoms of these elements increase in size in the order they are written above—lead being the largest (Fig. 13-5). We might expect, then, that electrons could be removed from an atom of lead or tin more easily than from an atom of any of the other Group 4 elements—that is, that lead and tin would have the lowest ionization energy among the elements of this family. And this is so. These elements show distinct electropositive character and are metals, having, for example, the metallic characteristics of lustre, malleability, and good electrical and thermal conductivity. Germanium shows both metallic and non-metallic characteristics. Silicon and carbon are non-metals, carbon being more non-metallic than silicon. Carbon in the form of diamond is a very poor conductor of electricity; its oxide is acidic (whereas the oxides of metallic elements are basic).

10. HYDROGEN, A UNIQUE ELEMENT. Hydrogen is the simplest element, in that its atom has only one electron. But the family relationships of hydrogen are not simple, because in some ways it resembles the elements of the alkali metal family and in other ways it resembles the elements of the halogen family. Hydrogen is best considered a family all to itself, and for this reason it is set apart in Table 31-1.

Like the alkali metals, hydrogen reacts with halogens to form halides (HCl, HBr, etc.) but these are primarily covalent compounds whereas the alkali metal halides (NaCl, KBr, etc.) are ionic compounds. The hydrogen halides do, however, yield positive ions (H_3O^+) and negative ions (Cl^-, Br^-, etc.) in aqueous solution (Sec. 26-8), and in this respect resemble the alkali metal halides.

Like the halogen elements, hydrogen forms diatomic molecules (H_2), and reacts with the alkali metals to form compounds such as sodium hydride, Na^+H^-, which, like sodium chloride, are crystalline ionic compounds.

The electron arrangement in hydrogen is unique and accounts for its unusual properties. The first shell contains the only electron an atom of hydrogen has; this shell is, then, the outermost shell—and in having one electron in the outermost shell (in an s orbital) the atoms of hydrogen are like the atoms of the alkali metals. But hydrogen is like a halogen in having atoms whose outer shell has one electron fewer than the outer shell of the atoms of the neighbouring inert gas (helium).

Another unique feature is that when an atom of hydrogen loses an electron, there are no electrons left in the atom. The symbol H^+ thus represents a nude nucleus.

11. CHANGES IN PROPERTIES ACROSS THE PERIODS. As we have seen, the Periods of the Periodic Table correspond to the gradual filling of electron orbitals and shells. Let us illustrate the effect of this on the properties of the elements, by considering the third Period (from sodium, $Z = 11$, to argon, $Z = 18$).

All these elements have atoms with a "closed" first shell containing two electrons, and a "closed" second shell containing eight electrons. In this third Period, it is the third shell of the atoms that is building up its population of electrons, from one to eight.

An atom of sodium ($Z = 11$) has one electron in the third shell. By the transfer of this electron to an atom of an electronegative atom, a sodium ion, Na^+, is formed, with the electron configuration of an atom of the inert gas neon. Sodium atoms readily surrender this single electron of their third shell (that is, sodium has a low ionization energy; see Fig. 13-2), so sodium is a highly electropositive element, an active metal prone to form compounds in which sodium has an ionic valence of $\div 1$ (Sec. 14-20).

Magnesium ($Z = 12$) is also an active metal (though less so than sodium—its ionization energy is higher); it readily forms ionic compounds. The formation of a magnesium ion, Mg^{2+}, involves the surrender by an atom of magnesium of two electrons to the atom(s) of an electronegative element. Notice that a magnesium ion, Mg^{2+}, has the same electron configuration as a sodium ion, Na^+, and as an atom of neon. Since the hydride, fluoride, and oxide ions have the ionic valences represented by H^-, F^-, and O^{2-}, the compounds of these ions with sodium ions must have (for electrical neutrality) the formulas NaH, NaF, and Na_2O, whereas the corresponding compounds with magnesium ions must have the formulas MgH_2, MgF_2, and MgO.

Aluminium ($Z = 13$) is a metallic element whose atoms can give up three electrons to form the ion Al^{3+}, a species with the same number of electrons as Ne, Na^+, and Mg^{2+}. But aluminium is a less active metal than magnesium or sodium. In fact, aluminium atoms show an appreciable tendency to share electrons with other atoms, as in the covalent compound Al_2Cl_6, in which each of the atoms has, or has a share in, eight electrons in its outer shell. And eight electrons in the outer shell is the electron configuration of the atoms of an inert gas (in this case, argon ($Z = 18$)).

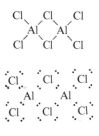

From silicon ($Z = 14$) to chlorine ($Z = 17$), the elements form compounds with covalent structures: silicon commonly shares four pairs of electrons, or has a covalence of four, as in SiF_4 (Sec. 14-20) and SiO_2 (Sec. 15-14). Phosphorus exhibits a covalence of five, as in PF_5 (Sec. 15-7), and sulphur six, as in SF_6 (Sec. 15-7).

The atoms of sulphur ($Z = 16$) and of chlorine ($Z = 17$) can attract electrons to become negatively charged ions, S^{2-} and Cl^-, that is, sulphur and chlorine show electronegative character (Sec. 13-5). By acquiring electrons the atoms of sulphur and chlorine attain, in S^{2-} and Cl^-, the electron configuration of argon.

12. Thus, as we move across a Period, we witness distinct trends. Although we chose the third Period to illustrate these, we could almost equally well have chosen the second Period (lithium to neon) as we did briefly in Sec. 12-9. The same considerations apply in the fourth and

We must not leave the impression that these particular covalences are the only ones exhibited by these elements. In fact, you have already encountered a compound of phosphorus, PCl_3 (Sec. 22-4), in which phosphorus has a covalence of three and another, P_4O_{10} (Sec. 5-9), in which it has a covalence of four. Sulphur exhibits other covalences, too; for example, two in H_2S and S_8 (Sec. 23-3), and four in SO_4^{2-} (Sec. 15-10).

When he was still in his thirties, D.I. Mendeléeff (1834-1907) developed the Periodic Table. Then, from the relationships it embodied, he predicted the existence—even the properties—of elements then unknown. These predictions proved to be impressively accurate.

This Russian stamp depicts him predicting the atomic mass of the element that was to be named gallium. It was discovered a few years later (1875) with the aid of the spectroscope, as Mendeléeff had said it probably would be.

later periods, although in these the situation is complicated by the occurrence of the transition elements (Sec. 31-6).

One evident trend is a *decrease in electropositive character* as we pass from left to right. A related trend is the *increase in electronegative character*. These trends are evident from increasing ionization energy, and can be related to the progressive increase in nuclear charge (Fig. 13-2). Elements on the left are metallic; those on the right are non-metallic.

In the third Period, electronegativity is in evidence in phosphorus, is appreciable in sulphur, and is pronounced in chlorine. The strongly electropositive elements "on the left" tend to lose electrons to form ionic compounds. The electronegative elements, sulphur and chlorine, either acquire electrons to form ionic compounds such as Na_2S or $MgCl_2$, or share electrons in covalent compounds such as H_2S or PCl_3. The elements "in the middle," silicon and phosphorus, form covalent compounds (or compound ions) by sharing electrons.

Another trend among the main-group elements within each period is a *progressive change in valence*. When Mendeléeff drew up his Periodic Table, he pointed out that the valence of each element toward oxygen or toward hydrogen could be related to Group number. These relationships are demonstrated in Table 31-3. Valence toward oxygen is today termed oxidation state (Sec. 28-5), and the highest oxidation state that an element may attain is its Group number in the Periodic Table. In ionic hy-

TABLE 31-3

FORMULAS OF SOME COMPOUNDS OF ELEMENTS OF THE THIRD PERIOD*

	Na	Mg	Al	Si	P	S	Cl	Ar
Atomic No. (Z)	11	12	13	14	15	16	17	18
Formula of Fluoride	NaF	MgF_2	AlF_3	SiF_4	PF_5	SF_6	**	—
Atom Ratio	1:1	1:2	1:3	1:4	1:5	1:6		—
Formula of Oxide	Na_2O	MgO	Al_2O_3	SiO_2	P_4O_{10}	SO_3	Cl_2O_7	—
Atom Ratio	2:1	1:1 (2:2)	2:3	1:2 (2:4)	4:10 (2:5)	1:3 (2:6)	2:7	
Formula of Hydride	NaH	MgH_2	AlH_3	SiH_4	PH_3	SH_2	ClH	—
Atom ratio	1:1	1:2	1:3	1:4	1:3	1:2	1:1	—

*In this tabulation we have not given all the oxides, fluorides, and hydrides of the elements of the third Period. For example, other oxides include P_4O_6 (Sec. 22-4), SO_2 (Sec. 23-6), and ClO_2 (Sec. 8-7); other fluorides include PF_3 and SF_4; other hydrides include Si_2H_6 and P_2H_4. You could not predict the existence of these compounds from the Periodic Table (although you might predict that they would be covalent compounds, as indeed they are). One of the weaknesses of the Periodic Table is that it gives no indication that some elements have more than one valence—and many elements have.

**ClF_7 "belongs" here, but there is apparently no such compound. However, another halogen, iodine, forms a heptafluoride, IF_7.

drides, in which hydrogen exists as H^- (with oxidation state −1), the valence toward hydrogen is also the Group number, but these hydrides occur only with electropositive metals. In non-metallic hydrides the oxidation state of the second element is the Group number *minus* eight.

13. SOME OTHER TRENDS. Another trend "across" a Period is *variation in the size of the atoms*: the atomic radius decreases with increasing atomic number (Table 31-4). This is a consequence of the increasing nuclear charge. As the nuclear charge, Z, increases the electrons are drawn in closer to the nucleus: that is, the effective radius of the atom decreases. When, however, electrons start to occupy a new shell—as at potassium ($Z = 19$)—there is a sharp increase in atomic radius (Table 31-4 and also Fig. 13-5), and then with increasing Z the radius decreases again.

TABLE 31-4

SIZES OF SOME ATOMS

Z	ELEMENT	ATOMIC RADIUS (picometres)
11	Na	157
12	Mg	137
13	Al	125
14	Si	117
15	P	110
16	S	104
17	Cl	99
19	K	203
20	Ca	174

Earlier (Sec. 13-3) we discussed the *variation in the ionization energy* of the elements as one moves "across" a Period. In Fig. 13-2 these energies are plotted for the elements of the first three Periods and the first two elements of the fourth Period. An extension of this plot shows similar trends and variations in the other Periods, the "peak" points being ionization energies for the inert gases and the "valley" points being those for the alkali metals. Such a plot very effectively illustrates the Periodic Law.

14. USEFULNESS OF THE TABLE. The regularities that are embodied in the Periodic Table, both in the Periods and the Groups, are a tremendous aid in correlating and predicting the properties of the elements and their compounds—so much so that the Periodic Law is regarded as the greatest single generalization in chemistry.

From the relationships of the Periodic Table you can, for example, predict the most likely formulas of compounds, and whether the compound is likely to have predominantly ionic bonding or covalent bonding. And, as we learned earlier (Sec. 14-7 and 26-3), certain properties

An interesting instance of prediction is afforded by the work of the American chemist Thomas Midgley. From the relationships of the Periodic Table, he predicted that the compound CCl_2F_2 (now known as Freon) would by an ideal refrigerant. A vast industry developed from this successful prediction.

(such as high melting point, high boiling point, and electrical conductivity) can be associated with ionic character. And, when you study chemistry further, you will learn how information from the Periodic Table can help predict the shapes of molecules and how, in turn, the shapes of molecules influence their properties.

But there is much chemistry that cannot be predicted from the Periodic Table. From the Table you could predict that carbon would form the covalent compounds CH_4 and CCl_4 and probably the similarly covalent compounds CH_3Cl(methyl chloride), CH_2Cl_2(methylene chloride), $CHCl_3$(chloroform)—and these all exist—but you would not likely predict that there are literally thousands of other compounds whose molecules contain carbon, hydrogen, and chlorine atoms. There are! And there is very good reason to believe that thousands more, which haven't yet been made, could be made!

In an earlier day the Periodic Table was very useful in predicting the existence of undiscovered elements, in the detection of errors in relative atomic masses and in the numerical values of other properties of the elements and their compounds, and as a stimulus to scientists' thinking about the structure of atoms.

15. HISTORICAL FOOTNOTE. The Periodic Law, and the Periodic Table that exemplifies it, were not sudden discoveries. Far from it. The development of the Table stretched over almost a hundred years. Döbereiner in Germany in 1817 and 1829 drew attention to relationships among the properties of certain elements in groups of three. Important and more fruitful efforts toward classification of the elements were made in the 1860s by de Chancourtois in France, by Newlands in England, and particularly by Meyer in Germany. The greatest contribution of all was made in 1869 by Mendeléeff in Russia.

Mendeléeff's Periodic Table was an arrangement of the elements based on the order of their atomic *masses* rather than on the order of their atomic *numbers*. Atomic numbers weren't known in Mendeléeff's time. It was only after the work of Moseley in England, in 1913, that scientists thought in terms of atomic numbers and recognized their importance. It happens that the arrangement of the elements in the order of their atomic numbers is almost the same as in the order of their atomic masses. But atomic number is a more fundamental property than atomic mass, and Moseley's work removed some anomalies in Mendeléeff's scheme of classification.

When Mendeléeff developed his Periodic Table, only 63 elements were known. Since then 42 elements have been discovered, and all of them fit into a Periodic Table that closely resembles Mendeléeff's original one. In fact, Mendeléeff predicted the existence of some of these elements and the properties they would have—even the density of the element and the boiling point of its chloride! And, what's more, he proved to be remarkably correct. (This pleased Mendeléeff, but didn't surprise him; he always had great confidence in the soundness of Mendeléeff's work!)

QUESTIONS

1. Review and be sure you understand the meaning of the following:

(a) orbitals
(b) shells
(c) closed shells
(d) electron configuration
(e) ground state
(f) building-up principle
(g) electropositive character
(h) electronegative character
(i) valence
(j) oxidation state

2. In the Periodic Table which are the Groups and which are the Periods?

3. How many Periods are in the Periodic Table? How does the Period number relate to the quantum number of the outermost shell of the atoms in that Period?

4. Explain the grouping of elements in the Periodic Table into "blocks." Quickly sketch an outline of the Table and mark the areas corresponding to s-block, p-block, d-block, and f-block elements.

5. What is meant by the following terms: main-group elements, transition elements, lanthanides, actinides, inner transition elements? Which are the elements mainly featured in this textbook?

6. State the Periodic Law. In what respect does the modern statement of the Periodic Law differ from Mendeléeff's statement of it?

7. There were 63 elements known when Mendeléeff drew up the first Periodic Table. How did Mendeléeff justify leaving gaps at certain places in the Table?

8. Give a brief explanation of the fact that Group 3 (boron, aluminium, etc.) is separated from Group 2 (beryllium, magnesium, etc.) beginning with the fourth Period in Table 31-1.

9. The element caesium is in the same family as sodium and potassium. On the basis of your knowledge of properties of the latter, predict two or three physical properties and two or three chemical properties you would expect caesium to have.

10. How do you account for the metallic properties of tin and lead as compared with the properties of the elements above them in Group 4?

11. Write possible formulas for:

(a) a chloride of bismuth, $Z = 83$
(b) a hydride of tellurium, $Z = 52$
(c) an oxide of germanium, $Z = 32$
(d) a sulphate of thallium, $Z = 81$
(e) a fluoride of indium, $Z = 49$
(f) a sulphide of arsenic, $Z = 33$

12. How can the Periodic Law be accounted for in terms of the structure of the atoms of the elements?

13. In what regions of the Periodic Table are found: metals, non-metals, the most electropositive elements, the most electronegative elements, the most inert elements?

14. In which main-group families has a gradation from non-metallic to metallic or almost metallic character been noted? By reviewing the appropriate chapters, identify elements that are borderline between non-metallic and metallic in character. Where are they located in the Periodic Table?

15. One of the snags that bothered scientists for many years after the introduction of the periodic classification of the elements was that there were places in the Table where elements had to be placed on the basis of family resemblances, with the result that they were then out of order according to their atomic masses. Now that atomic number is recognized as being more significant in the arrangement of the elements than atomic mass, this no longer matters. Find at least two pairs of elements whose atomic masses are out of order as they are arranged in Table 31-1.

16. Examine Fig. 13-5 again. Account for the trends in atomic diameter in passing down any Group, and in passing across any Period.

17. In seeking relationships between properties and atomic structure, the following gradations in properties of the inert gas elements are of interest.

ELEMENT	MELTING POINT (K)	BOILING POINT (K)	HEAT OF VAPORIZATION (kJ/mol)	ATOMIC NUMBER
Helium	——	4.2	0.082	2
Neon	24.6	27.1	1.69	10
Argon	83.8	87.3	6.53	18
Krypton	115.9	119.7	9.03	36
Xenon	161.3	165.0	12.6	54
Radon	202	211	16.4	86

(a) Plot the boiling points against atomic number. Comment on the trend.

(b) Plot the molar heats of vaporization (ordinates) against boiling points (abscissae). What relationship is suggested by the position of the points? (Compare Question 22, Chapter 24.)

(c) How do the trends in melting and boiling points for the inert gases compare with those of the halogens? (Table 8-1.)

*18. The metals sodium, magnesium, and aluminium differ only moderately in atomic mass, yet their boiling points are 889°C, 1120°C, and 2327°C, respectively. What significance can be attached to the increase in boiling point with increasing atomic number, and how can this be explained in terms of the structure of the atoms of these metals?

19. The elements that comprise an inner-transition series (such as the lanthanide series, $Z = 57-71$; Table 31-1) all have rather similar chemical properties. Account for this.

20. Applying principles outlined in this chapter, predict which you would expect to be more acidic: H_2SO_4 or H_2SeO_4. Which would you expect to be more basic, $Al(OH)_3$ or $In(OH)_3$?

21. Of the following pairs of compounds which would you expect to have predominantly ionic rather than covalent bonding? Why?

(a) $CsCl$ and $GeCl_4$

(b) $SnBr_2$ and $BaBr_2$

(c) Fr_2S and As_2S_3

22. Antimony, arsenic, bismuth, nitrogen, and phosphorus all belong to one Group in the Periodic Table. Predict which will be the most strongly metallic, what will be common valences of these elements, and which element will form the strongest acid. Account for your answers.

*23. The element germanium was discovered by Winkler in 1886, seventeen years after Mendeléeff had predicted not only its existence, but also properties of the element and some of its compounds. (Mendeléeff called the predicted element eka-silicon.) From the properties listed below for silicon and tin, predict reasonable values for comparable

properties for germanium. See if your school library has information enabling you to verify your predictions.

	SILICON	TIN
Atomic mass	28.1	118.7
Density (g/cm³)	2.4	5.75
Melting point (°C)	1420	231.9
Boiling point (°C)	2480	2337
Formula of chloride	$SiCl_4$	$SnCl_4$ ($SnCl_2$)
Melting point of chloride (°C)	−67.6	−33.2

*24. The names of the elements come from a wide variety of sources; from the names of towns and cities, countries and continents, planets and people, Greek gods and Scandinavian goddesses; from Latin and Greek words that describe properties of the elements; and from many other sources. How many of the names on the inside back cover of this book can you identify? (A fascinating reference book on this subject is *Discovery of the Elements* by M. E. Weeks and H. M. Leicester.)

POSTSCRIPT

This book, as its title implies, is only an outline of chemistry. We have said nothing about incomplete reactions, although many chemical reactions fall far short of going to completion. We have said nothing about how fast reactions proceed, yet it is of great value to know what conditions will yield a product in the shortest possible time. We have said very little about organic chemistry—the chemistry of the compounds of carbon—even though at least 85% of all known chemical substances are organic compounds. We have barely alluded to the transition metals, whose electron configuration gives rise to new kinds of compounds, to variability in valence, to colour in compounds, and to other properties. This brief list is far from complete because chemistry is a vast subject, and growing rapidly. Herein lies one of its challenges: the opportunity for doing creative work—for discovering new knowledge, and for applying it to new and useful purposes.

Chemistry is basic to a variety of applied sciences: chemical engineering, metallurgy, medicine, and agriculture, to name a few. Moreover, it is essential for understanding other sciences, such as biology and geology. And it is important in its own right—so important that modern education and industry need more chemists than scientists of any other kind.

The discoveries of chemists have been so extensively applied that it is difficult to imagine life without them. Just think what antibiotics mean in keeping us healthy, what fertilizers mean in keeping us fed, what synthetic fibres mean in keeping us clothed. What would transportation be like without rubber or steel or aviation fuel? What would entertainment be like without paper or photographic film or the plastics from which records and tape recordings are made? Almost everything we eat or drink or wear or use has in some way been affected, and often profoundly, by the science of the chemist.

The "science of the chemist" embraces a lot. Biochemists try to unravel and explain the complex chemical reactions that occur in living or-

We began this book with a definition of chemistry attributed to Linus Pauling, a definition which we hope you can now re-read with greater understanding.

At the California Institute of Technology, Dr. Pauling made outstanding contributions to our understanding of the chemical bond, the structure of proteins, and the chemical basis of blood diseases. He is also the author of textbooks that have greatly influenced the teaching of chemistry.

ganisms; geochemists study the composition and structure of rocks and minerals and the distribution of elements in them; astrochemists investigate the chemical species that are in outer space and seek their significance; industrial chemists develop new chemical processes and new products of commercial significance. And there are chemists of many specialties: agricultural chemists, polymer chemists, paint chemists, textile chemists, food chemists, pharmaceutical chemists, rubber chemists, petroleum chemists, and chemical educators, among others. It is no wonder that a definition adopted (1978) by the American Chemical Society is broad: "the chemical sciences deal with the composition, structure, and properties of substances and of the transformations they undergo." (You might compare this with what we attributed to Linus Pauling (1947) at the beginning of Chapter 1.)

Chemists do many different things. Some convert small molecules into huge molecules. Others analyze complex substances into their constituent parts, perhaps to measure harmful impurities or detect a cause of failure. Some chemists work with small glass apparatus in laboratories; others work with large metal equipment in manufacturing plants. Some test and evaluate raw materials and products, others help to make the products, and still others track down troubles in chemical processes. Some are concerned with the nature of chemical reactions, or with the structure of molecules, or with making substances never before known, or with devising new methods of analysis—these are the research chemists on whose work advances in chemistry depend. "For the research-minded chemist, limitless possibilities exist for work on the chemistry of the human body, the oceans, the atmosphere, the planets. Chemical research aimed at the conquest of disease is even now, in many cases, just on the threshold of discovery. Research on the development of new, improved materials for use in the home, in industry, or in outer space offers immense opportunities for the skilled, creative chemist" (*Chemical and Engineering News*).

We should not close this book without pointing out that chemistry is a profession for women as well as for men. It is true that there are many more male than female chemists, but the proportion of women chemists is increasing. They are following a very old tradition: the earliest chemist whose name we know was a Babylonian girl, with the delightful name of Tapputi, who 3200 years ago was extracting essential oils from plants and producing perfumes from them by a form of distillation.

APPENDIX: Answers to Numerical Questions

CHAPTER 1.
13. 375 mL.

CHAPTER 2.
11. 32.5 g of salt; 67.5 g of 25.9% solution.

CHAPTER 3.
9. 3.49:1.00 = 77.8%:22.2% = 0.186 g:0.0533 g. **10.** (a) 0.490 g (b) 19.6 g; 671 g. **13.** 2.89 g; 0.806 cm^3. **15.** 4.02 g sulphur/1.00 g copper. **20.** shrinkage 0.93 cm^3 to 0.88 cm^3.

CHAPTER 4.
6. 67.1% Zn. **7.** x = 12.5. **8.** mass oxygen/mass carbon = 1.33; 2.66. **9.** CO; CO_2; no. **11.** (a) increase 8.33-fold (b) nil. **12.** $CuO:Cu_2O$, $CuO_2:CuO$, etc; 4:1, 8:1, etc. **13.** 1:1, 3:2, 3:1, 6:1, 9:1, etc. **14.** CH_4, C_2H_8, etc.

CHAPTER 5.
5. 0.39 g; 273 mL.

CHAPTER 6.
18. 124 mL hydrogen; 62 mL oxygen. **19.** 11.2% hydrogen; 88.8% oxygen.

CHAPTER 7.
6. nitrogen 1.27 g; 1.0 L; hydrogen 0.27 g, 3.0 L; ammonia 2.0 L. **9.** 1.384 g nitride; 0.465 g ammonia. **15.** 156 g. **21.** left to right 12, 21, 21, 35, 17. **26.** (a) 129 g (b) 97.5 g nitrogen, 30.0 g oxygen (c) 1.5 g/L.

CHAPTER 8.
13. 3.17 g chlorine; 5.22 g sodium chloride. **15.** (a) 444 g (b) 272 L. **18.** $FeCl_2$, $FeCl_3$.

CHAPTER 9.
11. 1.26 kg. **12.** 0.48 g; 5.3 L.

CHAPTER 10.
12. 10.81. **13.** 60% ^{93}Ir. **15.** 0.027%. **17.** F, 19.0 u, 3.15×10^{-26} kg; P, 31.0 u, 5.15×10^{-26} kg. **18.** nine, five. **22.** 2.48×10^{18}; 3.00×10^{17}. **23.** 1.708×10^{-22} g; 4.03×10^{-17} g; 1.49×10^{-3} g. **24.** M/g = 127.9, 30.0, 98.1, 44.0, 284. **25.** n/mol = 0.041(Mg), 0.0141(Cl_2), 0.282(Cl^-), 0.0495(Ne), 0.0113(CS_2), 0.0039(S_8), 0.0030($Pb(NO_3)_2$), 0.006 67(NaI), 0.0356(Si), 0.0311(SiH_4). **29.** 0.5; 27.0, 102.0 g; 37.0; 18.5; 1.89 kg. **30.** 0.5; 0.0217; 0.0109; 0.690 g. **31.** 3.92×10^7; 1.54×10^{15}; 6.02×10^{22}; 6.35 g/cm^3.

CHAPTER 11.
4. 8.3×10^4. **5.** 1.5×10^5:1. **10.** 4.69×10^{14} s^{-1}; 3.10×10^{-19} J; 187 kJ/mol. **11.** 182.2, 246.0, 275.6 kJ/mol (red to violet). **12.** 1.60×10^{-19} J; 96.4 kJ/mol. **13.** 2.38×10^{-38} m. **22.** $E/kJ \cdot mol^{-1}$ = -1312, -328, -146, $-82 \rightarrow 0$. **24.** $^{234}_{90}Th$; $^{60}_{28}Ni$. **25.** $^{90}_{39}Y$; $^{90}_{40}Zr$.

CHAPTER 12.
15. 3.37×10^{-19} J; 202.9 kJ/mol.

CHAPTER 16.

2. 835 kg. **3.** C = 64.9%; H = 13.6%; O = 21.5%. **4.** 16.8 g; 6.3 g. **12.** methane; methane; propane. **14.** (b) 297 kJ. **15.** $Q_3 - Q_1 - \frac{1}{2}Q_2$. **16.** (a) 230 kJ (c) $2Q_3 - 3Q_1 - Q_2$. **19.** 20 g glucose/tbsp; 15.5 g alcohol/jigger. **20.** (a) 0.75 mol (b) 4.21 × 10²⁴ (c) 1.33 mol. **21.** (a) 1 mol (b) 2.0 g/mol (c) 22.2 L (d) 0.045 mol. **22.** (a) 0.0899 g H_2, 1.429 g O_2 (b) oxygen (c) 0.803 g (d) 0.716 g (e) 0.25 atm (25.3 kPa). **23.** (a) 699 kg (b) 225.6 kg.

CHAPTER 17.

7. 108.8 J; 0.907 J/g; 24.5 J/mol. **10.** calorie; 4.184; 6.0 to 6.4 cal/mol; 1.43 kcal/mol; 9.81 kcal/mol. **14.** heat capacity/J·mol⁻¹ 25.7, 24.8, 24.8, 25.2.

CHAPTER 18.

3. (b) 98.6 kPa; 0.974 atm; 740 Torr. **4.** 101.3 kPa. **5.** (a) 93.3 kPa (b) 0.947 atm (c) 2.28 × 10³ Torr (d) 7.50 Torr (e) 30.4 MPa (f) 0.025 atm. **6.** MP/°C −219, −101, −39, 119, 419.6, 1083, 1536, 2620. **7.** BP/K 4.1, 26.9, 87.1, 119.6, 164.9, 210.9. **9.** 400 L, 8 atm, 27.0 kPa, 2.5 m³, 187.5 atm. **10.** 5200 L. **12.** −124°C. **14.** 29.9 L, 99.5°C, 14.2 L, 325 K. **15.** 1.093 g/L. **16.** 64.1 L, 127.5°C, 100.7 Torr, 189.3 K, 215 kPa. **18.** 0.771 g/L. **19.** 1765 lb/in². **20.** 40.7 lb/in²; 2.77 atm; 281 kPa. **21.** 30.2 lb/in² (gauge pressure); 3.05 atm; 310 kPa.

CHAPTER 19.

5. $m_{H_2S}/m_{NH_3} \sim 2$. **7.** (a) different (b) different (c) different (d) same. **8.** (a) hydrogen (b) hydrogen (c) oxygen (d) hydrogen (e) neither (f) neither. **9.** (a) hydrogen greater (b) equal (c) equal (d) hydrogen greater (e) hydrogen greater. **18.** liquid and gas. **20.** 63.0%. **21.** 96.8 kPa. **23.** 4 atm. **24.** 99.2°C, 100.4°C.

CHAPTER 20.

1. (a) m_{Sn}/m_O could be 1.86, 3.72, 7.44, etc. (b) m_{Sn} could be 29.8, 59.5, 119, etc. **2.** 118.9, SnO_2. **5.** (a) 24.5 L (b) 31.0 L (c) 14.7 L (d) 1200 L. **6.** (a) 782 L (b) 3700 L. **7.** 72.1 g/mol. **8.** 88.1 g/mol. **9.** 93 g/mol. **10.** M/g mol⁻¹ (a) 51.7 (b) 33.6 (c) 47.5 (d) 44.8 (e) 47.5. **11.** 31 g/mol (P). **14.** 10.814 017. **15.** 6.942 597. **16.** 10 species, 6 masses; M = 16 strong; = 17 weak; = 18-21 very weak. **17.** (a) n = 1.5 mol (b) 0.0816 mol (c) 0.122 mol (d) 3.92 g (e) 2.74 L. **18.** (a) n = 3 mol (b) 1 mol, 2 mol (c) 67.2 L, 320 L (d) 67.2 L. **22.** NH_3, 17.3 (17.0); CO_2, 44.3 (44.0); Cl_2, 72.0 (71.0); H_2, 2.01 (2.00); CH_4, 16.1 (16.0); N_2, 28.0 (28.0); O_2, 32.0 (32.0); SO_2, 65.6 (64.1); H_2S, 34.4 (34.1). **23.** 0.003 94; 0.004 33. **26.** (a) 87.5% Si (b) 72.2% Mg (c) 93.8% C (d) 40.1% Ca, 12.0% C (e) 24.7% Ca, 1.24% H, 14.8% C (f) 36.7% Fe, 21.1% S (g) 27.9% Fe, 24.1% S (h) 49.0% C, 48.3% Cl (i) 10.0% C, 89.1% Cl (j) 77.8% Si. **27.** (a) 41.8% C, 4.7% H, 16.3% N, 18.6% S (b) 40.9% C, 3.7% H, 8.7% N, 22.0% Cl. **28.** (a) CS_2 (b) SCl (c) Cl_2O (d) $AgNO_3$ (e) K_2CrO_4 (f) $Na_2S_2O_3$ (g) $K_2Cr_2O_7$. **29.** P_2O_3, P_2O_5. **30.** (a) $CaSO_4$ (b) $NaHSO_4$ (c) $C_4H_{10}O$ (d) C_2H_6O (e) $NaHCO_3$ (f) $KAlSi_3O_8$. **31.** $CuCl_2$. **32.** $C_6H_{12}O_6$. **33.** (a) C_8H_{18} (b) C_2H_6O (c) $C_{10}H_8$ (d) $C_{40}H_{56}$ (e) $C_3H_6N_6$. **34.** (a) $C_4H_{10}O$ (b) C_2H_6O (c) $C_2H_4O_2$ (d) $C_2H_2O_4$ (e) $COCl_2$ (f) Al_2Cl_6 (g) $B_3N_3H_6$. **35.** C_2H_2, C_6H_6. **36.** (a) $C_6H_5NO_2$ (b) 123.1 g/mol. **37.** C_2H_4. **38.** (a) 26.2 g/mol (b) C_2H_2. **39.** N_2O_4. **40.** 1.07 g. **41.** 78.1 g/mol. **42.** C_2H_4O, $C_4H_8O_2$. **43.** C_6H_6. **44.** C_3H_8. **45.** 1.13 L. **46.** 0.332 g. **47.** 1.185 kg. **48.** (a) 11.4 mL (b) 3920 mL. **49.** (a) 1.27 mL (b) 6840 mL. **50.** 29.0 g/mol. **51.** 2.73 g/L. **52.** 836 mL. **53.** 0.415 g. **54.** 1.03 kPa. **55.** 2.69 × 10²². **56.** 1.33 × 10⁻⁴ Pa, 3.52 × 10¹³. **57.** 2.69 × 10²², 0.565 × 10²², 2.10 × 10²², 0.565 × 10¹⁹, 2.10 × 10²², 21%. **58.** 8.07 × 10¹⁵, 300 ppm. **59.** 2.52 cm³, 22 400 cm³. **60.** 1.185 g/L, 1.172 g/L, damp air rises.

CHAPTER 22.

12. superphosphate, 25% P_2O_5; $Ca(H_2PO_4)_2$, 61% P_2O_5; $(NH_4)_2HPO_4$, 21.2% N, 54% P_2O_5; $NH_4H_2PO_4$, 12% N, 62% P_2O_5. **13.** P_4 molecules. **16.** 200 kg.

CHAPTER 23.

3. 218 g/mol, some S_8 decomposed. **18.** $SOCl_2$. **19.** (a) 7.8 mL (b) 4020 mL.

CHAPTER 24.

19. $MgSO_3\cdot6H_2O$. **20.** 6. **22.** Trouton constants 110, 97, 115, 97, 95, 94, 91 J/(mol·K). **24.** 41 kJ/mol, 286 kJ/mol. **25.** HO, H : Ö : Ö : H.

CHAPTER 25.

14. 20% solute, 4 g. **15.** 40% sugar, 66.7 g/100 g water. **16.** 9.1% solute, 0.94 mol. **18.** 500 g water, 62.5 g. **19.** 13%. **20.** 228 g. **21.** 55 g. **22.** 3.56 mol. **23.** 11.8 mol/L. **24.** 32.2 g, 0.304 mol. **25.** 0.412 mol/L. **26.** 3.73 g. **27.** 36.8%. **28.** 15.8 mol/L. **29.** (a) 6.0 g (b) 9.62 g (c) 122 g (d) 107 g. **30.** (a) 76.3 g (b) 40.2 g. **31.** 5.8 mL. **32.** 80 mL. **34.** 36 mL. **35.** 0.100

mol/L. **36.** 0.160 mol/L. **37.** 0.0153 mol/L. **38.** 24.4%, 20.7 g/100 g water. **39.** (b) 6.7, 11.2, 20.8 (c) 34.7, 55.5, 41.0 (d) un-, super-, unsaturated (e) 4.9 g (f) 4.0 g (g) 6.9 g. **40.** (b) 116 g (c) 149 g (d) 39.2, 62.7 (e) 34°C.

CHAPTER 26.

16. 1.08×10^{15} of each; 55.5; 1.0×10^{-7} mol/L of each. **18.** –167.5°C. **22.** 2.24 L. **23.** 254 mL. **24.** 783 s or 13 min 3 s. **25.** 2.7×10^7 A. **26.** 0.618 g, 1515 s.

CHAPTER 27.

13. H_2SO_4, HCl, $HC_2H_3O_2$, H_2O, NH_3, NaOH, $Ba(OH)_2$. **14.** D, E, A. **15.** 8. **16.** 6. **23.** 33.8 g. **24.** 2.65 g. **25.** 1000 cm³. **26.** mass/g (amount/mol) 36.5(1.00), 63.0(1.00), 49.0(0.50), 32.7(0.33). **27.** 3.73 g, no. **28.** 0.200 mol/L. **30.** (a) 0.02 Mg^{2+}, 0.04 Cl^- (b) 0.02 Mg^{2+}, 0.03 K^+, 0.07 Cl^- (c) 0.1 Na^+, 0.03 CO_3^{2-}, 0.04 Cl^- (d) 0.01 Mg^{2+}, 0.02 K^+, 0.04 Cl^- (e) 0.02 K^+, 0.03 H^+, 0.05 NO_3^- (f) 0.1 $HC_2H_3O_2$ (g) 0.05 K^+, 0.05 $C_2H_3O_2^-$, 0.05 $HC_2H_3O_2$ (h) 0.05 K^+, 0.05 $H_2PO_4^-$ (i) 0.02 Mg^{2+}, 0.06 H^+, 0.1 ClO_4^-.

CHAPTER 28.

6. +5; +1; –4; +5; +5; –3; –3; +5; +4, –2; +7; +5; +4. **14.** heavier, 0.097 g. **15.** (a) 0.02 Mg^{2+}, 0.03 Pb^{2+} 0.01 NO_3^-, (b) 0.25 Zn^{2+}, 0.50 NO_3^- (c) 0.1 Fe^{2+}, 0.3 H^+, 0.5 Cl^-. **17.** (a) D, A, C, H, B (c) B (d) D. **19.** no, 5.13 g. **22.** 212.3 kJ.

CHAPTER 29.

20. 400 ppm $CaCO_3$. **21.** 92 ppm Na^+ (212 ppm Na_2CO_3). **25.** 504 kg. **26.** raise temp. to 100°C, boil off 363 g water. **27.** 299 g. **28.** 5.49 cm. **29.** 787 t. **30.** 209 g. **31.** ratios 1.95, 1.96, 1.94, 1.94, 1.92.

CHAPTER 30.

18. ratios 0.69, 1.23, 2.79, 4.41. **24.** 3.01 g/L. **25.** (a) CH_3Cl (b) 50.1 (c) CH_3Cl (50.5). **26.** 0.40 mol/L. **27.** 0.01 mol, 224 mL. **28.** 96 mL. **29.** 3.34 g/L, 3.59. **30.** 0.008 mol/L. **37.** $Q_3 - \frac{1}{2}Q_1 - \frac{1}{2}Q_2$ (evolved). **39.** 229.9 (cf. 253.8) g/mol. **40.** 49.9 (27°C), 20 (80°C).

INDEX

APPROXIMATE RELATIVE MASSES OF SOME ELEMENTS

RELATIVE ATOMIC MASSES OF SOME COMMON ELEMENTS ROUNDED TO ONE DECIMAL PLACE. THESE ARE SUFFICIENT FOR MOST CALCULATIONS.

ELEMENT	SYMBOL	RELATIVE ATOMIC MASS	ELEMENT	SYMBOL	RELATIVE ATOMIC MASS
Aluminium	Al	27.0	Lead	Pb	207.2
Antimony	Sb	121.8	Magnesium	Mg	24.3
Argon	Ar	39.9	Manganese	Mn	54.9
Barium	Ba	137.3	Mercury	Hg	200.6
Beryllium	Be	9.0	Neon	Ne	20.2
Boron	B	10.8	Nickel	Ni	58.7
Bromine	Br	79.9	Nitrogen	N	14.0
Calcium	Ca	40.1	Oxygen	O	16.0
Carbon	C	12.0	Phosphorus	P	31.0
Chlorine	Cl	35.5	Potassium	K	39.1
Chromium	Cr	52.0	Silicon	Si	28.1
Cobalt	Co	58.9	Silver	Ag	107.9
Copper	Cu	63.5	Sodium	Na	23.0
Fluorine	F	19.0	Sulphur	S	32.1
Helium	He	4.0	Thorium	Th	232.0
Hydrogen	H	1.0	Tin	Sn	118.7
Iodine	I	126.9	Xenon	Xe	131.3
Iron	Fe	55.8	Zinc	Zn	65.4